McGraw-Hill Electrical and Electronic Engineering Series

FREDERICK EMMONS TERMAN, *Consulting Editor*

Electronic Measurements

ELECTRONIC MEASUREMENTS

Frederick Emmons Terman, Sc.D.

*Professor of Electrical Engineering and
Dean of the School of Engineering
Stanford University*

*Past President
Institute of Radio Engineers*

Joseph Mayo Pettit, Ph.D.

*Associate Professor of Electrical Engineering
Stanford University*

SECOND EDITION

NEW YORK   TORONTO LONDON
McGRAW-HILL BOOK COMPANY, INC.
1952

ELECTRONIC MEASUREMENTS

Library of Congress Catalog Card Number: 51-12650

THE MAPLE PRESS COMPANY, YORK, PA.

PREFACE TO THE SECOND EDITION

"Electronic Measurements" succeeds "Measurements in Radio Engineering" (1935) as a college text, and as a reference book for the practicing engineer. The change in title is indicative of the increased scope of the new book, which now covers measurement fundamentals in numerous fields beyond conventional radio, including television, radar and other pulsed systems, microwaves, and a diversity of techniques of value to engineers in other areas who may use electronics in their instrumentation.

The revisions in this edition are extensive. Many sections in the present volume are devoted to technical subjects that were nonexistent at the time of the earlier book, or were perhaps then only scientific curiosities. Such topics include: waveguides and cavity resonators; standing-wave measurements; noise in amplifiers and receivers; frequency-modulation and television receivers; generation of special waveforms (pulses, square waves, sawtooth waves); generation of time delays; modern forms of vacuum-tube voltmeters; power measurement at microwave frequencies; antenna measurements into the microwave region, including directivity pattern, gain, and phase-front measurements; oscillators for laboratory signal sources covering the range from very low to microwave frequencies; transient and steady-state response of amplifiers and circuits; new oscilloscope techniques; stability of feedback amplifiers; etc. The length of the book is approximately twice that of the earlier volume. Many new illustrations have been added; the original volume had 198 figures, while the new one has 449. Most of the old illustrations have been supplanted by new drawings; all of them have been prepared to conform with present graphical standards.

As in the earlier volume which it supersedes, "Electronic Measurements" has as its aim the providing of a comprehensive engineering discussion of the measuring problems commonly encountered by radio or electronic engineers. The method of treatment and the degree of difficulty are much the same as in Terman's "Radio Engineering" (3d ed.). The two works are in a sense companion volumes, in that one deals with the general principles of radio while the other is devoted to measuring methods and measuring apparatus.

"Electronic Measurements" is intended to be of use as both a reference and a textbook. For the practicing engineer it gathers together information on measuring techniques and measuring equipment, and thereby provides him with a convenient place to obtain the background necessary to handle new problems as they arise.   As a further aid in this connection, extensive footnote references are given to the literature, so that the reader knows just where to turn for further details on any subject.   The thoroughness with which the literature is covered by these references is indicated by the fact that the Author Index contains over a thousand individual entries.   In a way, it can thus be said that in addition to presenting a reference book summary of measuring methods and principles, "Electronic Measurements" also presents a rather complete guide to the pertinent literature.

To the student, "Electronic Measurements" presents in an organized and systematic form a thorough coverage of the laboratory methods and laboratory measuring equipment in present-day use in radio and allied fields.

No detailed laboratory experiments for use in university courses are included.   It is believed that the main value of this type of book in connection with a university laboratory course is not as a manual of experiments, but rather as a textbook on general measuring principles suitable for supplementing the specific experiments being performed in a way that will increase greatly the value of these experiments to the student.

The authors have been fortunate in being intimately associated on the one hand with university students and staff, and on the other hand with nonacademic groups engaged in research, development, and production. It is hoped that this book will be a contribution to the work of all.

FREDERICK EMMONS TERMAN
JOSEPH MAYO PETTIT

STANFORD, CALIF.
January, 1952

PREFACE TO THE FIRST EDITION

The aim of "Measurements in Radio Engineering" is to provide a comprehensive engineering discussion of the measuring problems commonly encountered by radio engineers. The method of treatment and the degree of difficulty are much the same as in the author's book "Radio Engineering," and the two works are in a sense companion volumes in which one deals with the general principles of radio, while the other is devoted to measuring methods and measuring apparatus.

The present volume is intended to be of use as both a reference and a textbook. For the practicing engineer it gathers together information on measuring techniques and measuring equipment, and thereby will be found of assistance when new problems are to be attacked. To the student it presents in an organized and systematic form a complete picture of the laboratory methods and laboratory measuring equipment ordinarily used in radio and allied fields. This makes it possible for the student to study the experimental aspect of radio in the same comprehensive way that the general principles are ordinarily studied. In particular, the present volume will be found of especial value in connection with laboratory courses where emphasis is placed on training in laboratory and experimental methods. Its use under such circumstances ensures a broader viewpoint and better perspective than can be gained solely from a series of individual experiments, and also assists in the treatment of topics upon which experiments are not feasible.

Considerable attention has been given to the principles involved in the design and construction of laboratory equipment; partly because of the desirability of understanding thoroughly the equipment which one is using, and partly because of the fact that many circumstances arise where it is necessary to build one's own equipment in order to have any equipment at all. The latter situation arises particularly in university laboratories, where it is usually possible to construct valuable apparatus with the aid of student help. There are also many occasions in which special measuring equipment not commercially available is needed, and must be designed and built by the user.

"Measurements in Radio Engineering" has been written with the idea of presenting an engineering treatment of the subject, and is in no sense an encyclopedia of measuring methods. Success in making measurements in radio work is primarily a matter of having available a satisfactory technique that is thoroughly understood rather than of having available innumerable alternatives.   Emphasis has therefore been placed upon those methods which experience has shown to be the most practical, which require the minimum of equipment, and which are least likely of error.   Where alternatives are given, an attempt has been made to weigh their relative merits.

In view of the fact that in making radio measurements one is to a considerable extent utilizing expedients and ingenious practical applications of general principles, the techniques employed are much more subject to change than are fundamental principles.   The information available in the literature on laboratory methods and the details of laboratory equipment is scattered and in many cases incomplete.   The author is therefore fully aware that there is undoubtedly information which it would have been desirable to include in this book but which is known only to limited groups.   Any suggestions which readers may care to send in for incorporation in later editions will be greatly appreciated.

Little emphasis has been placed upon detailed laboratory experiments suitable for use in university courses devoted to radio.   This is because there are potentially many more experiments available than there is ever time to perform, and the particular ones which are selected depend to some extent upon the preference of the individual instructor and to a much greater extent upon the apparatus available.

Emphasis has chiefly been placed on the types of measurements that can be carried out within the limitations of a university laboratory course. It is believed that the main value of this type of book in connection with a university laboratory course is not as a manual of experiments, but rather as a textbook on general measuring principles which can be used to supplement the specific experiments carried out in the laboratory.

FREDERICK EMMONS TERMAN

STANFORD, CALIF.
July, 1935

CONTENTS

ix

CHAPTER 1

VOLTAGE AND CURRENT

1-1. Measurement of Direct Current and Voltage. Direct currents of the magnitudes encountered in communication work are ordinarily measured with portable instruments of the moving-coil (d'Arsonval) type. Such instruments are rugged, stable, and consume relatively little power. They are commercially available in a wide variety of ranges, types, and accuracies.

Voltmeters for d-c potentials are obtained by providing a d'Arsonval current instrument with a series resistance. The power (and current) required to operate such a voltmeter depends upon the current sensitivity of the instrument used, and is commonly expressed in ohms per volt. Thus if 0.5 ma is required to give full-scale deflection, the required series resistance is 2000 times the voltage that is to give full-scale deflection. Sensitivities commonly used range from 100 to 20,000 ohms per volt, with values of 1000 ohms per volt or more preferred for communication work. Even then the current required by the voltmeter will often seriously affect the magnitude of the voltage being measured.

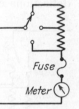

FIG. 1-1. A voltmeter multiplier circuit.

A particular voltmeter can be arranged to give full-scale deflection for different values of voltage by the expedient of providing the series resistance with taps at appropriate points, as illustrated in Fig. 1-1. These taps may lead either to binding posts or to a switch. In the latter case, the switch should be of the type that short-circuits between points. When several full-scale ranges are provided in this way, the scales should be arranged so that each division represents one, two, or five units. Hence when the meter scale is divided into 50 divisions, the full-scale ranges should be chosen out of the sequence 1-2.5-5-10-25, etc., while when 100 divisions are available they should be taken from the sequence 1-2-5-10-20, etc.

The current required to give full-scale deflection of an ammeter can be controlled by means of a resistance in parallel with the d'Arsonval instrument. Such a shunt may take the form illustrated in Fig. 1-2a, where different full-scale ranges are obtained by the use of different individual shunts connected into the circuit either by a switch, or by being clamped to binding posts. Alternatively, a fixed resistance may be shunted across

1

the meter with the input terminals appropriately tapped across a portion of this resistance, as illustrated in Fig. 1-2b. This latter arrangement is known as the *universal shunt*. An analysis based on Fig. 1-2c shows that the *relative* multiplying ratio is proportional to R/R_1, and is *independent both of the meter resistance and of the total shunt resistance R*. Hence, if resistance R is tapped at points which make R/R_1 successively 1, 2, 5, 10, then the *relative* multiplying factors at the same taps are 1, 2, 5, 10, respectively, and are the same for any meter whatever its resistance.

Shunts of the type shown in Fig. 1-2a for currents up to 1 amp can be wound on small spools turned out of doweling, and provided with an axial hole for mounting. The universal shunt can be more conveniently wound upon a card. Shunts can ordinarily be made of copper or any available resistance wire.[1] The only factor that must be kept in mind is that shunts of advance, nichrome, and certain other materials will generate sufficient thermoelectric voltages at their terminals to cause small deflections on sensitive microammeters and milliammeters immediately

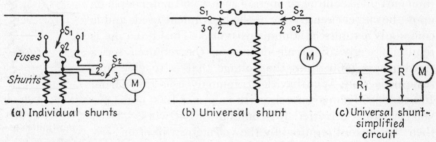

(a) Individual shunts   (b) Universal shunt   (c) Universal shunt-simplified circuit

FIG. 1-2. Possible circuit arrangements for current multipliers. The switches S_1 and S_2 should be of the short-circuiting type operated by a common shaft.

after the shunt is soldered, or when it is in a warm place. When this effect is to be avoided, one should use either copper or manganin.

When a shunt is used to extend the range of a current meter, care must be taken to arrange matters so that the contact resistance of the connections which carry the current to be measured is not included as part of the shunt resistance. Thus, in Fig. 1-2 the contact resistance of switch S_1 is external to the shunt system. The contact resistance of switch S_2 is much less troublesome, as it is in series with the meter resistance, which is much larger than the shunt resistance. Switches such as shown in Fig. 1-2 should be of the type that short-circuits between taps, so that the circuit will not be momentarily opened when the range is changed.

Meters used for laboratory and experimental purposes can be protected against accidental overloads by quick-acting fuses. Inasmuch as the

[1] Precision instruments having very low temperature coefficients require special shunting arrangements. See "Standard Handbook for Electrical Engineers," 7th ed., Sec. 3-92, McGraw-Hill Book Company, Inc., New York, 1941.

resistance of individual fuses can be expected to vary appreciably, fused current-measuring systems must be arranged so that the fuse resistance is not a part of the shunt resistance, but rather is external to the measuring system as illustrated in Fig. 1-2. This requires a separate fuse for each current range. In the case of voltmeter multipliers, the high resistance used in series with the instrument swamps the effect of variations in fuse resistance, and one can place the fuse in series with the meter as illustrated in Fig. 1-1, thereby enabling a single fuse to function for all ranges.

Calibration of D-C Instruments. The practical problem usually encountered in calibrating measuring instruments, or in adjusting multipliers, is to use a single standard instrument having a single range, for checking both voltmeters and milliammeters of a great variety of ranges.

Milliammeters and microammeters are conveniently checked by the arrangement illustrated in Fig. 1-3, in which the standard voltmeter V applies a known potential equal to or more than 10 volts to the meter A in series with a resistance R. The resistance R is so adjusted that this resistance, plus the resistance of the fuse, meter, etc., gives the desired current in the circuit when the known voltage is applied. The total

resistance actually in the circuit at any time can be determined by throwing switch S to the right and measuring on a Wheatstone bridge. The sensitivity of current instruments can be adjusted to a desired value by controlling the strength of the permanent magnet, using the technique and equipment employed

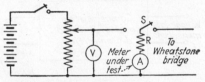

FIG. 1-3. Convenient circuit arrangement for calibrating a milliammeter A using a standard voltmeter V.

by garages to adjust speedometer magnets. It is possible in this way to vary the sensitivity by as much as 10 per cent.

Voltmeters are most easily calibrated by first adjusting or determining the current sensitivity of the moving-coil instrument. The series resistance that is required can then be readily calculated, and measured accurately by using a Wheatstone bridge.

The ultimate standard for all d-c calibrations is the standard cell. The potential of such a cell is known to a very high order of precision and can be balanced against other potentials by means of a sensitive galvanometer and suitable potentiometer. The technique and apparatus for carrying out the necessary operations have become well standardized and are to be found in any work on instruments.[1]

Vacuum-tube Voltmeters for Measuring D-C Voltages and Currents. Vacuum-tube amplifier systems are widely used for the measurement of

[1] For example, see Chap. V of F. A. Laws, "Electrical Measurements," 2d ed., McGraw-Hill Book Company, Inc., New York, 1938.

d-c voltages and currents.   They consist of a d-c amplifier provided with
a d-c meter to indicate the amplified output, as illustrated in Fig. 1-4,
where the voltage to be measured (or a suitable fraction thereof) is
applied to the input terminals of the amplifier.   In the case of current
measurements, the unknown current is passed through a known resistance, thus producing a voltage drop that is a measure of this current.
This voltage drop is then determined by the vacuum-tube voltmeter
system.

Direct-current amplifiers for use in d-c voltmeters must employ a circuit which minimizes the effects of variations in supply voltages and tube
aging upon the output zero indication.[1]   The calibration is normally
stabilized against variation in tube characteristics and supply voltages
by introducing negative feedback in some manner.

Vacuum-tube voltmeters for measuring d-c voltages and currents find
numerous and diversified applications.   They are, for example, widely
used in radio service work in place of ordinary voltmeters.   In such
instruments, the voltage to be determined is applied to the amplifier
through a resistance voltage divider having an input resistance that is
typically 10 to 100 megohms.   The
system is thereby able to achieve a
sensitivity of the order of megohms
per volt, representing negligible
power consumption, and at the
same time is very rugged and cannot be damaged by overload.   Since
a relative large voltage is available

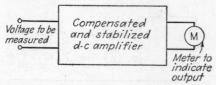

FIG.   1-4. Schematic   diagram   of   d-c
vacuum-tube voltmeter.

for the input terminals of such an instrument, a simple amplifier can be
used, and elaborate stabilization arrangements are unnecessary.

Another important application is in the measurement of very small d-c
voltages, of the order of millivolts or less.   In vacuum-tube voltmeters
of this type, where the potential to be measured is very small, it is necessary that the amplifier be carefully designed to minimize drifts that if
present in appreciable amount would obscure the small voltage being
determined.

[1] There is extensive literature on the subject of d-c amplifiers.   Useful references
include Chap. 11 of "Vacuum Tube Amplifiers" (vol. 18 of Radiation Laboratory
Series), McGraw-Hill Book Company, Inc., New York, 1948; E. L. Ginzton, D-C
Amplifier Design Technique, *Electronics*, vol. 17, p. 98, March, 1944; M. Artzt, Survey
of D-C Amplifiers, *Electronics*, vol. 18, p. 112, August, 1945; J. M. Brumbaugh and
A. W. Vance, A Feedback D-C Amplifier, *Electronics*, vol. 11, p. 16, September, 1938;
D. B. Penick, Direct-Current Amplifier Circuits for Use with the Electrometer Tube,
Rev. Sci. Instruments, vol. 6, p. 115, April, 1935; J. D. Close, Stable Voltmeter Ampli-
fier, *Wireless Engineer*, vol. 25, p. 231, July, 1948; also the references in footnote 3
on page 18.

Very small currents can be measured by sensitive vacuum-tube volt-meters. For example, a current of 10^{-12} amp passed through a resistance of 100 megohms will produce a potential of 0.1 mv, a value readily measured with a well-designed d-c vacuum-tube voltmeter. It is thus possible, by means of d-c vacuum-tube voltmeters, to obtain in a rela-tively portable and rugged instrument, a sensitivity as great as or greater than realizable with a wall galvanometer.

Small d-c voltages are sometimes measured by converting them into alternating voltages, and then amplifying and measuring the latter. Such an arrangement has the advantage that there is no danger that the quantity being amplified will be obscured by drifts in the amplifier itself, since these drifts are d-c effects, and therefore do not confuse indications that are based on the alternating current. This greatly simplifies the design of the amplifier, but in turn requires an inverter or modulator which must maintain a linear relationship between a-c output and d-c input, without at the same time introducing transients. Successful arrangements of this type have, however, been devised, and are used in some commercial equipment.

1-2. Methods of Measuring Alternating Voltages and Currents. The problem of measuring alternating voltages and currents in communica-tion work is complicated by the wide frequency range which must be covered, and by the resulting calibration difficulties. Among the means that find use are iron-vane, dynamometer, rectifier, thermocouple, and vacuum-tube voltmeter instruments. In some cases, particularly at the very highest radio frequencies, voltage and current are determined indirectly by measuring the power associated with a known resistance such as the characteristic impedance of a transmission line. In fact, at frequencies above about 500 Mc, determinations of this type are used almost exclusively in place of voltage or current measurements.

Iron-vane instruments are widely used for voltage and current measure-ments at 60 cycles. They are inexpensive, fairly accurate, and can be designed for use up to frequencies in the order of 2500 cycles without undue error.[1] They are available in maximum sensitivities of about 10 ma and hence a maximum ohms per volt of about 100. Dynamometer instruments are more accurate than iron-vane instruments, have similar sensitivity and frequency range, but are considerably more expensive.

Rectifier instruments, thermocouples, and vacuum-tube voltmeters are the principal measuring instruments used at frequencies much higher than 60 cycles, and are described in detail in subsequent sections.

The behavior of a-c measuring instruments with nonsinusoidal waves of current is particularly important because these instruments are nearly

[1] J. H. Miller, Compensation of A-C Instruments for Variations in Frequency, *Elec. Eng.*, vol. 70, p. 494, June, 1951.

always calibrated in terms of the effective value of the current, assuming a sine wave. Iron-vane, dynamometer, and thermocouple instruments give an indication that is dependent upon the square of the effective value of the wave passing through them. Thus, if this wave consists of components of different frequencies having effective magnitudes I_1, I_2, I_3, etc., these square-law instruments will give the same deflection as would a sine wave having an effective value of

$$\text{Effective value} = \sqrt{I_1{}^2 + I_2{}^2 + I_3{}^2 + \cdots} \qquad (1\text{-}1)$$

Substitution in this formula shows that the presence of a 20 per cent harmonic increases the reading by 2 per cent. The indication of a square-law instrument is not influenced by the relative phase positions of the various harmonics.

Rectifier and vacuum-tube voltmeter instruments are commonly operated so that they do not follow square-law behavior; the resulting situa-

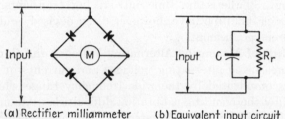

(a) Rectifier milliammeter   (b) Equivalent input circuit

FIG. 1-5. Actual and equivalent circuit of rectifier milliammeter.

tions that thus arise are discussed below and summarized in Table 1-1, (page 10).

1-3. Rectifier Instruments.[1] In the rectifier instrument the alternating current to be measured is passed through a full-wave copper-oxide rectifier unit[2], and the resulting direct current is indicated by a moving-coil d-c instrument, as in Fig. 1-5a. Rectifier instruments can be built to give full-scale deflection on currents less than 1 ma, and so make possible the construction of a-c voltmeters having sensitivities exceeding 1000 ohms per volt. The ruggedness and overload capacity compare favorably with moving-coil d-c instruments. The best accuracy obtainable is, however, only about 5 per cent, because of the variation of rectifier characteristics with temperature. Another disadvantage of rectifier current instruments is that they have a high voltage drop, a 1-ma instrument consuming about 1 volt at full-scale deflection.

[1] For further information, see Joseph Sahagen, The Use of the Copper Oxide Rectifier for Instrument Purposes, *Proc. IRE*, vol. 19, p. 233, February, 1931.

[2] Selenium rectifier units have been developed that also have characteristics suitable for instrument use; see J. J. A. Ploos van Amstel, Small Selenium Rectifiers, *Philips Tech. Rev.*, vol. 9, no. 9, p. 267, 1948.

The characteristics of the rectifier instrument depend primarily upon the properties of the rectifier element.   The most important of these for low audio frequencies such as 60 cycles are shown in Fig. 1-6.   It will be observed that the rectified direct current is almost exactly proportional to the alternating current.[1]   The resistance of the rectifier unit, however, depends very considerably upon the alternating current passing through the rectifier, being greatest when the current is small.[2]

As a consequence of these characteristics, an unshunted rectifier instrument used to measure current will have a scale that is approximately linear provided the full-scale current is not too small.   The same is true when a high series resistance is employed to give a high-range voltmeter.   However, when a small series resistance is used to produce a low-range voltmeter, the variable resistance of the rectifier element causes the current through the instrument to decrease appreciably faster than the voltage, so that the scale is bunched near the low end.   A similar behavior results when the terminals of a rectifier milliammeter are shunted to increase the current range.

The extent of this scale bunching for small deflection depends upon the ratio of the rectifier resistance to the equivalent resistance the input terminals of the rectifier see when looking toward the source of power, the bunching being less the higher the ratio of source to rectifier resistance.   The same degree of scale bunching, and hence the same scale graduations,

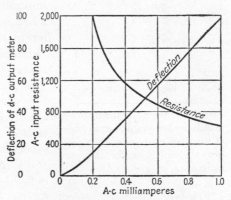

Fig. 1-6. Rectified direct current, and input resistance, as a function of the applied alternating current in a typical copperoxide rectifier type of instrument.

will exist for different ranges when the multiplier or shunt arrangement employed is of a type that presents the same source resistance to the rectifier input irrespective of the multiplying range.[3]   With current

[1] At very minute currents the direct current is, however, proportional to the square of the alternating current.

[2] The rise in resistance at low current densities is so rapid that increasing the current density in the rectifier by reducing the area of the rectifier actually *reduces* the resistance of the rectifier unit to a small current.   For this reason rectifiers for instrument purposes always have very small cross sections, even though a larger area would give less voltage drop for the current corresponding to full-scale deflection.

[3] For a more detailed discussion see F. E. Terman, Multirange Rectifier Instruments Having the Same Scale Graduation for all Ranges, *Proc. IRE*, vol. 23, p. 234, March, 1935

instruments this requires that the resistance which the input terminals of the rectifier see when the source of current is open-circuited, be constant irrespective of multiplying factor. The simplest arrangement satisfying this requirement is the universal shunt of the type illustrated in Fig. 1-2b. A voltmeter multiplier satisfying the same requirement must be so designed that the resistance which faces the rectifier when the source of voltage is short-circuited is constant. A simple method of accomplishing this is shown schematically in Fig. 1-7, in which the shunt resistance R_2 is decreased as the series resistance R_1 is increased.

With rectifier instruments a protecting fuse may be placed between the rectifier input and the associated multiplier or shunt as illustrated in Fig. 1-7. This location, not acceptable with d-c current meters, is permissible because with rectifier instruments the high input resistance of the meter and the relatively low inherent accuracy minimize the undesirable effects resulting when a replacement fuse has a slightly different resistance than the original fuse.

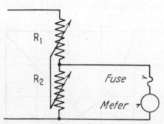

FIG. 1-7. Schematic diagram of multiplier for copper-oxide type of rectifier voltmeter that follows the same scale for different ranges.

Rectifier instruments are commonly calibrated by employing a 60-cycle sine wave. The scale is marked to indicate the effective value of such a sine wave, and the exact sensitivity for full-scale deflection is controlled by varying the sensitivity of the associated d-c milliammeter until the desired alternating current gives full-scale deflection.

Frequency and Waveform Effects in Rectifier Instruments. When a reverse voltage is applied across a copper-oxide rectifier element, the non-conducting barrier layer acts as the dielectric of a condenser. As a result, the equivalent circuit of a rectifier meter has the character illustrated in Fig. 1-5b, where C represents the equivalent capacitance formed by the series connection of the two rectifier units that are nonconducting at the moment, and R_r represents the meter resistance plus the sum of the resistances of the two rectifier units that are conducting at the moment.

At low audio frequencies, such as 60 cycles, the reactance of C is so much greater than the resistance R_r that the shunting capacitance is of no consequence. However, as the frequency becomes higher an increasing fraction of the current is diverted through the condenser and away from the rectifier and meter. The rectifier instrument accordingly gives an indication that decreases as the frequency is raised. In a typical instrument this error will be of the order of 0.5 per cent per thousand cycles, for full-scale deflection.[1] With small deflections, the error may be consider-

[1] By associating suitable equalizing networks with the copper-oxide unit, it is possi-

ably greater as a result of the increase in rectifier resistance that occurs with small currents, as illustrated in Fig. 1-6.

Rectifier instruments give an indication that is proportional to the average value of the a-c wave when the negative areas are treated as though they were positive. This is termed *full-wave linear* behavior. Since the ratio of average to effective values of a sine wave is 0.909, this means that the d-c meter used with the rectifier must have a d-c sensitivity approximately 10 per cent greater than the alternating current indicated on the scale.

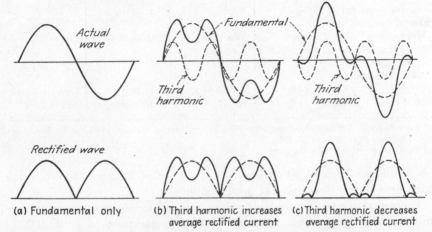

FIG. 1-8. Wave shapes before and after rectification, showing how the phase position of a third-harmonic component affects the average value of the rectified current.

Because the rectifier instrument gives an indication proportional to the average value of the wave, it is susceptible to waveform errors which, in general, will depend upon the phase as well as the magnitude of the harmonics that are present. This is illustrated in Fig. 1-8, which shows a fundamental wave alone, and fundamental waves with 50 per cent third harmonic in two phase relations. It is apparent that for the phase relation at (b) the rectified current is increased by the presence of the harmonic, while for the phase shown in (c) the harmonic produces a reduction in the average or rectified current. Further details are given in Table 1-1.

1-4. Thermocouple Instruments.[1] In a thermocouple instrument the current to be measured heats a short piece of resistance wire. This is

ble to compensate rectifier instruments so that their full-scale deflection will correctly read voltage up to frequencies as high as 100 kc.

[1] An ingenious method of employing an emission-limited diode in conjunction with negative feedback to provide an rms instrument that is equivalent to a thermocouple is described by R. D. Campbell, The Diotron, An Aid to RMS Instrumentation, *Electronics*, vol. 23, p. 93, July, 1950.

associated with a thermocouple that consists of a junction of two dissimilar wires so chosen that a voltage is generated by heating the junction. The output of the thermocouple is delivered to a sensitive d-c microammeter giving an indication of the alternating current passing through the heater wire. Calibration made with direct current or a

TABLE 1-1*

	Full-wave square law	Half-wave square law	Linear†	Peak
Turnover possible?....	No	Yes	No	Yes
Phase of harmonics affect reading?........	No	Yes	Yes	Yes
Effect of harmonic component on reading 50% second harmonic...........	11%	−6 to +27%	0 to 10%	−25 to +50%
50% third harmonic	11%	12.5%	−10 to +16%	8 to +50%

* From I. Wolff, Alternating-current Measuring Instruments as Discriminators against Harmonics, *Proc. IRE*, vol. 19, p. 647, April, 1931.
† Both half-wave and full-wave linear.

low frequency such as 60 cycles, will apply for all frequencies for which skin effect in the heater is not appreciable.

Thermocouple instruments are the standard means of measuring current at radio frequencies, and may be of several kinds, as illustrated in Fig. 1-9. The mutual type, in which the thermocouple also serves as its

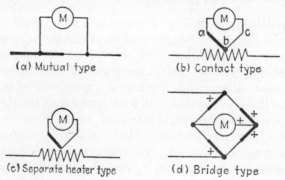

(a) Mutual type   (b) Contact type

(c) Separate heater type   (d) Bridge type

FIG. 1-9. Schematic diagram illustrating different types of thermocouple instruments.

own heater, is more sensitive than the contact type where there are separate thermocouple leads that conduct heat away from the heater, but has the disadvantage that the d-c microammeter shunts the heater. This difficulty is overcome in the bridge circuit, which preserves the high sensitivity of the mutual-type thermocouple, and yet avoids the shunting effect by placing the microammeter across the neutral arm of a bridge. In the separate heater arrangement, the thermocouple is held near to but insulated from the heater by a small glass bead.   This makes the instrument sluggish, and also less sensitive than the contact type because of the temperature drop in the glass, but the separation of heater and thermocouple has advantages for some types of work.

The sensitivity of a thermocouple arrangement may be increased by placing the thermocouple and associated heater in a vacuum.   In this way the loss of heat by conduction to the surrounding air is avoided; at the same time the absence of oxygen in contact with the heater makes it permissible to operate the heater at a much higher temperature than would be possible in air.   Vacuum thermocouples associated with small general-purpose microammeters can be designed to give full-scale deflection on approximately 1 ma.   A corresponding bridge arrangement of thermocouples in air will require about 100 ma for full-scale deflection. When a d-c instrument of very high sensitivity is used, such as a wall galvanometer, currents that are very much smaller than these values can be readily measured.

A variety of materials may be used to form the thermocouple.   A common combination is constantan (or advance) against copper, manganin, or a platinum alloy.   Such a junction gives a thermal emf of approximately 45 μv per °C.   The heating element of open-air heaters is typically made of a noncorroding platinum alloy, while carbon-filament heaters are commonly used in the vacuum type.

Thermocouple heaters operate so close to the burnout point under normal conditions that they can withstand only small overloads without damage, commonly only 50 per cent.   This is one of the serious limitations of thermocouple instruments, and also makes it impossible to use a fuse for protection.   Care must be taken to avoid passing surges of even very brief duration through a thermocouple instrument.   Thus the rush of charging current that results when several hundred volts is applied to a 4-μf condenser will invariably burn out the thermocouple of a 125-ma instrument even though the steady current flowing in the circuit is zero.

The heat generated by the passage of current through the thermocouple heater is proportional to the square of the effective value of the current.   Accordingly, harmonic components affect the indication in accordance with their influence on the square of the effective value of the wave, as in Eq. (1-1) (also see Table 1-1, page 10); thus a 20 per cent harmonic increases the effective value of the wave by 2 per cent.   When the generated heat is carried away primarily by conduction, the heater temperature is proportional to the square of the effective current.   This is the situation in all air thermocouples, and also in vacuum thermocouples when the heater current is not too large.   However, when the heater current in a vacuum thermocouple is sufficient to develop a high temperature, an appreciable part of the heat is lost by radiation.   Under these conditions the temperature, and hence the thermocouple voltage, increases less rapidly than the square of the effective value of the current, as shown in Fig. 1-10 by region *a-b*.   A further complicating factor is that at the higher operating temperatures, the resistance of the heater changes.

The microammeter of a thermocouple instrument will deflect slightly in the absence of a current if there is a temperature difference between the thermocouple junction *b*, and the "cold" junction indicated by *a* in Fig. 1-9*b*. Also, the reading resulting from a given current will vary with time if the temperature difference between hot and cold junctions is modified by unequal distribution of the heat produced by the heater. These effects become more pronounced as the thermal capacity of the heater is increased, and some form of equalization or compensation is required in instruments employing heaters designed for large currents.[1]

Frequency Effects, and Calibration Considerations in Thermocouples. Although the chief value of the thermocouple instrument results from the relative independence of its behavior with frequency, nevertheless frequency effects can occur as a result of skin effect, nonuniform current distribution along the length of the heater, and spurious capacitive currents.

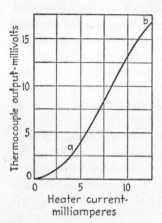

FIG. 1-10. Relationship between heater current and thermocouple output, for a vacuum thermocouple.

When the frequency becomes sufficiently high, skin effect causes the heater resistance to be greater than for lower frequencies and for direct currents.   This causes the heater temperature produced by a given current to be greater than at low frequencies, resulting in the thermocouple instrument reading high. As the frequency at which skin effect first becomes appreciable is greater the smaller the heater wire, thermocouples designed for small currents can in general be used without frequency correction at frequencies higher than can corresponding thermocouples designed for larger currents.

It is possible to construct low-current heaters for use in vacuum thermocouples that have a skin-effect error of less than 1 per cent at frequencies up to 30,000 Mc.[2]   Heaters for larger currents, such as 1 amp, will have a

[1] See W. N. Goodwin, Jr., The Compensated Thermocouple Ammeter, *Elec. Eng.*, vol. 55, p. 23, January, 1936.

[2] A good discussion of the upper frequency limit of a thermocouple from the point

less satisfactory high-frequency behavior, with the details depending on the kind of heater. Ribbon heaters, while often used to carry large currents, have relatively large skin effects. Solid wire is much better, while thin-walled tubing behaves excellently from the point of view of skin effect, and is now used for large currents where good high-frequency behavior is important.[1]

At frequencies so high that the heater length is an appreciable fraction of a wavelength, the current distribution along the heater will not be uniform. The relation between the indication of the thermocouple instrument and the current being measured then becomes uncertain. To avoid this, the heater and its associated leads must accordingly be quite short (less than a tenth of a wavelength), if high accuracy is to be maintained.

When a thermocouple instrument is connected in a circuit in such a manner that both terminals of the heater are at a potential above ground, then as the frequency is raised, an increasingly large current flows through the capacitance formed by the thermocouple leads and microammeter acting as one electrode, and the ground acting as the other electrode. This action causes the current flowing into one end of the heater to differ from that flowing out of the other end, thus introducing an uncertainty as to what current is being indicated. The resulting error is greater the higher the frequency, the smaller the current being measured, and the greater the potential difference that exists between the thermocouple and ground. These effects can be minimized by connecting the thermocouple into the circuit at a point where the impedance to ground has the lowest possible value; also in some cases shielding can be arranged so that no capacitive current will flow through the heater.[2]

The frequency characteristics of thermocouples employing heaters consisting of a short-length round wire or thin-walled tubing can be determined with fairly good reliability on the basis of theoretical skin-effect calculations. Where a check of such calculations is desired, or where skin-effect calculations cannot be made with accuracy, an experimental calibration can be made at high frequencies by the oscillating ring ammeter, the hot-wire air-expansion milliammeter, etc.[3]

---

of view of skin effect is given by L. S. Nergaard, A Survey of Ultra-high Frequency Measurements, *RCA Rev.*, vol. 3, p. 156, October, 1938; also see "Technique of Microwave Measurements" (Vol. 11 of Radiation Laboratory Series), p.188, McGraw-Hill Book Company, Inc., New York, 1947.

[1] Formulas, curves, and tables for calculating skin effect of solid-wire, tubular, and ribbon conductors are given on pp. 30–34 of F. E. Terman, "Radio Engineers' Handbook," McGraw-Hill Book Company, Inc., New York, 1943.

[2] For further information see J. D. Wallace, The Shielding of Radio-frequency Ammeters, *Proc. IRE*, vol. 29, p. 1, January, 1941.

[3] For further information on the absolute calibration of thermocouples see H. M.

The calibration of a thermocouple is reasonably permanent, although it must be periodically checked if precision is important. When calibrating contact- and mutual-type thermocouple instruments with direct current, it is always necessary to reverse the polarity of the direct-current and take the average of the readings for the two polarities as the true reading. This is because the resistance drop in the heater at the contact may cause a small amount of d-c current to flow through the microammeter; reversing the calibrating current averages out of this effect.

Measurements of Very Large Currents by Thermocouples. The measurement of large high-frequency currents introduces a number of difficulties. Thermocouple instruments with heaters large enough to carry very large currents may have excessive skin effect. Ordinary shunts cannot be

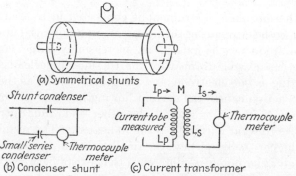

(a) Symmetrical shunts

(b) Condenser shunt   (c) Current transformer

Fig. 1-11. Methods that can be successfully employed to measure large radio-frequency currents.

employed to carry the major part of the current since the shunting ratio will be affected by the relative inductances as well as resistances, thus introducing a considerable frequency effect.

Several solutions to this problem are available. One consists of minimizing skin effect by employing a heater that is a tube of large diameter, but possessing very thin walls. An alternative is an array of shunts of identical resistance arranged symmetrically as in Fig. 1-11a, for example.

Turner and P. C. Michel, An Electrodynamic Ammeter for Use at Frequencies from One to One Hundred Megacycles, *Proc. IRE*, vol. 25, p. 1367, November, 1937; Harry R. Meahl, A Bearing-type High Frequency Electrodynamic Ammeter, *Proc. IRE*, vol. 26, p. 734, June, 1938; J. D. Wallace and A. H. More, Frequency Errors in Radio-frequency Ammeters, *Proc. IRE*, vol. 25, p. 327, March, 1937; John H. Miller, Thermocouple Ammeters for Ultra-high Frequencies, *Proc. IRE*, vol. 24, p. 1567, December, 1936; Herbert C. Hazel, A New Method for the Calibration of Ammeters at Radio Frequencies, *Proc. IRE*, vol. 16, p. 70, January, 1928: G. F. Gainsborough, Experiments with Thermocouple Milliammeters at Very High Radio Frequencies, *J. IEE*, pt. III, vol. 91, p. 156, September, 1944; M. J. O. Strutt and K. S. Knol, Measurements of Current and Voltage down to a Wavelength of 20 Centimeters, *Proc. IRE*, vol. 27, p. 783, December, 1939.

Here each filament of wire possesses the same inductance, so that the inductance causes the current to divide at high frequencies in the same way as does the resistance at low frequencies. The condenser shunt shown in Fig. 1-11b has also been used successfully in the measurement of large currents.[1] The current will divide between the two parallel condensers directly as their capacitance, and will maintain this ratio independent of frequency as long as the condenser that is in series with the thermocouple has a much higher impedance than the thermocouple heater, and provided that the lead inductances of the two branches of the circuit are in inverse proportion to the condenser capacitances.

Current transformers analogous to those used in electrical power work and illustrated schematically in Fig. 1-11c, can be employed to measure very large radio-frequency currents of low or moderate frequencies, using thermocouple instruments of ordinary range. Such transformers commonly, but not necessarily, employ a magnetic dust core. The current ratio is given by the equation:[2]

$$\frac{\text{Primary current}}{\text{Secondary current}} = \frac{1}{k}\sqrt{\frac{L_s}{L_p}}\sqrt{1 + \frac{1}{Q_s^2}} \tag{1-2}$$

where L_s = secondary inductance
L_p = primary inductance
k = coefficient of coupling between L_s and L_p
R_s = resistance of secondary, including meter resistance
$Q_s = \omega L_s/R_s = Q$ of secondary circuit taking into account meter resistance

It will be noted that if the Q of the secondary winding is appreciable (i.e., greater than 5), the transformation ratio is substantially independent of frequency. Current ratios up to 1000 or more can be obtained at low and moderate radio frequencies by using a many-turn secondary wound on a toroidal ring, through the hole of which the wire carrying the current to be metered is looped once or twice.

1-5. Vacuum-tube Voltmeters.[3] A vacuum-tube voltmeter is a vacuum-tube rectifier or detector in which the rectified direct current produced as the result of application of an alternating voltage is used as a measure of this voltage. Vacuum-tube voltmeters consume little or no

[1] Alexander Nyman, Condenser Shunt for Measurement of High-frequency Currents of Large Magnitude, *Proc. IRE*, vol. 16, p. 208, February, 1928.

[2] This is derived as follows: The voltage induced in the secondary by the primary current I_p is $-j\omega M I_p$. The secondary current I_s is this voltage divided by the impedance of the secondary circuit, or $I_s = -j\omega M I_p/(R_s + j\omega L_s)$. Solving this for $|I_p/I_s|$, and substituting $M = k/\sqrt{L_p L_s}$ gives Eq. (1-2).

[3] The first use of a vacuum tube to measure voltage was in 1915 by R. A. Heising; see Historic First: Vacuum-tube Voltmeter, *Bell Lab. Rec.*, vol. 24, p. 270, July, 1946.

power from the voltage being measured, and have an input capacitance that can be as small as 1 to 2 $\mu\mu f$. Sensitivities corresponding to full-scale deflection with an applied alternating potential of less than 1 volt are readily obtainable; at the same time the instrument can be designed to indicate very large voltages, such as hundreds or thousands of volts. The response of a vacuum-tube voltmeter can be made independent of frequency over wide frequency ranges; thus it is not unusual for the same calibration curve to apply for frequencies as low as 60 cycles and as high as 60 Mc.   As a result of these desirable characteristics, the vacuum-tube voltmeter is the most widely used instrument for making measurements at radio frequencies.

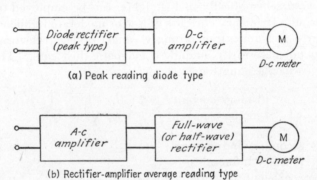

(a) Peak reading diode type

(b) Rectifier-amplifier average reading type

Fig. 1-12. Schematic diagrams of diode peak-reading and amplifier-rectifier average-reading types of vacuum-tube voltmeters.

Two commercial forms of vacuum-tube voltmeters are in wide use. In the first of these, the alternating voltage to be measured is rectified by a peak-type diode detector.   The output of the diode is amplified and indicated by a d-c amplifier and meter, as illustrated schematically in Fig. 1-12a.   Such an arrangement gives an indication of the peak amplitude of the positive half cycles of the applied voltage.   With proper attention to design, frequencies from the lowest to values of the order of 100 to 500 Mc can be covered in a single instrument.   The maximum sensitivity that can be obtained corresponds to full-scale deflection with an input voltage of the order of 0.5 volt peak.

In the other type of vacuum-tube voltmeter in wide commercial use (illustrated schematically in Fig. 1-12b), the alternating voltage to be indicated is first amplified by a wide-band amplifier stabilized by means of negative feedback.   The output of this amplifier is then rectified by a half-wave or a full-wave rectifier, and the resulting direct current used to operate a d'Arsonval type of instrument.   This amplifier-rectifier arrangement gives an indication proportional to the average amplitude of the wave, just as does the copper-oxide instrument, instead of an indication of the peak as in the case of the diode type.   The sensitivity is greater than for the diode type of voltmeter as it is a simple matter to provide sufficient amplification to give full-scale deflection with alternating voltages as low as 1 mv.   The frequency range of the amplifier-rectifier arrangement is, however, limited by the amplifier to a maximum of about 10 Mc.

In addition to the above types, many other forms of vacuum-tube voltmeters have been devised.   These include arrangements employing plate rectification, slide-back vacuum-tube voltmeters, and vacuum-tube voltmeters having logarithmic characteristics.

1-6. Diode Peak-reading Vacuum-tube Voltmeters.   The most common of the many vacuum-tube arrangements that can be employed as

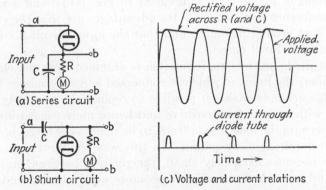

Fig. 1-13. Circuits for peak-reading diode voltmeter together with associated voltage and current waveforms.

vacuum-tube voltmeters is the diode peak-reading voltmeter, a simple form of which is shown in Fig. 1-13a.   This is an ordinary diode detector employing a high load resistance R.   The mechanism of operation is illustrated by the oscillograms of Fig. 1-13c.   At each positive peak of the applied voltage the condenser C is charged to a potential that is almost equal to the peak voltage.   Between peaks a small portion of the total charge on condenser C leaks off through the resistance R, causing a slight falling off in the condenser voltage.   At the positive peak of the next cycle the charge that has been lost in this way is replenished by a pulse of plate current through the diode.   The voltage across C, and hence across the resistance R, is thereby again built up almost to the peak value of the applied wave.   Either the average (d-c) voltage across R, or the average (d-c) current through R, can be used to indicate the peak of the applied voltage.   When this applied voltage is not too small, the relationship between the peak potential and the rectified output is almost linear.

The diode voltmeter consumes power from the applied voltage as a result of the current pulses that pass through the tube at the positive peak of each cycle. To a rough approximation, the power consumed in this way by the diode is the same as though the diode voltmeter offered an input resistance to the applied voltage equal to $R/2$.[1,2] By making R of the order of tens to hundreds of megohms, as is readily possible when the diode is associated with a d-c amplifier, the input resistance of the diode will be so high as to be of negligible consequence. This behavior implies an applied voltage of sufficient amplitude to cause the system to act as a peak device. If the applied signal is very small, then some current flows throughout the cycle of the voltage as a result of the velocity of emission of the electrons, and the input resistance may be only a few hundred ohms.

The circuit of Fig. 1-13b is equivalent to Fig. 1-13a, and is commonly used in preference to that at a. Its advantages are that the cathode of the tube is at ground potential, and that the input circuit need not provide a path for direct current.

In most diode voltmeters, indication is obtained from the output of a d-c amplifier, the input of which is connected across terminals bb in Fig. 1-13. This not only makes it possible to replace the relatively sensitive meter M with a much less sensitive and hence more rugged instrument, but also permits the load resistance R to be made very large, of the order of tens to hundreds of megohms. In this way the power consumed by the diode becomes extremely small, the relation between peak applied voltage and meter indication becomes more nearly linear, and the performance of the diode with inputs consisting of pulses and modulated waves is also improved (see below). The d-c amplifier associated with the diode rectifier should be provided with stabilizing means to prevent drift in the indication of the output meter; in general, a voltage-regulated power supply, combined with some form of compensating circuit, is employed.[3]

The diode tube is ordinarily mounted in a housing located at the end of a flexible cable that connects the tube to the remainder of the voltmeter

---

[1] See F. E. Terman, "Radio Engineering," 3d ed., p. 505, McGraw-Hill Book Company, Inc., New York, 1947.

[2] This is at frequencies for which the transit time of the electrons can be neglected. At frequencies so high that the transit time is an appreciable fraction of a cycle, the input resistance is less than $R/2$ as a result of energy absorbed by the electrons. The input resistance will then also depend upon the applied voltage, being less the smaller the voltage, since the transit time is increased as the voltage becomes less.

[3] Examples of commercial diode-amplifier voltmeter systems are described by C. A. Woodward, Jr., A New Vacuum-tube Voltmeter, *Gen. Rad. Expt.*, vol. 2, p. 1, September, 1946; The Type 1803 Vacuum-tube Voltmeter, *Gen. Rad. Expt.*, vol. 24, p. 1, April, 1950; W. N. Tuttle, The Type 727-A Vacuum-tube Voltmeter, *Gen. Rad. Expt.*, vol. 16, p. 1, May, 1942.

system, and which is so arranged that lead *a* in Fig. 1-13*b* forms a short
probe projecting from the housing.   In this way the tube can be brought
to the voltage being measured, ensuring minimum lead effects.   This is
necessary in dealing with radio-frequency circuits, since otherwise the
inductance and capacitance effects introduced by the voltmeter would
alter in a significant way the conditions in the circuit being measured.

**1-7. Waveform Effects in Diode Voltmeters, Including Response to
Modulated Waves and Pulses.**   Although the scale of the meter associated with a diode-type voltmeter is normally marked in effective (rms)
values on the assumption that the applied voltage is a sine wave, the
response is actually determined by the peak positive voltage applied to
lead *a* in Fig. 1-13.   As a result, the indication is very sensitive to the
presence of harmonics in the applied wave.   Thus a 20 per cent harmonic
can increase the indication by as much as 20 per cent, whereas with a

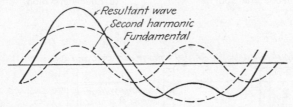

Fig. 1-14. Waveform illustrating the effect a second-harmonic component can have
on the peak amplitude of the positive and negative half cycles of an alternating
wave.

thermocouple instrument the same harmonic would increase the indication by only 2 per cent.   Also, whereas the relative phase of the harmonics has no effect on a square-law device such as a thermocouple, it is
very important in a peak-reading device.   As apparent from Fig. 1-14
(and as indicated in Table 1-1, page 10), the presence of a harmonic may
either increase or decrease the positive peak amplitude, depending on the
phase, amplitude, and order of the harmonic.

When even harmonics are present, the peak amplitudes of the positive
and negative half cycles are not necessarily the same, as is apparent in
Fig. 1-14.   Under these conditions, reversal of the input terminals of a
diode-type vacuum-tube voltmeter will change the voltage indicated by
the meter.   This polarity effect is sometimes called *turnover;* when it
exists the average of the direct and reverse polarity readings will approximate the effective value of the applied voltage more accurately than
either reading alone.

Response of Diode Voltmeter to Pulses.   When pulses such as produced
by a pulse generator are applied to the input of a diode voltmeter, it is
commonly found that when the pulse duration is short compared with the
length of time between pulses, the voltage indicated by the meter reading

is considerably less than 0.707 times the peak amplitude of the applied pulses even when the voltage across the diode condenser C does not decrease appreciably during the interval between pulses. This arises from the fact that all of the charge leaking off the condenser C during the relatively long period between pulses must be replaced by a current that flows through the diode only during the very brief interval represented by the pulse length. Thus if the pulse repetition frequency is 100 cycles, and the pulse length 1 μsec, then for accurate results the charge leaking

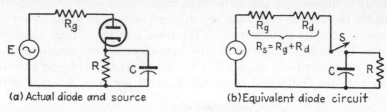

(a) Actual diode and source   (b) Equivalent diode circuit

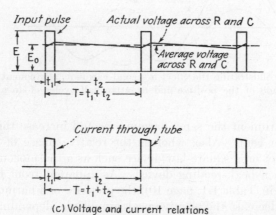

(c) Voltage and current relations

FIG. 1-15. The equivalent circuit, and voltage and current relations, for the case of a pulse applied to a peak-reading diode voltmeter.

off of condenser C during 10,000 μsec must be replaced by a current that averages 10,000 times as great flowing through the diode for 1 μsec. This pulse of current has a peak amplitude great enough to produce a large voltage drop in the diode and generator resistance R_s as defined below. Unless the time constant R_sC of the charging circuit as defined below is small compared with the pulse length t_1, the condenser C will not be charged to the peak amplitude of the applied pulse. Under ordinary circumstances the quantitative relations applying to this situation are given approximately by the relation:[1]

[1] This relation can be derived with the aid of the equivalent circuit of Fig. 1-15b, in which the diode tube is replaced by a switch S_1 that is closed during the interval

$$\left.\begin{array}{c}\text{Peak amplitude}\\ \text{of pulses}\end{array}\right\} = \left(\begin{array}{c}\text{scale reading}\\ \text{of meter}\end{array}\right) \times 1.414\left(1 + \frac{t_2}{t_1}\frac{R_s}{R}\right) \quad (1\text{-}3)$$

where, as indicated in Fig. 1-15,

R = resistance determining rate at which condenser C discharges, including shunting resistance together with leakage resistance of this condenser

R_s = equivalent source resistance, including actual source resistance R_g of applied voltage, and equivalent plate-cathode resistance R_d of diode

t_1 = pulse length

t_2 = time between pulses

$T = t_1 + t_2$ = reciprocal of pulse repetition frequency

The ratio t_1/T is termed the duty cycle; for short pulses $t_2 \approx T$, and the duty cycle approximates t_1/t_2.

The assumptions involved in Eq. (1-3) are that the plate-cathode resistance of the diode can be represented by a fixed resistance R_d, that $R \gg R_s$, and that the time constants R_sC and RC are appreciably greater than the pulse length t_1, and the time t_2 between pulses, respectively. The first assumption, while not strictly accurate, is satisfactory for ordinary purposes, while the remaining assumptions are realized with typical circuit proportions when the pulse duration is sufficiently short and the pulse repetition frequency is not excessively low. Results computed with the aid of Eq. (1-3) are given in Fig. 1-16 in general form, while the results for a particular case are illustrated in Fig. 1-17.[1]

---

the pulse voltage is applied, and is then open during the remainder of the time. In this equivalent circuit, the source of voltage E is assumed to have an equivalent internal resistance R_g, while the plate-cathode resistance of the diode is replaced by an equivalent fixed resistance R_d.

When the time constants R_sC and RC are appreciably greater than times t_1 and t_2, respectively, then the percentage change in voltage across condenser C is small during both charge and discharge periods, as illustrated in Fig. 1-15c. Under these assumptions the charge delivered to condenser C during a pulse is $t_1(E - E_0)/R_s$, where E_0 is the average voltage across C and is the output voltage indicated by the system. The charge that leaks off the condenser during the interval between pulses is t_2E_0/R. Since these two charges must be equal, one can then write

$$\frac{t_1(E - E_0)}{R_s} = \frac{t_2E_0}{R}$$

or, solving for E_0

$$E_0 = \frac{E}{1 + (t_2/t_1)(R_s/R)} \quad (1\text{-}3a)$$

Equation (1-3) follows when allowance is made for the fact that the meter is ordinarily calibrated in equivalent rms instead of peak values.

[1] For additional examples, see A. Easton, Pulse Responses of Diode Voltmeters, *Electronics* vol. 19, p. 146, January, 1946.

It is apparent that diode-voltmeter readings can be expected to be considerably in error under many conditions occurring in practice. Examination of Eq. (1-3) and Figs. 1-16 and 1-17 shows that this error

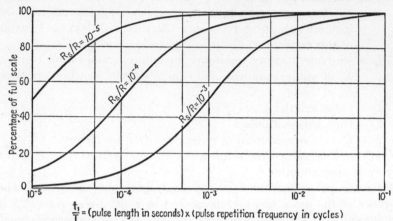

$$\frac{t_1}{T} = \text{(pulse length in seconds)} \times \text{(pulse repetition frequency in cycles)}$$

Fig. 1-16. Generalized curves showing the behavior of a peak-reading diode voltmeter when the input wave is a pulse.

increases the shorter the pulse length, the lower the repetition frequency, and the greater the ratio R_s/R of equivalent source resistance to equivalent discharge resistance. To avoid error in any particular situation, it is not only necessary to make R large enough so that $t_2 R_s/t_1 R \ll 1$, but

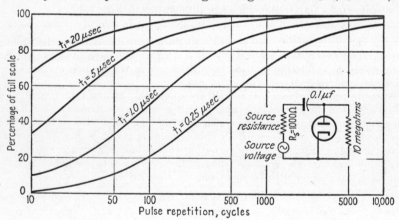

Fig. 1-17. Curves showing the relative output reading of a particular diode voltmeter as a function of repetition frequency, when the input wave is a pulse of various lengths t_1.

also it is necessary that $RC \gg t_2$. This is equivalent to saying that to avoid error in indication, the charging time constant $R_s C$ must be small compared with the time t_1 available for charging C, while the discharge time constant must be large compared with the time t_2 available for the discharge of condenser C.

A diode voltmeter used with pulses not only reads less than the peak amplitude of the pulse, but at the same time has a relatively low input resistance as compared with the input resistance that would be obtained with a sinusoidal voltage. This arises from the fact that during the interval the pulse voltage is applied, a very large current flows through the tube. To the same approximations involved in Eq. (1-3), the input resistance of the diode voltmeter to a pulse is[1]

$$\left. \begin{array}{l} \text{Equivalent input resistance} \\ \text{of diode to pulses} \end{array} \right\} = R_s \left(1 + \frac{Rt_1}{R_s t_2} \right) \qquad (1\text{-}4)$$

When the applied voltage has negligible internal impedance ($R_g = 0$), then the input resistance will approach the equivalent plate-cathode resistance of the tube for conditions which make the parentheses in the right-hand side of Eq. (1-3) appreciably greater than unity. This corresponds to an input resistance that is often below 1000 ohms, an altogether different order of magnitude from the equivalent input resistance $R/2$, typically in excess of 1 megohm, that the same diode voltmeter would have with a sinusoidal voltage.[2]

If the voltage applied to a diode voltmeter is a pulse-modulated radio-frequency wave, rather than a simple pulse, the behavior is the same as would be calculated from Eqs. (1-3) and (1-4) for a pulse length t_1 taken as between 0.3 and 0.1 times the length of the actual pulse.[3] This results from the fact that with the pulse-modulated radio-frequency wave, current flows through the diode only during part of the positive radio-frequency half cycles. The exact value of the factor by which the pulse length t_1 is to be multiplied depends upon how nearly the voltmeter is able to indicate the peak pulse voltage, the factor being larger the greater the error in the indication.

[1] This is derived from the fact that the input resistance is the applied voltage E divided by the diode current, while the diode current is the voltage $E - E_0$ between diode plate and cathode, divided by the equivalent source resistance R_s. Thus input resistance is $R_s E/(E - E_0)$, which gives Eq. (1-4) upon substitution from Eq. (1-3a).

[2] The problem presented by the low input impedance can be most readily handled by applying the pulse to a cathode-follower amplifier that is used to excite the diode voltmeter tube. Thus see D. E. Howes, High Impedance Pulse Voltmeter, *Rev. Sci. Instruments*, vol. 16, p. 322, November, 1945. More complicated solutions are described by Y. P. Yu, An Improved Peak Voltmeter for Pulses, *Rev. Sci. Instruments*, vol. 19, p. 447, July, 1948; F. H. Shepard and F. Osterland, Peak-to-peak Voltmeter, *Electronics*, vol. 21, p. 101, October, 1948.

[3] A quantitative analysis is given by R. E. Burgess, The Response of a Diode Voltmeter to Single and Recurrent Pulses of Various Shapes, *J. IEE (Radio Section)*, vol. 95, pt. III, p.106, March, 1948.

Response of Diode Voltmeters to Modulated Waves. When the voltage applied to a diode voltmeter is a sinusoidally modulated radio-frequency wave, the behavior of the instrument is much the same as in the case of a pulse-modulated radio-frequency wave. During the positive peaks of the modulation cycle a relatively large current will flow through the diode in an attempt to charge the condenser C to the highest radio-frequency voltage reached during the modulation cycle. Between positive peaks of modulation, the diode becomes nonconducting and condenser C slowly discharges through the resistance R, as shown in Fig. 1-18. The result is a tendency for the instrument to give an indication moderately

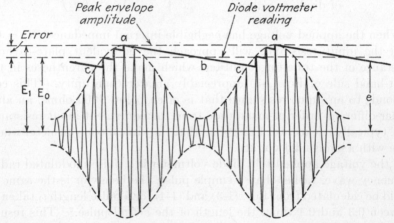

Fig. 1-18. Voltage waveforms showing behavior of a peak-reading diode voltmeter when the input wave is a modulated radio-frequency oscillation.

less than the peak amplitude of the modulation envelope. This error in peak indication will be less the larger the quantity R/X, where X is the reactance of the diode condenser C at the modulation frequency, and R is the diode load resistance. For good peak action, R/X should preferably be over 150 (corresponding to about 2 per cent error for a fully modulated wave).[1]

---

[1] This is arrived at as follows: The curve abc in Fig. 1-18 follows the equation $e = E_1\epsilon^{-t/RC}$. If now $t/RC \ll 1$, as is the case when the error is not large, then $\epsilon^{-t/RC}$ can be replaced by $1 - (t/RC)$, giving $e = E_1(1 - t/RC)$. The average amplitude E_0 of e during the interval from a, corresponding to $t = 0$, to c, corresponding to $t = t_1$, is $E_0 = E_1[1 - (t_1/2RC)]$. Noting that if the interval ca is much shorter than the interval abc, then to a rough approximation $t_1 = 1/f_m$, where f_m is the modulation frequency

$$\frac{\text{Error}}{E_1} = \frac{E_1 - E_0}{E_1} = \frac{t_1}{2RC} = \frac{\pi}{2\pi f_m CR} = \frac{\pi}{R/X} \qquad (1\text{-}5)$$

For $R/X = 150$, the error becomes 0.02.

1-8. Effect of Frequency on Behavior of Diode Voltmeters. At very high frequencies the indication of a diode voltmeter will be in error as a result of partial resonance in the input leads, and because of the transit time of the electrons passing from cathode to plate.

The equivalent input circuit of a diode voltmeter is shown in Fig. 1-19, and consists of lead inductance L and tube capacitance C_{pf}. These form a series resonant circuit, which causes the alternating voltage E_{pf} actually existing between plate and cathode to differ from the applied alternating voltage E. When not too close to resonance the relationship is[1]

$$\frac{\text{Actual plate-cathode alternating voltage}}{\text{Applied alternating voltage}} = \frac{E_{pf}}{E} = \frac{1}{1 - (f/f_r)^2} \quad (1\text{-}6)$$

where f/f_r is the ratio of actual to series resonant frequency. The relationship represented by Eq. (1-6) is plotted in Fig. 1-20 for the region below resonance. When the ratio f/f_r is appreciably less than unity, the fractional error is proportional to the square of the frequency, and is 12.5 per cent at one-third the resonant frequency.

The capacitance C_{pf} of the series resonant circuit depends primarily upon the plate-cathode capacitance of the tube. The inductance L consists of the inductance of the cathode and plate leads inside and outside the tube, including the inductance of the probe commonly attached to anode lead a in Fig. 1-13b. The resonant frequency f_r for the Type 9005 acorn diode when mounted in a housing carefully designed to minimize frequency effects, is about 1000 Mc, while values up to about 2000 Mc can be obtained with specially designed very small close-spaced diodes.

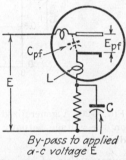

By-pass to applied
a-c voltage E

Fig. 1-19. A schematic diagram of diode input, indicating the inductance of the cathode and plate leads, and the plate-cathode capacitance.

Thus the upper frequency limit possible in diode voltmeters without lead effects exceeding 10 per cent is about 700 Mc, while if ordinary tubes are used the upper frequency limit will be substantially lower than this.

Transit-time Effects. Transit time at very high frequencies causes the diode voltmeter to indicate a potential less than the value actually existing between cathode and plate.[2] Consider the situation in Fig. 1-21,

[1] This follows from the fact that the voltage ratio is

$$\frac{1/j\omega C_{pf}}{j\omega L + (1/j\omega C_{pf})} = \frac{1}{-\omega^2 L C_{pf} + 1}$$

Equation (1-5) results upon substitution of the relation $(2\pi f_r)^2 = 1/LC_{pf}$.

[2] Transit time also causes the input resistance of the diode voltmeter to become less and to depend upon the amplitude of the voltage being measured, as explained in the footnote on page 18.

where it is assumed that when transit time is taken into account the diode condenser C in Fig. 1-13b charges to a potential E_0 that is ΔE less than the peak value E of the applied wave. Consider now an electron leaving the cathode at some time such as t_1; this electron is accelerated by a potential equal to the difference in voltage between E_0 and the instanta-

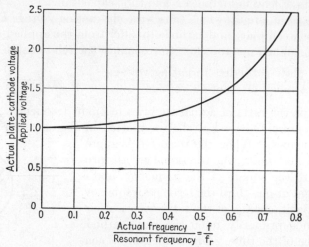

FIG. 1-20. A generalized curve showing effect of partial resonance in the input lead on the voltage actually appearing between the plate and cathode electrodes of a diode.

neous value of the applied wave. Assume also that this particular electron arrives at the plate just as it is slowed down to zero velocity. This time of arrival will be t_2, and the fact that the electron is able to reach the plate when the plate is less positive than E_0 (i.e., plate negative with

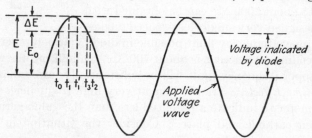

FIG. 1-21. Diagram illustrating effects of transit time on the voltage indicated by a peak-reading diode.

respect to its cathode) is a result of the acceleration obtained earlier in the transit period. Electrons leaving the cathode during the interval t_0 to t_1 reach the plate, but all electrons leaving the cathode at times subsequent to t_1, such as t_1', start toward the plate but before they reach it are slowed down to zero velocity, and turned back toward the cathode.

Thus because of transit time only the electrons leaving the cathode in the interval $t_0 t_1$ reach the plate and are available to charge condenser C, whereas at low frequencies electrons leaving the cathode in the longer time interval t_0 to t_3 reach the plate. The magnitude of ΔE is accordingly less than when the transit is significant. This effect of transit time is sometimes referred to as "premature cutoff." As a result of it, the larger the transit time the lower will be the voltage to which the diode condenser C is charged, and hence the greater will be the error in the diode indication. Furthermore, since the velocity with which the electrons move is proportional to the square root of the voltages involved, *the error will be greater the smaller the input voltage applied to the anode.*

Mathematical analysis verified by experiment shows that the transit-time error is given quantitatively by the relation[1]

$$\text{Fractional error} = \frac{\Delta E}{E} = \frac{kX_a}{\lambda \sqrt{E}} \tag{1-7}$$

where k = constant that is approximately 1050 for cylindrical electrodes, and 2100 with plane electrodes

X_a = clearance between plate and cathode, cm

E = peak amplitude of signal applied between cathode and plate

λ = wavelength, cm

This relation is derived on the assumption that the error is small or moderate, and indicates that under these conditions the error is proportional to the frequency, and inversely proportional to the square root of the peak value of the applied signal. For the Type 9005 acorn diode tube the transit-time error for an input potential of 2 volts peak is about 6 per cent at 200 Mc. With ordinary tubes the transit-time effect will be considerably more serious than this, and even with specially designed close-spaced diodes it begins to be appreciable at about 500 Mc.

It will be noted that the transit-time error is of the opposite sign from the error introduced by the leads, and furthermore, the two vary with frequency according to different laws. Moreover, one of the errors varies with the amplitude of the applied voltage, while the other does not. The over-all result obtained with a close-spaced diode specially designed for voltmeter use is shown in Fig. 1-22;[2] the behavior of the acorn and other tubes is much inferior. When such a correction curve is available, the

[1] This is from Leon S. Nergaard, Electrical Measurements at Wave Lengths Less than Two Meters, *Proc. IRE*, vol. 24, p. 1207, September, 1936. Equivalent results are also given by E. C. S. Megaw, Voltage Measurement at Very High Frequencies, *Wireless Eng.*, vol. 13, p. 64, February, p. 135, March, and p. 201, April, 1936, and C. L. Fortescue, Thermionic Peak Voltmeters, for Use at Very High Frequencies, *J. IEE (Wireless Sec.)*, vol. 10, p. 262, September, 1935.

[2] This figure is adapted from information supplied by the Hewlett-Packard Company.

useful frequency range of the diode voltmeter may be extended by perhaps one octave. However, at best the diode voltmeter is of little value for accurate measurement beyond 1000 Mc even when special close-spaced tubes are employed.

Low-frequency Considerations. The low-frequency limit of a diode voltmeter is determined by the fact that the meter will read low when the frequency is so low that the potential across diode condenser C in Fig.

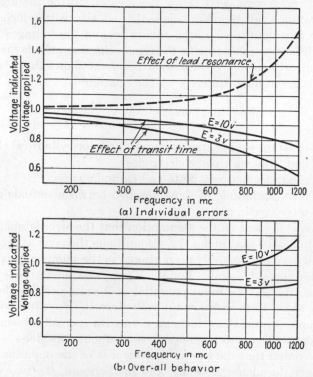

Fig. 1-22. Curve showing behavior of a particular peak-reading diode at very high frequencies and indicating the contributions made by transit time and partial resonance in the input circuit to the resultant behavior.

1-13*b* drops off appreciably in value between positive peaks as a result of leakage through resistance R. When the error from this source is not excessive (less than about 15 per cent), it is given approximately by the relation[1]

$$\text{Error in diode indication} = \frac{\pi}{R/X} \qquad (1\text{-}8)$$

[1] This follows from the fact that in the time $1/f$ of one cycle, the voltage across C decays by the factor $e^{-1/fCR}$ due to leakage through R. When $1/fCR$ is small, then $e^{-1/fCR} = 1 - (1/fCR)$, and the average loss in voltage is

$$1/2fCR = \pi/2\pi fCR = \pi/(R/X)$$

where R/X is the ratio of resistance R (see Fig. 1-13b) to the reactance of condenser C at the input frequency. It will be noted that this result is identical with Eq. (1-5), and that if the error is not to exceed about 2 per cent, then R/X must be not less than 150.

It is a simple matter to realize circuit proportions that will keep the error as calculated by Eq. (1-8) to a negligible value at frequencies well below 60 cycles. It is thus possible to design diode voltmeters so that they can be calibrated at 60 cycles, and used with the same calibration for all frequencies up to 200 Mc. However, the large capacitance C required to obtain good behavior at low frequencies is commonly of sufficient physical size to lower appreciably the series resonant frequency

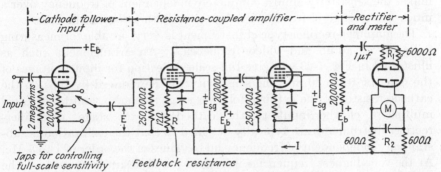

FIG. 1-23. Schematic diagram of amplifier-rectifier type of vacuum-tube voltmeter.

of the input circuit (see Fig. 1-19). Accordingly, diode voltmeters are sometimes arranged so that two values of capacitance can be used, a large value for low frequencies and when low-frequency calibrations are being made, and the other, a much smaller capacitance with a correspondingly shorter probe and smaller housing, for use when making measurements at very high frequencies.

1-9. Amplifier-Rectifier Type of Vacuum-tube Voltmeters. The fundamental features of an amplifier-rectifier vacuum-tube voltmeter have already been indicated in Fig. 1-12b. Briefly, the voltage to be measured is amplified, and then rectified, and the resulting direct current taken as a measure of the voltage.

A circuit diagram illustrating the principal features usually incorporated in practical amplifier-rectifier voltmeters is shown in Fig. 1-23. Here the amplifier system consists of a cathode-follower input tube followed by two stages of resistance-coupled amplification designed to amplify uniformly over a wide frequency band. The amplifier output delivers a current I to a rectifier, which in Fig. 1-23 is a full-wave rectifier employing a double diode; in other cases a crystal rectifier is employed, and also half-wave rectification is sometimes used. The current I

delivered by the amplifier output to the rectifier system is passed through resistance R, thereby developing a voltage in the cathode circuit of the first resistance-coupled stage that is proportional to the current I. This introduces negative feedback of a character such as to make the current I faithfully reproduce the voltage E that is delivered to the resistance-coupled amplifier by the output of the cathode-follower input stage. As a result of this negative feedback, together with the negative feedback that is implicit in the cathode-follower connection, the calibration of the entire system is substantially independent of supply voltage, tube characteristics, and of circuit constants except for the particular resistance R that produces the negative feedback. The use of negative feedback also makes the sensitivity almost completely independent of frequency over a much wider range of frequencies than would otherwise be the case.

The amplifier-rectifier type of instrument is very suitable for measuring voltages, at audio and video frequencies. An arrangement such as illustrated in Fig. 1-23 will give full-scale deflection for input voltages of the order of 10 to 30 mv; the sensitivity can be reduced by taps on the cathode resistor of the cathode-follower stage as shown, and by external multipliers of the input to the cathode-follower stage. Amplifier-rectifier instruments are typically designed so that the calibration is substantially independent of frequency up to values of the order of 1 to 5 Mc. At the very highest frequencies it is often found desirable to arrange the cathode-follower input tube in the form of a probe, as in the case of the diode peak voltmeter at high frequencies.

When the voltage being measured is a distorted wave shape, the behavior of the amplifier-rectifier instrument is the same as that of a copper-oxide rectifier, and so corresponds to the linear case in Table 1-1 (page 10). This behavior is obtained by making the load impedance in the rectifier output a resistance that is substantially constant up to the highest frequency that is being rectified; in Fig. 1-23 this means making the resistances R_1 and R_2 small enough so that the stray shunting capacitances have negligible by-passing action at the highest frequency of measurement.

1-10. Vacuum-tube Voltmeters Employing Plate Rectification. Plate rectification (plate detection) using a triode tube is sometimes employed in vacuum-tube voltmeters instead of a diode rectifier. A typical circuit arrangement of this type is illustrated in Fig. 1-24a. Here the curvature of the plate-current grid-voltage characteristic of the tube causes the d-c current to change by an amount which is a measure of the applied voltage. This change in plate current is indicated by a d-c milliammeter in the plate circuit, which is well by-passed to all a-c components. The steady plate current flowing through the milliammeter when no signal is applied is customarily balanced out so that the full scale of the instrument is available for reading change in plate current.   Means of doing this are shown in Fig. 1-24d and e.

The characteristics of a plate-rectifier type of voltmeter depend upon the circuit adjustment, and upon the amplitude of the applied signal. If the control grid bias is a fixed value independent of plate current (not derived from a bias resistor), and is appreciably less than the grid bias required to cut off the plate current, as in Fig. 1-25a, then the change in plate current produced by an applied voltage that is not too large, is almost exactly proportional to the square of the effective value of the applied voltage.   Such action is termed *full-wave square-law action*, and results because the tube characteristic over a limited range of grid voltage

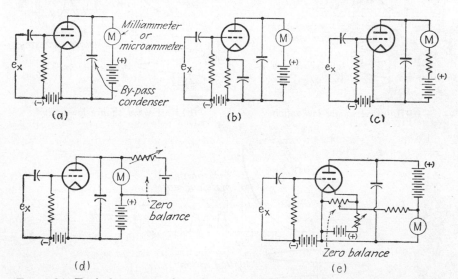

FIG. 1-24. Typical vacuum-tube voltmeter circuits employing plate rectification.

can be approximated by a parabola.   Under these conditions, harmonics in the applied wave affect the indication in proportion to the contribution of the harmonics to the square of the effective value [see Eq. (1-1)].   The phase of the harmonics has no effect on the reading, and no turnover effect is present when the polarity of the applied voltage is reversed. Further details of behavior are given in Table 1-1 (page 10).

If the grid bias of a plate rectifier is so chosen that the operating point approximates plate current cutoff, as is shown in Fig. 1-25b, then the negative half cycles of the applied voltage are entirely suppressed and have no effect.   The change in plate current, the "rectified" current, accordingly depends only upon the positive half cycles of the wave.   If the amplitude is not too great, the rectified current will be proportional to the square of the effective value of the positive half cycles, giving *half-*

wave square-law action. When the applied voltage contains harmonics, the phase as well as the amplitude of the harmonics will affect the reading, and turnover is also present, as indicated in Table 1-1 (page 10).

If the grid bias is made greater than cutoff, as shown in Fig. 1-25c, then plate current flows only at the positive peaks of the applied voltage, and the instrument tends to become a peak voltmeter.

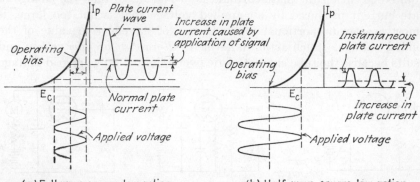

(a) Full-wave square-law action   (b) Half-wave square-law action

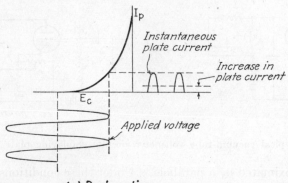

(c) Peak action

Fig. 1-25. Voltage and current relations in plate-rectifier voltmeters adjusted to give different types of action.

The calibration curve of full-wave and half-wave square-law voltmeters is a straight line when plotted on log-log paper, as shown in Fig. 1-26. This fact can be used to obtain a complete calibration curve from a relatively small number of points; also departure of the curve from a straight line gives a simple means of indicating when the behavior ceases to be of the square-law type.

Other possible plate-rectification circuits include a self-biased system, as illustrated in Fig. 1-24b, and an arrangement with a high resistance in series with the plate milliammeter, as illustrated in Fig. 1-24c. Although both of these arrangements have calibration curves that tend to be linear, they have the disadvantage that with large applied potentials they tend to be peak devices.   This results from the fact that the large increase in d-c plate current produced by a large applied signal increases the bias in Fig. 1-24b, and reduces the voltage actually at the plate of the tube in Fig. 1-24c, to such an extent that the effective operating point corresponds to a condition that is beyond cutoff, as in Fig. 1-25c.

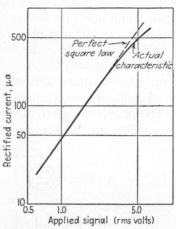

FIG. 1-26. Calibration curve of plate-rectifier type of vacuum-tube voltmeter, illustrating how departure from square-law action can be readily detected by plotting the calibration on a log-log scale.

The maximum sensitivity obtainable with vacuum-tube voltmeters in which plate current flows in the absence of an applied voltage, such as the full-wave square-law type, is limited by the stability that can be achieved in balancing out the quiescent d-c plate current from the meter.   This is because the less the current change that is to be measured, the more precise must be the balance of the initial current.   Otherwise the deflection in the absence of a signal will drift appreciably from zero in comparison with the amplitude of the deflection produced by the signal.   The chief difficulty in maintaining an accurate zero balance comes as a result of variations in the tube voltages, although variations in the tube characteristics either through aging, or merely as a result of "warming up" of the tube, are also troublesome.   It is accordingly important that all voltages applied to a vacuum-tube voltmeter of this type, including filament as well as plate, bias, and balancing voltages, be carefully regulated. It is also helpful to employ circuit arrangements that are inherently stabilized against voltage changes.   Thus it is possible to balance out the plate current by means of a similar auxiliary tube that is affected in the same way by supply-voltage changes, tube warm-up, etc., as is the voltmeter tube.   This is illustrated schematically in Fig. 1-27.[1]

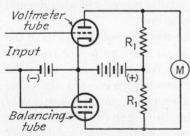

FIG. 1-27. A simple d-c voltmeter circuit employing a balancing tube.

[1] For an example of a more elaborate balancing arrangement see C. Williamson and J. Nagy, Push-pull Stabilized Triode Voltmeter, *Rev. Sci. Instruments*, vol. 9, p. 270. September, 1938.

It is customary to employ triode tubes in vacuum-tube voltmeters of the plate-rectification type. If pentodes are used, they are preferably reconnected as triodes, since the pentode connection gives no advantages and adds complications. The amplification factor of the tube is not important beyond the fact that with a given grid bias (which defines the peak amplitude that the applied signal may have without grid current flowing), the required plate-supply voltage is less the smaller the amplification factor. If high sensitivity to a small applied signal is desired, the tube should have a high transconductance in proportion to d-c plate current, such as characterizes tubes designed for video-frequency or wideband radio-frequency amplification.

The practical high-frequency limit of a plate-rectifier type of vacuum-tube voltmeter is determined by the fact that the input conductance

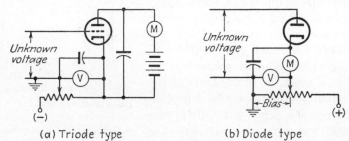

(a) Triode type   (b) Diode type

Fig. 1-28. Schematic diagram of slide-back vacuum-tube voltmeters.

becomes excessively high at very high frequencies, as a result of transit-time effects and cathode lead inductance. This behavior is analogous to that encountered in amplifier tubes at corresponding frequencies, except that if the vacuum-tube voltmeter is biased at or beyond cutoff, the transit-time effects, and hence the input conductance, will also depend upon the amplitude of the voltage being measured.

As compared with diode voltmeters, plate-rectifier voltmeters have the advantage that they can be so operated as to draw no power from the applied voltage; also, they can be made to follow a square law with accuracy, which is sometimes but not always preferred. At the same time the high-frequency limit of plate-rectifier arrangements is ordinarily poorer, they are less stable as a result of requiring careful balance of the quiescent d-c plate current, and they require more frequent recalibration.

1-11. Slide-back Vacuum-tube Voltmeters. Typical examples of slide-back vacuum-tube voltmeters are shown in Fig. 1-28. The triode type of slide-back voltmeter, illustrated in Fig. 1-28a, consists of a plate-rectifier voltmeter provided with an adjustable grid bias that is read by voltmeter V. In the absence of signal, this bias is adjusted so that the plate current is reduced to a few microamperes as indicated on the meter

M.   The voltage to be measured is then applied to the grid of the tube, and the negative bias on this grid is increased until the d-c current in the plate circuit is again reduced to a few microamperes.   The peak amplitude of the positive half cycle of the applied wave is very closely equal to the increase in the bias.[1]

A slide-back arrangement employing diode rather than plate detection is illustrated in Fig. 1-28*b*.   Here the current indicated by meter *M* in the absence of an applied signal is very small, representing only the current flowing to the plate as a result of emission velocity.   When a voltage is applied, the bias voltage is adjusted until the current through meter *M* is reduced almost to zero.   The peak amplitude of the applied voltage is then assumed equal to the reading of voltmeter *V*.[2]

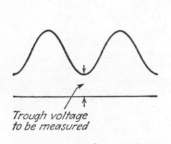

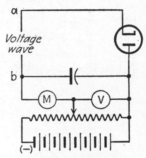

(a) Wave consisting of alternating voltage superimposed on a direct voltage

(b) Trough meter for determining minimum positive voltage

FIG. 1-29. Trough meter for reading trough value of a pulsating positive wave. Note that battery polarity has been reversed from that in Fig. 1-28*b*.

It is to be noted that the slide-back voltmeter will correctly indicate the peak amplitude of pulses if the meter *M* is quite sensitive.

A modification of the diode slide-back voltmeter arranged to measure minimum positive voltage of an alternating wave superimposed on a larger d-c voltage, is illustrated in Fig. 1-29.   This arrangement, which can be termed a "trough" meter, is operated in the same manner as the

---

[1] The voltages indicated by a slide-back voltmeter are slightly low by an amount that becomes less the larger the applied signal and the sharper the cut-off characteristics of the tube.   If the initial plate current is only a few microamperes, and the applied signal is relatively large, the error is then quite small.   A detailed analysis of this situation, which includes means of determining this error, is given by C. B. Aiken and L. C. Birdsall, Sharp Cut-off in Vacuum Tubes with Applications to the Slide-back Voltmeter, *Trans. AIEE*, vol. 57, p. 171, April, 1938.

[2] A modification of this arrangement, in which the slide-back bias is obtained automatically by amplification of the rectified output of the diode, is described by C. J. Creveling and Leonard Mautner, An Automatic Slide-back Peak Voltmeter for Measuring Pulses, *Proc. IRE*, vol. 35, p. 208, February, 1947.

diode slide-back voltmeter of Fig. 1-28*b*, but because of the reversal of bias polarity, and the interchange of cathode and plate, the voltage indicated is now the minimum positive voltage of lead *a* with respect to lead *b*.

1-12. Logarithmic Vacuum-tube Voltmeters. The term *logarithmic* is applied to a vacuum-tube voltmeter when the current or voltage produced in the indicating instrument by an applied voltage is proportional to the logarithm of the applied voltage. Such a characteristic leads to a linear decibel scale for the indicating instrument, and therefore finds numerous practical uses.

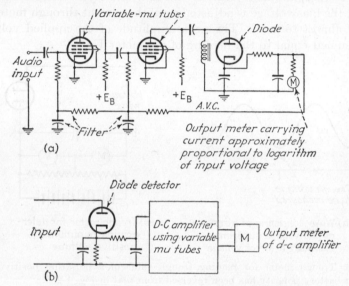

Fig. 1-30. Logarithmic vacuum-tube voltmeters.

There are three principal methods used for obtaining a logarithmic characteristic.[1] The first of these is illustrated schematically in Fig. 1-30*a*, and is particularly suitable where the input voltage is too small to be measured directly, as in field-strength recorders, sound-intensity measurements, etc.[2] Here the voltage to be indicated is passed through

[1] Still another principle that can be used to give logarithmic indication consists in utilizing each positive crest of the voltage being measured to initiate an exponentially decaying wave that has an initial amplitude proportional to the peak amplitude to be measured. The output meter indicates the time it takes this exponential wave to decay to a convenient and arbitrarily selected amplitude. Because of the properties of the exponential curve this time is proportional to the logarithm of the initial amplitude, and hence to the peak of the wave being measured. Apparatus for carrying out these operations is described by A. W. Nolle, Electronic Circuit as Logarithmic Response, *Electronics*, vol. 21, p. 166, September, 1948.

[2] For more information see H. A. Wheeler and V. E. Whitman, Acoustic Testing of High-fidelity Receivers, *Proc. IRE*, vol. 23, p. 610, June, 1935; S. Ballantine, High

an amplifier consisting of several stages of variable-mu tubes. The amplified output is then rectified and used to develop an automatic volume control bias for the grids of the variable-mu tubes. The relationship obtained between input voltage and the rectified current in the automatic volume control of such a system can be made reasonably close to logarithmic over a range of amplitudes up to 60 db if the automatic volume control operates on several tubes.

A second form of logarithmic voltmeter is illustrated schematically in Fig. 1-30b, and is particularly suitable for large input voltages. Here a diode (or other type) rectifier is used to develop a d-c voltage proportional to the peak input voltage. This rectified output or a fraction of it, is then amplified by a d-c amplifier employing a variable-mu tube. A logarithmic characteristic over a 20-db range can be obtained in this way, with still greater logarithmic range obtainable by employing auxiliary tubes to introduce a correcting nonlinearity in the amplifier.[1]

The third type of logarithmic voltmeter makes use of the fact that the velocities of the electrons emitted from a hot cathode are distributed according to the Maxwellian law. As a result, when the plate current of a diode tube is sufficiently small (typically not over 10 to 100 μa), the actual difference in potential between plate and cathode resulting from the passage of a current I is related to the voltage drop E across the tube according to the equation

$$E = A - B \log_{10} I \tag{1-9}$$

where A and B are constants.[2] It is clear that if a direct current proportional to the amplitude of whatever is to be measured is passed through the tube under conditions where Eq. (1-9) applies, then the voltage developed between plate and cathode of the tube as a result of the passage of this current will vary exactly in proportion to the logarithm of the current. Moreover, because the logarithmic characteristic is controlled by a

Quality Radio Broadcast Transmission and Reception, *Proc. IRE*, vol. 35, p. 618, June, 1935; K. R. Sturley and R. P. Skipway, A Visual Selectivity Meter with a Uniform Decibel Scale, *J. IEE*, vol. 87, p. 189, 1940 (*Wireless Sec.*, *J. IEE*, vol. 15, p. 215, September, 1940).

[1] J. P. Taylor, A D-C Amplifier for Logarithmic Recording, *Electronics*, vol. 10, p. 24, March, 1937; F. V. Hunt, A Vacuum-tube Voltmeter with Logarithmic Response, *Rev. Sci. Instruments*, vol. 4, p. 672, December, 1933.

[2] The constant B, which controls the logarithmic behavior, is given by the relation $B = 690(kT/e)$, where k is Boltzmann's constant, T is the absolute temperature, and e is the change of an electron. This constant accordingly always has the same value for the same cathode temperature, irrespective of type of cathode, cathode emission, tube geometry, etc. The constant A on the other hand depends upon such factors as tube geometry, cathode emission, and contact potential between plate and cathode, but its value does not affect the logarithmic nature of the current characteristic.

fundamental physical law, it is constant and predictable.   Under practical circumstances the logarithmic relationship can be maintained almost
ideally over a range of 40 db, and approximated rather well over a range
of 100 db.[1]

1-13. Crystal Voltmeters and Galvanometers.[2]   A silicon or germanium crystal rectifier has properties similar to those of a diode, and so can
replace the tube in a diode type of vacuum-tube voltmeter.

Such a crystal voltmeter, moreover, has certain advantages over the
corresponding diode arrangement.   The performance at very high frequencies is superior because of the very small transit-time effects in the
crystal even at the highest radio frequencies, and because the small
physical size of the crystal in relationship to its input capacitance results
in the resonant frequency of the input system being higher than when a
tube is employed.   In addition the crystal does not have a cathode that
needs to be heated, and which as a result of velocity of emission produces
some plate current even in the absence of an applied signal.   The crystal
also is a more effective rectifier of very small input voltages, since for a
crystal the curve of current as a function of applied voltage has a greater
curvature for small applied voltages than does the corresponding diode
characteristic.   At the same time the crystal has a number of disadvantages; its characteristics are appreciably affected by ambient temperature, its characteristics vary more from crystal to crystal than do tube
characteristics from tube to tube, and most important of all, a crystal
suffers permanent damage if severely overloaded even momentarily.

A crystal voltmeter of the peak-reading type, using a circuit such as
shown in Fig. 1-13b but with the tube replaced by a crystal, possesses an
input resistance approximately one-third the "back" resistance of the
crystal, or typically from 5000 to 30,000 ohms.   The frequency at which
partial resonance in the input lead becomes significant is commonly 50 to
100 per cent greater than for the corresponding diode type of instrument.
Accurate measurements can be made at still higher frequencies by employing a simple curve giving the correction for lead effects.   In addition a
crystal voltmeter will accurately indicate *relative* voltages well above the
resonant frequency of the probe assembly; this is not the case with the
corresponding diode instrument because the latter possesses transit-time
effects which depend upon the amplitude of the applied signal.   The

[1] Logarithmic voltmeters based on this principle are described by R. E. Meagher
and E. P. Bentley, Vacuum-tube Circuit to Measure the Logarithm of a Direct Current, *Rev. Sci. Instruments*, vol. 10, p. 336, November, 1939; Walter J. Ives, Logarithmic Scale Noise Meter, *Electronics*, vol. 22, p. 100, August, 1949.

[2] For further information see Arnold Peterson, A Peak-reading Voltmeter for the
U-H-F Ranges, *Gen. Rad. Expt.*, vol. 21, p. 1, October, 1946; Vacuum-tube and Crystal
Rectifiers as Galvanometers and Voltmeters at Ultra-high Frequencies, *Gen. Rad.
Expt.*, vol. 19, no. 12, p. 1, May, 1945.

range of input voltages handled most satisfactorily by a crystal voltmeter is between 0.1 and 2.0 volts. When the applied potential is of the order of 10 volts or more, a multiplier or attenuator must be used on the *input* side to reduce the voltage actually applied to the crystal to a safe value.

When the input voltage to a crystal voltmeter is small, as for example a few hundredths of a volt, the rectified current is proportional to the square of the effective value of the applied signal. This full-wave square-law type of rectification behavior results from the fact that over a small range of voltage, the voltage-current characteristic of the crystal (see Fig. 1-31) can be approximated by a section of a parabola. By using a sensitive microammeter to indicate the rectified current under these conditions, it then becomes possible accurately to compare power associated with

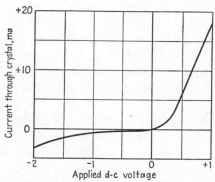

Fig. 1-31. Typical relationship existing between applied voltage and resulting current in a crystal rectifier.

different input voltages, since power is proportional to the square of the effective value of the voltage. The maximum voltage that may be applied to a crystal and still obtain square-law behavior is affected by the internal impedance of the source of power exciting the crystal, by the d-c impedance encountered by the rectified current, and by the characteristics of the individual crystal.[1] In some instances the square-law relationship is maintained for inputs up to several tenths of a volt, or for rectified current in excess of 100 μa.

Crystal rectifiers operated under square-law conditions can be expected to have an input resistance that is quite low, typically 1000 ohms or less. This is in contrast with the much higher input resistance of the peak-reading type of crystal voltmeter, where the combination of large input voltage and high d-c resistance encountered by the rectified current, accounts for the difference.

[1] For further discussion see R. C. Robbins and F. W. Black, An Investigation into the Use of Crystal Rectifiers for Measuring and Monitoring Purposes, *J. IEE (Radiolocation Conv.)*, vol. 93, pt. IIIA, p. 1343, March–May, 1946.

CHAPTER 2

POWER

2-1. Power Measurements. The importance of power measurements depends upon the frequency. At most radio frequencies it is ordinarily easier and more convenient to measure voltage, current, and impedance than it is to measure power. Under these conditions the direct determination of power is of only limited importance. On the other hand, at microwave frequencies, voltage, current, and impedance are difficult to determine, may differ greatly at slightly different points in a circuit, and are appreciably affected by small changes in geometry. Accordingly at the highest radio frequencies, the most significant quantity is the power, the measurement of which then becomes of primary rather than secondary importance.[1]

The measurement of power at audio and radio frequencies may be approached in a number of ways. One common method consists in determining the circuit resistance and then measuring the current that flows through this resistance, thus obtaining power as I^2R. When the circuit consuming the power is a resistance without a series reactive component of impedance, one can alternatively measure voltage across the circuit instead of current in the load, and then obtain power from the relation $P = E^2/R$, instead of as I^2R. These methods of determining power from a knowledge of resistance and current (or voltage) are widely used to measure the power output of oscillators and radio transmitters. The idea is to substitute for the normal load a specially designed resistor having low reactance and low skin effect, and able to dissipate large amounts of energy. Such resistors are commonly called dummy loads, or dummy antennas, and are available commercially in a variety of types (see Sec. 14–6).

Another widely used power-measuring technique is to convert the power to be determined into heat, and then to observe the resulting temperature effects. When large amounts of power are involved, this method usually takes the form of a water calorimeter (see Sec. 2-3), while with small amounts of power some form of bolometer is customary (see Sec. 2-2).

---

[1] The transition region where one shifts to power measurements is of the order of 100 to 300 Mc. This is discussed by T. I. Jones and F. M. Colebrook, *J. IEE* (*Radio Sec.*), vol. 95, pt. III, p. 315, September, 1948.

Many additional methods have been proposed for measuring power. These include the use of a cathode-ray tube so connected as to trace a pattern having an area proportional to power per cycle,[1] the use of a multigrid vacuum tube so operated that when potentials proportional, respectively, to current and voltage are applied to different grids the rectified plate current is an indication of power,[2] two square-law devices such as thermocouples[3] or full-wave square-law vacuum-tube voltmeters[4] combined in such a manner as to indicate power, and the three-ammeter method of power indication. While all of these methods will measure power accurately, most of them find little practical use, and in the main merely represent interesting laboratory stunts.

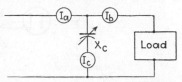

A possible exception to this is the three-ammeter method, which is sometimes used to measure transmitter power. The circuit arrangement is given in Fig. 2-1. An analysis shows that the power

Fig. 2-1. Three-ammeter shunt-reactance method of measuring power.

flowing past the measuring point toward the load is given by the relation[5]

$$\text{Watts} = 2X_c \sqrt{S(S - I_a)(S - I_b)(S - I_c)} \qquad (2\text{-}1)$$

where X_c = reactance of shunt condenser, ohms
I_a, I_b, I_c = currents in the three meters (see Fig. 2-1)
$$S = \frac{I_a + I_b + I_c}{2}$$

The best accuracy is obtained when the reactance X_c of the shunt condenser is of the same order of magnitude as the load impedance. The accuracy becomes poor when the load is highly reactive.

[1] See A. Hoyt Taylor, the Measurement of Radio-frequency Power, *Proc. IRE*, vol. 24, p. 1342, October, 1936; Harris J. Ryan, A Power Diagram Indicator for High Tension Current, *Trans. AIEE*, vol. 30, pt. II, p. 1089, 1911.

[2] M. A. H. El-Said, Electronic Wattmeter Circuits, *Proc. IRE*, vol. 37, p. 1003, September, 1949; John R. Pierce, A Proposed Wattmeter Using Multi-electrode Tubes, *Proc. IRE*, vol. 24, p. 577, April, 1936; Raymond J. Wey, A Thermionic Wattmeter, *Wireless Eng.*, vol. 14, p. 490, September, 1937.

[3] G. Pession and T. Gorio, Measurement of Power and Efficiency in Radio Transmitting Apparatus, *Proc. IRE*, vol. 19, p. 377, March, 1931; George H. Brown, J. Epstein, and D. W. Peterson, Direct-reading Wattmeters for Use at Radio Frequencies, *Proc. IRE*, vol. 31, p. 403, August, 1943.

[4] For further information see E. O. Peterson, U.S. Patent 1,586,553; H. M. Turner and F. T. McNamara, An Electron Tube Wattmeter and Voltmeter and a Phase-shifting Bridge, *Proc. IRE*, vol. 18, p. 1743, October, 1930; L. P. Malling, Electronic Wattmeter, *Electronics*, vol. 18, p. 133, November, 1945.

[5] For further discussion, and for derivation of this relation, see P. M. Honnel and E. B. Ferrell, The Measurement of Harmonic Power Output of a Radio Transmitter, *Proc. IRE*, vol. 22, p. 1181, October, 1934; J. L. Hollis, Measuring R-F Power with Three Ammeters, *Electronics*, vol. 18, p. 142, June, 1945.

A very simple method of measuring power approximately with a minimum of equipment is illustrated in Fig. 2-2. Here the alternating power to be determined is passed through some form of rectifier and filter, and the resulting d-c power on the output side of the rectifier-filter combination is determined by ordinary methods.[1] If the power being handled is not too small, and if the rectifier tube has a plate-cathode resistance while conducting that is small compared with the d-c load resistance, then the d-c power will be only slightly less than the radio-frequency power absorbed by the device.

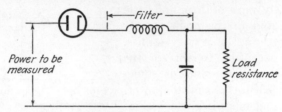

Fig. 2-2. Diagram showing method of converting alternating power to be measured into d-c power consumed in a load resistance.

2-2. Power Measurement by the Bolometer Method.[2]

In the bolometer method the unknown power is absorbed in a specially constructed bolometer element of resistive material. The resultant temperature rise is then detected by measuring the change in bolometer resistance by means of an auxiliary bridge circuit. Powers ranging from a few microwatts to a fraction of a watt are commonly measured in this way.

[1] P. M. Honnel, R-F Power Measurements, *Electronics*, vol. 13, p. 21, January, 1940.

[2] Comprehensive discussions of details and refinements of the bolometer method can be found in the literature. Thus see Chap. 3 of "Technique of Microwave Measurements" (Vol. 11, Radiation Laboratory Series), McGraw-Hill Book Company, Inc., New York, 1947; also "Very High Frequency Techniques," Radio Research Laboratory Staff, McGraw-Hill Book Company, Inc., New York, 1947, Vol. 2, pp. 593, 1023. The following journal articles are helpful: F. J. Gaffney, Microwave Measurements and Test Equipments, *Proc. IRE*, vol. 34, p. 755, October, 1946; Theodore Moreno and Oscar C. Lundstrom, Microwave Power Measurements, *Proc. IRE*, vol. 35, p. 514, May, 1947; B. Bleaney, Radio-frequency Power Measurement by Bolometer Lamps at Centimetre Wavelengths, *J. IEE (Radiolocation Conv.)*, vol. 93, pt. IIIA, p. 1378, March–May, 1946; E. M. Hickin, Bolometers for V.H.F. Power Measurement, *Wireless Eng.*, vol. 23, p. 308, November, 1946; John Collard, The Enthrakometer, An Instrument for the Measurement of Power in Rectangular Wave Guides, *J. IEE (Radiolocation Conv.)*, vol. 93, pt. IIIA, p. 1399, March–May, 1946; G. F. Gainsborough, Some Sources of Error in Microwave Milliwattmeters, *J. IEE (Radio & Comm.)*, vol. 95, pt. III, p. 229, July, 1948.

The bolometer method was one of the earliest means used for the detection of radio-frequency energy, but then became largely superseded by methods using the thermocouple ammeter and vacuum-tube voltmeter as described in the preceding sections. With the relatively recent expansion of activity into the microwave region the bolometer has again come into common use, as it has advantages at extremely high frequencies.

A typical arrangement for a bolometer power measurement is shown in Fig. 2-3. Here the radio-frequency power enters from a coaxial line, with a short tapered section to transform the line impedance to that of the bolometer. A quarter-wave stub provides a ground return for the bolometer bridge connection, but does not influence the radio-frequency portion of the circuit. The by-pass capacitor provides a return for the radio-frequency currents and an insulated connection to the bolometer. The resistance change in the bolometer is measured with the bridge *ABCD*, in which the arm *CD* is supplied by the resistance of the bolometer element. The bridge is excited simultaneously by direct current from the voltage *E* and by an alternating voltage of audio (or quite low radio)

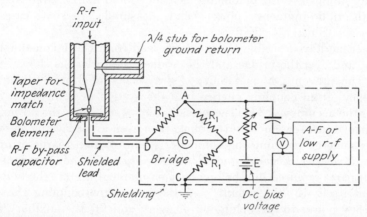

Fig. 2-3. Typical bolometer power-measuring arrangement for coaxial system, using manually adjusted bridge of the balanced type.

frequency.[1,2] Thus the bolometer element is simultaneously heated by d-c power, audio-frequency power, and the radio-frequency power being measured. However, the resistance of the bolometer is dependent upon the total power and is independent of where this power comes from.

To measure radio-frequency power with the arrangement of Fig. 2-3, a nominal voltage is applied from the audio supply, superimposed upon the radio-frequency power being measured. The direct current from voltage *E* is next adjusted by rheostat *R* until the heating of the bolometer causes

---

[1] The frequency of this supply must be high enough so that the bolometer resistance will not vary appreciably as the alternating current varies during a single cycle. With bolometers of the thermistor type the thermal lag is so great that frequencies as low as 60 cycles are often satisfactory; however, with the barretter type element a high audio or low radio frequency ordinarily must be employed.

[2] When two sources of power are applied to a bolometer bridge, the one that is not used to detect balance in the neutral arm is said to be a *bias* supply. The bias supply is for the purpose of controlling or biasing the operating conditions, and hence resistance, of the bolometer element.

its resistance to have the value required to balance the bridge, as indicated by the galvanometer G.   The radio-frequency power is then turned off, which unbalances the bridge because of the change in resistance of the bolometer as a result of less heating.   Balance is restored by increasing the amount of power from the audio-frequency supply.   Since the bolometer resistance depends upon the total power dissipated in it regardless of frequency, the radio-frequency power being measured is exactly equal to the audio-frequency power that must be added to rebalance the bridge. If the voltage from the auxiliary supply is V_1 before the radio-frequency power is turned off, and is V_2 after the second balance, the radio-frequency power[1] is $(V_2{}^2 - V_1{}^2)/4R_1$.   For greatest accuracy the audio power initially supplied to the bolometer element should not be large compared with the radio-frequency power being measured.   In some cases it is convenient to make $V_1 = 0$.

It is generally desirable to shield the lead from the bolometer to the bridge, and also the bridge and the bridge accessories, as shown in Fig. 2-3.   This prevents the possibility of stray fields (of either audio or radio frequency) from coupling energy into the system in a way that would impair the accuracy.   This is especially important when the power being determined is a few microwatts, since then even a very slight amount of spurious energy reaching the bolometer will introduce a large error.

The Bolometer Element and Bolometer Mount.   The principal component parts required in a bolometer measurement are (1) the bolometer element itself, (2) the mount, *i.e.*, the means for coupling the radio-frequency power to the bolometer element, and (3) the auxiliary bridge circuit required for detecting the change in resistance of the bolometer element.   The same bridge circuit may be used in a variety of measuring systems, and several types are commercially available.   Likewise a variety of bolometer elements is commercially available.   The mount, on the other hand, is most often "tailor-made" for each specific radio-frequency-measurement application.

The word bolometer embraces two subdivisions, *viz.*, barretters,[2] which are normal resistive elements with a positive temperature coefficient of resistance, and thermistors,[3] which are compounded of metallic oxide materials possessing a negative temperature coefficient.   The barretters

---

[1] If the resistance of the bolometer element at the balance condition is equal to R_1, then the power delivered by the audio supply to the bolometer element is $V^2/4R_1$. The change in this audio power to compensate for turning off the radio-frequency power is then obviously $(V_2{}^2 - V_1{}^2)/4R_1$.

[2] "Technique of Microwave Measurements," *op. cit.*, pp. 156–169.

[3] "Technique of Microwave Measurements," *op. cit.*, pp. 89–103; J. A. Becker, C. B. Green, and G. L. Pearson, Properties and Uses of Thermistors, *Trans. AIEE*, vol. 65, p. 711, November, 1946; G. L. Pearson, The Physics of Electronic Semiconductors, *Elec. Eng.*, vol. 66, p. 638, July, 1947.

can, in the simplest cases, be short lengths of fine wire, such as instrument fuses,[1] or metallized film resistors.   For special applications the individual laboratory worker can easily fabricate his own barretter, using Wollaston wire.   For a given sensitivity the barretter tends to be less rugged than the thermistor, but has the advantage of operating at a higher temperature, thereby being less sensitive to changes in the temperature of the surroundings.

The thermistor, while suffering the disadvantage of operating at lower temperatures, and thus usually requiring some compensation against ambient temperature changes, tends to be less susceptible to burnout due to overload, and is somewhat stronger mechanically.   It consists of a

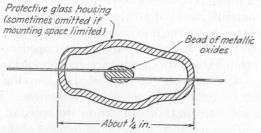

FIG. 2-4. Thermistor construction (bead type).

very small bead of the special thermistor material that joins the two ends of the contact wires as in Fig. 2-4.   The whole assembly is then usually mounted in a protective envelope, as shown.

Thermistors and barretters are both in widespread use, and there seems to be no clear-cut preference between them.   During the Second World War the thermistor was more widely used, but since then the barretter has come into increased use, and is now more common.

Both the thermistor and barretter can be made in very small sizes, and can be easily mounted in waveguide or transmission-line systems.   They are both very sensitive elements, and can be used in measurement of powers as small as tens of microwatts.   Furthermore, they are more stable with respect to time and exposure to overload than are detectors for very high frequencies, such as the silicon crystal, and in most circuits can be replaced without recalibration.   While the thermistor and barretter display their greatest advantage in measuring very small amounts of power, they can also be used to monitor large amounts of power by inserting a directional coupler (see Sec. 2-5) between the bolometer element and the main radio-frequency system.

[1] Thus the very inexpensive Littel fuses make excellent barretter elements, and are useful up to frequencies of about 4000 Mc.   The $\frac{1}{200}$-amp Littel fuse has a resistance of about 400 ohms when carrying a direct current of 5 ma, while for the $\frac{1}{100}$-amp Littel fuse the resistance is about 200 ohms at 10 ma direct current.

Of primary importance in the choice of the bolometer element is the desired sensitivity, *i.e.*, the radio-frequency power level to be measured. The sensitivity is a function of how much change in resistance occurs for a given radio-frequency energy absorbed in the bolometer element, and also of the characteristics of the associated bridge circuit. That is to say, the sensitivity figure is specified in terms of the radio-frequency power required to produce full-scale deflection of the indicating element of the bridge circuit. A typical value for a sensitive commercial instrument is 100 microwatts for full-scale reading. Full-scale sensitivities as small as 10 μw and as large as 100 mw are not unusual, however.

Another item of importance in the choice of the bolometer element is the impedance it presents to the radio-frequency circuit. The bolometer element is customarily matched to the radio-frequency power source in such a manner as to absorb the maximum possible power from the source. It is therefore convenient if the radio-frequency impedance of the bolometer element is comparable with the characteristic impedance of the transmission system. One may also be interested in knowing how much the impedance varies over the frequency band of interest. Finally, it may be important in some circumstances to know the speed of response of the bolometer element; for instance, in the measurement of the average power of a pulsed system with low-duty cycle, the slower response of the thermistor may provide some advantage over a barretter of the same sensitivity. Conversely the barretter is less sluggish to sudden changes in power level.

The bolometer mount has the important function of coupling the radio-frequency energy into the bolometer element, including the means used to provide impedance matching.[1] At low radio frequencies the bolometer may be connected into the circuit in much the same manner as a thermocouple, except that the bridge circuit must be isolated from the radio-frequency circuits. In the arrangement of Fig. 2-3 the isolation is provided by the by-pass capacitor. In coaxial and waveguide transmission systems considerable care must be exercised in order that the bolometer mount provide the necessary impedance transformation between the bolometer and the transmission-line system. In a coaxial cable this typically involves transforming a 50-ohm transmission-line impedance to something on the order of 125 to 200 ohms to match a typical bolometer.[2] This is usually done by means of a short tapered section as shown in Fig. 2-3. In Fig. 2-5 is shown a typical arrangement[3]

[1] A variety of thermistor and barretter mounts are described on pp. 130–156, and 175–179, respectively, of "Technique of Microwave Measurements," *op. cit.*

[2] A 50-ohm bolometer could be provided instead, but 200 ohms is a better compromise where both waveguide and coaxial applications are needed, and bridge circuits are commonly designed to balance when the bolometer resistance is 200 ohms.

[3] Gaffney, *op. cit.*, p. 781.

for a waveguide system. Here impedance matching is accomplished through the use of the two tunable stubs. In coaxial systems, where the bolometer impedance is usually considerably higher than that of the transmission line, a useful technique is the utilization of two bolometers

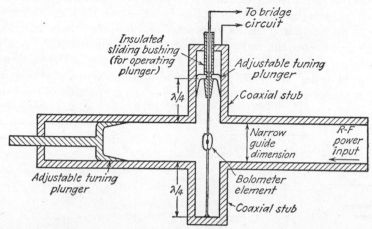

FIG. 2-5. Bolometer mount for use with a waveguide system.

as shown in Fig. 2-6. Here, two 100-ohm bolometers act in parallel to present 50 ohms to the line, but act in series to present 200 ohms to the bridge. This arrangement has the advantage of eliminating both the stub and the tapered section shown in Fig. 2-3, and thus is more suitable for broad-band operation. In general the transformation problem is

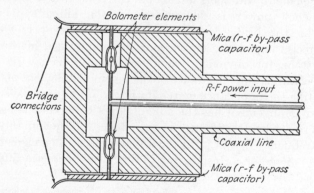

FIG. 2-6. Arrangement for using two bolometers in coaxial system.

made more difficult by large ratios of impedance, especially if a broad-band system is desired.

Bolometer Bridge Circuits. The bridge circuit used for measuring the resistance change of the bolometer element may take a variety of forms.

Some of these are quite simple, while others are very complex and include self-balancing features and arrangements to compensate for variations in the ambient temperature.[1] The bridge circuit of Fig. 2-3 is generally referred to as the balanced type, and is a common arrangement. A variation consists in omitting the audio-frequency source, and adjusting the d-c excitation so that the bridge is first balanced with the radio-frequency power being dissipated in the bolometer element, and then brought into balance again after the radio-frequency power is turned off.[2] A simpler arrangement is shown in Fig. 2-7a, and is generally referred to as the unbalanced type. Here in the absence of radio-frequency power, the bridge is brought into balance by adjusting the amplitude of the exciting

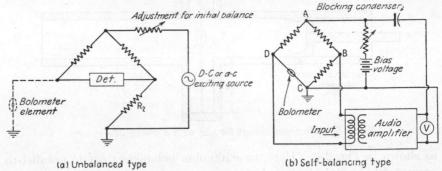

(a) Unbalanced type   (b) Self-balancing type

FIG. 2-7. Examples of bolometer bridges. Radio-frequency connections are not shown.

voltage applied to the bridge. Radio-frequency power dissipated in the bolometer element will then unbalance the bridge, and the amount of radio-frequency power is determined by the amount of unbalance indicated by the bridge detector. This arrangement is not suitable where a precise impedance match must be maintained in the radio-frequency system, for obviously when the radio-frequency power in the bolometer changes, the impedance of the bolometer element also changes, thus upsetting the impedance match in the radio-frequency system. The unbalanced arrangement has the advantage of being direct-reading, so is often preferred when the change in impedance will not unduly influence the radio-frequency circuit. In the unbalanced arrangement the impedance of the bolometer corresponding to the initial balance adjustment can be controlled by varying the value of the resistance R_2.

[1] Examples of bridges are given in "Technique of Microwave Measurements," *op. cit.*, pp. 103–130, 169.

[2] The design features of a power-measuring system of this type are described by H. J. Carlin and J. Blass, A Direct Reading D-C Bridge for Microwave Power Measurement, *Trans. AIEE*, vol. 67, p. 311, 1948; also see "Technique of Microwave Measurements," *op. cit.*, p. 169; R. A. Soderman, A Bolometer Bridge for the Measurement of Power at High Frequencies, *Gen. Radio Expt.*, vol. 25, July, 1950.

The next step of complexity beyond the balanced bridge, and one which is incorporated in some of the commercially available bolometer arrangements for measuring power, is the self-balancing bridge.[1] Such an arrangement is illustrated schematically in Fig. 2-7b, and consists of an amplifier the output of which is coupled back to the input through the bridge, as shown in the figure. With the bolometer element at room temperature the bridge is unbalanced, permitting transmission to take place through the bridge from AC to BD, and resulting in the system breaking into oscillation. However, as the oscillations increase in amplitude, the resistance of the bolometer element changes in such a manner as to bring the bridge more nearly in balance. By making the amplification large, the amplitude of oscillations will assume whatever value is required to make the bridge almost but not quite exactly balanced. A smaller amplitude than this will cause the bridge to be considerably unbalanced, resulting in a large input voltage to the amplifier and hence increased output. At the same time, a slightly larger amplitude will bring the bridge into exact balance, giving no transmission between amplifier input and output, and hence no oscillations. If now radio-frequency power is dissipated in the bolometer element, this will reduce correspondingly the amount of power that the oscillations must supply the bolometer to make the bridge approach a balanced condition. The radio-frequency power can hence be indicated by the meter V that measures the amplitude of the oscillations, a large radio-frequency power corresponding to a small amplitude of oscillations, and vice versa. The initial amplitude of the oscillations in the absence of radio-frequency power can be adjusted to a predetermined value corresponding to full-scale deflection of V by applying a d-c "biasing" voltage to the bridge as indicated in Fig. 2-7b.

Calibration of bolometer measuring arrangements employing the balanced type of bridge presents no problem, since the power being measured is matched exactly by the measured change in power from the low-frequency or d-c auxiliary supply. In the case of the unbalanced type of bridge, or when a calibration check is desired upon any type, two methods are available. The first takes advantage of the fact that with most commercial barretters and thermistors designed for microwave work, the skin depth of the radio-frequency current is large compared with the diameter of the element even at frequencies of several thousand megacycles. The impedance of the bolometer under these conditions is very closely the same at low audio frequencies as at several thousand megacycles. The calibration may accordingly be carried out at a low frequency where a

[1] A self-balancing bridge that also provides compensation for changes in ambient temperature is described by C. C. Bath and H. Goldberg, Self-balancing Thermistor Bridge, *Proc. Natl. Electronics Conf.*, vol. 3, p. 47, November, 1947.

variety of accurate power-measuring techniques are available for use in the calibration. The second method of calibration has the advantage of making no such assumptions. In it one starts with sufficient power to be measured accurately by calorimetric methods (see Sec. 2-3). The bolometer is then calibrated by using a small known fraction of this power, derived with the aid of a directional coupler (see Sec. 2-4), or by the known attenuation undergone by the power in passing through the calorimeter.[1]

Bolometer as a Square-law Demodulator.[2] An important application of the bolometer in measurement work is as a demodulator of modulated or pulsed waves. The idea is illustrated in Fig. 2-8. Here the modulated (or pulsed) radio-frequency power is delivered to a bolometer element through which is simultaneously passed a direct current. Assuming the thermal time constant of the bolometer element is small compared

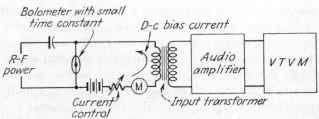

Fig. 2-8. Bolometer-amplifier arrangement for measuring amplitude-modulated waves.

with the modulation frequency of the radio-frequency power, then the additional heating caused by the radio-frequency power will cause the bolometer resistance to the direct current to vary in accordance with the modulation envelope. The result is that a modulation-frequency voltage is developed across the primary terminals of the input transformer, which is then amplified, and measured by means of a vacuum-tube voltmeter.

The bolometer-amplifier combination will accurately follow a square-law behavior (*i.e.*, output voltage proportional to the radio-frequency power or to the square of the radio-frequency voltage), provided the d-c power dissipated in the bolometer element is much greater than the radio-frequency power. For a given element, type of modulation, and amplifier, the sensitivity will be determined by the d-c bias current. Thus an accurately reproducible sensitivity can be obtained by using an amplifier

[1] For further details see R. Street, The Absolute Measurement of Low Power at 300 Mc/s, *Proc. IEE* (*Radio & Comm.*), vol. 96, pt. III, p. 237, May, 1949.

[2] For further discussion see "Microwave Antenna Theory and Design" (Vol. 12, Radiation Laboratory Series), pp. 601–607, McGraw-Hill Book Company, Inc., New York, 1949.

stabilized by negative feedback, and always adjusting the direct current to the same value.

Satisfactory operation of the system of Fig. 2-8 requires that the thermal time constant of the bolometer be small enough to permit the bolometer temperature to be able to follow the modulation envelope of the radio-frequency wave. Barretters of the type used to measure small amounts of radio-frequency power meet this requirement at audio modulation (or repetition) frequencies. However, the greater thermal sluggishness of most thermistors limits their use as demodulators to modulation frequencies below the audio range.

The sensitivity of the bolometer-amplifier combination of Fig. 2-8 depends upon the bolometer characteristics, the d-c bias current, the percentage modulation, and the amplifier. When the amplifier has a response band no wider than necessary, and the amplifier gain is so great that the minimum useful signal is limited by noise, then it is possible under practical conditions to obtain a power sensitivity of less than 1 μw when dealing with a square-wave-modulated radio-frequency signal.

While the sensitivity of the bolometer-amplifier combination of Fig. 2-8 is considerably less than that of a crystal-amplifier combination, the former is generally preferred for measurement work wherever it can be used. This is because the bolometer can always be depended upon to have a square-law behavior and a reproducible sensitivity. In contrast, both the crystal sensitivity and the range of amplitude over which it follows a square law may be changed by momentary overloads.

High-power Bolometer.[1] Although the bolometer method of measuring power is generally applied to powers of the order of microwatts or milliwatts, the same principles can be used to determine larger powers. For example, if the power to be measured is dissipated in a dummy load consisting of a vacuum or gas-filled lamp (see Sec. 14-6), then the temperature of the lamp filament is a function of the power. The temperature in turn determines the filament resistance. As a consequence the radio-frequency power may be obtained by determining the resistance of the lamp filament to direct current with the aid of an ohmmeter or d-c bridge. Alternatively the heating of the filament may be evaluated by using a photocell or an optical pyrometer to determine the brilliancy temperature of the filament. The relationship between the filament resistance (or temperature), and the power dissipated in the filament, can be determined by calibration with direct current or at 60 cycles. Powers ranging from a fraction of a watt to about 50 watts may be readily measured in this way. The method is moreover independent of frequency provided the filament length does not exceed about a tenth of a wavelength.

[1] See "Technique of Microwave Measurements," *op. cit.*, pp. 180–183; also "Very High Frequency Techniques," *op. cit.*, pp. 579–580.

2-3. Power Measurement by Calorimeter Methods.[1]   The calorimeter method of measuring radio-frequency power involves conversion of the radio-frequency energy into heat, absorbing this heat in a fluid (usually water) which flows through the system, and then measuring the temperature rise of the fluid.   The radio-frequency power may be absorbed directly in the calorimeter fluid, or the fluid may be used as a coolant for a resistive load of solid material.   In any case, it is essential that all of the radio-frequency energy be transferred to the fluid; this means that the system must have no radio-frequency leakage, either by radiation or in lossy joints.   Likewise the heat radiation from the fluid must be minimized until after the point in the system where the temperature measurement is made.

The calorimeter method is especially suited to the measurement of large power.   Although large power can also be measured with the aid of a bolometer in a directional-coupler arrangement, and indeed such a system is well suited to the monitoring of the power delivered to an antenna in a transmitting system, the calorimeter method has definite advantages in the laboratory.   For laboratory performance, it is usually necessary to provide an artificial load to absorb the power, and for very high power this load may be fluid-cooled.   In such cases, most of the elements of a calorimeter measurement are already at hand.

The power dissipated in a calorimeter can be calculated directly from the temperature rise, the specific heat of the fluid, and the rate of flow of the fluid, according to the following relationship:

$$P = 4.18 m s_p \, \Delta t \qquad (2\text{-}2)$$

where m = flow, g per sec

s_p = specific heat, calories per g per °C

Δt = temperature rise, °C

P = power, watts

Alternatively the relationship between temperature rise and power dissipated can be determined experimentally by dissipating known amounts of 60-cycle or d-c power in the calorimeter system.

As in the bolometer method of power measurement, the radio-frequency portion of the calorimeter system must be designed to provide a proper transformation of impedance in order that the load impedance may be adequately matched to the power source.   This is commonly accomplished with a tapered arrangement.   It is also important that the radio-

[1] For general discussion and further details of the calorimeter method see "Very High Frequency Techniques," *op. cit.*, vol. 2, pp. 581–591, McGraw-Hill Book Company, Inc., New York, 1947; "Technique of Microwave Measurements," *op. cit.*, pp. 194–217; M. C. Crowley-Milling, D. S. Gordon, C. W. Miller, and G. Saxon, The Measurement of Power at Centimetric and Decimetric Wavelengths, *J. IEE* (*Radiolocation Conv.*), vol. 93, pt. IIIA, p. 1452, March–May, 1946.

frequency power be transferred to the fluid in such a manner as to avoid hot spots where boiling of the fluid might occur.

The rate of fluid flow, and the mass of fluid exposed to the heating, should be proportioned so that a measurable temperature rise is obtained with as small an amount of fluid as can absorb the desired power. This assures a system that will not be too sluggish to changes in the power level.

Some typical arrangements will serve best to illustrate the various forms that the calorimeter method may assume. The first of these, shown in Fig. 2-9, utilizes a length of lossy cable for absorbing power. This cable is available in the standard impedance of 50 ohms, and hence there is no problem of impedance matching to the radio-frequency system.

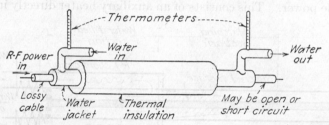

FIG. 2.9. Calorimeter load using lossy coaxial cable. Total cable length should give at least 10 db one-way attenuation.

The fluid serves as a coolant, absorbing no radio-frequency power itself. The length of the cable should be sufficient to provide an attenuation of 10 db or more at the operating frequency. This ensures at least 20 db of attenuation for the reflected power, and thus the load absorbs virtually all of the incident radio-frequency power delivered from the source. This type of calorimeter has been used for power levels ranging from 5 to 500 watts.

A second arrangement,[1] also for use in coaxial systems, is shown in Fig. 2-10. Here the radio-frequency power is absorbed in a water-filled section of line. The water serves as a lossy dielectric that absorbs the power because of its high power factor, and simultaneously functions as the calorimeter fluid. An impedance match between the section of coaxial line having air dielectric, and the portion having water dielectric, is provided by a tapered section of titanium dioxide, as shown. This material has a dielectric constant very closely equal to that of water

[1] William R. Rambo, A Coaxial Load for Ultra-high-frequency Calorimeter Watt-meters, *Proc. IRE*, vol. 35, p. 827, August, 1947. Other arrangements for coaxial systems are described in R. C. Shaw and R. J. Kircher, A Coaxial-type Water Load and Associated Power-measuring Apparatus, *Proc. IRE*, vol. 35, p. 84, January, 1947; F. M. Leslie, R. F. Generator Load, *Wireless Eng.*, vol. 24, p. 105, April, 1947; "Technique of Microwave Measurements," *op. cit.*, pp. 195–199.

(approximately 80), and so is ideally suited to match air to water. Titanium dioxide is a ceramic, and must be machined to the proper shape before firing, with due allowance made for shrinkage. In Fig. 2-10 the temperature difference between the incoming and outgoing water is measured with a thermopile instead of by thermometers as in Fig. 2-9. The thermopile consists of a succession of thermocouple junctions connected in series as shown, with alternate junctions placed in the incoming (cold), and outgoing (hot), fluid. A thermopile mounted in this way responds directly to the difference in temperature between the hot and cold fluids, and also has a greater sensitivity than does a simple thermocouple system having single hot and cold junctions.

The arrangement of Fig. 2-10 shows a means for calibrating, using d-c or 60-cycle power. This consists of an auxiliary heater directly immersed

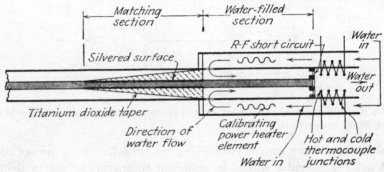

FIG. 2-10. Coaxial water load with titanium dioxide taper.

in the flow system, as illustrated. Calibration is carried out by observing the thermopile response produced by the dissipation of a known amount of 60-cycle or d-c power in this heater.

A variety of calorimeter arrangements are possible for use with waveguides.[1] A typical arrangement is shown in Fig. 2-11, where the power is absorbed by the fluid flowing in a glass tube. This tube enters through the middle of the broad side of the waveguide, and passes obliquely through the guide and out the end as shown. The fluid, commonly tap water or salt water, serves as a lossy dielectric that both absorbs the power and carries it off. A metal ridge is placed between the glass tube and one wall of the waveguide as illustrated. This ridge concentrates the field in the vicinity of the fluid, and thereby increases the amount of power absorbed per unit length toward the exit end of the guide, where the power that still remains tends to be small. In this way the total

[1] See "Very High Frequency Techniques," *op. cit.*, p. 590; "Technique of Microwave Measurements," *op. cit.*, p. 199; L. B. Turner, Balanced Calorimeters for 3000 and 10,000 mc/s with Tapered Water Loads for H_{01} Rectangular Pipes, *J. IEE (Radiolocation Conv.)*, vol. 93, Part IIIA, p. 1467, March–May, 1946.

length the section must have in order to obtain substantially complete absorption of the power is reduced. The combination of the ridge and the slanting tube that gradually enters the waveguide, produces a tapered effect that minimizes reflection as the power to be measured enters the calorimeter section. The absorbed power is determined by the difference in temperature of the incoming and outgoing fluid. Since the volume of fluid in the glass tube can be quite small, the system will respond very quickly to changes in power level.

The fluid must flow through the calorimeter at a very constant rate. There are two general types of flow systems. The first of these is known as the open-flow system, in which an elevated, constantly overflowing

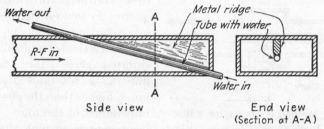

Side view　　　　　　　　　　　End view
　　　　　　　　　　　　　　　　　(Section at A-A)

FIG. 2-11. Waveguide water load using tapered ridge for impedance matching.

reservoir is used to maintain a constant head of liquid. The system exhausts into the drain, and is conveniently used with tap water. The other system is the so-called "closed-flow" system, in which the same fluid is recirculated, being alternately heated in the calorimeter unit and cooled in a radiator or other heat exchanger. This arrangement permits the use of special fluids such as salt water, but requires some care in maintaining a constant flow. The choice between the systems depends primarily upon convenience and upon available components.

2-4. Special Considerations Relating to Power Measurements on Transmission Lines. The power on a *perfectly terminated* transmission line can be readily obtained by taking advantage of the fact that the impedance everywhere along such a line is equal to the characteristic impedance. In lines having low loss at radio frequencies, this impedance is a resistance which can be calculated from the geometrical dimensions of the line, or from measurements that can be made at any convenient audio or radio frequency (see Sec. 4-2). The power on such a non-resonant transmission line is then I^2R or E^2/R, where R is the characteristic impedance (resistance) of the transmission line, I is the current flowing along the line, and E the voltage across it. Power measurements made in this way will be accurate provided the load impedance of the transmission line closely approximates the characteristic impedance, and provided the arrangement employed to measure the voltage or current on the line does not introduce an irregularity that produces an appreciable reflected wave.[1,2]

Transmission-line currents up to the very highest frequency used in radio work can be measured by means of a thermocouple in series with the line. The accuracy obtainable with a thermocouple is quite high provided either that the heater wire is small enough to have negligible skin effect, or provided that a correction for skin effect is made. By proper attention to constructional details it is possible to minimize the tendency for the series thermocouple to introduce reflections.[3]

The voltage across a transmission line may be determined satisfactorily by means of a diode-type vacuum-tube voltmeter provided the frequency is low enough so that the input capacitance of the voltmeter (or the voltmeter multiplier) that is shunted across the transmission line has a reactance that is very much higher than the characteristic impedance of the line. When the frequency is so high that this requirement is not satisfied, then the voltmeter introduces a large reflected wave.

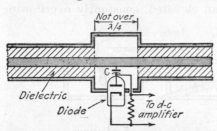

Fig. 2-12. Method of employing a diode voltmeter to determine voltage existing on a coaxial transmission line without introducing reflection from the input capacitance of the diode tube.

An ingenious method of minimizing this undesirable effect of input capacitance of a diode voltmeter at high frequencies for the case of coaxial lines is illustrated in Fig. 2-12. Here the diode is shunted across a specially designed section of the line which has greater spacing between inner and outer conductors than the rest of the line, and which has a length somewhat less than a quarter of a wavelength at the highest frequency for which the arrangement is to be employed. The enlarged spacing increases the inductance per unit length of line, while reducing the capacitance per unit length; the absence of dielectric in the enlarged

---

[1] When a reflected wave is present, then

$$\left.\begin{array}{c}\text{Sum of powers of incident}\\ \text{and reflected waves}\end{array}\right\} = \frac{E_1{}^2 + E_2{}^2}{2R} \qquad (2\text{-}3)$$

where E_1 and E_2 are the voltages of the standing-wave pattern at points spaced a quarter of a wavelength apart along the line. A special case is when E_1 and E_2 are the maximum and minimum voltages, respectively, of the standing-wave pattern.

[2] In some cases the line can be a lossy line that absorbs the power and so acts as a "dummy" load. No problem of termination is then present if the line attenuation is large, as is customary in such arrangements.

[3] For further details on the use of thermocouples to measure line current see "Very High Frequency Techniques," *op. cit.*, pp. 574–575, p. 606; also "Technique of Microwave Measurements," *op. cit.*, p. 187.

section further reduces the capacitance.   At the same time the shunting capacitance of the voltmeter acts as though it were distributed along the enlarged section, and therefore adds to the capacitance.   By proper design, the ratio of inductance to effective capacitance for the special section can be made to have the same value as the ratio of inductance to capacitance for the remainder of the coaxial line.   The special section then has the same characteristic impedance as the remainder of the system, and accordingly introduces negligible reflection; moreover, for all frequencies appreciably less than the frequency for which the special section is a quarter wavelength long, the behavior is independent of fre-

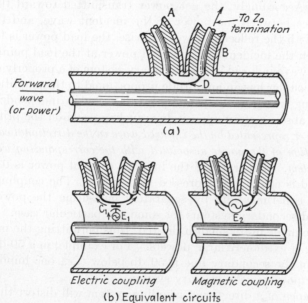

FIG. 2-13. A simple type of directional coupler, together with equivalent circuits showing the action of the electric and magnetic induction.

quency. [*] It is possible in this way to employ a vacuum-tube voltmeter up to the highest frequencies at which the very best diode meter will operate satisfactorily.[1]

2-5. Power Measurements and Power Monitoring Using Directional Couplers.   A directional coupler is a device which, when coupled to a transmission line or waveguide, will respond only to the wave traveling in a particular direction on the primary transmission system, while being unaffected by a wave traveling in the opposite direction on the primary line.   For example, the arrangement illustrated in Fig. 2-13a can be so designed that a wave traveling toward the right in the coaxial line will

[1] This arrangement is due to W. R. Hewlett of the Hewlett-Packard Company.

induce a wave traveling toward the left in part A of the coupled coaxial cable, while a wave traveling toward the left in the coaxial line will produce no effect in part A of the secondary line.

The usefulness of a directional coupler in power measurements arises from the fact that in radio-frequency transmission systems, each wave on the system can be considered as transmitting power in the direction in which that wave travels, and in an amount proportional to the square of the amplitude of the wave. The power that is associated with each individual wave is, moreover, independent of the presence or absence of a companion wave traveling along the transmission system in the opposite direction.[1] Accordingly, the net power transmitted toward the load is the difference between the power of the incident wave, and the power associated with the reflected wave; likewise, the load power is the difference between the incident and reflected power at the load point.

Since the wave induced in the secondary system of a properly operating directional coupler has an amplitude proportional to the amplitude of the corresponding wave on the primary system, and is independent of the presence or absence of an oppositely traveling wave on the primary system, *the power represented by the induced wave in the directional coupler is a definite fraction of the power associated with the corresponding wave on the primary system.* This ratio of the induced to total power is termed the *coupling* and is commonly expressed in decibels. The coupling may be determined experimentally by separately measuring the power on the primary and secondary systems for some one particular case. The coupling can be made quite small if desired, thus permitting the monitoring or sampling of extremely large powers. For example, in a 50-db coupler the power in the secondary line is 50 db below (*i.e.*, one hundred-thousandth) the power in the primary system.

The presence of a directional-coupling system will distort the fields in the primary line or waveguide. In general, this irregularity can be expected to produce a reflected wave in the primary system. The magnitude of the reflected wave will depend upon the coupling, but will in any case be quite small unless the coupling is unusually great.

A single directional coupler determines the power flowing in only one direction on the primary line. By using two directional couplers on the same primary system, with one directional coupler responsive only to the wave traveling toward the load, and the other responsive only to the reflected wave, then one can separately measure the powers of the two

---

[1] The only exception to this is when the characteristic impedance of the transmission line is not a pure resistance, or when the dielectric and wall losses in a waveguide are so great and so related as to cause the magnetic and electric field vectors to be out of time phase. These conditions never occur in radio-frequency systems, however, unless the transmission losses are very high.

primary waves, and by subtraction can obtain the net load power.[1] However, for most monitoring purposes it is sufficient to measure only the power in the incident wave.   In particular, when the reflection coefficient of the load is small or moderate, the amount of power represented by the reflected wave is so small that the power in the incident wave is a good indication of the power delivered to the load.   For example, when the reflection coefficient of the load is 0.25 corresponding to a voltage standing-wave ratio of 1.67, the reflected wave has only 6.7 per cent as much power as does the incident wave.   Even when the reflection coefficient is 0.5, corresponding to a voltage standing-wave ratio of 3.0, the reflected wave still represents only 25 per cent as much energy as the incident wave. It is thus apparent that power sampling by means of a single directional coupler responsive only to the incident wave is a much more significant indication of power relations when a reflected wave is present, than is the sampling of the voltage or current on the line or guide by means of a single small probe or loop.

Directional-coupler systems find extensive use for monitoring and measuring power in microwave systems.   In particular, radar transmitters often have built-in directional couplers that check the power output by withdrawing a small known fraction or sample of the power in the wave traveling from transmitter toward the antenna.   Other applications include determination of reflection coefficients (see Sec. 4-10), and their use as attenuators (see Sec. 15-6).

Types of Directional Couplers.   A great variety of directional-coupling systems have been devised.[2]   One type is shown in Fig. 2-13a; this is

---

[1] A direct-reading wattmeter based on this principle is described by H. C. Early, A Wide-band Wattmeter for Wave Guide, *Proc. IRE*, vol. 34, p. 803, October, 1946.

[2] A detailed consideration of different types of directional couplers and their properties is beyond the scope of this work.   The reader desiring further information on types and properties of directional couplers is referred to W. W. Mumford, Directional Couplers, *Proc. IRE*, vol. 35, p. 160, February, 1947; N. I. Korman, The Theory and Design of Several Types of Wave Selectors, *Proc. Natl. Electronics Conf.*, vol. 2, p. 404, 1946; M. Surdin, Directive Couplers in Wave Guides, *Jour. IEE (Radiolocation Conv.)*, vol. 93, pt. IIIA, p. 725, 1946; J. F. Morrison and E. L. Younker, A Method of Determining and Monitoring Power and Impedance at High Frequencies, *Proc. IRE*, vol. 36, p. 212, February, 1948; H. C. Early, A Wide-band Directional Coupler for Wave Guides, *Proc. IRE*, vol. 34, p. 883, November, 1946; H. R. Allan and C. D. Curling, The Reflectometer, *Proc. IEE (Radio & Comm.)*, vol. 96, pt. III, p. 25, January, 1949; B. Parzan and A. Yalow, Theory and Design of the Reflectometer, *Electrical Commun.*, vol. 24, p. 94, March, 1947; H. J. Riblet and T. S. Saad, A New Type of Waveguide Directional Coupler, *Proc. IRE*, vol. 36, p. 61, January, 1948; S. Rosen and J. T. Bangerts, A Consideration of Directivity in Wave Guide Directional Couplers, *Proc. IRE*, vol. 37, p. 393, April, 1949; G. W. O. Howe, An Instrument for Direct Measurement of Traveling Wave Coefficient in Feeders, *Wireless Eng.*, vol. 20, p. 365, August, 1943; "Very High Frequency Techniques," *op. cit.*, p. 594–602; "Technique of Microwave Measurements," pp. 854–897.

chosen for initial discussion because although not as commonly used as some other types, it is particularly easy to understand. Here, the primary system is a coaxial line, and the secondary system consists of two coaxial lines A and B interconnected by loop D that projects into the primary line, and is subjected to the simultaneous influence of the electric and magnetic fields that exist in it.[1] Consider now the case of a wave traveling toward the right on the primary system. The electric field of this wave induces a charge on the loop D that produces waves in both parts A and B of the secondary systems. The equivalent circuit that describes this action is illustrated in Fig. 2-13b, and consists of a voltage E_1 that is applied to coaxial systems A and B in parallel through series capacitance C_1, producing currents as indicated by the arrows.

The loop D links with the magnetic flux from the wave in the primary line, and therefore has a voltage E_2 induced in series with it, as illustrated by the equivalent circuit of Fig. 2-13b. This series voltage gives rise to waves in parts A and B of the secondary system, which are characterized by currents flowing in the direction indicated by the arrows. The two waves in section A produced by magnetic and electrostatic coupling, respectively, are of the same polarity and so add, while the two waves produced in section B are of opposite polarity and so tend to cancel each other. It is accordingly apparent that if the electric and magnetic couplings are so proportioned that the waves induced by the magnetic affect have the same amplitude as the waves induced by the electric coupling, then complete cancellation takes place in section B. With a wave traveling to the right in the primary line, the net effect is then to produce only one resultant wave in the secondary system, this being a wave that travels in the direction of A. By terminating A of the secondary system in its characteristic impedance this induced wave is absorbed. No wave travels in direction B.

The relative magnitude of electric and magnetic couplings in Fig. 2-13a can be readily controlled by the design of the coupling loop D. The electric coupling depends on the amount of electric field that terminates on the loop, and so is determined by the length of the loop, and the width (or diameter) of its conductor. Similarly, the magnetic coupling is determined by the amount of magnetic flux that links with the loop, and so is determined by the area enclosed between the loop and the outer conductor of the line, and by the orientation of the loop with respect to the axis of the line.

Assuming now that the coupling arrangement in Fig. 2-13 has been

---

[1] While this particular type of directional coupler couples a coaxial primary to a coaxial secondary, it is possible to couple from waveguide to coaxial line, from coaxial line to a waveguide secondary system, or from waveguide to waveguide. Further information can be obtained from the references given in the footnote on page 59.

designed so that a wave traveling to the right on the primary system produces no induced wave in section B, then consider the effect of a wave traveling to the left in the primary system. The component waves induced in A and B by the electric and magnetic fields in the primary coaxial line will again be equal to each other, since the magnitudes are not affected by the direction of travel on the primary line. However, the polarity of the wave produced by magnetic coupling will now be reversed with respect to the polarity of the induced wave resulting from electric coupling. Accordingly, the two waves induced in A now cancel each other, while the two waves produced in B add. Consequently, a wave traveling to the left in the primary line produces no effect in section A, but does produce an induced wave in section B. By terminating B of the secondary system in its characteristic impedance, this induced wave is absorbed. The final result is then that any wave that appears in section A is determined only by the wave traveling to the right in the primary system, and is independent of the presence or absence of a wave traveling to the left in the primary system. Thus one has achieved a directional-coupling system.

It is to be noted that to obtain the directional action it is absolutely necessary that B be terminated in its characteristic impedance. If the impedance terminating B produces a reflection, the resulting reflected wave will return along B, pass through the coupling loop, and enter A. The actual wave existing in A will then be a resultant of the desired effect produced by the wave traveling to the right in the primary line, and an undesired effect proportional to the product of the amplitude of the wave traveling to the left in the primary system and to the reflection coefficient at the termination of B.

The magnitude of the wave induced in section A of the secondary system by a wave traveling to the right on the primary system can be determined by terminating section A with a bolometer, thermocouple, crystal detector, or equivalent device, and measuring the power absorbed when the terminating impedance of the coaxial line matches the characteristic impedance. Since this induced wave is proportional to the wave on the primary system, the power of the latter can be determined from the power of the induced wave, combined with a knowledge of the coupling system. It will be noted that this determination of power on the primary system is made without absorbing the primary power, or without disturbing the primary system in any way except for the diversion to the secondary of a negligibly small fraction of the power.

It is apparent that if in the system shown in Fig. 2-13a, sections of A and B of the coaxial cable A are *both* terminated in characteristic impedance loads, then the wave present in section B will be determined only by the wave traveling to the left in the primary line, while any wave existing in A will be proportional only to the wave traveling to the right in the primary line. The arrangement then is equivalent to two directional systems, and can be used to determine separately the amplitudes (or powers) of the incident and reflected waves, and also the ratio of these waves (*i.e.*, the load reflection coefficient).

A different method of achieving the same result as Fig. 2-13 consists in obtaining the coupling between the primary and the secondary systems by means of a hole, as shown in Fig. 2-14. This arrangement is known as the single-hole or Bethe coupler. It makes use of the fact that when a hole exists in the wall between two systems involving either waveguides or coaxial lines, both electric and magnetic coupling result.[1] The electric

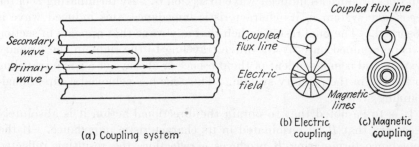

(a) Coupling system

(b) Electric coupling

(c) Magnetic coupling

FIG. 2-14. Single-hole directional coupler for coaxial lines.

coupling arises from the fact that electric lines of force project through the hole from the primary into the secondary system; similarly magnetic coupling arises from the fact that the interference to the lines of current flow in the walls of the primary system which results from the presence of the hole, causes magnetic flux to project through the hole and induce a voltage in the secondary system. The ratio of electric to magnetic coupling is determined by the orientation of the hole with respect to the fields of the primary system, the shape of the hole, and the angle between the axes of the secondary and primary transmission systems. In particular, if the hole is in the form of a narrow slot, then the electric coupling will predominate if the axis of the slot is so oriented that the coupling slot interferes as little as possible with the lines of current flow in the walls of the primary system (*i.e.*, is at right angles to the magnetic flux). In contrast, magnetic coupling will predominate when the slot is oriented so that its axis is at right angles to the lines of current flow and thus interferes with them to the maximum possible extent, or, what is equivalent, is

[1] The theory of coupling through a hole is given by H. Bethe, Theory of Diffraction by Small Holes, *Phys. Rev.*, vol. 66, p. 163, October, 1944. When the diameter of the coupling hole is not small compared with an eighth wavelength, it is necessary to compensate for discontinuity effects; see Edward L. Ginzton and Paul S. Goodwin, A Note on Coaxial Bethe-Hole Directional Couplers, *Proc. IRE*, vol. 38, p. 305, March, 1950.

parallel to the lines of magnetic flux in the primary system. It is apparent that the single-hole coupler is essentially equivalent to the arrangement of Fig. 2-13, and that by making the electric and magnetic couplings
equal, directional-coupler action results.

A quite different type of directional-coupling system is shown in Fig.
2-15. This is known as a two-hole coupler, and consists of primary and
secondary systems which are coupled *either* electrically or magnetically
at two points separated by an odd multiple of a quarter wavelength.[1] It
is essential that the coupling at each of these two points be either primarily electric, or primarily magnetic. This result can be achieved by
using probes (for electric coupling), or loops (for magnetic coupling), or

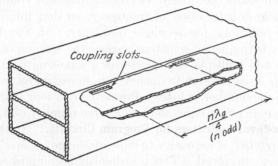

Fig. 2-15. Two-hole directional coupler for waveguides, using electric coupling
provided by narrow slots parallel to guide axis.

by suitably shaped and oriented slots that favor either one or the other
type of coupling. In the two-hole coupler a wave traveling to the right
in the primary system gives rise to a wave that also travels to the right in
the secondary system, but no wave traveling to the left; similarly, a wave
traveling to the left in the primary system gives rise to a wave traveling
to the left in the secondary system, but there is no wave traveling to the
right on the secondary. This result comes about because, although each
hole induces waves that travel in the secondary system in both directions
away from the coupling point, the induced waves in the favored direction
add in phase, while those in the reverse direction cancel exactly if they
are of equal amplitude and the coupling points are spaced an odd multiple
of a quarter wavelength apart.

Directivity of Directional Couplers. In an ideal directional coupler a
wave on the primary system will induce only one wave in the secondary
system. However, in actual directional couplers it is ordinarily found
that there are two induced waves, a large one in the favored direction in
the secondary system, and a small one in the other direction. This

[1] In the case of waveguides, this is based on the wavelength in the guide, rather than
the free-space wavelength.

results from failure to realize the ideal condition as a result of mechanical imperfections, frequency differing from the design value, second-order effects, etc. The ratio of the desired to the undesired induced waves is termed the *directivity*, and is commonly expressed in decibels. Thus a directivity of 30 db means that the undesired induced wave is 30 db weaker than (or represents only one-thousandth as much power as) the desired induced wave.

The directivity of the loop-type directional coupler of Fig. 2-13 is theoretically independent of frequency at least in so far as first-order effects are concerned. In the case of single-hole couplers this is also true if the walls separating the primary and secondary system have zero thickness; with finite walls the ratio of electric to magnetic coupling produced by a given hole is a function of frequency, so that infinite directivity can be achieved only for a single frequency. In two-hole couplers the directivity is frequency-sensitive because the spacing of the holes can be exactly an odd multiple of a quarter of a wavelength only at one frequency. This sensitivity to frequency can, however, be reduced greatly by increasing the number of holes;[1] alternatively a long, narrow slot may be used to give an effect equivalent to a large number of holes.

2-6. Power-level Indicators for Program Circuits.[2] In the monitoring of program circuits it is necessary to indicate the power level of the audio-frequency energy involved. This is ordinarily accomplished by bridging the audio-frequency transmission line or circuit by a rectifier voltmeter having such a high ohms per volt that the measuring instrument has negligible effect upon the circuit in which it is used.

Inasmuch as audio-frequency currents representing speech and music fluctuate rapidly in intensity, the ballistic characteristics of such power-level indicators are fully as important as the characteristics under steady-state conditions. Standards have therefore been established for the dynamic characteristics of power-level indicators for program circuits. The standard power-level indicator system consists of a rectifier voltmeter having an input impedance of 3900 ohms, and associated with a 600-ohm transmission line through a 3600-ohm series resistance, as indicated in Fig. 2-16. The equivalent impedance of the source of energy connected across the input terminals xx of the rectifier in this system is 3900 ohms (note that the line acts as 300 ohms since the right- and left-hand sections of the line are in parallel to the power-level indicator), or alternatively, the total resistance shunted across the trans-

---

[1] For details see particularly, Mumford, *loc. cit.*; also Rosen and Bangert, *loc. cit.*

[2] For further information see H. A. Chinn, D. K. Gannett, and R. M. Morris, New Standard Volume Indicator and Reference Level, *Proc. IRE*, vol. 28, p. 1, January, 1940; H. A. Affel, H. A. Chinn, and R. M. Morris, New Standard Volume Indicator and Reference Level, *Electronics*, vol. 12, p. 28, February, 1939.

mission line by the power-level measuring equipment is 7500 ohms.[1] The ballistic characteristics of the standard power-level indicator are such that when used in this circuit, a sudden application of a single-frequency voltage giving a steady-state reading of zero level will cause the pointer to overswing by 1 to 1.5 per cent, and to reach 99 per cent of the steady-state deflection in 0.3 sec. The instrument accordingly does not read the actual instantaneous power level of speech, but rather indicates a mean level based on an average amplitude over a short period of time.

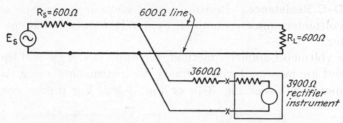

FIG. 2-16. Schematic circuit of a power-level indicator for monitoring the power level in audio-frequency program circuits.

The scale of the standard power-level indicator is calibrated in terms of decibels for a steady sine-wave voltage, with 1 mw flowing in a 600-ohm line taken as the reference, or zero level. The deflections actually obtained when monitoring speech are, however, customarily called volume units, abbreviated VU.[2] This is done to make clear that such readings are averages achieved by a particular set of ballistic characteristics. Only when the wave being monitored is sinusoidal and of constant amplitude will the VU reading be the same as the instantaneous power level in decibels; with speech the VU reading represents the power level in decibels corresponding to this averaged power level of the speech.

[1] The power level that is indicated with an arrangement of the type shown in Fig. 2-16 can be increased by inserting an attenuator at xx. This attenuator is calibrated in decibels (or volume units), and must have constant input and output impedances of 3900 ohms when used with load and source impedances of 3900 ohms.

[2] Power expressed in decibels (db) relative to 1 mw is commonly referred to as dbm. Thus 1 VU corresponds to 0 dbm dissipated in 600 ohms. Further discussion of types of scales for expressing power is given by J. L. Merrill, Meter Scales for Transmission Measurements, *Bell Labs. Record*, vol. 27, p. 16, January, 1949.

CHAPTER 3

CIRCUIT CONSTANTS OF LUMPED CIRCUITS

3-1. D-C Resistance. Resistance to direct current can be measured by the voltmeter-ammeter method, by a Wheatstone bridge, or with an ohmmeter.

In the voltmeter-ammeter method, the applied voltage and the resulting current are measured with ordinary d-c instruments, using the circuit arrangements of either Fig. 3-1a or Fig. 3-1b. For precise results one

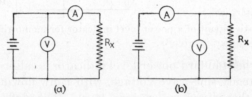

FIG. 3-1. Circuit arrangements for measuring resistance by the voltmeter-ammeter method.

must take into account the fact that in arrangement a the voltage actually existing across the unknown resistance R_x is the value indicated by V *minus the voltage drop in the ammeter A.* Similarly, in b the current flowing through the unknown resistance is the value indicated by ammeter A *less the current drawn by the voltmeter V.* When the resistance being measured is large, the correction required in a is so small as to be commonly negligible, and this is then the preferred arrangement of meters. However, when the resistance being measured is small, so that the impedance of the ammeter is not negligible in comparison, then arrangement b has the smallest correction.

Wheatstone Bridge. The Wheatstone bridge is the most accurate method available for measuring resistance, and is standard for general laboratory use where accuracy is important. The circuit diagram and constants of a typical Wheatstone bridge are shown in Fig. 3-2. The resistance R_x to be measured is connected in one arm of the bridge as indicated, and the remaining three arms are adjusted to give zero deflection of the galvanometer G when the battery is connected to the bridge. Under these conditions one has

$$R_x = R_S \frac{R_A}{R_B} \tag{3-1}$$

The measuring procedure is to choose a suitable ratio R_A/R_B, and then balance the bridge by adjusting R_S. The ratio R_A/R_B should be so chosen that the unknown resistance is determined to the full number of significant figures available, which is usually four. Also the magnitudes of the resistances used in arms A and B to obtain the desired ratio should be so chosen as to give maximum sensitivity to unbalances. The proper values depend on the resistance being measured, the galvanometer resist-ance, etc., and are usually stated in the instructions accompanying the bridge.[1]

Special difficulties are encountered in the measurement of very low and very high resistances. With low resistances the un-certainty introduced by the resistance of leads and contacts can be eliminated by using the Kelvin double bridge, a descrip-tion of which is found in any book on electrical measurements.

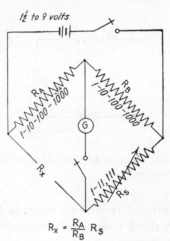

$$R_x = \frac{R_A}{R_B} R_S$$

FIG. 3-2. Circuit diagram and constants of typical Wheatstone bridge for measuring d-c resist-ance.

When the resistance being measured is very high, the bridge galvanometer becomes a relatively insensitive indicator of un-balance because of the high source imped-ance that the bridge then presents to the galvanometer. This difficulty can be over-come by using a d-c vacuum-tube voltmeter in place of the galvanometer. It is also desirable when measuring very high resist-ances to use a fixed standard resistance R_s of 1 megohm or more, and to balance the bridge by varying R_A.

Ohmmeters. Ohmmeters are suitable for making approximate resist-ance measurements, and are widely used in the servicing of communica-tion equipment.

Circuit arrangements that are employed in ohmmeters are illustrated in Fig. 3-3. To operate circuits a and b, an initial adjustment is made by short-circuiting the terminals xx and adjusting the resistance R until full-scale reading is obtained on the milliammeter M. When a resistance is then inserted between the terminals xx, the reading will be less than full scale by an amount that depends upon the inserted resistance. The meter scales can accordingly be calibrated directly in ohms. Different resistance ranges can be provided by various combinations of resistance

[1] When the resistance being measured is associated with an inductance or capaci-tance, it is important to press the battery key *before* pressing the galvanometer key. Otherwise the transients that result when the battery is connected will give the galvanometer needle an initial spurious kick.

values for R and R_0, by changing the number of cells in the battery, and by shunts across the milliammeter.

The arrangement of Fig. 3-3a operates on the assumption that the battery generates a constant voltage during its life, but that the internal resistance of the battery increases with age and so can be compensated for by changing a series resistance. The arrangement of Fig. 3-3b operates on the assumption that as the battery ages its voltage drops, but that the

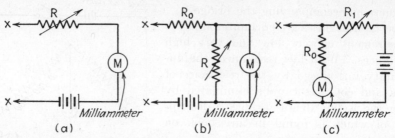

FIG. 3-3. Circuit arrangements used in ohmmeters employed for servicing electronic equipment.

internal resistance remains the same. Although neither assumption is realized completely, ohmmeters built in either way are satisfactory for test work.

The ohmmeter arrangement of Fig. 3-3c is particularly suitable for measuring small resistances of the same order of magnitude as R_0. Here the initial adjustment is made by varying R_1 with terminals xx open until full-scale deflection is obtained. The unknown resistance is then connected across xx, reducing the reading by an amount depending on the resistance involved. To avoid excessive battery current, it is customary to use a sensitive meter, so that R_1 can be made much larger than R_0.

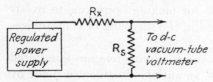

FIG. 3-4. Ohmmeter for measuring very high resistances.

When the resistance to be measured by an ohmmeter is extremely large, i.e., tens to hundreds of megohms, instruments of the type shown in Fig. 3-3 are impractical because of the excessive sensitivity that must then be possessed by the milliammeter M. An ohmmeter suitable for measuring such high resistances[1] is illustrated in Fig. 3-4, and consists of a

[1] See W. N. Tuttle, An Improved Megohm Meter for A-C Operation, *Gen. Rad. Expt.*, vol. 20, November, 1945; T. J. Rehfisch, An Insulation Resistance Meter, *Wireless Eng.*, vol. 19, p. 49, February, 1942.

voltage source (50 to 100 volts), preferably a regulated voltage obtained from a rectifier-filter system, which is applied to the unknown resistance R_x in series with a fixed known resistance R_s that has a magnitude comparable with the unknown.   The voltage across R_s is then indicated by means of a d-c vacuum-tube voltmeter, the output indication of which can be calibrated directly in ohms.   Multiplying factors for the scale reading may be obtained by changing the resistance R_s.

3-2. A-C Wheatstone Bridges.   Impedance at audio and radio frequencies is commonly determined by means of an a-c Wheatstone bridge. The schematic circuit of an a-c bridge is shown in Fig. 3-5, and is similar

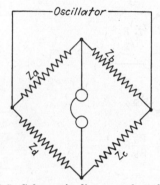

FIG. 3-5. Schematic diagram of a-c bridge.

to the d-c bridge of Fig. 3-2 except that instead of being regarded as simple resistances, the arms are now impedances which may have reactive components; also the bridge is excited by alternating rather than direct current, and the galvanometer is replaced by some means, such as a telephone receiver, for detecting alternating currents.   When the bridge is balanced,

$$\frac{Z_a}{Z_b} = \frac{Z_d}{Z_c} \tag{3-2}$$

where Z_a, Z_b, Z_c, and Z_d are the impedances of the arms, and are vector complex quantities that commonly possess phase angles.   It is thus necessary to adjust both the magnitudes and the phase angles of the impedance arms to achieve balance, *i.e.*, the bridge must be balanced both for the reactance and for the resistance components.

3-3. Common Types of Bridges.   Since the impedance composing each arm of an a-c bridge may be a combination of resistances, inductances, and capacitances, an unlimited variety of bridge types is possible.   Some

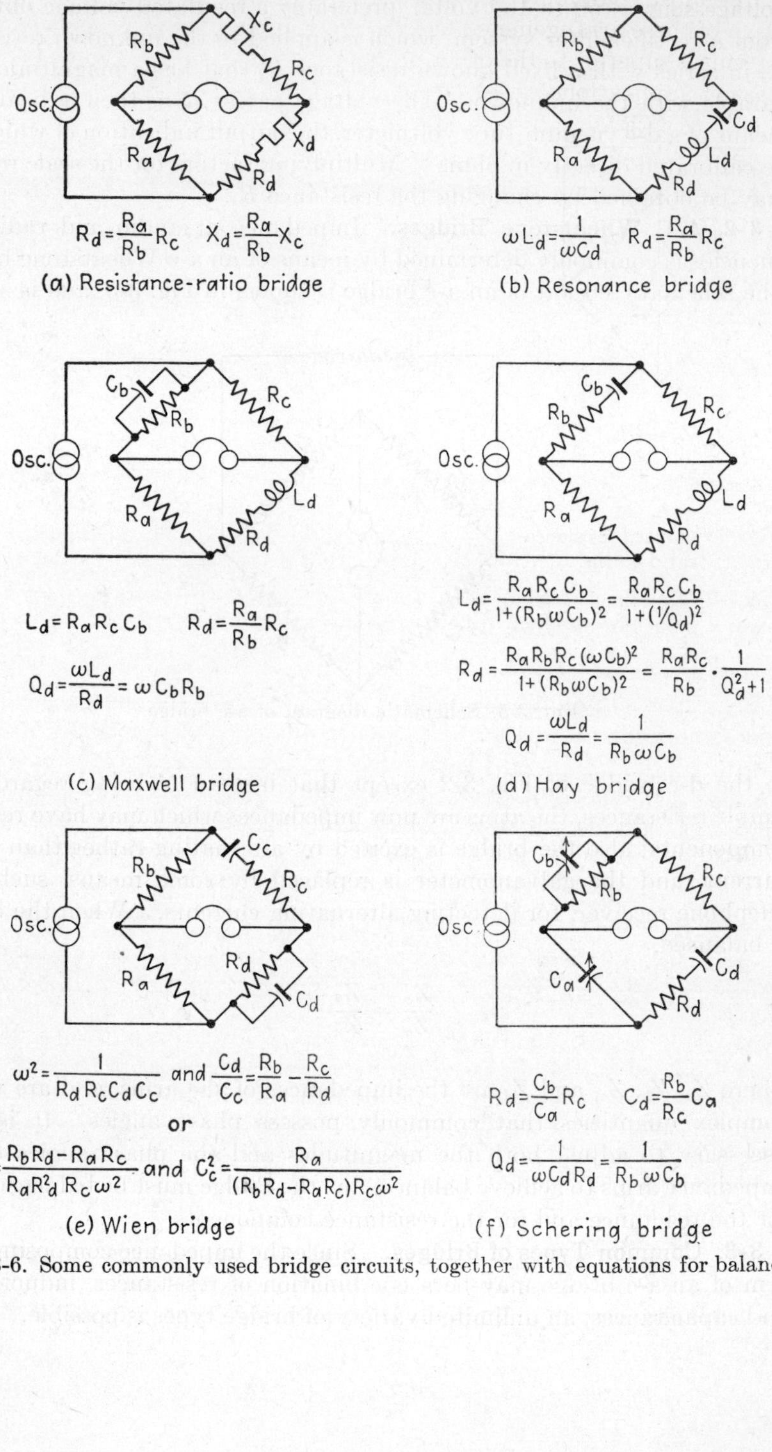

(a) Resistance-ratio bridge

$$R_d = \frac{R_a}{R_b} R_c \qquad X_d = \frac{R_a}{R_b} X_c$$

(b) Resonance bridge

$$\omega L_d = \frac{1}{\omega C_d} \qquad R_d = \frac{R_a}{R_b} R_c$$

(c) Maxwell bridge

$$L_d = R_a R_c C_b \qquad R_d = \frac{R_a}{R_b} R_c$$

$$Q_d = \frac{\omega L_d}{R_d} = \omega C_b R_b$$

(d) Hay bridge

$$L_d = \frac{R_a R_c C_b}{1 + (R_b \omega C_b)^2} = \frac{R_a R_c C_b}{1 + (1/Q_d)^2}$$

$$R_d = \frac{R_a R_b R_c (\omega C_b)^2}{1 + (R_b \omega C_b)^2} = \frac{R_a R_c}{R_b} \cdot \frac{1}{Q_d^2 + 1}$$

$$Q_d = \frac{\omega L_d}{R_d} = \frac{1}{R_b \omega C_b}$$

(e) Wien bridge

$$\omega^2 = \frac{1}{R_d R_c C_d C_c} \quad \text{and} \quad \frac{C_d}{C_c} = \frac{R_b}{R_a} - \frac{R_c}{R_d}$$

or

$$C_d^2 = \frac{R_b R_d - R_a R_c}{R_a R_d^2 R_c \omega^2} \quad \text{and} \quad C_c^2 = \frac{R_a}{(R_b R_d - R_a R_c) R_c \omega^2}$$

(f) Schering bridge

$$R_d = \frac{C_b}{C_a} R_c \qquad C_d = \frac{R_b}{R_c} C_a$$

$$Q_d = \frac{1}{\omega C_d R_d} = \frac{1}{R_b \omega C_b}$$

Fig. 3-6. Some commonly used bridge circuits, together with equations for balance.

of the most commonly used bridge circuits are illustrated in Fig. 3-6.[1,2] Each of these arrangements has its own combination of properties, and as a result is superior to the other bridge types in Fig. 3-6 for some particular class of applications.

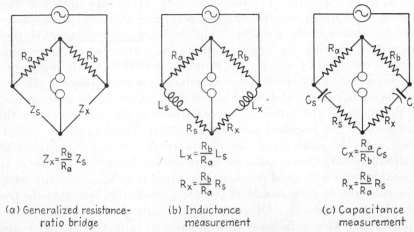

$$Z_x = \frac{R_b}{R_a} Z_s$$

$$L_x = \frac{R_b}{R_a} L_s$$

$$R_x = \frac{R_b}{R_a} R_s$$

$$C_x = \frac{R_a}{R_b} C_s$$

$$R_x = \frac{R_b}{R_a} R_s$$

(a) Generalized resistance-
ratio bridge

(b) Inductance
measurement

(c) Capacitance
measurement

Fig. 3-7. Details of resistance-ratio bridge, with particular reference to the measurement of inductance and capacitance, together with equations for balance.

The resistance-ratio bridge of Fig. 3-6a, shown in greater detail in Fig. 3-7, measures the unknown impedance in terms of a known impedance of the same kind. Thus an unknown inductance and its series resistance

[1] For a more complete catalog of bridge types the reader is referred to one of the standard books on electrical measurements. Some additional types of more limited application than those of Fig. 3-6 are shown in Figs. 3-30, 3-35, 3-36, 3-37, and 3-40.

[2] For further information on these bridges, including design features, shielding arrangements, and problem arising from residual impedances, see L. Behr and A. J. Williams, Jr., The Campbell-Shackelton Shielded Ratio Box, *Proc. IRE*, vol. **20**, p. 969, June, 1932; W. J. Shackelton, Shielded Bridge for Inductive Impedance, *Trans. AIEE*, vol. 45, p. 1266, 1946; I. G. Easton, A Wide-range Capacitance Test Bridge, *Gen. Rad. Expt.*, vol. 23, p. 1, July, 1948; W. D. Voelker, An Improved Capacitance Bridge for Precision Measurements, *Bell Labs. Record*, vol. 20, p. 133, January, 1942; H. T. Wilhelm, Impedance Bridge with a Billion-to-one Range. *Bell Labs. Record*, vol. 10, p. 133, January, 1942; C. L. Fortescue and G. Mole, A Resonance Bridge for Use at Frequencies Up to 10 Megacycles per Second, *J. IEE (Wireless Sec.)*, vol. 13, p. 122, June, 1938; H. W. Lamson, A Handy Pair of Bridges, *Gen. Rad. Expt.*, vol. 20, p. 3, February, 1946; R. F. Field and I. G. Easton, A Wide Frequency Range Capacitance Bridge, *Gen. Rad. Expt.*, vol. 21, p. 1, April, 1947; D. B. Sinclair, A Radio-frequency Bridge for Impedance Measurements from 400 Kilocycles to 60 Megacycles, *Proc. IRE*, vol. 28, p. 497, November, 1940; D. W. Dye and T. I. Jones, A Radio-frequency Bridge for Impedance and Power-factor Measurements, *J. IEE*, vol. **72**, p. 169, 1933 (*Wireless Sec., IEE*, vol. 8, p. 22, March, 1933); J. G. Ferguson, Classification of Bridge Methods of Measuring Impedances, *Bell System Tech. J.*, vol. 12, p. 452, October, 1933.

are measured in terms of a standard inductance and a standard resistance, as indicated by the circuit and balance equations given in Fig. 3-7b, while similarly an unknown capacitance and its equivalent series resistance are measured in terms of a standard capacitance C_s and a known series resistance R_s as in Fig. 3-7c. The resistance-ratio bridge can employ a fixed ratio R_b/R_a, in which case the standard reactance and standard resistance must be continuously variable. The balance for reactance is then achieved by varying the standard reactance, while the resistance component is balanced by varying the standard resistance.[1] Alternatively a fixed capacitance (or inductance) standard can be employed. In this case the equations of balance are satisfied by adjusting the resistance R_a (or R_b) to make the ratio R_b/R_a correspond to the ratio between the reactances of the standard and the unknown capacitances (or inductances). At the same time, the resistance R_s (or R_x) is adjusted as required to satisfy the equation for the resistance balance. The use of an adjustable ratio with fixed standard reactance is satisfactory only when measuring coils or capacitances that have a reasonably high Q at the frequency of measurement. Otherwise a fixed ratio for the resistance arms is preferred. This is because with a variable ratio the reactance and resistance balances are not independent, and unless the Q of the reactance being measured is at least reasonably high, the interaction is so great that a long series of successive adjustments of first the ratio, then the resistance R_s, then the ratio, etc., is required to obtain a good balance.[2]

The resonance bridge of Fig. 3-6b is a special form of resistance-ratio bridge. Here the reactances are all concentrated in one arm, and are adjusted to give series resonance so that this arm offers a resistance impedance which can be balanced by varying R_c. The resonance bridge can be used to measure frequency in terms of inductance and capacitance, and is also sometimes used to measure capacitance in terms of frequency and a variable inductance, or inductance in terms of frequency and a variable capacitance.

The Maxwell bridge of Fig. 3-6c compares an inductance with a

[1] It will be noted that if the unknown reactance has a higher Q than the standard reactance, then in adjusting the bridge to obtain resistance balance it is necessary to do so with a variable resistance in series with the unknown reactance, rather than in series with the standard. The resistance of the unknown reactance is then $R_x - R_s'$, where R_x is the total resistance in the x arm as calculated by the balance equation, and R_s' is the resistance that must be added to the x arm to obtain a resistance balance.

[2] In contrast, the reactance and resistance balances with a variable reactance standard and a fixed ratio are independent; i.e., the adjustment of the standard reactance that gives the best balance with improper adjustment of the standard resistance, is also the best adjustment of the reactance when the standard resistance has exactly the correct value, and vice versa.

capacitance and two resistances. This bridge is particularly suitable for measuring inductance, since ordinary capacitances come closer to being ideal lossless standards of reactance than do the very best coils. In addition, the balance equation of the Maxwell bridge for the inductance component is independent of the losses associated with the inductance, and also is independent of the frequency of measurement. As ordinarily arranged for inductance measurements, the Maxwell bridge employs a fixed capacitance standard, the inductance balance being achieved by varying either resistance R_a or R_c. It will be noted that the scale of this variable resistance can be calibrated to read inductance directly. The losses R_d associated with the unknown inductance are then taken care of by adjusting R_b. When the bridge is operated at a specified frequency, it is possible to mark the scale of R_b to read directly the Q of the inductance. The Maxwell bridge is suitable for measuring inductances of all magnitudes, provided only that the Q of the inductance at the frequency of measurement is not too high. If the Q is very large, R_b becomes excessively large, and it is impractical to obtain a satisfactory variable standard resistance in the range of values required. The Maxwell bridge using a fixed capacitance has the disadvantage that there is interaction between the resistance and reactance balances. This can be avoided by varying the capacitance to obtain a reactance balance instead of varying R_a or R_c; however, the bridge then cannot be made direct-reading in Q. Furthermore a continuously variable condenser having the maximum capacitance ordinarily required means that decade condensers must be used, which leads to poorer accuracy than when a fixed condenser is employed.

The Hay bridge (Fig. 3-6d) also compares an inductance with a capacitance, but differs from the Maxwell bridge in that the resistance associated with the capacitance is a series instead of a shunt resistance. An inconvenient feature of this bridge is that the equation giving the balance for inductance contains the multiplier $1/[1 + (1/Q^2)]$. The inductance balance hence depends upon the losses (or Q) of the inductance, and also upon frequency, unless Q is absolutely independent of frequency. This correction makes it impossible to calibrate the dials to indicate inductance directly except for high values of Q (for $Q = 10$ the error is 1 per cent, for $Q = 30$ it is only 0.1 per cent). For this reason the Maxwell bridge is generally preferred to the Hay bridge for coils of low Q, while the Hay bridge is preferable for coils having high Q. The Hay bridge also finds extensive use in the measurement of incremental inductance (see Sec. 3-11).

The Wien bridge of Fig. 3-6e is a particular form of the resistance-ratio bridge that measures capacitance in terms of resistance and frequency.

This bridge finds use for measuring frequency in the audio range. It is also useful in the precision determination of capacitance, since the standards of frequency and resistance are known to very great accuracy.[1]

The Schering bridge (Fig. 3-6f) is extensively used for measuring the capacitance and power factor of condensers. It can be thought of as a modification of the resistance-ratio capacitance bridge of Fig. 3-7c, in which the loss R_d of the unknown condenser C_d in Fig. 3-6f is balanced by variable condenser C_b, rather than by a resistance in series with the standard capacitance C_a. For a fixed ratio R_b/R_c of the resistance arms of the Schering bridge, the unknown capacitance is directly proportional to the standard capacitance C_a, thereby permitting the latter to be calibrated directly in terms of the unknown capacitance, irrespective of losses. At the same time, the Q of the condenser under test is determined only by the frequency and the value of capacitance C_b required to achieve balance. Therefore, for a specified frequency the scale of the variable condenser C_b can be calibrated directly in Q (or in terms of the dissipation factor, which is defined as $1/Q$) of the condenser under test. The accuracy with which the dissipation factor can be measured in this way is very good even when the dissipation factor is small; as a consequence the Schering bridge is almost universally used in capacitance measurements where accurate determination of the dissipation factor is desired.

3-4. Shielding and Grounding of Bridges.[2] The bridge circuits of Fig. 3-6 are idealized in that they neglect the stray capacitances that are inevitably present. The various stray capacitances that are associated with a bridge circuit are illustrated schematically in Fig. 3-8a for a typical case. In general, these capacitances are uncertain in magnitude, often vary with the adjustment of the bridge and the position of the operator's body, etc.; also in some instances they are quite large. If these capacitances are not properly controlled or taken into account, serious errors may result in measurements made with the bridge. This situation is handled by grounding and shielding, and in some cases by using guard circuits.

The principles involved in shielding and grounding are illustrated by Fig. 3-8. Here Fig. 3-8a shows an unshielded and ungrounded resistance-ratio bridge arranged for measuring capacitance with a variable condenser standard. Various stray capacitances are schematically indicated by C_1 to C_{12}. Figure 3-8b shows the same bridge after shielding and

---

[1] See J. G. Ferguson and B. W. Barlett, The Measurement of Capacitance in Terms of Resistance and Frequency, *Bell System Tech. J.*, vol. 7, p. 420, July, 1928.

[2] For further information the reader should consult the references in footnote 2, p. 71; also see J. G. Ferguson, Shielding in High-frequency Measurements, *Bell System Tech. J.*, vol. 8, p. 560, July, 1929.

grounding.   The effect of the shielding and grounding is to make the stray capacitances definite, and to localize them so that they act in a known way, as shown in Fig. 3-8c.   Thus the ground short-circuits oscillator stray capacitance C_2 in Fig. 3-8a, and places oscillator capacitance C_1 in shunt with the oscillator output terminals, where it has no effect.   Similarly the shield surrounding the resistances R_a and R_b replaces capacitances C_3, C_6, C_7, and C_{11} by capacitances C_{21}, C_{22}, and C_{27},

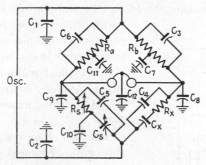

(a) Schematic illustration of stray capacitances in unshielded and ungrounded bridge

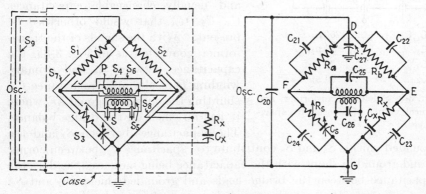

(b) Bridge with shields and ground   (c) Schematic circuit of shielded and grounded bridge

Fig. 3-8. Bridge circuits, showing the effect of shielding.

which are associated with corner D in a definite manner, and which are independent of everything external to the interior of shields S_1 and S_2. Thus by making these ratio arms and their shields absolutely identical and symmetrical, the bridge ratio will always be unity irrespective of frequency, in spite of the associated capacitances.   The capacitance between the outside of shields S_1 and S_2 and ground contributes to the capacitance C_{20} that shunts the oscillator terminals (as likewise do C_1 and C_{27}) and so has no adverse effect.   The shield S_3 around the standard impedance

$C_s R_s$ introduces a known fixed capacitance C_{24} in shunt with this arm. For the usual case where $R_s \ll 1/\omega C_s$ this capacitance can be considered to be in shunt with only C_s, affecting the calibration of the latter accordingly.

The various capacitances associated with the output diagonal EF of the bridge are prevented from causing trouble by employing a shielded output transformer as illustrated. In this transformer the primary and secondary windings are provided with separate electrostatic shields S_4 and S_5 enclosed in another shield S_6 (the transformer case), to which the transformer core is attached. The equivalent circuit of such a shielded transformer is shown in Fig. 3-9, which gives typical values for the various capacitances. A further discussion of shielded transformers is given in Sec. 3-12.[1]

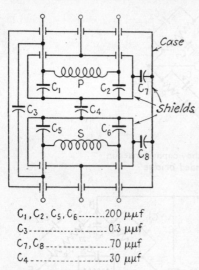

C_1, C_2, C_5, C_6 .... 200 μμf
C_3 .... 0.3 μμf
C_7, C_8 .... 70 μμf
C_4 .... 30 μμf

FIG. 3-9. Shielded transformer, and typical values of associated capacitances.

The use of an output transformer in this manner places known and small capacitances at specified locations, in place of the commonly large, unknown, and usually changeable capacitances C_8, C_9, C_{12} that would otherwise be present. With the shields of the transformer connected as in Fig. 3-8b, the capacitance between S_4 and primary winding P results in a capacitance C_{25} shunting the output diagonal EF, where it has no effect on the bridge balance. The capacitances between S_4 and the grounded shields S_5 and S_6 contribute to capacitance C_{23} between corner E and ground in shunt with the capacitance being measured, as does the capacitance between the bridge leads and grounded shields S_7 and S_8. The secondary leads of the transformer are brought out of the case through grounded shields.

The entire bridge in Fig. 3-8b is enclosed in a shielded case which acts as a ground for the system, and makes all capacitances to ground have a definite value independent of external objects or leads. It is also usually

[1] Also see Sinclair, loc. cit.

Current appearing in the transformer secondary circuit as a result of residual capacitance coupling between primary and secondary windings, can be neutralized with some bridge arrangements by injecting an adjustable current into the detector circuit, the current being derived from the voltage applied to the bridge, using an adjustable phase splitter. For further information see Easton, loc. cit.

desirable to enclose the oscillator leads external to the case in a grounded shield (S_9).

The effect of the shielding in Fig. 3-8b is seen to eliminate some stray capacitances, and to make definite and to localize the others so that their effects will always be the same and so can be taken into account when using the bridge.[1] The shielding also makes the behavior of the bridge independent of the characteristics of the oscillator or output detector systems. It is, for example, possible to interchange the oscillator and output indicator terminals of the shielded bridge without in any way affecting the functioning of the bridge, or changing the calibration.

The need for shielding in a bridge system becomes greater as the frequency is increased and as the impedance level of the bridge arms becomes greater. Shielding is absolutely essential in all bridges operating at audio frequencies, and on down to 60 cycles, although the Wagner ground guard circuit is sometimes used in place of shielding for these conditions.

The Wagner Ground. In resistance-ratio audio-frequency bridges intended for measuring impedances on the order of a few thousand ohms or less, the principal sources of trouble from stray capacitances are the capacitances to ground associated with the oscillator

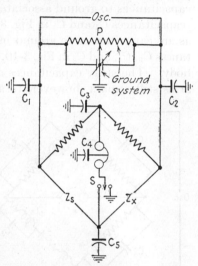

FIG. 3-10. Resistance-ratio bridge with Wagner ground connection.

and the output indicator. When the utmost in precision is not required, this problem can be handled without resorting to shielding, by the use of a Wagner ground, illustrated in Fig. 3-10. Here potentiometer P is connected across the oscillator as indicated, and is often but not always associated with a three-terminal double-stator balancing condenser as indicated. The procedure for carrying out a measurement with such a system involves three steps as follows: (1) The bridge is balanced as well as possible, ignoring the Wagner ground system. It will generally be found that it is impossible to obtain a complete null. (2) Switch S is next thrown to connect the telephone receivers from one corner of the bridge

---

[1] Thus by adjusting the shields so that $C_{22}/C_{21} = R_a/R_b$, the ratio of the bridge is independent of frequency. Again, the capacitance C_{24} can be taken into account in the calibration of C_s, as has been mentioned. Finally, the capacitance C_{23} can be measured, and its shunting effect across the unknown impedance allowed for by calculation.

to ground, and the Wagner ground system is then adjusted to give a null indication in the telephone receivers. (3) Switch S is thrown to reconnect the telephone receivers across the output diagonal of the bridge, and the balance is then completed in the usual manner. In some cases it may be desirable to repeat the second and third steps to ensure the highest possible accuracy.

It will be observed that the effect of the Wagner ground is to place a ground connection on the oscillator in such a manner as to bring the output diagonal of the bridge to ground potential. In this way the stray capacitances to ground associated with the generator terminals and leads (capacitances C_1 and C_2 in Fig. 3-10) are removed from the bridge circuit, as are capacitances to ground in the output circuit, representing capacitances C_3, C_4, and C_5 in Fig. 3-10, which include the effects of the operator's body. The stray capacitances associated with impedances of the bridge arms still remain, however, to affect the accuracy of the measurement; these capacitances are not shown in Fig. 3-10, but correspond to capacitances C_3 to C_6, C_7, C_{10} and C_{11} in Fig. 3-8a.

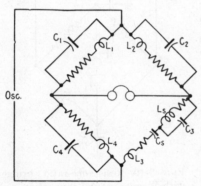

FIG. 3-11. Bridge circuit showing residual inductances L_1 to L_4 and capacitances C_1 to C_4 associated with the bridge arms.

3-5. Miscellaneous Aspects of Bridges. *Residual Impedances of Bridge Arms.*[1] The simple impedances in the arms of the bridges in Fig. 3-6 are only approximated in actual practice. This is because resistances and capacitances always have lead inductance associated with them, while resistances and inductances have at least some distributed capacitance. Again, inductances and capacitances always have losses, and so have an equivalent shunt or series resistance that in general depends upon the frequency. Even air-dielectric condensers, which are more nearly perfect than other reactance standards, have some loss and some residual inductance (see Sec. 14-1). The result is illustrated schematically in Fig. 3-11 for a resonance bridge. All of these residual impedances must be taken into account if errors are to be minimized in bridge measurements.

The effect of the residual parameters becomes more serious as the frequency is increased. This is because a series inductance has an impedance proportional to frequency, while a shunt capacitance produces a shunting effect proportional to frequency. However, it is sometimes necessary to take into account these residual quantities even at audio fre-

[1] For further information see the references in footnote 2, p. 71.

quencies. For example, when measuring very small inductances, such as values of the order of 10 μh, the series inductances of the bridge leads and resistances are by no means negligible in comparison. Under these circumstances, the lead inductances in the various arms must either be equalized or minimized; furthermore, variable resistances must be of the inductively compensated type, so that as the resistances are adjusted, the inductances that they introduce remain fixed.

In a properly shielded bridge, these residual impedances are the principal factor that determines the accuracy at the higher radio frequencies. Their evaluation and minimization accordingly become one of the principal considerations involved in radio-frequency bridges, and

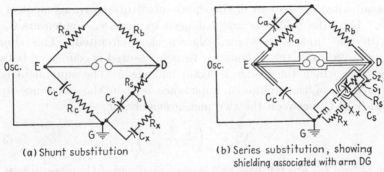

(a) Shunt substitution

(b) Series substitution, showing shielding associated with arm DG

Fig. 3-12. Substitution method of measurement, as applied to a bridge, showing shunt substitution at a, and series substitution at b.

represent a problem that must be worked out with great care for each individual design. The solution involves an appropriate combination of three approaches, $viz.$, (1) minimizing the magnitude of the residual impedances as far as possible, (2) evaluating the residuals so that correction can be made for their effects, and (3) using the substitution method of measurement.

With proper design and careful attention to details, it is possible to obtain useful results with bridges operating at frequencies up to about 200 Mc.[1]

Substitution Method as Applied to Bridge Measurements. The principle of the substitution method can be understood by reference to the example in Fig. 3-12a. Here adjustable standard impedances R_s and C_s are connected in the standard arm. With the unknown capacitance disconnected, the bridge is balanced in the usual manner. The unknown impedance $C_x R_x$ is then connected in shunt with C_s, and C_s and R_s are

[1] For example, see R. A. Soderman, A New Bridge for the Measurement of Impedance between 10 and 165 Mc, *Gen. Rad. Expt.*, vol. 24, February, 1950.

readjusted to restore balance.[1] The unknown capacitance C_x and its equivalent series resistance R_x (assumed small compared with the reactance of C_x) are then obtained from the changes ΔR_s and ΔC_s required in R_s and C_s, according to the relations

$$C_x = \Delta C_s \tag{3-3a}$$

$$R_x = \Delta R_s \left(\frac{C'_s}{C_x}\right)^2 \tag{3-3b}$$

where ΔC_s and ΔR_s are the changes in C_s and R_s obtained when the bridge is rebalanced, and C'_s is the capacitance required in the initial balance.

A slightly different method of carrying out the substitution principle is illustrated in Fig. 3-12b, where a Schering bridge is employed,[2] using series substitution instead of the shunt substitution arrangement of Fig. 3-12a. Here the bridge is first balanced by variable condensers C_s and C_a with the "unknown" terminals mn short-circuited. This short is then removed, and the impedance to be measured is connected between them, after which the bridge is again balanced. The equivalent series reactance X_x of the unknown impedance is then the difference in the reactance of C_s between the two measurements, or

$$X_x = \frac{1}{\omega}\left(\frac{1}{C'_s} - \frac{1}{C''_s}\right) \tag{3-4a}$$

where C'_s and C''_s are the first and second readings of C_s, respectively. A positive sign indicates that X_x is capacitive, while a negative sign corresponds to an inductive X_x. Similarly, the equivalent series resistance R_x of the unknown impedance is the difference in the equivalent series resistances for the two cases, as determined from the adjustment of C_a.[3] From the formula for the Schering bridge this is

$$R_x = R_b \frac{C''_a - C'_a}{C_c} \tag{3-4b}$$

where C'_a and C''_a are the values of C_a for the first and second measurements, respectively, while R_b and C_c are as shown in Fig. 3-12b.

Attention is called to the arrangement of shields for arm DG indicated in Fig. 3-12b, which eliminates the stray capacitances that are in shunt

[1] If the leads are not properly handled when connecting the condensers in parallel, it is possible to introduce errors as great as 1 $\mu\mu$f from lead capacitance effects. This point is discussed by R. F. Field, Correction Errors in Capacitance Measurements, *Gen. Rad. Expt.*, vol. 21, p. 1, May, 1947.

[2] For further details relating to this arrangement, with particular reference to the higher radio frequencies, see Sinclair, *loc. cit.*

[3] By providing a variable standard resistance R_s, and keeping C_a fixed after the initial adjustment with mn short-circuited, then R_x is the change required in R_s to achieve balance after the unknown impedance has been inserted into the system.

with the unknown impedance.   This is achieved by surrounding shield S_1, which is connected to corner D, by shield S_2, which is connected to corner E.   Capacitance between S_1 and S_2 is accordingly placed in shunt with the telephone receivers (or other output indicator) and thereby has no effect.   Capacitance between S_2 and ground is placed in shunt with arm EG and can be allowed for when adjusting the capacitance C_c to the proper value for bridge operation.   Capacitance between C_sR_s and S_1 is effectively in shunt with C_s and so merely modifies the calibration of C_s. It will be noted that this arrangement eliminates all capacitance between C_sR_s and ground, and so prevents C_sR_s from placing a stray capacitance in shunt with the unknown impedance C_xR_x being measured.   This is an excellent illustration of the value of a properly designed shielding arrangement.

The substitution method has the advantage that the accuracy of the measurement depends almost solely upon the accuracy with which one knows the changes in impedance of the adjustable circuit elements.   Stray capacitances anywhere in the circuit, stray couplings, imperfect shielding, residual impedances, and inaccuracies in the magnitude and phase angles of the impedances composing the other three bridge arms do not introduce errors, since these effects are the same both with and without the unknown impedance in the circuit.   The substitution method is often the only means by which reasonable accuracy can be obtained at radio frequencies; in addition its use will also still further increase the relatively high accuracy normally associated with measurements made at audio frequencies.

Input and Output Impedances of Bridges, and Calculation of Bridge Sensitivity.[1]   In designing bridge systems an important consideration is the impedance that the bridge presents to the oscillator when the bridge is balanced or almost balanced.   Under these conditions the current through the output branch is either zero or negligibly small, so that the behavior is the same as though the output branch were open-circuited. The input impedance of the bridge of Fig. 3-5 when balanced is accordingly the impedance formed by $Z_a + Z_b$ in parallel with the impedance $Z_c + Z_d$, or

$$\begin{matrix} \text{Input impedance of} \\ \text{bridge} \end{matrix} \Bigg\} = \frac{(Z_a + Z_b)(Z_c + Z_d)}{Z_a + Z_b + Z_c + Z_d} \qquad (3\text{-}5)$$

When viewed from its output terminals, a bridge can be represented by the equivalent circuit of Fig. 3-13b, which consists of an equivalent generator V in series with an equivalent source of output impedance Z_{eq}.   The value of this equivalent output impedance is, by Thévenin's theorem, the impedance that is measured at the output terminals, looking

[1] Also see Raymond J. Wey, A New Treatment of the Wheatstone Bridge Network, *Wireless Eng.*, vol. 21, p. 308, July, 1944.

into the bridge with the oscillator inactive. When the bridge is balanced or nearly balanced, this impedance is independent of the internal impedance of the oscillator, and so can be calculated on the assumption that the oscillator connection is open-circuited. The output impedance of the bridge in Fig. 3-13a accordingly has the value shown in Fig. 3-13c, assuming that the bridge adjustment approximates balance. For maximum sensitivity, the output indicator (such as the telephone receiver) should possess an impedance Z_L that matches the output impedance of the bridge in a manner that provides for maximum power transfer to the indicator. If the equivalent output impedance is high, the indicating equipment

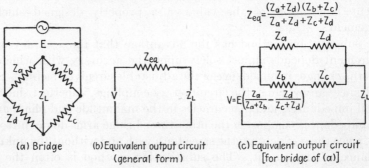

(a) Bridge   (b) Equivalent output circuit (general form)   (c) Equivalent output circuit [for bridge of (a)]

Fig. 3-13. Equivalent input and output circuits of a bridge.

should then also present a high load impedance Z_L to the bridge, and vice versa.

The equivalent voltage V acting in series with the equivalent circuit of Fig. 3-13b is, according to Thévenin's theorem, the potential that appears across the output terminals when these are open-circuited. This voltage will depend upon the adjustment of the bridge, being zero with balance, and increasing as the bridge becomes unbalanced. It value can be calculated as indicated in Fig. 3-13c.

Bridge Oscillator and Detector. A wide variety of arrangements can be employed to detect the bridge output. In the frequency range 250 to 5000 cycles telephone receivers are customary, usually connected directly to the bridge through a transformer, but sometimes in association with an amplifier (preferably tuned) to increase sensitivity. At lower and higher audio frequencies, where the ear is not particularly satisfactory as an indicating device, a tuned amplifier with visual output indicator such as a meter or cathode-ray tube is common.[1] When available, a wave analyzer forms a convenient tuned-amplifier–indicator combination.

[1] Arrangements have been devised for presenting a visual indication of the balance on a cathode-ray tube in a manner that shows separately the conditions of the balances for the resistance and reactance components. This is achieved by synchroniz-

At radio frequencies an ordinary radio receiver is customarily employed as a bridge indicator. The only special consideration involved is that the receiver, and also the leads between its input and the bridge output, should be shielded in order to prevent direct coupling with the oscillator. It is also sometimes desirable to disconnect the automatic volume control of the receiver, and replace it with a manual control.

The amount of oscillator power required to operate a bridge is determined by the sensitivity of the indicator employed to detect the bridge output. When a telephone receiver is used without amplification, an oscillator power of 50 to 200 mw is generally adequate in the frequency range 500 to 2000 cycles, where the ear is most sensitive. More power will be required at lower and higher audio frequencies unless amplification is employed, in which case the power required will depend upon the amount of amplification. In radio-frequency bridges, the power used to operate may be quite small, since the radio receivers employed as output indicators are quite sensitive.

The bridge oscillator may be of any convenient type having the required power and frequency. However, it is generally desirable that the waveform be relatively free of harmonics. This arises from the fact that the bridge adjustment which gives balance for the fundamental frequency will commonly not result in a balance for the harmonic component, either because the bridge is of a type in which the condition of balance depends on frequency (such as the Wien bridge), or because the impedance being measured has a loss, or an effective inductance, or an effective capacitance, that depends upon frequency.[1] A tuned indicator will of course eliminate this problem by suppressing the interfering harmonics. Good waveform therefore becomes of prime importance only in the audio-frequency case where the indicator is a telephone receiver; here extremely low harmonic content is very advantageous.

At radio frequencies it is important that the oscillator be shielded and

---

ing the horizontal sweep of the cathode-ray tube with the bridge oscillator in a suitable phase relation, and then applying the output of the bridge to the vertically deflecting electrodes. The result is an elliptical pattern, in which the tilt of the axis is controlled by the resistance component of the bridge balance, while incorrect reactance balance causes an opening up of the ellipse. For further information see H. W. Lamson, Electronic Null Detector for Impedance Bridges, *Rev. Sci. Instruments*, vol. 9, p. 272, September, 1938; E. H. Eveland, A Cathode-ray Bridge Detector, *Bell Labs. Record*, vol. 23, p. 93, March, 1945. These papers also discuss tuned amplifiers suitable for use with bridges.

[1] Similar harmonic effects are also produced when the impedance being measured has a nonlinear characteristic, as when a magnetic core or a nonlinear resistance is involved. This situation requires either that a tuned indicator be used, or that the amplitude of the oscillator output be reduced to the point where the nonlinear effects are not excessive.

that it be connected to the bridge through a shielded cable, in order to minimize any direct leakage of energy from the oscillator to the bridge indicating system. When available, a signal generator makes an excellent source of energy for operating a radio-frequency bridge, but simpler arrangements are satisfactory provided they are at least moderately well shielded.

3-6. Twin-T and Bridged-T Null Networks.[1] The Wheatstone bridge with its four impedances arranged on the sides of a square is not the only network that gives zero transmission between input and output terminals for some particular adjustment of the circuit constants. Equivalent

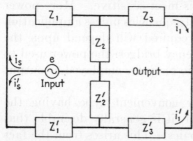

FIG. 3-14. General form of twin-T network.

arrangements that find extensive use are provided by the twin-T and bridged-T circuits.

The twin-T network, also sometimes called the parallel-T network, is shown schematically in Fig. 3-14. It consists of two unlike T networks arranged with input and output terminals in parallel. Zero output is obtained when the circuit impedances of the individual branches are so arranged that the trans-

mission through the two T networks to the output terminals is equal in magnitude but opposite in phase; this corresponds to the condition for balance in a Wheatstone bridge The twin-T arrangement has the desirable feature, not present in a bridge, of possessing a common input and output terminal which can be grounded. This eliminates the necessity of the shielded transformer required with the Wheatstone bridge, and simplifies the shielding problem. The twin-T arrangement also lends itself to simple circuit layouts which minimize stray capacitances and residual reactances.

In analyzing the behavior of the twin-T arrangement under conditions corresponding to balance, it is convenient to assume that the output terminals are short-circuited, and then to determine the conditions for which the short-circuit currents transmitted through the individual T networks will be equal and opposite. The output current i_1 for the T network $Z_1Z_2Z_3$, assuming that the output terminals are short-circuited, is[2]

---

[1] For further information see W. N. Tuttle, Bridged-T and Parallel-T Null Circuits for Measurements at Radio Frequencies, *Proc. IRE*, vol. 28, p. 23, January, 1940.

[2] This relation is derived as follows: Assuming the output terminals are short-circuited, then the impedance offered by the input terminals to an applied voltage e_1 is $Z_s = Z_1 + Z_2Z_3/(Z_2 + Z_3)$, and the input current $i_s = e/Z_s$. The part i_1 of i_s that flows through Z_3 is then $i_1 = i_sZ_2/(Z_2 + Z_3) = eZ_2/Z_s(Z_2 + Z_3)$. This readily reduces to Eq. (3-6a) by substituting for Z_s.

$$i_1 = \frac{e}{Z_1 + Z_3 + (Z_1 Z_3 / Z_2)} \qquad (3\text{-}6a)$$

where e is the input voltage, and the impedances are as indicated in Fig. 3-14. Similarly the current i_1' simultaneously transmitted through the short-circuited load by the second T network is

$$i_1' = \frac{e}{Z_1' + Z_3' + (Z_1' Z_3' / Z_2')} \qquad (3\text{-}6b)$$

Zero output, corresponding to balance, will result when $i_1 + i_1' = 0$; the

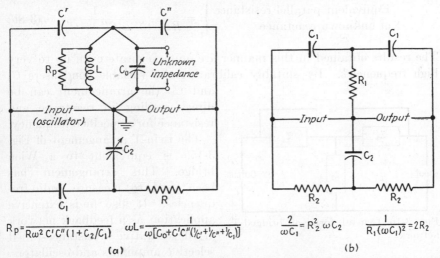

$$R_p = \frac{1}{R\omega^2 C'C''(1 + C_2/C_1)} \qquad \omega L = \frac{1}{\omega[C_0 + C'C''(1/c' + 1/c'' + 1/c_1)]} \qquad \frac{2}{\omega C_1} = R_2^2\, \omega C_2 \qquad \frac{1}{R_1(\omega C_1)^2} = 2R_2$$

(a)   (b)

FIG. 3-15. Examples of twin-T circuits.

general null condition accordingly becomes

$$Z_1 + Z_3 + \frac{Z_1 Z_3}{Z_2} + Z_1' + Z_3' + \frac{Z_1' Z_3'}{Z_2'} = 0 \qquad (3\text{-}7)$$

Examples of twin-T circuit arrangements that have been found to be of practical value are shown in Fig. 3-15, together with equations for balance. The arrangement of Fig. 3-15a is particularly suitable for the general run of impedance measurements at radio frequencies where the impedances to be determined are not too small in magnitude.[1] For this purpose it complements the radio-frequency Wheatstone bridge of Fig. 3-12b, which tends to be most suitable in dealing with low and moderate impedances. The substitution method is normally employed for measuring impedances with this circuit. The procedure consists first in making a preliminary

[1] This circuit is discussed in considerable detail by D. B. Sinclair, The Twin-T, a New Type of Null Instrument for Measuring Impedance at Frequencies up to 30 Megacycles, *Proc. IRE*, vol. 28, p. 310, July, 1940.

balance before connecting the unknown impedance. This is done by adjusting C_0 and C_2 to values C_0' and C_2' as required to give zero output. The unknown impedance is then connected in shunt with C_0 and L and the network brought back to balance by readjusting C_0 and C_2 to the values C_0'' and C_2'' required to restore balance. The reactance and the equivalent parallel resistance of the unknown impedance are then given by the equations

$$\text{Reactance of unknown} = \frac{1}{\omega(C_0' - C_0'')} \qquad (3\text{-}8a)$$

$$\left.\begin{array}{l}\text{Equivalent parallel resistance} \\ \text{of unknown reactance}\end{array}\right\} = \frac{C_1}{R\omega C'C''}\frac{1}{\omega(C_2'' - C_2')} \qquad (3\text{-}8b)$$

The results obtained in this manner are quite accurate even up to very high frequencies. By suitably calibrating the variable condensers C_0 and C_2 the arrangement can be direct reading in reactance and resistance for a specified frequency.

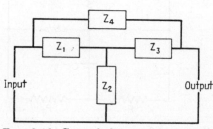

The twin-T arrangement of Fig. 3-15b is equivalent to a Wien bridge. This arrangement has been used to measure audio-frequencies. It also finds extensive

Fig. 3-16. General form of bridged-T network.

application as a feedback network in degenerative resistance-tuned selective amplifiers and oscillators.

The bridged-T circuit is shown schematically in Fig. 3-16, and is a degenerated form of the twin T in which the shunt impedance Z_2' of Fig. 3-14 has become an open circuit. The general balance equation for the bridged-T network accordingly follows directly from Eq. (3-7), and in the notation of Fig. 3-16 is

$$Z_1 + Z_3 + \frac{Z_1 Z_3}{Z_2} + Z_4 = 0 \qquad (3\text{-}9)$$

Because the bridged-T network is a degenerated form, it has less flexibility, and finds fewer applications as a substitute for the Wheatstone bridge, as compared with the twin-T arrangement.

Examples of practical bridged-T networks, together with equations for balance, are given in Fig. 3-17. The circuit of Fig. 3-17a is useful in the measurement of incremental inductance (see Sec. 3-11), and also has been proposed for determining the inductance and Q of radio-frequency coils. The circuit of Fig. 3-17b has been used to compare coils, and is also suitable for the measurement of impedance by the substitution method. In the latter case, a variable condenser and the unknown impedance are connected in parallel with each other and in parallel with L_p, and the unknown reactance and its equivalent shunt resistance determined from the readjustments required in the variable condenser and the resistance R, respectively, to restore balance when the unknown is removed.[1]

The twin-T and bridged-T networks are troubled with stray capacitances and residual circuit impedances just as are Wheatstone bridges. This results in errors, particularly at the higher frequencies, where the effect of the residual and stray parameters is greatest.   The situation with these networks is handled in the same manner as in Wheatstone

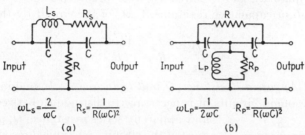

$$\omega L_s = \frac{2}{\omega C} \qquad R_s = \frac{1}{R(\omega C)^2}$$
(a)

$$\omega L_p = \frac{1}{2\omega C} \qquad R_p = \frac{1}{R(\omega C)^2}$$
(b)

FIG. 3-17. Examples of bridged-T networks.

bridges, by appropriate shielding, by arranging matters so that effects of the stray and residual parameters are least harmful, and by employing the substitution method of measurement.   The details involved differ from the Wheatstone-bridge case because of the different circuit arrangements, but if anything the problems are simpler than with bridges as a result of the fact that no shielded transformer is required. The general principles that must be given consideration are the same, however, as is likewise the general method of attack.[2]

3-7. Resistance and Q of Resonant Circuits.   The resistance and Q of a resonant circuit can be determined in a number of ways.   An obvious method of obtaining the resistance is to use a radio-frequency bridge or a twin-T null network.   When such equipment is conveniently available,

---

[1] An excellent discussion of the practical possibilities of the two circuits of Fig. 3-17 for the null measurement of circuit constants, is given by W. N. Tuttle, Bridged-T and Parallel-T Null Circuits for Measurements at Radio Frequencies, *Proc. IRE*, vol. 28, p. 23, January, 1940.   This reference also includes a consideration of the effects of stray capacitances and residual impedances.

[2] An excellent discussion of the effects of the residual and stray parameters, with particular reference to the problem of accurate impedance measurement at radio frequencies, is given by D. B. Sinclair, A Radio-frequency Bridge for Impedance Measurements from 400 Kilocycles to 60 Megacycles, *Proc. IRE*, vol. 28, p. 497, November, 1940; also see I. G. Easton, Corrections for Residual Impedances in the Twin-T, *Gen. Rad. Expt.*, vol. 19, p. 4, January–February, 1945.

and covers the frequency range required, this method is very satisfactory. The series resistance of resonant circuits may be measured by arranging the circuit as a series circuit in a resonance bridge, and then determining the equivalent series resistance. Alternatively, one may measure the parallel resonant impedance of a tuned circuit with the aid of twin-T network, which is more suitable for measuring high impedances at radio frequencies than is a Wheatstone bridge.

In addition to these bridge or null methods, a number of other arrangements are in common use for determining circuit resistance and Q. Some of these methods measure Q, others the series resistance R; in any case these two quantities are related to each other through the inductive reactance ωL or capacitive reactance $1/\omega C$ of the circuit by the equation

$$ Q = \frac{\omega L}{R} = \frac{1/\omega C}{R} \qquad (3\text{-}10) $$

True and Apparent Resistance, Q, and Inductance. In making measurements on resonant circuits, it is necessary to distinguish between the true

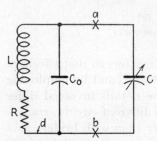

FIG. 3-18. Resonant circuit showing relationship of distributed capacitance C_0 to coil terminals ab.

and apparent series resistance, Q, and inductance of the circuit. A typical resonant circuit is illustrated in Fig. 3-18. Here the circuit inductance L has associated with it a distributed capacitance C_0 and is tuned to resonance by condenser C. The circuit resistance R is usually due almost entirely to losses in the coil; it is therefore shown in series with the inductance. While the condenser C will have some series resistance, this is usually negligible in comparison.

In this slightly idealized circuit the true inductance of the circuit is L, the true series resistance is R, and the true circuit Q is $\omega L/R$. However, if the inductance is viewed from its terminals ab across which the tuning capacitance C is connected, then the situation is somewhat different. The equivalent inductance that appears to the left of terminals ab is now greater than the inductance L; this is the apparent inductance and has the value[1]

---

[1] This relation is derived by noting that if the resistance R is neglected, the impedance of L and C_0 in parallel is

$$ \frac{j\omega L(1/j\omega C_0)}{j\omega L + (1/j\omega C_0)} = \frac{j\omega L}{-\omega^2 L C_0 + 1} $$

Thus the equivalent inductance is $L/(1 - \omega^2 L C_0)$. Substituting the resonant condition $\omega^2 = 1/L(C + C_0)$ gives Eq. (3-11a), while substituting $m^2 = \omega^2/\omega_0^2$, where $\omega_0^2 = 1/LC_0$, gives Eq. (3-11b).

$$\text{Apparent inductance} = L\,\frac{C + C_0}{C} \qquad (3\text{-}11a)$$

$$\text{Apparent inductance} = \frac{L}{1 - m^2} \qquad (3\text{-}11b)$$

where C is the capacitance required to tune the coil to resonance at the frequency for which the apparent inductance is desired, and m is the ratio of this frequency to the frequency at which the distributed capacitance C_0 acting alone is in resonance with the coil inductance. Similarly, the equivalent series resistance that appears to exist to the left of the terminals ab is greater than the actual series resistance R of the circuit as the result of the presence of distributed capacitance C_0. This enhanced resistance is termed the apparent resistance, and has the value

$$\text{Apparent resistance} = R\left(\frac{C + C_0}{C}\right)^2 = \frac{R}{(1 - m^2)^2} \qquad (3\text{-}12)$$

The ratio of the apparent inductive reactance to the apparent series resistance gives the apparent Q, which accordingly is

$$\text{Apparent } Q = (\text{true } Q)\,\frac{C}{C + C_0} = (\text{true } Q)(1 - m^2) \qquad (3\text{-}13)$$

Equations (3-11) to (3-13) apply strictly only to the part of the circuit in Fig. 3-18 that is to the left of ab. However, since in most instances the series resistance of the capacitance C is negligible, these relations that give the apparent series inductance, apparent Q, and apparent series resistance of the coil, can also ordinarily be used to define the relationship between the corresponding apparent and true quantities for the entire resonant circuit.

The value C_0 of the distributed capacitance can be determined as explained in Sec. 3-10.

The true and apparent values commonly differ appreciably. For example, when $C_0/C = \frac{1}{10}$ in Fig. 3-18, which corresponds to $m = 0.30$, then the true resistance is only 83 per cent of the apparent resistance, while the true and apparent Q and inductance differ by 9 per cent.

It will be noted that the difference between the true and apparent values of a circuit is essentially a difference in reference point in the circuit. The true values correspond to a reference point such as d that is in series with the total capacitance that tunes the circuit (including distributed capacitance); in contrast, the apparent values refer to a reference point b that is in series with the tuning condenser C but is not in series with the total effective capacitance that is present in the system.

Separation of Losses. The following methods of measuring circuit resistance and Q give the total resistance of the circuit, but say nothing as to how this total is distributed between the coil and condenser. When well-constructed air-dielectric condensers are used for tuning, the condenser losses are quite low, and under most practical circumstances it is permissible to assume that the coil is responsible for substantially the entire circuit loss.

When it is desired to know the exact division of losses between coil and condenser, it becomes necessary to make a separate investigation of the condenser losses. The coil losses can then be determined by subtraction

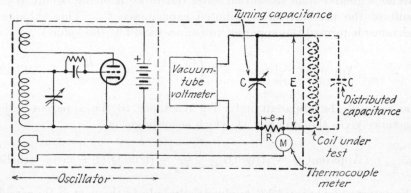

FIG. 3-19. Simplified diagram of Q meter.

of the condenser resistance from the measured total resistance of the circuit. A discussion of condenser losses is given in Sec. 14-1.

Q Meter. The Q meter is the most widely used means of obtaining circuit Q. The fundamental circuit diagram of the Q meter is shown in Fig. 3-19. Here a small voltage e is introduced in series with the tuned circuit under test by passing a known current through a small resistance R, as shown. The circuit under test is then tuned to resonance with the oscillator frequency (or the oscillator frequency is adjusted to the resonant frequency of the circuit), and the voltage E developed across the tuning condenser is observed on a vacuum-tube voltmeter. The circuit Q is then taken as $Q = E/e$.

The results obtained in this way involve certain approximations.[1] In the first place, the resistance R, and also the input resistance of the vacuum-tube voltmeter, are charged against the resonant circuit. By

[1] For further discussion see V. V. L. Rao, The Q Meter and Its Theory, *Proc. IRE*, vol. 30, p. 502, November, 1942. A modified form of Q meter having some advantages at very high frequencies is described by A. J. Briggs and J. E. Houlden, The Development of Q Meter Methods of Impedance Measurement, *Proc. IEE*, vol. 96, pt. III, p. 295, July, 1949.

proper design the vacuum-tube voltmeter will have negligible losses, except possibly at extremely high frequencies where transit-time effects become significant. The effect of resistance R is to augment the series resistance of the circuit, thereby causing the observed Q to be low, according to the relation

$$\text{Actual } Q = (\text{observed } Q) \frac{1}{1 + (R/R_s)} \tag{3-14}$$

where R_s is the apparent series resistance of the circuit. By making R small (a value of 0.04 ohm is used in typical commercial Q meters), the difference between the observed and actual Q is negligible except when the series resistance of the circuit under test is unusually low.

A second approximation in the indication of the Q meter is usually more serious. It arises from the fact that the Q meter measures apparent Q, so that if the coil has distributed capacitance, then the true Q of the circuit under test is higher than that indicated by the Q meter.

Q meters are widely used for the measurement of coil Q and coil inductance, and generally in measurements which involve substitution in a tuned circuit (see Sec. 3-5). The commercial instruments for this purpose are provided with a calibrated tuning condenser so that the apparent coil inductance can be determined from the condenser setting and the oscillator frequency. In these instruments, the injected voltage e is held at a predetermined value, such as 0.02 volt, and the vacuum-tube voltmeter is then calibrated directly in Q rather than volts.

Resistance-neutralization Method of Measuring Parallel Impedance of a Tuned Circuit.[1]   In this method, an adjustable negative resistance is connected in parallel with the condenser of the tuned circuit being measured. The magnitude of this negative resistance is varied until oscillations are just on the verge of being started. The negative resistance required thus to neutralize the positive resistance of the circuit is exactly equal in absolute magnitude to the parallel resonant impedance of the tuned circuit. If the series resistance or the Q of the circuit is desired, they may be obtained from the relations

$$\text{True } Q = \frac{R_n}{\omega L} \tag{3-15}$$

$$\text{True series resistance} = \frac{(\omega L)^2}{R_n} \tag{3-16}$$

Here R_n is the negative resistance required to neutralize the resistance of the circuit, and L is the true inductance. No error is caused by dis-

[1] Iinuma Hajime, A Method of Measuring the Radio-frequency Resistance of an Oscillatory Circuit, *Proc. IRE*, vol. 18, p. 537, March, 1930; Resonant Impedances and Effective Series Resistance of Shortwave Parallel Resonant Circuits, *Proc. IRE*, vol. 19, p. 467, March, 1931.

tributed capacitance, stray wiring capacitance, and tube capacitance, as these merely assist the tuning condenser in bringing the circuit to resonance.

The required adjustable negative resistance can be obtained in a number of ways with the aid of vacuum tubes.[1] One method, illustrated in Fig. 3-20, utilizes the negative plate-cathode resistance of a screen-grid tube operated as a dynatron. An alternative possibility is a pentode tube connected as a transitron. In either case the magnitude of the negative resistance can be adjusted by varying the control-grid bias of the tube.

The value of negative resistance corresponding to neutralization of the circuit resistance can be conveniently determined by an audio-frequency measurement, using a bridge designed to measure negative resistance, as discussed in connection with Fig. 3-36. An alternative procedure, suitable for use with the dynatron, consists in adding a small increment to the plate voltage and observing the resulting change in plate current.

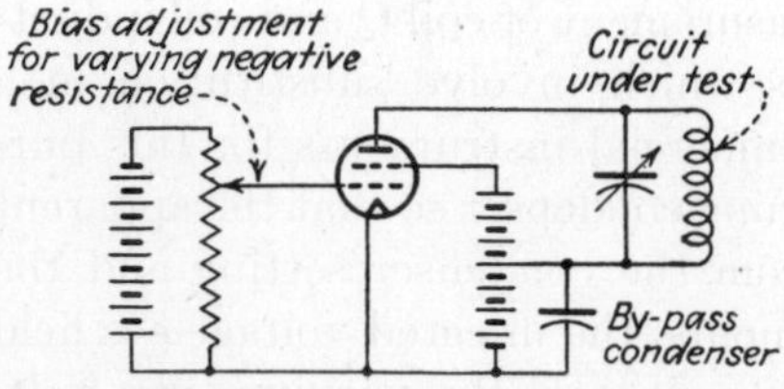

FIG. 3-20. Schematic diagram illustrating the resistance-neutralization method of measuring the resistance of a resonant circuit.

3-8. Variation Methods of Measuring Q and Resistance. *Resistance-variation Method of Measuring Tuned-circuit Resistance.*[2] The resistance-variation method of determining the resistance of tuned circuits makes use of the fact that at resonance the current in a circuit is equal to the applied voltage divided by the series resistance of the circuit. If the applied voltage is kept constant, it is then possible to deduce the actual circuit resistance by the current change that results when a known resistance is added in series with the circuit.

Circuit arrangements suitable for carrying out the necessary measuring operations are shown in Fig. 3-21a. The circuit under test is loosely coupled to a driving oscillator, and has in series with it a thermocouple milliammeter M and an adjustable resistance R. The circuit is first tuned to resonance with the driver by means of condenser C, and the current in the milliammeter is observed when the added resistance R is zero. A known amount of resistance R is then added, the circuit is

---

[1] A good summary is given by E. W. Herold, Negative Resistance and Devices for Obtaining It, *Proc. IRE*, vol. 23, p. 1201, October, 1935.

[2] A good discussion of the considerations involved in carrying out this method is given by D. B. Sinclair, Parallel-resonance Methods for Precise Measurements of High Impedance at Radio Frequencies and a Comparison with the Ordinary Series-resonance Methods, *Proc. IRE*, vol. 26, p.1 466, December, 1938. This paper contains a bibliography of 138 titles.

retuned to resonance (if this is necessary) without changing the coupling to the driver, and the resulting current noted. The apparent series resistance of the circuit is then[1]

$$\left.\begin{array}{l}\text{Apparent series resistance}\\\text{of tuned circuit}\end{array}\right\} = R\,\frac{I_1}{I_0 - I_1} \qquad (3\text{-}17a)$$

where I_0 and I_1 are the thermocouple currents when the added resistance is, respectively, zero and R. If R is adjusted until $I_1 = 0.5I_0$, then the apparent series resistance equals R; this condition also gives maximum accuracy.

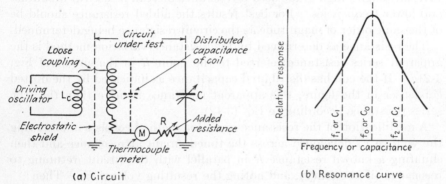

(a) Circuit   (b) Resonance curve

FIG. 3-21. Circuit arrangement for measuring radio-frequency resistance by variation methods, together with resonance curve showing how response is much less critical with respect to small changes in frequency and capacitance at resonance than on the sides of the resonance curve.

A modification of the arrangement shown in Fig. 3-21a consists in using a vacuum-tube voltmeter connected across the capacitance C as an indicator, rather than the milliammeter. The procedure in using a vacuum-tube voltmeter is the same as outlined above, except that I_1 and I_0 in Eq. (3-17a) are replaced by the corresponding voltages E_1 and E_0.

In order to obtain accurate results with the resistance-variation method, it is necessary that the current through the coupling coil L_c be constant throughout the measurement and that the only coupling between the oscillator and the circuit under test be inductive. These require-ments can be most satisfactorily met by loose coupling between the two circuits, and by the use of an electrostatic shield as shown in Fig. 3-21a.

The resistance of the thermocouple heater in Fig. 3-21a is included in the apparent circuit resistance calculated from Eq. (3-17a) and must be

---

[1] The derivation of Eq. (3-17a) follows: If E_0 is the voltage induced in the cir-cuit, and R_0 is the apparent resistance of the circuit, then with no added resistance $I_0 = E_0/R_0$, while, when the resistance R has been added, $I_1 = E_0/(R_0 + R)$. Solving these two equations to eliminate E_0 leads to Eq. (3-17a).

subtracted for accurate results. When a vacuum-tube voltmeter is used as an indicator, then if the voltmeter has an input resistance R_s that is shunted across the tuned circuit, the true series resistance as determined from the experimental results is greater than the actual value by an amount $R_s/(\omega L)^2$, where L is the true inductance of the coil.

To avoid errors from capacitances to ground, it is necessary to ground one side of the condenser and place the milliammeter and added resistance on the grounded side of the circuit, as shown in Fig. 3-21a. The added resistance must have negligible skin effect and a reasonably good phase-angle characteristic. It commonly consists of a short link of resistance wire, although a high-grade decade resistance box can be used at broadcast and lower frequencies. For best results the added resistance should be of the same order of magnitude as the circuit resistance being determined.

The resistance as determined by the resistance-variation method is the apparent series resistance referred to the point R in the circuit of Fig. 3-21a. If the coil has distributed capacitance as indicated by the dotted condenser in the figure, this apparent resistance is more than the true series resistance according to Eq. (3-12).

A modification of the resistance-variation method consists in observing the voltage E_0 developed across the tuned circuit at resonance and then shunting a known resistance R in parallel with the circuit, retuning to resonance (if necessary), and noting the resulting voltage E_1. Then

$$\left.\begin{array}{l}\text{Parallel resonant impedance}\\ \text{of tuned circuit (true value)}\end{array}\right\} = R_2 = R\,\frac{E_0 - E_1}{E_1} \qquad (3\text{-}17b)$$

The relationship between true parallel resonant impedance R_2 and true series resistance R_1 is

$$R_1 = \frac{(\omega L)^2}{R_2} \qquad (3\text{-}18)$$

where ωL is the reactance of the true (not apparent) inductance of the tuned circuit.

Reactance-variation Method of Measuring the Resistance and Q of Tuned Circuits.[1] In this method, also called the capacitance-variation method, the circuit under test is loosely coupled to a driving oscillator of the desired frequency using the circuit arrangement of Fig. 3-21a, and the induced current I_0 observed at resonance. The tuning capacitance of the circuit under test is then increased to some value C_2 at which the current has dropped to some convenient value I_1, after which the capacitance is

---

[1] A good discussion of this method, with particular reference to sources of error, is given by D. B. Sinclair, Parallel-resonance Methods for Precise Measurements of High Impedances at Radio Frequencies and a Comparison with the Ordinary Series-resonance Methods, *Proc. IRE*, vol. 26, p. 1466, December, 1938.

reduced to a value C_1 such that the current is again reduced to the value I_1. Then[1,2]

$$\text{Series resistance} = \frac{C_2 - C_1}{2\omega C_1 C_2} \sqrt{\frac{I_1{}^2}{I_0{}^2 - I_1{}^2}} \tag{3-19}$$

where ω is 2π times the driver frequency. The resistance as measured includes the heater resistance of the thermocouple meter used to read current. Maximum accuracy results when the detuning is such that $I_1 = 0.707 I_0$; under these conditions the quantity under the radical becomes unity.

The resistance obtained from Eq. (3-19) will be the *apparent* series resistance if, as is usually the case, the capacitances C_1 and C_2 are taken as the added tuning capacitances, i.e., do not include the distributed capacitance of the coil. To obtain the true series resistance a correction must be made by using Eq. (3-12). If C_1 and C_2 do include the distributed capacitance, or if the distributed capacitance is negligible, then Eq. (3-19) gives true series resistance.

The circuit for the reactance-variation method is the same as that used for resistance variation (see Fig. 3-21a). However, no added resistance need be provided, and the tuning condenser must either be accurately

---

[1] This equation can be derived as follows: When tuned to resonance,

$$E_0 = I_0 R$$

where E_0 is the voltage induced in the circuit, and R is the series resistance. When detuned, the circuit has a reactance ΔX, so that the series impedance is $R + j \Delta X$. Hence

$$E_0 = I_1 \sqrt{R^2 + \Delta X^2}$$

Solving these two equations simultaneously yields

$$R = \Delta X \sqrt{\frac{I_1{}^2}{I_0{}^2 - I_1{}^2}}$$

Now $2 \Delta X = (1/\omega C_1) - (1/\omega C_2)$, and Eq. (3-19) follows at once when this relation is used to eliminate ΔX.

[2] An alternative procedure consists in expressing the apparent series resistance in terms of $C_0 - C_1$, the difference between capacitance C_0 at resonance and the detuned capacitance C_1 corresponding to I_1. The results obtained this way are related to Eq. (3-17a) through the fact that to a high degree of accuracy, $2(C_0 - C_1) = C_2 - C_1$ and $C_1 C_2 = C_0{}^2$.

Although it might seem that this alternative is of equal merit, this is not the case. The reason is that the flat top of the resonance curve makes it impossible to determine accurately the value of C_0 corresponding to resonance merely by observing the circuit voltage or current response. In contrast, C_1 and C_2 can be determined quite accurately in relation to I_1 because the response on the sides of the resonance curve varies rapidly with tuning capacitance. This is illustrated in Fig. 3-21b.

calibrated or, what is still better, be shunted by a small calibrated vernier condenser.

The measuring procedure described above is sometimes modified by observing the variation in response on a vacuum-tube voltmeter shunted across the tuning condenser, and omitting the thermocouple. In this case, assuming $C_2 - C_1 \ll C_1$, one has to good accuracy

$$\text{Series resistance} = \frac{C_2 - C_1}{2\omega C_1 C_2} \sqrt{\frac{E_1^2}{E_0^2 - E_1^2}} \qquad (3\text{-}20)$$

where the notation is as before except that E_0 is now the voltage read by the voltmeter at resonance, and E_1 is the voltage read by the voltmeter when the tuning capacitance is either C_1 or C_2. Equation (3-20) follows from Eq. (3-19) by noting that if C_0, C_1, and C_2 differ only very slightly in magnitude, as is the case if the circuit Q is at least moderate, then the voltage across the circuit is almost exactly proportional to the current in the tuning condenser. Input losses of the vacuum-tube voltmeter cause the experimentally determined series resistance to be too high; if the error involved is appreciable, a correction must be made, as explained in connection with the resistance-variation method.

The reactance-variation method can be used to give Q directly by noting that for all practical purposes $C_0 = \sqrt{C_1 C_2} = (C_1 + C_2)/2$, and that at resonance $Q = (1/\omega C_0)/R$, where R is the series resistance and C_0 is the tuning capacitance at resonance. Making these substitutions in Eqs. (3-19) and (3-20) gives

$$Q = \frac{2C_0}{C_2 - C_1} \sqrt{\frac{I_0^2 - I_1^2}{I_1^2}} = \frac{C_1 + C_2}{C_2 - C_1} \sqrt{\frac{I_0^2 - I_1^2}{I_1^2}} \qquad (3\text{-}21a)$$

$$Q = \frac{2C_0}{C_2 - C_1} \sqrt{\frac{E_0^2 - E_1^2}{E_1^2}} = \frac{C_1 + C_2}{C_2 - C_1} \sqrt{\frac{E_0^2 - E_1^2}{E_1^2}} \qquad (3\text{-}21b)$$

The values of Q calculated from these equations will be either the true or the apparent Q, according to whether the values of C_0, C_1, and C_2 include or do not include the distributed capacitance of the coil, respectively. In the latter case the true Q can be calculated with the aid of Eq. (3-13).

Frequency-variation Method of Measuring the Q of Tuned Circuits. In this method of measurement, the circuit under test is loosely coupled to an oscillator, as in Fig. 3-21a, and the response at resonance noted. The frequency of the driving oscillator is then increased to some value $f_2 = \omega_2/2\pi$ at which the response has dropped to a convenient reference value, after which the frequency is decreased to below resonance to a value $f_1 = \omega_1/2\pi$ at which the response is the same as at f_2. It can then be shown that to an accuracy sufficient for all practical purposes[1,2]

$$\text{True circuit } Q = \frac{\dfrac{f_0}{f_2 - f_1}}{\sqrt{\dfrac{D_1{}^2}{D_0{}^2 - D_1{}^2}}} = \frac{\dfrac{1}{2}\left(\dfrac{f_2 + f_1}{f_2 - f_1}\right)}{\sqrt{\dfrac{D_1{}^2}{D_0{}^2 - D_1{}^2}}} \qquad (3\text{-}22)$$

where f_2 and f_1 are the frequencies above and below resonance for which the circuit response (either voltage or current) is D_1, and f_0 is the frequency at resonance, where the response is D_0. The Q obtained in this way is the true Q, no correction being required for distributed capacitance of the coil. Losses in the indicating instrument do, however, make the experimentally determined values lower than the actual circuit Q. Correction for this effect can be made in the same manner as in the resistance-variation method. Maximum accuracy is obtained when $D_1 = 0.707D_0$; this condition makes the radical in Eq. (3-22) become unity.

The accuracy of the frequency-variation method is determined largely by the precision with which $f_2 - f_1$ is known. This can be made very great by measuring the difference directly by using a beat-frequency technique instead of determining f_2 and f_1 individually and then subtracting to obtain their small difference.

3-9. Impedance Measurement by Substitution in Tuned Circuits with Lumped Constants. A very common method of determining an imped-

[1] This relation assumes that $f_2 - f_0 = f_0 - f_1$, that $f_2 - f_0 \ll f_0$, and that circuit resistance and Q do not change significantly over the frequency range f_1 to f_2. On the basis of these assumptions, the relation of the response D_1 at a frequency $f_2 - f_0$ cycles off resonance to the response D_0 at resonance is, assuming R and L are the true circuit resistance and inductance, respectively,

$$\frac{D_1}{D_0} = \left| \frac{R}{R + j2\pi(f_2 - f_0)L \times 2} \right|$$

or, noting that $f_2 - f_1 = 2(f_2 - f_0)$,

$$\frac{D_1}{D_0} \approx \left| \frac{1}{1 + j\left(\dfrac{2\pi f_0 L}{R}\dfrac{f_2 - f_1}{f_0}\right)} \right|$$

$$\left(\frac{D_1}{D_0}\right)^2 = \frac{1}{1 + Q^2\left(\dfrac{f_2 - f_1}{f_0}\right)^2}$$

Solving for Q gives Eq. (3-22).

[2] An alternative procedure is to express the circuit Q in terms of the difference $f_0 - f_1$, instead of the difference $f_2 - f_1$. However, as explained in footnote 2, page 95, this results in lowered experimental accuracy, since as shown in Fig. 3-21b the flat top of the resonance curve makes the response insensitive to frequency in the vicinity of resonance. In contrast, f_2 and f_1 can be quite accurately determined because the response on the sides of the resonance curve varies rapidly with frequency.

ance consists in associating it with a resonant circuit. The reactance component of the unknown impedance is then determined by the change of tuning capacitance necessary to restore the original resonant frequency after the unknown impedance has been added. The resistance or conductance component at the unknown impedance is obtained from the change in Q, or the change in series or shunt resistance of the resonant circuit, resulting from the introduction of the unknown impedance. Measurements of this type are usually made with a Q meter, using a coil supplied with the instrument to provide an appropriate resonant circuit. Other methods for measuring the characteristics of the resonant circuit, such as the reactance-variation method using a calibrated tuning condenser (see Fig. 3-21a), may, however, be employed with equally satisfactory results.

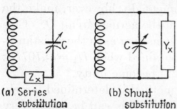

(a) Series substitution   (b) Shunt substitution

Fig. 3-22. Schematic diagrams illustrating measurement of impedance and admittance by substitution in a resonant circuit.

The unknown impedance may be placed either in series or in shunt with the resonant circuit, as illustrated in Fig. 3-22. The choice of arrangements depends upon the magnitude. When the unknown impedance is small compared with the inductive reactance of the tuned circuit, then it is always connected in series, as illustrated in Fig. 3-22a; alternatively, when the unknown impedance is large compared with the inductive reactance of the resonant circuit, it is ordinarily connected in shunt, as in Fig. 3-22b. Intermediate values may employ either method of connection, provided only that the power factor of the unknown impedance is not too high. However, if the unknown impedance is of the same order of magnitude as the inductive reactance of the resonant circuit, and the power factor is quite high, then the losses introduced into the resonant system by association with the unknown impedance are so great as largely to destroy resonance. The method of measurement involving substitution in a resonant circuit as in Fig. 3-22 is then not satisfactory.

When the series substitution arrangement of Fig. 3-22a is employed, the unknown impedance Z_x is determined in terms of its equivalent series resistance and reactive components R_x and X_x (that is, $Z_x = R_x + jX_x$). The measuring procedure is as follows: With the unknown impedance short-circuited or otherwise removed from the system, the tuned circuit is adjusted to resonance at the frequency for which the results are desired. The circuit Q (or series resistance R) is next determined, and the value of tuning capacitance C required is likewise noted. The unknown impedance is then connected in series with the circuit, and the tuning capacitance readjusted to a new value C' required to restore the original

resonant frequency.   The circuit Q (or series resistance R') is determined
with the unknown impedance in the circuit.   The following relations then
exist between the values obtained with and without the presence of the
unknown impedance:

$$X_x = \frac{1}{\omega C'} - \frac{1}{\omega C} = \frac{1}{\omega C}\frac{C - C'}{C'} \tag{3-23}$$

$$R_x = \omega L \frac{Q - Q'}{QQ'} = R' - R \tag{3-24}$$

Here the results obtained with the unknown impedance in the circuit are
indicated by primes.   The values in Eq. (3-24) must be referred to the
point in the circuit where the unknown impedance Z_x is inserted; *i.e.*,
they must be apparent values.   In Eq. (3-23) a positive value for X_x
denotes inductive reactance; it will be noted that X_x can be determined
irrespective of whether it is inductive or capacitive.

When the unknown impedance is measured by connecting it in parallel
with the resonant circuit, as in Fig. 3-22b, the unknown impedance is
determined as a susceptance B_x shunted by a conductance G_x (that is,
$Y_x = G_x + jB$).   The measuring procedure followed in this case is
analogous to that for series insertion of the unknown impedance, except
for the fact that the unknown impedance is connected in shunt with the
condenser, and is removed from the circuit by disconnecting rather than
by short circuiting.   The equations that apply in this case are

$$B_x = \omega(C - C') \tag{3-25}$$

$$G_x = \frac{1}{\omega L}\frac{Q - Q'}{QQ'} \tag{3-26}$$

The notation is the same as in Eqs. (3-23) and (3-24), with the understanding that in the equation for G_x it is necessary that either both ωL
and Q be apparent, or that they both be true values.   A negative value
of B_x indicates inductive susceptance.

The accuracy with which reactance may be determined by the method
of substitution in a tuned circuit is quite high.   The principal errors that
may be present arise from two causes: The first is inability to determine
accurately the capacitance corresponding to exact resonance because of
the fact that the resonance curve is flat on top.[1]   This results in errors
which will be larger on a percentage basis the smaller the change in tuning

[1] This trouble can be eliminated where only reactance (not resistance) is to be
measured by making the resonant circuit the frequency-determining circuit of a small
oscillator.   One then adjusts the capacitance on the basis of the generated frequency,
a procedure that can give high accuracy.   An example of measuring equipment that
utilizes this means of accurately measuring small values of inductance is described by
Harold A. Wheeler, R-F Inductance Meter, *Electronics*, vol. 20, p. 105, September,
1947.

capacitance required to take into account the added reactance. The second error arises from the fact that at high frequencies the small residual inductance associated with the tuning condenser causes the change in capacitance per unit division on the condenser scale to be greater than given by the calibration curve of the condenser applying to ordinary frequencies. This introduces errors at very high frequencies unless the residual inductance is known and is taken into account.[1]

The accuracy with which the resistance (or conductance) component of the unknown impedance is obtained by substitution in a tuned circuit is affected by several factors. The accuracy will in general be poor if the losses in the unknown impedance are so small as to have only slight effect on the equivalent series resistance or equivalent Q of the resonant circuit. Also, the substitution method implies that the equivalent series resistance (or equivalent shunt conductance) of the tuning condenser C is not affected by the capacitance setting of this condenser. Although this assumption is not strictly true, the resulting error will be small provided the series resistance (or shunt conductance) of the unknown is considerably greater than the corresponding variation arising in the tuning condenser. Thus, the substitution method is quite satisfactory for measuring losses of coils, and the power factor of condensers with solid dielectrics, but is not satisfactory for measuring losses of air-dielectric condensers.

Impedance measurement by substitution in a resonant circuit represents a simple and particularly easily applied measuring technique. Moreover, the essential equipment can when necessary be easily assembled from parts ordinarily available in every radio laboratory.[2]

3-10. Special Types of Capacitance Measurements. *Distributed Capacitance of Coils.* Every inductance has a small amount of capacitance associated with it as a result of dielectric stress between various parts of the coil. This distributed capacitance acts very much as though it were lumped across the terminals of the coil, and is important because it limits the frequency range over which a coil can be tuned with a given variable condenser. The distributed capacitance also causes the coil to have an apparent inductance that differs from the true inductance as measured at low frequencies, as discussed in connection with Eqs. (3-11).

The distributed capacitance which may be considered as being lumped across the coil terminals can be determined by adding a known capaci-

---

[1] An excellent discussion of these and other errors is given by D. B. Sinclair, Impedance Measurements at High Frequencies with Standard Parts, *Gen. Rad. Expt.*, vol. 14, no. 4, September, 1939; Parallel-resonance Methods for Precise Measurements of High Impedances at Radio Frequencies and a Comparison with the Ordinary Sales-resonance Methods, *Proc. IRE*, vol. 26, p. 1466, December, 1938.

[2] An example of such "homemade" equipment is described by D. Stanley Henry, VHF Impedance Measurements, *Electronics*, vol. 18, p. 156, December, 1945.

tance in parallel with the coil and measuring the resonant frequency of the resulting tuned circuit. Knowing the true inductance of the coil and the frequency, one can calculate the total tuning capacitance, from which by subtraction of the added capacitance one obtains the distributed capacitance. It is more accurate, however, to make tests with several added capacitances. Then if one plots $1/f^2$ as a function of the added capacitance, as shown in Fig. 3-23, a straight line will result. This line when extrapolated will intersect the capacitance axis at a negative capacitance which is equal to the distributed capacitance, and the slope of the line is a measure of the true inductance of the coil according to the equation

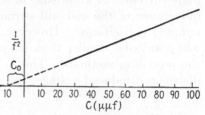

True coil inductance in henrys
$$= 0.0253m \quad (3\text{-}27)$$

FIG. 3-23. Determination of the distributed capacitance by plotting $1/f^2$, where f is the resonant frequency, as a function of external tuning capacitance C.

where m is the slope of the curve of $1/f^2$ plotted against capacitance, when f is in megacycles and capacitance is in micromicrofarads.[1]

The necessity of plotting a curve such as shown in Fig. (3-23) can sometimes be avoided by using a calibrated condenser to tune the coil to resonance with an oscillator, and then reducing the condenser capacitance until the coil is brought to resonance with the second harmonic of the oscillator. If C_1 is the tuning capacitance required for the fundamental frequency, and C_2 the capacitance at the second harmonic, one then has[2]

[1] This is derived as follows: The relation between circuit constants and frequency in a resonant circuit is

$$2\pi fL = \frac{1}{2\pi f(C + C_0)}$$

where $C + C_0$ is the total tuning capacitance (including distributed capacitance C_0). Solving this equation for $1/f^2$ gives

$$\frac{1}{f^2} = 4\pi^2 LC + 4\pi^2 LC_0$$

This is the equation of a straight line intersecting the C-axis at $-C_0$, and having a slope of $4\pi^2 L$.

[2] Equation (3-28) is derived by the following reasoning: The actual tuning capacitances effectively present in the two cases are $C_1 + C_0$ and $C_2 + C_0$, where C_0 is the distributed capacitance. These capacitances must be in the ratio of 4:1, since the tuning capacitance is inversely proportional to the square of the frequency. That is,

$$C_1 + C_0 = 4(C_2 + C_0)$$

Equation (3-28) follows at once by solving for C_0. This method is due to Ralph R. Batcher, Rapid Determination of Distributed Capacity of Coils, *Proc. IRE*, vol. 9, p. 300, August, 1921.

$$\text{Distributed capacitance} = \frac{C_1 - 4C_2}{3} \qquad (3\text{-}28)$$

A method sometimes proposed for determining distributed capacitance consists in measuring the resonant frequency of the coil when tuned only by the distributed capacitance. This can be done by loosely coupling the coil to an oscillator and observing the frequency at which the coil reacts upon the oscillator to cause a sudden change in the grid or plate current. A knowledge of this self-resonant frequency and the true inductance of the coil will permit a determination of an apparent distributed capacitance. However, the capacitance obtained in this way will always be smaller than when the same capacitance is measured by the preceding methods. This is because when the driving voltage is a distributed induced voltage, the voltage and current distribution in the coil with no external tuning condenser is quite different from the distribution when an appreciable capacitance is shunted across the coil terminals. For this reason *the distributed capacitance of a coil normally should not be determined by the self-resonant-frequency method.*

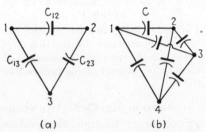

Fig. 3-24. Capacitances associated with three- and four-electrode systems.

Direct Capacitance.[1] In a system involving more than two electrodes, it is possible for a capacitance to exist between each pair of terminals. This is illustrated in Fig. 3-24 for systems involving three and four terminals. The capacitance existing between any two terminals in such an arrangement, for example the capacitance C_{12} between terminals 1 and 2 in Fig. 3-24a, is termed the *direct capacitance* between these electrodes. A typical practical example is a triode tube, where capacitances C_{12}, C_{23}, and C_{13} could be considered the grid-plate, plate-cathode, and grid-cathode capacitances, respectively.

The direct capacitance between a pair of electrodes in a complex system, such as that of Fig. 3-24b, may be measured by connecting the electrodes involved in the X arm of a capacitance bridge in the usual manner for measuring an unknown capacitance.[2] The remaining electrodes of the

[1] For further discussion of this subject, including references to the measurement of the direct capacitance between tube electrodes, see George Campbell, Direct Capacity Measurement, *Bell System Tech. J.*, vol. 1, p. 18, July, 1922; Lincoln Walsh, Direct-capacity Bridge for Vacuum-tube Measurements, *Proc. IRE*, vol. 16, p. 482, April, 1928; E. T. Hoch, A Bridge Method for the Measurement of Inter-electrode Admittance in Vacuum Tubes, *Proc. IRE*, vol. 16, p. 487, April, 1928.

[2] A bridged-T equivalent of such a direct-capacitance bridge is described by R. F. Proctor and E. G. James, A Radio-frequency Capacitance and Conductance Bridge,

system are then all connected together, thus reducing the arrangement to a three-terminal one, such as shown in Fig. 3-24a. This third terminal is connected to one of the two remaining corners of the bridge, or is returned to a guard circuit. The application of this procedure to the resistance-ratio capacitance bridge of Fig. 3-7c is shown in Fig. 3-25a. Here the capacitance to be measured is C_{12}, and the third terminal is returned to corner B of the bridge. This causes capacitance C_{23} to be shunted across the oscillator, where it cannot affect the bridge behavior. At the same time capacitance C_{13} is shunted across resistance

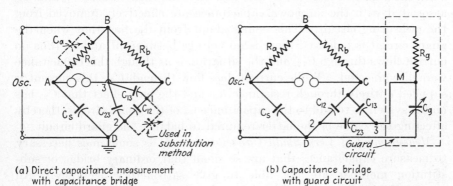

(a) Direct capacitance measurement
with capacitance bridge

(b) Capacitance bridge
with guard circuit

Fig. 3-25. Measurement of direct capacitance by means of the capacitance bridge shown in Fig. 3-7c.

R_b. This requires the addition of a compensating capacitance C_a such as that $C_a/C_{13} = R_b/R_a$, in order to achieve balance and maintain the bridge ratio at the value R_b/R_a defined by the resistance arms. With the capacitances C_{13} and C_{23} thus removed from consideration, the direct capacitance C_{12} can be measured as an ordinary capacitance, by substitution or otherwise, and without the necessity of determining the associated capacitances C_{12} and C_{23}. It would be possible to return the third terminal of the capacitance system to corner A of the bridge, instead of to corner B as in Fig. 3-25a. However, this would place C_{23} in shunt with C_s, thereby affecting a portion of the bridge that is involved in the determination of the desired capacitance C_{12}.

A guard circuit is shown in Fig. 3-25b for removing the capacitances C_{13} and C_{23} from the circuit that is being used to measure the direct

J. IEE, vol. 92, pt. III, p. 287, December, 1945. In this, the unknown capacitance bridges a T network, and is measured by substitution, while the third terminal is connected to the ground or common lead; the associated capacitances C_{13} and C_{23} are thereby placed in shunt with the input and output terminals of the bridged T, where they have no effect on the measurement.

capacitance.[1]   Here terminal 3 is connected to the point M in the guard circuit.   The guard circuit $C_g R_g$ is then so adjusted that there is no difference in potential between point M and corner C of the bridge; this is done by switching the output indicator of the bridge across CM.   The measuring procedure consists in alternately balancing the bridge and the guard circuit, until both are simultaneously in balance.   Under these conditions

$$R_a C_s = R_b C_{12} = R_g (C_g + C_{23}) \qquad (3\text{-}29)$$

With the guard circuit balanced in this way, the capacitances C_{13} and C_{23} associated with the unknown capacitance are effectively removed from the measuring circuit.   This comes about from the fact that when the guard circuit is balanced there is no voltage between M and C; thus no current flows through C_{13}, and the situation is as though this capacitance were disconnected.   While current does flow through C_{23}, this current is supplied entirely through resistance R_g, and the only effect that C_{23} has on the system is to add to the capacitance C_g of the guard circuit, thereby affecting the value of the latter required to balance the guard circuit.

Measurement of Very Small Capacitances.   It is sometimes necessary to measure capacitances that are so small that ordinary bridge or substitution methods are not able to give satisfactory accuracy.[2]   An example is the direct capacitance between the control grid and plate of a pentode tube, which is typically of the order of 0.005 $\mu\mu$f.   To meet needs of this type, special measuring techniques have been devised.

Examples of arrangements that find practical use in measuring capacitances ranging from less than 0.001 $\mu\mu$f up to several micromicrofarads, such as grid-plate tube capacitances, are shown in Fig. 3-26.   At a,[3] a known alternating potential E of several hundred volts is applied to the unknown capacitance C_x in series with a much larger known capacitance C_s, such as 10 to 20 $\mu\mu$f, that can be accurately measured by other means.   The capacitance C_x is obtained by measuring the applied voltage, and the voltage across C_s, by means of vacuum-tube voltmeters.   In Fig. 3-26b, a large voltage of known amplitude and frequency is applied to the unknown capacitance, and the resulting current is determined by means of a thermocouple.   The arrangement at c is a modification of that at b,

---

[1] For further information on guard circuits, see R. F. Field, A Guard Circuit for Capacitance Bridge Measurements, *Gen. Rad. Expt.*, vol. 14, March, 1940.

[2] It is possible to devise special bridges for this purpose, however.   Thus a rather complicated bridge circuit capable of reading direct capacitances smaller than 10^{-5} $\mu\mu$f, and associated shunt conductances of less than 10^{-5} μmho, is described by C. H. Young, Measuring Interelectrode Capacitances, *Bell Labs. Record*, vol. 24, p. 443, December, 1946.

[3] T. I. Jones, The Measurement of the Grid-Anode Capacitance of Screen-grid Valves, *J. IEE*, vol. 74, p. 589, 1934 (*Wireless Sec., IEE*, vol. 9, p. 161, June, 1934).

in which the unknown capacitance is connected in parallel with a standard adjustable capacitance so designed that small increments of capacitance of the latter can be accurately determined.[1] A large voltage is applied to the combination, and the resulting current observed by a thermocouple. The unknown capacitance is then disconnected, and the known capacitance readjusted to give the same current. By making the total capacitance C_s relatively small, it is possible to measure values of C_x smaller than 0.1 $\mu\mu f$ with accuracy; the other methods illustrated in Fig. 3-26 will, however, all measure much smaller capacitances.

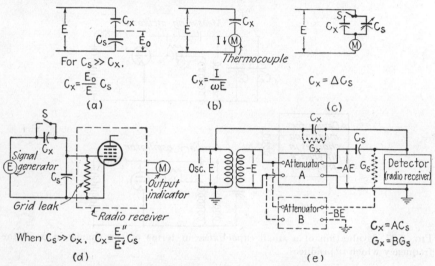

FIG. 3-26. Various methods for measuring very small capacitances.

The arrangement at Fig. 3-26d employs a radio-frequency signal generator to apply a voltage E' to the unknown capacitance in series with a much larger known capacitance C_s. A relative indication of the voltage across the latter is obtained as shown by means of a radio receiver, the output of which is equipped with an indicating meter. The small unknown capacitance is then short-circuited, after which the signal-generator voltage is reduced to a value E'' as required to restore the same output in the radio receiver. Since the two signal-generator voltages under these two conditions are accurately known even when very different, it is possible to measure very small capacitances in this manner.

A null method for measuring small capacitances is shown at Fig. 3-26e.[2]

[1] A. A. Barco, An Improved Interelectrode Capacitance Meter, *RCA Rev.*, vol. 6, p. 434, April, 1942; A. V. Loughren and H. W. Parker, The Measurement of Direct Interelectrode Capacitance of Vacuum Tubes, *Proc. IRE*, vol. 17, p. 957, June, 1929.

[2] I. G. Easton, A Method for Measuring Small Direct Capacitances, *Gen. Rad. Expt.*, vol. 19, p. 1, September, 1944.

Here radio-frequency voltages that are equal in magnitude but opposite in phase are applied, respectively, to the unknown capacitance C_x, and to a much larger known capacitance C_s in series with an adjustable attenuator A. This attenuator is adjusted until zero-output indication is obtained as determined by a radio receiver. By using large values of attenuation, unknown capacitances very much smaller than the known capacitance can be determined. In case the unknown capacitance has a shunt conductance associated with it, a third circuit shown dotted in Fig. 3-26e can be added to determine the conductance component in

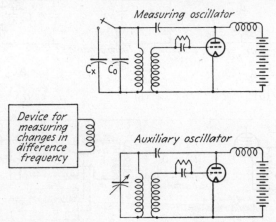

Fig. 3-27. Evaluation of a small capacitance in terms of the change in oscillator frequency which it produces.

terms of a known conductance G_s and the setting of the associated attenuator B.

Still another approach to the problem of measuring very small capacitances, or small capacitance changes, is illustrated in Fig. 3-27. Here the unknown capacitance is arranged so that it can be made part of the tuning capacitance of an oscillator. The size of the capacitance is then determined by the change in oscillator frequency which it produces. An auxiliary oscillator is used as a fixed standard, and the frequency changes of the measuring oscillator are obtained by observing changes that develop in the beat note.[1,2] The relation between frequency change

[1] In observing the change in beat note, care must be taken either to ensure that the beat note does not go through zero as the frequency varies, or if it does, to allow for this fact.

[2] The considerations that must be taken into account when the capacitance change involved takes place over an extended rather than short time interval are discussed by W. Schick, Temperature Coefficient of Capacitance, *Wireless Eng.*, vol. 21, p. 65, February, 1944.

and capacitance is given by the equation

$$C_x = C_0 \left[\left(\frac{f_0}{f_1} \right)^2 - 1 \right]$$ (3-30)

where C_x is the unknown capacitance, C_0 the original oscillator tuning capacitance, f_0 the oscillator frequency when tuned only by C_0, and f_1 the oscillator frequency when tuned by C_0 and C_x in parallel. In the special case where C_x is small compared with C_0, Eq. (3-30) can be rewritten as

$$C_x = 2C_0 \frac{f_0 - f_1}{f_0}$$ (3-31)

The oscillator tuning capacitance C_0 includes tube, wiring, and stray capacitances and may be determined experimentally by using a known capacitance for C_x, and noting the resulting frequency f_1. Since this calibrating capacitance can be large enough to be measured very accurately by other methods, it is possible to evaluate C_0 very accurately.

This method is capable of measuring extremely small capacitances. Thus if $C_0 = 50$ μμf, and $f_0 = 10,000,000$ cycles, a capacitance C_x of 10^{-5} μμf will cause a change in frequency of 1 cycle per sec, which is readily measured with accuracy.

3-11. Measurement of Incremental Inductance. Incremental inductance is the inductance that is offered by an iron-cored coil to the flow of an alternating current superimposed upon a direct current. Incremental inductance is of importance because it is the inductance that is effective in power-supply filter reactors, shunt-feed inductances, and the primary windings of interstage and output transformers that carry direct current.

The magnitude of the incremental inductance is affected by the intensity of both the a-c and the d-c magnetization of the magnetic core in the general manner illustrated in Fig. 3-28. In addition, the incremental inductance for a given alternating and direct magnetization will depend upon the previous magnetic history, and may change with subsequent magnetic history. Exactly reproducible results can be obtained only by first demagnetizing the core and then carefully following the same procedure in making each measurement. This situation means that very precise determination of incremental inductance is generally not of great importance; practically one desires to know the inductance to within 10 per cent rather than to within 1 per cent or closer.

The most convenient bridge for measuring incremental inductance is the Hay circuit arranged as in Fig. 3-29,[1] with the balance obtained

[1] This application of the Hay bridge is discussed by V. D. Landon, A Bridge Circuit for Measuring the Inductance of Coils while Passing Direct Current, *Proc. IRE*, vol. 16, p. 1771, December, 1928.

by varying resistances R_a and R_b. To the accuracy normally required in incremental-inductance measurements, one can assume $1 + (1/Q_x^2) \approx 1$, so that the inductance calibration can accordingly be considered as depending only upon the variable resistance R_a and fixed condenser C_b.

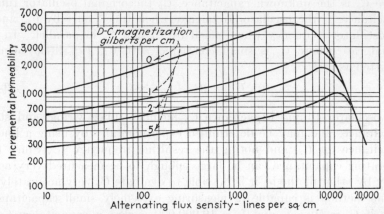

Fig. 3-28. Curves giving incremental permeability of typical silicon steel as a function of d-c magnetization, for several values of superimposed direct current.

The direct current can be introduced and metered in the neutral arm, and its value is not affected by the process of balancing the bridge; arm R_c must, however, be designed to carry the direct current. The alternating magnetization can be calculated from a knowledge of the inductance, and the alternating voltage developed across the inductance as observed by a vacuum-tube voltmeter. The fact that the Hay bridge measures inductance in terms of resistance and capacitance makes it possible to cover a large range of inductance with a minimum of difficulty with respect to the standards.

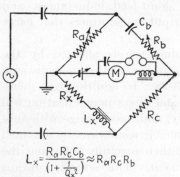

$$L_x = \frac{R_a R_c C_b}{\left(1 + \frac{1}{Q_x^2}\right)} \approx R_a R_c R_b$$

Fig. 3-29. Hay bridge arranged to measure incremental inductance.

An alternative bridge possibility is to employ an Owen bridge, as shown in Fig. 3-30, varying R_c and C_c to obtain balance.[1] Here the direct current is introduced through the neutral arm, and the d-c magnetization in the unknown inductance is not affected by the process of balancing the bridge. As compared with the Hay bridge, the Owen bridge has the advantage that the balance equation for inductance is independent of the coil Q, but the

[1] The advantages of this arrangement are developed by E. H. Meier and D. L. Waidelich, *Communications* (*N.Y.*), vol. 21, p. 5, November, 1941.

disadvantage of requiring a continuously variable condenser C_c, the maximum capacitance of which is ordinarily much greater than can be obtained with an air-dielectric condenser.

The bridged-T circuit of Fig. 3-31 is an adaptation of the bridged-T network of Fig. 3-17a, arranged for the measurement of incremental inductance. This circuit has the desirable feature that the alternating voltage applied to the unknown induct-
ance is always the oscillator voltage E_{ac}, irrespective of the magnitude of the impedance being measured or the state of the null balance. The disadvantages of the arrangement are that the balance depends upon frequency, and that twin variable condensers of excessively large maximum capacitance that can be achieved only by elaborate switching systems are required in the inductance balance if the measuring frequency is low and the inductance is small to moderate in magnitude. Also, unless

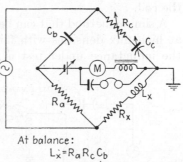

At balance:
$$L_x = R_a R_c C_b$$
$$R_x = R_a C_b / C_c$$

FIG. 3-30. Owen bridge arranged to measure incremental inductance.

appropriate suppressor resistors are employed, sparking troubles may be expected in the condenser switches as a result of the d-c voltage across the coil.

Several means of determining incremental inductance which do not involve null balances are illustrated in Fig. 3-32. One method of approaching the problem is to apply a known alternating voltage to the

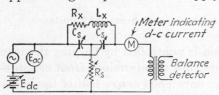

FIG. 3-31. Bridged-T circuit arranged to measure incremental inductance.

inductance, and then observe the resulting alternating current that flows superimposed upon the appropriate d-c magnetization. In such systems it is often convenient to employ two identical inductances, with the direct current introduced as shown in Fig. 3-32a, in order to avoid passing this current through the source of alternating voltage. In the arrangement for measuring incremental inductance shown in Fig. 3-32b, an adjustable capacitance is placed in parallel with the unknown inductance, which is supplied with the direct current and alternating current by sources as shown.[1] The condenser C is then adjusted until the alternating current registered by meter M is the same

[1] See H. M. Turner, The Constant Impedance Method for Measuring Inductance of Choke Coils, *Proc. IRE*, vol. 15, p. 1559, November, 1928.

with switch S open as with it closed.   It can then be shown that

$$\omega L = \frac{1}{2}\,\frac{1}{\omega C} \tag{3-32}$$

where $\omega/2\pi$ is the frequency of the supply, and the remaining notation is as in Fig. 3-32b.   This relation holds irrespective of the resistance of the coil.

A simple method that can be used to determine incremental inductance at high flux densities with fair accuracy is shown in Fig. 3-32c.   Here the inductance under test is used as the first choke of a choke-input

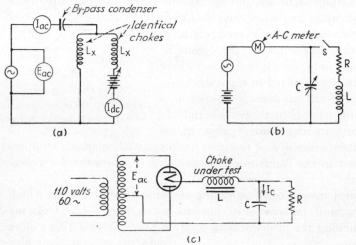

(a)

(b)

(c)

FIG. 3-32. Miscellaneous methods of measuring incremental inductance.

filter system.   The d-c magnetization is controlled by varying the load resistance R.   The incremental inductance is determined from measurements of the alternating voltage E_{ac}, developed across half of the transformer secondary, and the alternating current I_c which flows through the filter condenser C.   Both of these measurements can be made with rectifier-type instruments.   It can be readily shown that with a single-phase full-wave rectifier the effective value of the fundamental component of the ripple voltage that is applied to the input of the choke is 0.424 times the effective alternating voltage E_{ac}.   Virtually this entire voltage is applied to the input inductance L, and nearly all of the resulting alternating current flows through the filter condenser C.   While there are other frequencies applied to the first choke, these are comparatively small in amplitude and also produce proportionally less current because of their higher frequency.   Hence to a fair degree of accuracy the reactance of the input choke to the ripple frequency is[1]

$$\text{Reactance of incremental inductance} = \frac{0.424 E_{ac}}{I_c} \qquad (3\text{-}33)$$

where E_{ac} is the rms voltage across half of the transformer secondary, while I_c is the rms current flowing in the first filter condenser. The alternating flux density can be varied as desired by controlling the primary voltage of the rectifier transformer.

In making measurements of incremental inductance it is always necessary to employ a relatively low frequency. Sixty cycles is preferable if possible; however, when a null balance is to be obtained by ear then frequencies such as 250–400 cycles are suggested. At higher frequencies the distributed capacitance of the coil to be measured may cause the apparent inductance to differ appreciably from the true inductance (see Sec. 3-7). When the measurement is to be made at a high alternating flux density, the use of a low frequency also helps prevent the voltage required from becoming excessively large.

When bridge measurements of incremental inductance are being made at high alternating flux densities, harmonics will be generated by the nonlinearity of the magnetic core even when the bridge oscillator supplies a sine wave. Such harmonics will confuse the bridge balance point, since they are present when the bridge is properly balanced for the fundamental frequency. This makes it desirable to employ a low-pass filter in the bridge output, particularly when high alternating flux densities are involved.

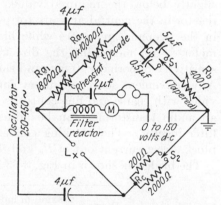

FIG. 3-33. Details of Hay bridge for measuring incremental inductance.

Constructional Features of Incremental-inductance Hay Bridge for Laboratory Use. Although bridges for the measurement of incremental inductance are not commonly available, they can be readily assembled from standard parts. Circuit details, including suitable numerical values of circuit constants, are shown in Fig. 3-33 for a Hay bridge capable of measuring inductances up to 1000 henrys. In this bridge the

[1] This equation assumes that one has a true choke input system, *i.e.*, that current flows continuously through the inductance under test. This requirement is satisfied when the d-c magnetizing current I_{dc} equals or exceeds the peak value of I_c. For 60-cycle supply this corresponds to $R \leq 1130L$, where R is the effective d-c load resistance (including choke resistance), and L is the incremental inductance.

inductance balance is obtained by varying R_a, which consists of a decade resistance unit R_{a2} having 10,000-ohm steps, supplemented by a high-grade wire-wound rheostat R_{a1} to give continuous adjustment. A hand-calibrated scale, marked in thousands of ohms, should be provided for the rheostat, if necessary. The two condensers marked C_b are for covering different inductance ranges, and can be built up to the correct capacitance by combining commercial paper condensers. The rheostat R_b is preferably tapered, and can be any inexpensive wire-wound type. It need not be calibrated unless it is necessary to know the resistance component of the coil impedance. The resistances R_c must carry the full direct current to be passed through the inductance being measured, and so must have a generous wattage rating; they are most satisfactorily made by padding out vitreous-enamel units which have resistances slightly below the required value. The blocking condenser and filter reactor in the neutral arm are for permitting alternating current to flow in the telephone receivers while blocking out the direct current. The meter M for measuring the direct current should have an unshunted sensitivity of perhaps 10 ma, and shunts to extend the range as required. Any convenient source of direct current is suitable, and should be provided with coarse and fine control so that a current of 1 or 2 ma through an audio transformer can be adjusted as accurately as 250 ma for a filter reactor. The blocking condensers in the oscillator circuit are to block direct current out of R_a and the oscillator.

The bridge as shown in Fig. 3-33 provides three ranges as follows:

Range	Maximum inductance, henrys	C_b, μf	R_c, ohms
1	11.8	0.5	200
2	118	5.0	200
3	1180	5.0	2000

It will be noted that for Range 2 the inductance in henrys is equal to R_a in thousands of ohms, so that if R_a is suitably calibrated the bridge can be made direct-reading in inductance to the extent that the coil Q is high enough so that $Q^2 \gg 1$.

3-12. Measurement of Lumped Circuit Constants—Miscellaneous Methods and Considerations. *Mutual Inductance.* The mutual inductance between two coils can be measured in a number of ways. A simple method consists in connecting the two coils in series and measuring the equivalent inductance of the combination. The terminals of one of the coils are next reversed, and the measurement repeated. The mutual inductance is then one-fourth of the difference of the two measured inductances.[1] This method is quite satisfactory if the coefficient of coupling between the inductances is not too small; otherwise the mutual inductance becomes the difference between two relatively large and not greatly different quantities, with resulting poor accuracy.

In the case of an autotransformer such as illustrated in Fig. 3-34, the foregoing procedure is not possible. In this case one can determine mutual inductance by measuring the impedance at the terminals 1-2 when the secondary terminals 3-4 are open, and when they are short-circuited. This, coupled with a measurement of the impedance at 3-4 with the primary terminals 1-2 open, will give all of the data needed to calculate the mutual inductance. The formula, assuming negligible resistance as compared with the reactance, is then[2]

$$M = \sqrt{(L_p - L'_p)L_s} \qquad (3\text{-}34)$$

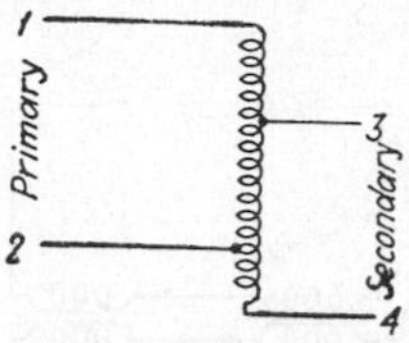

FIG. 3-34. Autotransformer coupling.

where M is the mutual inductance between primary and secondary portions of the autotransformer, L'_p is the inductance at terminals 1-2 with the secondary terminals 3-4 short-circuited, L_p is the inductance at terminals 1-2 with the secondary open (the primary inductance), and L_s the inductance measured at 3-4 when the primary terminals 1-2 are open (the secondary inductance).

Another method of obtaining mutual inductance consists in passing a known current I_p through one coil, and measuring the voltage induced across the terminals of the other coil. By the laws of coupled circuits, the magnitude of the induced voltage is $\omega M I_p$, so that the mutual inductance M is readily calculated when the primary current I_p, the frequency, and the induced voltage are known.

An unknown mutual inductance can be compared with a calibrated variable mutual inductance using the Felici mutual inductance balance, illustrated in Fig. 3-35a. Here the secondaries of the unknown and standard mutual inductances are connected in such relative polarity that when the two values of mutual inductances are the same, the two voltages induced in the secondary system by the primary current will be equal in magnitude and opposite in phase, giving a null indication.

[1] This follows from the fact that, when the coils are in series aiding, the total inductance is $L_p + L_s + 2M$, while when the coils are in series opposition, the inductance is $L_p + L_s - 2M$. The difference between these values is then $4M$.

[2] Following the analysis given in F. E. Terman, "Radio Engineering," 3d ed., p. 52, McGraw-Hill Book Company, Inc., New York, 1947, the difference $L_p - L'_p$ between primary inductance when the secondary is open and when it is short-circuited is the coupled inductance, which is $(\omega M)^2/\omega^2 L_s$. That is, $L_p - L'_p = M^2/L_s$, and Eq. (3-34) follows at once. If the resistances are not negligible compared with the reactances, then the situation becomes rather involved because there is resistive as well as inductive coupling. The situation can then be analyzed by the approach given on p. 67 of "Radio Engineering."

Mutual inductance may be compared with an inductance by means of the Campbell mutual inductance bridge, illustrated in Fig. 3-35b. This is an ordinary resistance-ratio inductance bridge in which the primary winding of the mutual inductance is connected in the "unknown" arm while the secondary winding of the mutual inductance is connected in series with the detector branch, as shown. In utilizing the balance equation to determine the mutual inductance, it is necessary to know the primary inductance L_p; this can be readily determined by throwing switch S to point 1, and making a second balance as an ordinary resistance-ratio

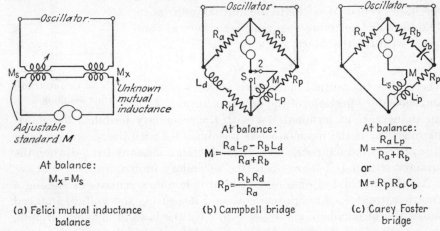

(a) Felici mutual inductance balance

At balance:
$$M_x = M_s$$

(b) Campbell bridge

At balance:
$$M = \frac{R_a L_p - R_b L_d}{R_a + R_b}$$

$$R_p = \frac{R_b R_d}{R_a}$$

(c) Carey Foster bridge

At balance:
$$M = \frac{R_a L_p}{R_a + R_b}$$
or
$$M = R_p R_a C_b$$

FIG. 3-35. Bridge arrangements for measuring mutual inductance.

inductance bridge. The accuracy of this bridge is limited by the fact that the mutual inductance is expressed as the difference between two quantities; when the mutual inductance is small, the accuracy therefore suffers.

Mutual inductance may be obtained in terms of capacitance by means of the Carey-Foster bridge of Fig. 3-35c. This arrangement has the advantage that the expression for mutual inductance does not involve a difference; as a result, the percentage accuracy that it is possible to attain is essentially the same as in the general run of bridge measurements. The Carey-Foster circuit has the disadvantage, however, that either the inductance L_p or the resistance R_p (which includes the loss resistance of the primary L_p of the mutual inductance) must be obtained by a separate measurement on another bridge.

In mutual-inductance bridges it is necessary to give the usual considerations to residual impedances, shielding, and grounding. In addition, errors may arise as a result of capacitive coupling between the primary and secondary windings.

Coefficient of Coupling. When the mutual inductance M and the self-inductances L_p and L_s of the two coils are known, the coefficient of coupling can then be calculated by the formula

$$\text{Coefficient of coupling} = k = \frac{M}{\sqrt{L_p L_s}} \tag{3-35}$$

The coefficient of coupling represents the ratio of the actual mutual inductance to the maximum possible mutual inductance which can be obtained with the given primary and secondary inductances.

An alternative procedure for determining the coefficient of coupling is to measure the inductances L_p and L'_p across the primary terminals when the secondary terminals are first open-circuited, and then short-circuited, respectively. If the Q of the windings is not too low, one then has

$$k = \sqrt{1 - \frac{L'_p}{L_p}} \tag{3-36a}$$

Values of L'_p and L_p are often measured with the aid of a Q meter, by connecting the primary terminals of the coupled system across the condenser of the Q meter in place of the coil in Fig. 3-19. Then if C_{oc} and C_{sc} are the Q meter capacitance values required to resonate the system to a particular frequency with the secondary coil open-circuited, and short-circuited, respectively, then

$$k = \sqrt{1 - \frac{C_{oc}}{C_{sc}}} \tag{3-36b}$$

Bridge Method of Measuring Negative Resistance. A negative resistance, such as is produced by certain vacuum-tube arrangements, can be accurately determined by a bridge measurement, just as can a positive resistance. Suitable circuit arrangements are shown in Fig. 3-36a, together with the equations that give the negative resistance in terms of the bridge arms for the condition of balance.[1] These simple bridge circuits assume that the negative resistance has no reactive component associated with it. Actually the negative resistances produced by tubes will normally be shunted by a small capacitance consisting of the inter-electrode capacitance of the tube plus lead capacitance. When this is the case, it is necessary to modify the bridge circuits, as shown in Fig. 3-36b, in which the effect of the capacitance in shunt with the negative

---

[1] Edward N. Dingley, Jr., Development of a Circuit for Measuring the Negative Resistance of Pliodynatrons, *Proc. IRE*, vol. 19, p. 1948, November, 1931.

resistance is balanced by the condenser C.[1,2] The addition of this capacitance balance has no effect upon the resistance balance, and adjustments of the two are quite independent.

Null Circuits in Which Transformer Windings Act as Bridge Arms. In the circuit of Fig. 3-37a, a transformer with one primary and two secondaries provides a combined shielded input transformer and pair of ratio

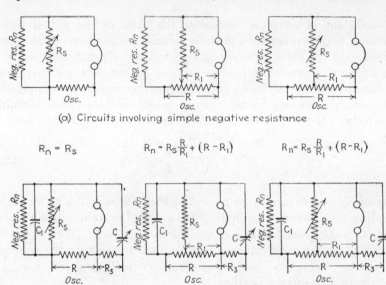

(a) Circuits involving simple negative resistance

$$R_n = R_s \qquad\qquad R_n = R_s \frac{R}{R_1} + (R - R_1) \qquad\qquad R_n = R_s \frac{R}{R_1} + (R - R_1)$$

(b) Circuits involving negative resistance shunted by a capacitance

FIG. 3-36. Bridge circuits for measuring negative resistance.

arms. Thus when the two secondary windings have identical characteristics, identical voltages are induced in them from the primary;[3] under these circumstances no output voltage will be developed across the terminals BG when the impedance Z_s equals the impedance Z_x. Accordingly when the impedance Z_s consists of a variable capacitance in series with a variable resistance, as illustrated in Fig. 3-37a, then the capaci-

[1] F. E. Terman, Improved Circuits for Measuring Negative Resistance, *Electronics*, vol. 6, p. 340, December, 1933.

[2] The constructional features of a practical bridge for measuring negative resistance of dynatron and other analogous tube arrangements is given on pp. 76–78 of F. E. Terman, "Measurements in Radio Engineering," McGraw-Hill Book Company, Inc., New York, 1935.

[3] It will be noted that if the transformer has low leakage inductance, stray capacitances across AB and BC have negligible effect on the ratio of voltages across these two windings. Also, the shielding shown places capacitance from ABC to ground in shunt with the neutral arm BG, where it can do no harm. Thus this tapped transformer has a behavior equivalent to a bridge with a Wagner ground, which is one of its principal virtues.

tance and equivalent series resistance of an unknown capacitive impedance Z_x can be determined by a procedure identical with that used in an
ordinary Wheatstone bridge of the type illustrated in Fig. 3-7c. In fact,

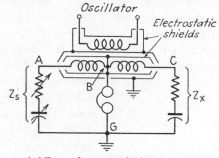

(a) Transformer bridge

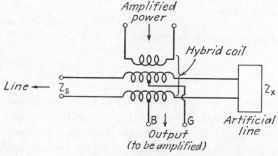

(b) Hybrid coil equivalent of
transformer bridge

FIG. 3-37. Bridge arrangements in which the ratio arms are obtained by means of
transformer windings.

the arrangement is in every respect identical with the resistance-ratio
bridge in Fig. 3-7 except for the method of obtaining the ratio arms.[1,2]

[1] It will be observed that the circuit of Fig. 3-37a is exactly equivalent to the hybrid
coil arrangement used in telephone repeater systems to couple amplified power into a
telephone line. In the hybrid coil system, as shown in Fig. 3-37b, the characteristic
impedance of the telephone line (represented by Z_s) to which amplified power is
delivered is balanced by a characteristic impedance of similar value (represented by
Z_x) produced by an artificial line. The amplified power to be delivered to the telephone line is introduced as shown, and to the extent that the balance between Z_s and
Z_x is perfect, does not produce output across terminals BG. At the same time, terminals BG are responsive to signals originating on the line.

[2] This arrangement is not the only means by which a multiwinding transformer
may be employed to obtain a null network. For further examples of bridge arrangements involving transformers, see H. L. Kirke, Radio Frequency Bridges, *J. IEE*,
vol. 92, pt. III, p. 2, March, 1945; Young, *loc. cit.*; H. A. M. Clark and P. B. Vanderlyn,
Proc. IEE (Radio & Comm.), vol. 96, pt. III, p. 189, May, 1949; W. C. Weatherley,

Measurement of Balanced Impedances.[1]   It is sometimes necessary to measure the impedance between two terminals that are balanced with respect to ground.   A typical example is the impedance between the two wires of a balanced transmission line.   The only equipment available to carry out such a measurement often has one terminal grounded, which introduces a difficulty.

In the case of two terminals associated with ground, as indicated in Fig. 3-38, the system can be considered as a three-terminal arrangement analogous to that of Fig. 3-24a, in which the direct admittances Y_1, Y_2, and Y_3 are involved.   The admittance Y_{AB} between terminals A and B is then

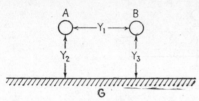

FIG. 3-38. Admittances associated with a two-wire transmission line.

$$Y_{AB} = \frac{1}{Z_{AB}} = Y_1 + \frac{Y_2 Y_3}{Y_2 + Y_3} \quad (3\text{-}37a)$$

When the terminals A and B are perfectly balanced with respect to ground, $Y_2 = Y_3$ and Eq. (3-37a) reduces to

$$Y_{AB} = Y_1 + \tfrac{1}{2} Y_2 \qquad (3\text{-}37b)$$

The usual method of measuring the admittance or impedance between A and B, and also of determining whether or not there is any difference in the admittances Y_2 and Y_3, is to make three measurements as follows: (1) the admittance Y' between electrode A and ground with electrode B grounded; (2) the admittance Y'' between A and ground with AB short-circuited; (3) the admittance Y''' between B and ground with A grounded. These measurements give

$$\begin{aligned} Y' &= Y_1 + Y_2 \\ Y'' &= Y_2 + Y_3 \\ Y''' &= Y_1 + Y_3 \end{aligned} \qquad (3\text{-}38a)$$

Solving successively for Y_1, Y_2, and Y_3 gives

$$Y_1 = \frac{Y' - Y'' + Y'''}{2}$$

$$Y_2 = \frac{Y' + Y'' - Y'''}{2} \qquad (3\text{-}38b)$$

$$Y_3 = \frac{-Y' + Y'' + Y'''}{2}$$

The Design and Construction of a Comparison Impedance Bridge for Frequencies of 40–270 Mc., *Proc. IEE*, vol. 96, pt. III, p. 429, September, 1949.

   [1] This discussion follows D. B. Sinclair, Measuring Balanced Impedances with the R-F Bridge, *Gen. Rad. Expt.*, vol. 17, p. 3, September, 1942.

This method is quite tedious to apply, but is highly accurate and is particularly useful when it is necessary to determine unbalance between the admittances Y_2 and Y_3. In the special case when it is known that the impedance can be assumed to be balanced with respect to ground, then only measurements (1) and (2) above need be made, and Eqs. (3-38b) reduce to

$$Y_1 = Y' - \frac{Y''}{2}$$
$$Y_2 = Y_3 = \frac{Y''}{2}$$

$$(3\text{-}38c)$$

An alternative procedure that is suitable for use with impedances that are reasonably well balanced with respect to ground, is illustrated in Fig. 3-39. Here the terminals of the bridge are connected to an artificial line $L_1L_2C_1C_2$ that is adjusted to be exactly a half wavelength long at the frequency of measurement. The balanced line is connected to this artificial line, as shown. It is a property of a half-wavelength line that the voltage across the output terminals 3-4 will always be equal in magnitude but opposite in phase from the voltage applied to the line input 1-2; accordingly, the balanced line will be excited with a voltage that is symmetrical with respect to

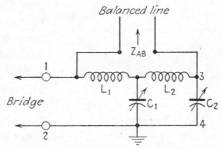

FIG. 3-39. Method of measuring the impedance of a transmission line that is balanced with respect to ground.

ground. It can be further shown that the impedance appearing across bridge terminals 1-2 is exactly one-fourth of the impedance Z_{AB} between A and B of the balanced line, as given by Eq. (3-37b); this assumes that the line under test is balanced, and that the artificial line is exactly a half wavelength long, and has negligible losses.

In the artificial line the coils L_1 and L_2 should be identical, and should have a reactance at the frequency of measurement that is of the same order of magnitude as the impedance to be measured. The line is adjusted by disconnecting Z_{AB}, and then short-circuiting terminals 3-4 and adjusting condenser C_1 to give series resonance at terminals 1-2, as determined by minimum and resistive impedance observed by the bridge. The short circuit across C_2 is next removed, and this condenser is then adjusted to give parallel resonance across terminals 1-2 as observed by the bridge.

Bridges for Measuring Vector Impedance. All of the bridges that have been previously described express the unknown impedance in terms of its resistance and reactance (or conductance and susceptance) components. It is, however, possible to devise a bridge that measures the magnitude and phase angle of a vector impedance directly.   An example of such a vector-impedance bridge is illustrated in Fig. 3-40a.[1]   This consists of an ordinary resistance-ratio bridge with the addition of the auxiliary circuit $L_pC_pR_p$ connected across the oscillator, as shown, with a secondary wind-

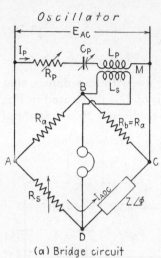

ing L_s coupled to L_p and connected in series with the neutral arm of the bridge.   In using this bridge, a preliminary adjustment is made which consists in tuning the condenser C_p to resonance with L_p at the frequency of measurement, so that the auxiliary circuit presents a resistance impedance to the oscillator.   This adjustment can be conveniently carried out by connecting $L_pC_pR_p$ in place of the unknown impedance of the bridge, disconnecting the secondary L_s from the neutral arm, and adjusting C_p and R_p until a balance is obtained.   An unknown impedance $Z\underline{/\Phi}$ can then be determined by connecting it in the bridge as shown, and varying resistances R_p and R_s until a null balance is obtained. Under these conditions one has

$$|Z| = R_s \qquad (3\text{-}39a)$$

$$\tan \frac{\Phi}{2} = \frac{2\omega M}{R_p} \qquad (3\text{-}39b)$$

(a) Bridge circuit

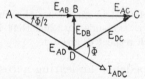

(b) Vector diagram

Fig.   3-40. Vector-impedance bridge for directly measuring magnitude and phase angle of an impedance.

where M is the mutual inductance between L_p and L_s.   Negative phase angles can be obtained by reversing the polarity of the secondary winding L_s, thereby reversing the phase of the voltage introduced into the neutral arm by this mutual inductance.

The operation of the bridge in Fig. 3-40a can be explained with the aid of the vector diagram on Fig. 3-40b, which is drawn for the conditions that exist when the bridge is balanced.   The oscillator voltage E_{AC} is taken as the reference vector.   Since $R_a = R_b$, then $E_{AB} = E_{AC}/2$.   The current I_{ADC} flowing in the arms ADC under conditions of balance will lag

[1] Further discussion of this and other bridge arrangements that can be used for measuring vector impedance are given by A. Serner, A New Bridge for the Direct Measurement of Impedance, *Wireless Eng.*, vol. 14, p. 59, February, 1937; G. W. O. Howe, Bridge for Direct Impedance Measurement, *Wireless Eng.*, vol. 14, p. 227, May 1937.

the oscillator voltage by exactly $\Phi/2$; this arises from the fact that, at balance, R_s and Z have identical magnitudes so that the sum of their impedances has a phase angle that is half the phase angle of Z. The voltage drop E_{AD} across R_s is in phase with the current I_{ADC} as shown, while the voltage drop E_{DC} across the impedance Z leads the current by the phase angle of the impedance; the sum $E_{AD} + E_{DC}$ equals E_{AC}. The vector E_{DB} now represents the voltage that must be inserted in the neutral arm if a null balance is to be achieved. Because of the geometry of Fig. 3-40b, this voltage is exactly 90° out of phase with the oscillator voltage E_{AC}. Since the preliminary adjustment of the auxiliary arm $R_p C_p L_p$ was such as to make the current in this arm in phase with E_{AC}, the voltage induced in L_s will be exactly 90° out of phase with E_{AC}, and so is in exactly the correct phase to supply E_{BD}. The magnitude of the voltage E_{BD} is $\omega M I_p = \omega M E_{AC}/R_p$, and so can be adjusted by varying R_p. From the geometry of Fig. 3-40b it is also seen that

$$\tan\,(\Phi/2) = E_{BD}/E_{AB} = \omega M I_p / \tfrac{1}{2} E_{AC} = 2\omega M / R_p$$

CHAPTER 4

CIRCUIT CONSTANTS IN
SYSTEMS INVOLVING DISTRIBUTED CONSTANTS

4-1. Introduction.[1] Waveguides and two-conductor transmission lines involve a wide range of frequencies, from the voice-frequency telephone line at one extreme, to the waveguide operating at thousands of megacycles at the other. There is a natural division between two-conductor transmission lines and waveguides (even though the transmission line can be thought of as a waveguide operating in the *TEM* mode). Accordingly, the first portion of the chapter will be devoted to the transmission line, and the second portion to the waveguide.

At higher frequencies, when one cannot use conventional bridges for the measurement of impedances, the transmission line (or waveguide) itself serves as an important measuring tool. Hence, a considerable portion of the chapter will be concerned with measurements made *using* transmission lines, as well as measurement *on* transmission lines.

4-2. Transmission-line Parameters.[2] Any two-conductor transmission line can have its electrical properties expressed in terms of a combination of physical parameters. Perhaps the most basic, although not the most directly useful parameters, are the series inductance L, shunt capacitance C, series resistance R, and shunt conductance G, per unit length of transmission line. From these constants one can define a line series impedance Z, and a line shunt admittance Y, as follows:

$$Z = R + j\omega L \qquad (4\text{-}1a)$$
$$Y = G + j\omega C \qquad (4\text{-}1b)$$

---

[1] Two recent books give extensive details on measurements peculiar to the so-called "microwave region," *i.e.*, frequencies roughly above 1000 Mc: H. M. Barlow and A. L. Cullen, "Microwave Measurements," Constable & Co., Ltd., London, 1950; "Technique of Microwave Measurements" (Vol. 11, Radiation Laboratory Series), McGraw-Hill Book Company, Inc., New York, 1947. A brief survey will be found in F. J. Gaffney, Microwave Measurements and Test Equipments, *Proc. IRE*, vol. 34, p. 775, October, 1946.

[2] The reader wishing to study the detailed properties of transmission lines should consult one of the numerous books on the subject. Among those available, attention is called to H. H. Skilling, "Electric Transmission Lines," McGraw-Hill Book Company, Inc., New York, 1951, and Walter C. Johnson, "Transmission Lines and Networks," McGraw-Hill Book Company, Inc., New York, 1950.

The Characteristic Impedance. In calculating the electrical properties of a line, the quantities Z and Y are used to express two derived constants, the characteristic impedance[1] Z_0, and the propagation constant γ, defined as follows:

$$Z_0 = \sqrt{ZY} = R_0 + jX_0 \tag{4-2}$$

$$\gamma = \sqrt{\frac{Z}{Y}} = \alpha + j\beta \tag{4-3}$$

where α = attenuation constant
      β = phase constant
Both Z_0 and γ are complex numbers in the general case.

The characteristic impedance Z_0 of the usual radio-frequency transmission line can be assumed to be resistive with a value[2]

$$Z_0 = \sqrt{\frac{L}{C}} \tag{4-4}$$

This relation follows from Eqs. (4-1) and (4-2), for the situation where the frequency is so high that $\omega L \gg R$, and $\omega C \gg G$.

The Attenuation and Phase Constants, and Phase Velocity. The complex number γ representing the propagation constant has a real part α and an imaginary part β. The real part is called the *attenuation constant*, and is a direct measure of the rate at which the amplitude of a wave diminishes as it travels along the line. The imaginary part of the propagation constant is called the *phase constant*, and is a measure of the rate at which the phase of a wave varies as it travels along the line. The

[1] Sometimes called *surge* impedance.
[2] In terms of line dimensions, this leads to the relations

For coaxial lines:

$$Z_0 = \frac{138}{\sqrt{\varepsilon}} \log_{10} \frac{b}{a} \qquad \text{ohms} \tag{4-5a}$$

where a = outside diameter of inner conductor
      b = inside diameter of outer conductor
      ε = dielectric constant of insulation material (if any) filling the line

For parallel-wire lines:

$$Z_0 = 276 \log_{10} \frac{2D}{d} \tag{4-5b}$$

where D = distance between centers of the two conductors
      d = diameter of each conductor
For more complicated forms of line, see F. E. Terman, "Radio Engineers' Handbook," p. 174, McGraw-Hill Book Company, Inc., New York, 1943; also H. A. Wheeler, Transmission Line Impedance Curves, *Proc. IRE*, vol. 38, p. 1400, December, 1950; Federal Telephone and Radio Corp., "Reference Data for Radio Engineers," 3d ed., p. 322, 1949.

phase constant at the same time determines a *phase velocity* v_p of the line. Also, the phase constant is related to the *line wavelength* λ_l, which is defined as the distance along the wave corresponding to a phase difference of 2π radians. This concept of line wavelength is one of great generality; many of the equations involving it will apply to waveguides as well as to two-conductor lines. The relationships between the phase constant, wavelength, and phase velocity, are

$$\lambda_l = \frac{2\pi}{\beta} \qquad (4\text{-}6)$$

$$v_p = f\lambda_l = \frac{2\pi f}{\beta} \qquad (4\text{-}7)$$

where λ_l = line wavelength, m

f = frequency, cycles per sec

v_p = phase velocity, m per sec

In the case of radio-frequency lines with air dielectric, λ_l approximates the free-space wavelength of a radio wave of the same frequency.[1] In the case of cables with solid dielectric having a constant ε, the wavelength is very closely the free space wavelength divided by $\sqrt{\varepsilon}$.

4-3. Voltage and Current Relations, Reflection Coefficient, and Standing-wave Ratio. The voltage and current existing on a transmission line can be considered as representing the sum of the voltages and currents of two waves. The first wave, which can be called the *incident wave*, travels from the generator toward the receiving end of the line, and carries energy toward the load. It consists of a voltage E_i and an associated current I_i that are everywhere related by the equation

$$\frac{\text{Voltage of incident wave}}{\text{Current of incident wave}} = \frac{E_i}{I_i} = Z_0 \qquad (4\text{-}9)$$

The magnitude of the incident wave becomes smaller as the wave travels along the line toward the load, according to the relation

$$\left.\begin{array}{l}\text{Voltage of incident wave} \\ \text{at distance } l \text{ from load}\end{array}\right\} = |E_i| = E'_L \epsilon^{\alpha l} \qquad (4\text{-}10)$$

where E'_L is the voltage of the wave at the receiving or load end of the line, α is the attenuation constant as defined by Eq. (4-3), and l is the distance from the *load* end of the line. The value αl_t for the total length l_t of the line is termed the *line attenuation*.

[1] If $\omega L \gg R$, and $\omega C \gg G$, as is usually true at high frequencies, the line losses can be assumed zero when calculating β and v_p. From Eqs. (4-1) and (4-3) this leads to

$$\beta = \omega\sqrt{LC} \qquad \text{radians per unit length} \qquad (4\text{-}8a)$$

$$v_p = \frac{1}{\sqrt{LC}} \qquad (4\text{-}8b)$$

It will be noted from Eq. (4-10) that the incident wave becomes smaller as it travels toward the receiver, *i.e.*, as the distance l from the receiver decreases. The phase of the incident wave also drops back (becomes more lagging) by β radians for each unit of length that the wave travels toward the load, or 2π radians for a distance corresponding to the line wavelength λ_l. As a result, the phase position at a distance l from the load is βl radians leading with respect to the phase at the load. The incident wave thus travels *toward* the load with the phase velocity v_p defined by Eq. (4-7).

If the load impedance Z_L differs from the characteristic impedance Z_0 of the line, some of the energy of the incident wave is reflected by the load producing a reflected wave that travels from the load toward the generator. This reflected wave is similar to the incident wave except that it is traveling toward the generator. As a result, its voltage E_r is associated with a current I_r such that everywhere on the line

$$\frac{\text{Voltage of reflected wave}}{\text{Current of reflected wave}} = \frac{E_r}{I_r} = -Z_0 \qquad (4\text{-}11)$$

The negative sign arises from the fact that the current in the reflected wave flows toward the generator, whereas the current of the incident wave flows toward the load. The magnitude of the reflected wave becomes smaller as the wave travels away from the receiver (*i.e.*, as l increases) according to the relation

$$\left. \begin{array}{l} \text{Voltage of reflected wave} \\ \text{at distance } l \text{ from load} \end{array} \right\} = |E_r| = E_L'' \epsilon^{-\alpha l} \qquad (4\text{-}12)$$

Here E_L'' is the magnitude of the reflected wave at the load. The phase of the reflected wave drops back β radians for each unit of distance the wave travels toward the generator, or 2π radians in a distance equal to one line wavelength λ_l. Thus the reflected wave at a distance l from the load lags its phase position at the load by βl radians. As a result, the reflected wave travels *away* from the load with the phase velocity v_p.

Reflection Coefficient. The vector ratio of the reflected wave to the incident wave is termed the *reflection coefficient*, commonly designated by the symbol ρ. Thus

$$\frac{\text{Reflected wave}}{\text{Incident wave}} = \rho = \frac{|E_r|}{|E_i|} \underline{/\theta} \qquad (4\text{-}13)$$

where θ is the phase difference between E_r and E_i. If the line has no losses (that is, $\alpha \approx 0$), the magnitude of ρ is everywhere constant, although its phase angle will depend upon position. If the line has losses, the magnitude of ρ decreases as one recedes from the load, because the reflected wave becomes smaller and the incident wave simultaneously becomes larger; the quantitative relation is given by Eq. (4-38).

In any case, at the load end of the line the reflection coefficient is determined by the ratio of the load impedance Z_L to the characteristic impedance Z_0 of the line by the equation

$$\left.\begin{array}{l}\text{Reflection coefficient}\\\text{at load end of line}\end{array}\right\} = \rho = \frac{(Z_L/Z_0) - 1}{(Z_L/Z_0) + 1} \qquad (4\text{-}14)$$

Several special cases are to be noted.   When the load is open-circuited $(Z_L = \infty)$, the reflection coefficient of the load is $+1.0$; this means that the incident wave is completely reflected with no change in polarity of voltage.   Likewise, when the load is a short circuit, $\rho = -1.0$, which means that the incident wave is completely reflected by the load, but with a reversal in polarity of voltage.   Again, if $Z_L = Z_0$, one has $\rho = 0$, and there is no reflected wave present; in this case the line is said to be terminated or matched.   Finally, if Z_L is a pure reactance, then assuming Z_0 is a resistance, the reflection coefficient of the load is unity, denoting complete reflection of the incident wave; however, the phase angle of the reflected wave relative to the incident wave will depend upon the magnitude and sign of the load reactance.

Standing-wave Patterns and Standing-wave Ratio.   The actual voltage E on the line at any point is the sum $E_i + E_r$ of the voltages of the incident and reflected waves at that point.   This results in voltage distributions on the line such as illustrated in Fig. 4-1,[1] that are called *standing-wave* patterns.   At certain places on the line the voltages of the two waves are in the same phase, and so add to give voltage maxima; at other places they are in phase opposition, and so subtract to give minima. The difference between the maxima and minima will be more pronounced the larger the reflection coefficient, as shown.   In particular, when the reflection coefficient of the load is unity, the minima are very deep,[2] while when the reflection coefficient of the load is zero (that is, $Z_L = Z_0$), there is no standing-wave pattern (see Fig. 4-1d).   Intermediate values of ρ give intermediate behavior, as shown.

The distance between adjacent minima (or maxima) is exactly half of the line wavelength λ_l as defined by Eq. (4-6).   In this distance $\lambda_l/2$ an individual traveling wave suffers a phase shift of exactly π radians.

The ratio of the maximum to minimum values of voltage (or current) in

[1] Standing-wave patterns of current are also present.   These are exactly the same as the voltage patterns, except that the current minima occur at the voltage maxima, and vice versa.

[2] The minima would theoretically be zero for $\rho = \pm1.0$ in the case of an ideal line with zero losses.

the standing-wave pattern is termed the *standing-wave ratio*.[1]   That is,

$$\text{Voltage standing-wave ratio} = S = \frac{E_{max}}{E_{min}} \qquad (4\text{-}15)$$

where E_{max} and E_{min} have the meanings indicated in Fig. 4-1.   It will be

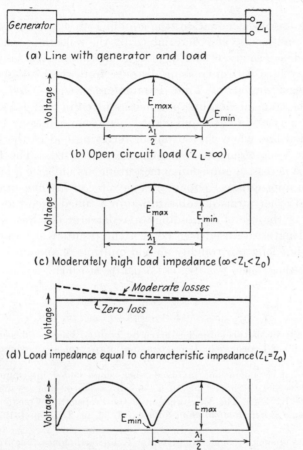

(a) Line with generator and load

(b) Open circuit load ($Z_L = \infty$)

(c) Moderately high load impedance ($\infty < Z_L < Z_0$)

(d) Load impedance equal to characteristic impedance ($Z_L = Z_0$)

(e) Short-circuited load impedance

Fig. 4-1. Standing-wave patterns corresponding to various load conditions.

noted that $S = 1$ corresponds to no reflected wave (Fig. 4-1d), while S will increase as the reflected wave becomes larger, and approaches infinity as the incident wave is completely reflected.   The relationship

[1] This *voltage* standing-wave ratio is often abbreviated VSWR, principally to distinguish it from the power standing-wave ratio.   If the detecting element used to observe a standing-wave pattern is a square-law device, then its output is proportional to power.   When desired, such power readings can be converted to relative voltage by taking the square root.

between the magnitude $|\rho|$ of the reflection coefficient, and the standing-wave ratio S is[1]

$$|\rho| = \frac{S - 1}{S + 1} \tag{4-16}$$

$$S = \frac{1 + |\rho|}{1 - |\rho|} \tag{4-17}$$

If the line has no attenuation, the standing-wave ratio S is everywhere the same, and has a value determined by the reflection coefficient of the load impedance as given by Eq. (4-14). If the line has losses, however, then S decreases with increasing distance from the load (see page 148).

4-4. Measurement of Line Parameters.[2] *Open- and Short-circuit Tests.* The transmission line parameters listed in Sec. 4-2 can be determined by measuring the input impedance of an arbitrary length of the transmission line when the output or receiving end of the transmission line is first open-circuited and then short-circuited. The technique of making the necessary impedance measurements must be selected according to the appropriate frequency range; it can involve bridges,[3] the Q meter, and other forms of substitution in a tuned circuit as described in Chap. 3,[4] or the use of a standing-wave detector (see Sec. 4-5). Unless resonant lengths are used (see below), the results will be most accurate when the line length is roughly an odd multiple of an eighth wavelength.

---

[1] These relations follow from Eq. (4-15) and the fact that

$$E_{max} = |E_i| + |E_r|$$
$$E_{min} = |E_i| - |E_r|$$
$$|E_r| = |\rho||E_i|$$

[2] A good survey of this subject is given by Ivan G. Easton, Measurement of the Characteristics of Transmission Lines, *Gen. Rad. Expt.*, vol. 18, November–December, 1943.

[3] The special considerations involved when single-ended impedance bridges are used for measuring the impedance of a two-wire balanced line are discussed in Sec. 3-12: also see L. Essen, The Measurement of the Propagation Constants of Screened Twin Cables, *J. IEE (Radiolocation Conv.)*, vol. 93, pt. IIIA, p. 1319, March–May, 1946.

[4] Examples of such methods are given by T. Iorwerth Jones, The Measurement of the Characteristics of Concentric Cables at Frequencies between 1 and 100 Megacycles per Second, *J. IEE (Wireless Sec.)*, vol. 89, pt. III, p. 213, December, 1942; J. M. Miller, Methods of Electrical and Mechanical Testing of Radio-frequency Cables at the Naval Research Laboratory, *Trans. AIEE*, vol. 64, p. 934, 1945; F. Jones and R. Sear, Testing High Frequency Cables, *Wireless Eng.*, vol. 21, p. 512, November, 1944; W. T. Blackband and D. R. Brown, The Two-point Method of Measuring Characteristic Impedance and Attenuation of Cables at 3,000 Mc/s, *J. IEE (Radiolocation Conv.)*, vol. 93, pt. IIIA, p. 1383, March-May, 1946; Ballantine Laboratories, Measurement of Transmission Line Constants, *Electronics*, vol. 11, p. 26, April,1938; L. Essen, The Measurement of Balanced and Unbalanced Impedances at Frequencies near 500 Mc/s, and Its Application to the Determination of the Propagation Constants of Cables, *J. IEE (Wireless Sec.)*, vol. 91, pt. III, p. 84, June, 1944.

Once the open- and short-circuit-impedance measurements have been made, the transmission-line parameters can be systematically computed. Suppose that the sample of transmission line used in the measurement has a length l_1; then the open-circuit impedance Z_{oc} and short-circuit impedance Z_{sc} are

$$Z_{oc} = \frac{Z_0}{\tanh \gamma l_1} \qquad (4\text{-}18)$$

$$Z_{sc} = Z_0 \tanh \gamma l_1 \qquad (4\text{-}19)$$

By manipulating Eqs. (4-7) and (4-8), they readily yield expressions as follows for the characteristic impedance, and the propagation constant:

$$Z_0 = \sqrt{Z_{oc}Z_{sc}} \qquad (4\text{-}20)$$

$$\tanh \gamma l_1 = \sqrt{\frac{Z_{sc}}{Z_{oc}}} \qquad (4\text{-}21)$$

In order to determine the attenuation constant α and the phase constant β, it is often convenient to use the following expressions, which represent a form of Eq. (4-21) that involves only real numbers. In this way only tables of real hyperbolic tangents[1] and ordinary tangents are required.

$$\tanh 2\alpha l_1 = \frac{2A}{1 + A^2 + B^2} \qquad (4\text{-}22)$$

$$\tan 2\beta l_1 = \frac{2B}{1 - A^2 + B^2} \qquad (4\text{-}23)$$

where A = real part of $\sqrt{Z_{sc}/Z_{oc}}$
B = imaginary of $\sqrt{Z_{sc}/Z_{oc}}$

The series impedance Z and shunt admittance Y of a transmission line can be computed from Z_0 and γ by the use of Eqs. (4-2) and (4-3). This gives

$$Z = R + j\omega L = Z_0\gamma \qquad (4\text{-}24)$$

$$Y = G + j\omega C = \frac{\gamma}{Z_0} \qquad (4\text{-}25)$$

Open- and Short-circuit Tests with Resonant Lines. The open-circuit and short-circuit impedances discussed above can be the impedance associated with any arbitrary length of transmission line. Considerable simplification results, however, if the sample is so cut that its length is exactly an odd or an even multiple of one quarter wavelength. The line is then in resonance, and its impedance is resistive. In practice, resonance can be achieved by cutting the line approximately to length, and

---

[1] In order to use Eq. (4-23), it is necessary to know the quadrant of $2\beta l_1$. This can be determined from the actual line length, and an estimate made in accordance with the discussion given in connection with Eq. (4-6), of the distance corresponding to one wavelength.

then varying the frequency to give resonance as indicated by maximum or minimum impedance, or by a resistive impedance.

In the resonant line, let R_{oc} be the input resistance measured when the receiving end is open-circuited, and R_{sc} the input resistance when the receiver is short-circuited.

Then Eq. (4-20) becomes

$$Z_0 = \sqrt{R_{oc}R_{sc}} \qquad (4\text{-}26)$$

The attenuation constant α can be simply expressed in terms of the resonant-circuit resistances by the relations[1]

Length l_1, an odd number of quarter wavelengths:

$$\alpha l_1 = \sqrt{\frac{R_{oc}}{R_{sc}}} \qquad (4\text{-}27a)$$

Length l_1, an even number of quarter wavelengths:

$$\alpha l_1 = \sqrt{\frac{R_{sc}}{R_{oc}}} \qquad (4\text{-}27b)$$

The phase constant β of the resonant line in radians per unit length is

$$\beta = \frac{n}{l_1}\frac{\pi}{2} \qquad (4\text{-}28)$$

where l_1 is the actual line length, and n is the number of quarter waves represented by this length. The applicable value of n can usually be estimated from supplementary data, particularly if n is small such as 1, 2, or 3. Thus for lines with air dielectric the wavelength on the line approximates the wavelength in free space, while a dielectric with constant ε reduces the length corresponding to a wavelength by the factor $1/\sqrt{\varepsilon}$.

---

[1] The derivation of these relations from Eq. (4-22) is as follows:
For resonance, $B = 0$, so that

$$\tanh 2\alpha l_1 = \frac{2A}{1 + A^2}$$

Here $A = \sqrt{R_{sc}/R_{oc}}$. Now when l_1 is an odd number of quarter wavelengths, R_{sc} is large and R_{oc} small. Under these conditions $A \gg 1$, and

$$\tanh 2\alpha l_1 \approx 2\alpha l_1 \approx \frac{2}{A}$$

Similarly, when l_1 is an even number of quarter wavelengths, R_{oc} is large and R_{sc} small; under these conditions $A \ll 1$, and

$$\tanh 2\alpha l_1 \approx 2\alpha l_1 = 2A$$

Solving these relations for αl_1 give Eqs. (4-27).

Use of Q Meter to Determine Attenuation.   The Q meter provides a simple means of determining the attenuation constant of a line.[1]   The line is associated with the resonant circuit of the Q meter in the manner illustrated in Fig. 4-2.   Here C is the tuning capacitance of the meter, and L is an auxiliary inductance that with C forms the resonant output circuit of the Q meter.   The line must be resonant; if in parallel resonance it is connected in parallel with LC as in Fig. 4-2a, while if in series resonance it is connected in series with L as in Fig. 4-2b.[2]   Exact resonance

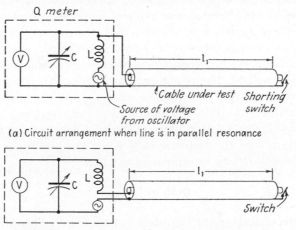

(a) Circuit arrangement when line is in parallel resonance

(b) Circuit arrangement when line is in series resonance

Fig. 4-2.   Circuit arrangements for measuring the input impedance of a resonant line with the aid of a Q meter.

can be achieved for any given length of line by adjusting the frequency of the Q-meter oscillator until disconnecting the line in a or short-circuiting its input in b does not alter the setting of C required to give resonance with the Q-meter oscillator.

The measuring procedure is then as follows: *First*, with the line terminated to give parallel resonance, the value of Q_1 is determined in Fig. 4-2a for the resonant system consisting of LC shunted by the line.   *Next*, with the line terminated to give series resonance, the value Q_2 is deter-

[1] C. Stewart, Jr., A Method of Measuring Attenuation of Short Lengths of Coaxial Cable, *Proc. IRE*, vol. 33, p. 46, January, 1945; C. C. Fleming, Report of Conference on Radio-frequency Cables: Electrical Tests over a Range of Frequencies, *Trans. AIEE*, vol. 64, p. 936, 1945.

[2] Parallel resonance (*i.e.*, high input impedance) occurs when the receiver is shorted and the line is an odd number of quarter wavelengths long, or when the receiver is open-circuited and the line is an even number of quarter wavelengths long.   Series resonance (*i.e.*, low input impedance) is obtained with a short-circuited receiver when the line is an even number of quarter wavelengths long, and with an open-circuited receiver when the length is an odd number of quarter wavelengths.

mined in Fig. 4-2b for the system consisting of LC in series with the line. Finally, with the line disconnected, the value Q_0 is determined for LC alone. Then [1,2]

$$\tanh \alpha l_1 = \sqrt{\left(\frac{1}{Q_1} - \frac{1}{Q_0}\right)\left(\frac{1}{Q_2} - \frac{1}{Q_0}\right)} \qquad (4\text{-}29)$$

The same procedure and formula are used irrespective of whether the line is an even or odd multiple of a half wavelength long. The difference in these two cases is that whereas series and parallel resonance are obtained with the receiver open- and short-circuited, respectively, when the line is an odd multiple of a quarter wavelength long, the reverse is the case when the length is an even multiple of a quarter wavelength.

An alternative procedure[3] consists in obtaining the input resistance R' of the parallel resonant line by comparison with known resistances of the same order of magnitude. The idea is to observe the response of the Q-meter indicator V as different known values of resistance are shunted across the tuned circuit LC in place of the parallel resonant line. With this information, and the response of V when the line is shunted across LC, one can obtain R' by interpolation. Then

$$\tanh \alpha l_1 = \frac{Z_0}{R'} \qquad (4\text{-}30)$$

where Z_0 is the characteristic impedance of the line. This procedure has the advantage that the accuracy of the result depends only upon the accuracy with which the resistances of the test resistors is known, and not upon the absolute accuracy of the Q readings, which may be rather poor at very high frequencies.[4,5]

[1] In most practical cases $\alpha l_1 \ll 1$; under these conditions $\tanh \alpha l_1 \approx \alpha l_1$.

[2] It is sometimes desirable to use different values of inductance for the coils L in a and b of Fig. 4-2. The modifications in Eq. (4-29) that this causes are given by Stewart, *op. cit.*

[3] See Fleming, *op. cit.*

[4] A unique method of obtaining an adjustable known shunting resistance is described by J. C. Simmonds, Tuned Circuit Parallel Resistance Apparatus for Measurements on Balanced Pair Cables at Frequencies Up to 10 Mc/s, *J. IEE*, vol. 92, pt. III, p. 120, June, 1945; Apparatus for Measurements on Balanced-pair High-frequency Cables in the Range 10–200 Mc/s, *J. IEE*, vol. 92, pt. III, p. 282, December, 1945.

[5] Still another Q-meter method of measuring the attenuation constant consists in using a short-circuited length of line approximately $0.15\lambda_1$ long as the unknown inductance in the standard Q-meter test of a coil (see p. 90). The attenuation constant at a particular frequency can then be calculated from the tuning capacitance required to resonate the cable at this frequency, the Q reading, and the characteristic impedance of the cable. For full details see Chandler Stewart, Jr., The S-function Method of Measuring Attenuation of Coaxial Radio-frequency Cable, *Trans. AIEE*, vol. 64, p. 616, 938, 1945. This method of measurement will yield accurate results in the frequency range 1 to 100 Mc.

Attenuation by Standing-wave-ratio Measurements. At the higher frequencies, where a standing-wave detector can be used (see Sec. 4-5), the attenuation of a length l_1 of line can be determined from the value of standing-wave ratio S observed at the sending end of a line that is short-circuited at the receiver. The apparatus arrangement is illustrated in Fig. 4-3. The basic relationship is[1]

$$\tanh \alpha l_1 = \frac{1}{S} \tag{4-31}$$

For this relation to be valid, two conditions must be rigorously met. First, the standing-wave detector itself must have zero or negligible losses

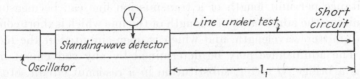

Fig. 4-3. Measurement of attenuation of a line with the aid of a standing-wave detector.

compared with the attenuation in the line sample, and *second*, the characteristic impedance of the standing-wave detector must be exactly the same as that of the line sample (or a reflectionless matching section must be interposed between them). The first condition can easily be met by using a long enough sample of cable so that its total attenuation αl_1 is high compared with the attenuation of the standing-wave detector. If the second condition is impossible to meet with sufficient precision, there is a more general but complicated measuring technique described on page 189 which takes account of the reflections at the junction of the standing-wave detector and the line sample.

Direct Measurement of Attenuation. Under certain circumstances, it may be convenient to measure the total attenuation of a sample of transmission line by direct voltage or current measurement when the line is terminated in its characteristic impedance, *i.e.*, when there is no reflected wave on the line. In the simplest case, the voltage V_L existing at the receiving end is compared with the voltage V_S applied to the sending end;[2] the attenuation constant α of a line of length l_1 is then given by

---

[1] This is derived as follows: Define E_0 as the amplitude of the incident and reflected waves at the receiving end of the line. Then the amplitudes of these waves at the sending end of the line are $E_0 \epsilon^{\alpha l_1}$ and $E_0 \epsilon^{-\alpha l_1}$ respectively. Equation (4-31) then follows by substituting $E_{\max} = E_0 \epsilon^{\alpha l_1} + E_0 \epsilon^{-\alpha l_1}$, and $E_{\min} = E_0 \epsilon^{\alpha l_1} - E_0 \epsilon^{-\alpha l_1}$, in Eq. (4-15), and noting that $\tanh \alpha l_1 = (\epsilon^{\alpha l} - \epsilon^{\alpha -l_1})/(\epsilon^{\alpha l_1} - \epsilon^{-\alpha l_1})$.

[2] Typical examples of how this method may be carried out are given by H. H. Race and C. V. Larrick, Coaxial Cable Attenuation Measurements at 300 Mc/s, *Gen. Elec. Rev.*, vol. 44, p. 507, September, 1941; and Miller, *op. cit.*

$$\frac{V_S}{V_L} = \epsilon^{\alpha l_1} \tag{4-32}$$

At ordinary radio frequencies the voltage measurement can be made with a vacuum-tube voltmeter. In some cases it may be more convenient to measure current instead of voltage, using a thermocouple, for instance. In this case, the sending-end current I_S replaces the voltage V_S, and the receiving-end current I_L replaces V_L in Eq. (4-32).

When the attenuation is measured in this manner, it is important that there be no standing waves due to reflection.

Direct Measurement of Capacitance and Inductance of Lines. The capacitance per unit length of a transmission line can be measured by determining the admittance of a length of the line which is short compared with a quarter wavelength, and which is open-circuited at the receiving end. The admittance may be determined by any convenient method such as a bridge, Q meter, substitution in a resonant circuit, etc. The measurement can be made at an audio frequency such as 1000 cycles, or alternatively it is possible to employ a radio frequency, as for example 1 Mc. The only limitation on frequency is that it must be low enough so that the test sample employed will have a length short compared with a quarter wavelength along the line. If the observed admittance of the line under test is $Y = G_t + j\omega C_t$, then the capacitance per unit length is the total capacitance C_t divided by the actual length of the line. Similarly, the conductance of the line per unit length at the frequency used in making the test, will be the total observed conductance G_t divided by the actual line length. The observed conductance will ordinarily depend upon the frequency, particularly in the case of cables with solid dielectric; on the other hand the line capacitance per unit length can be expected to be independent of frequency.

The inductance per unit length of a transmission line can be directly measured by determining the input impedance of a length of line that is short compared with a quarter wavelength along the line, when the receiving end of the test length is short-circuited. As in the case of the capacitance measurement, any convenient measuring method may be employed, and the measurement may be carried out either at audio or at radio frequencies; it is merely necessary that the frequency be such in relationship to the length of the test specimen as to make the length of the specimen short compared with a quarter wavelength. From the observed impedance $Z = R_t + j\omega L_t$, the inductance per unit length is obtained by dividing the total inductance L_t by the physical length. Similarly, the resistance per unit length is obtained by dividing the total observed resistance R_t by the physical length. The inductance measured in this way will be independent of frequency; however, the resistance will depend upon frequency, increasing because of skin effect as the frequency becomes higher.

Measurement of Characteristic Impedance.   The characteristic impedance of a cable can be calculated from the measured values of inductance and capacitance per unit length, using Eq. (4-4).   Alternatively, the characteristic impedance can be obtained from observed values of the capacitance C per unit length and the phase velocity v_p, using the relation[1]

$$\text{Characteristic impedance} = \frac{1}{v_p C} \tag{4-33}$$

This relation is obtained from Eqs. (4-4) and (4-8b).   The phase velocity v_p can be obtained from the length of line required to give half-wave or quarter-wave resonance, and then employing Eq. (4-7).

Again, the characteristic impedance of a line can be obtained by terminating it with a calibrated adjustable resistance and measuring the input impedance of the line as this load resistance is varied.   One value of load resistance will be found that makes the input impedance of the line equal to a resistance that is the same as the load resistance; this particular value of resistance is then the characteristic impedance.

4-5. Measurement of Standing-wave Ratio by the Use of a Slotted-line Standing-wave Detector.[2]   The value of standing-wave ratio that exists on a line is ordinarily determined by a standing-wave detector, such as shown in Fig. 4-4b and c for a coaxial line.   This consists of a length of line with an axial slot, along which moves a traveling carriage carrying a probe that projects through the slot.   To this probe is connected a voltage- (or power-) measuring device, which in the simplest case could be a crystal detector and microammeter.   An oscillator is connected to one end of the standing-wave detector, and to the other end is connected the unknown impedance, as in Fig. 4-4a.   The standing-wave pattern is obtained by moving the probe along the carriage, and observing the resulting variation in the crystal-detector output.

Not shown in Fig. 4-4 are some of the mechanical arrangements

---

[1] A modification of this procedure is sometimes useful in the case of twisted-pair and similar lines, involving a mixture of air and solid dielectric.   This consists in observing the ratio k of the wavelength of the actual line, as compared with the wavelength in free space, and calculating from Eqs. (4-5) the characteristic impedance Z_{00} that would be obtained if all of the solid dielectrics were replaced by air.   Then

$$\text{Actual characteristic impedance} = kZ_{00} \tag{4-34}$$

This method is due to Andrew Alford, Measuring the Impedance of Twisted Pairs, *Electronics*, vol. 13, p. 48, August, 1940.

[2] For further details, see "Technique of Microwave Measurements," *op. cit.*, Chap. 8, pp. 473–514.

required for the standing-wave detector.   The mechanical supports for
the traveling carriage must be accurately constructed so that the probe
projects into the line to a constant depth as the carriage moves along the
line.   A scale must be provided so that the position of the probe can be
accurately defined with respect to the end of the line where the unknown
impedance is to be connected.   In order to minimize electrical losses in

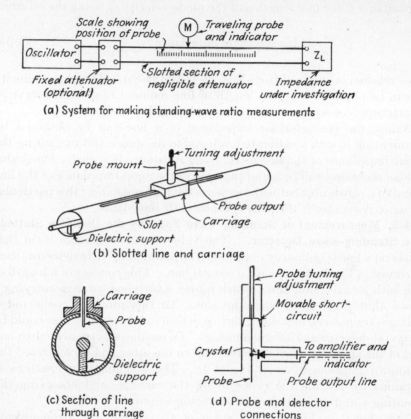

(a) System for making standing-wave ratio measurements

(b) Slotted line and carriage

(c) Section of line
through carriage

(d) Probe and detector
connections

FIG. 4-4. Details of slotted line for making standing-wave-ratio measurements on a
coaxial system.

the standing-wave detector, a minimum of dielectric is used, the amount
being just sufficient to provide the necessary mechanical support.   One
possible arrangement is shown in Fig. 4-4b, in which the line is continuously supported from the bottom; this arrangement is particularly well
suited for very long standing-wave detectors in which the center conductor would sag excessively if supported only from the ends.   Further
design details will be discussed in Sec. 4-6.

The Probe, and Its Detector and Amplifier.[1] The objective of the standing-wave detector is to sample the voltage along the transmission line.   The probe that projects through the slot into the line provides this sampling, since some of the electric-field lines will then terminate upon the probe, and thus cause a voltage to appear between the probe and the outer conductor of the line leading from the probe.   As shown in Fig. 4-4*d*, a crystal detector can be used to rectify this radio-frequency voltage; the rectified voltage is then amplified and indicated upon a meter.   A stub line is usually included as a part of the probe, and is provided with a movable short circuit in order to tune the system to give maximum rectified voltage.   This adjustment also ensures that the probe circuit, as seen from the main transmission line, presents a very high impedance; in this way the probe causes a minimum of disturbance to the fields within the coaxial line.   As a further means of minimizing the effect of the probe, it is extended into the line the shortest distance that will give a satisfactory indication.   The slot for the probe is made sufficiently narrow, and the slot walls sufficiently thick, so that the power radiated from the slot is negligibly small.

It is possible, at least theoretically, to sample the current along the standing-wave detector instead of the voltage.   In this case, the probe would consist of a small loop projecting through the slot, one end of the loop being the extension of the inner conductor of the probe line, and the other end of the loop being grounded to the carriage.   The difficulty is that such a loop tends to give an indication that depends on the line voltage as well as the line current.   This is because in addition to the voltage induced in the loop by the magnetic field, which is proportional to the current in the line, there is also an induced voltage resulting from the electric field that terminates on the loop.   The voltage probe in Fig. 4-4, on the other hand, is relatively free from the influence of the magnetic field, and hence gives an output voltage determined by the voltage on the main line.

It is possible to use a bolometer instead of the crystal, and for precise work this may be highly desirable.   The bolometer is accurately a square-law device; *i.e.*, the rectified voltage is proportional to the square of the radio-frequency voltage applied to it.

The crystal, on the other hand, approximates a square-law device only below a limited and uncertain value of amplitude.   For accurate measurements with a crystal it is therefore often necessary to make a calibration that gives the experimentally observed relation between relative line voltage and relative crystal response.   Moreover, if accuracy is impor-

[1] See *ibid.*, pp. 483–488, 496–503.

tant, the calibration must be checked frequently, as the characteristics of crystals often change appreciably with use.[1,2] The simplest way of checking the crystal calibration is to short-circuit the receiving end of the slotted line. The resulting voltage distribution between adjacent minima is then a half sine wave, thus giving a *relative* voltage that is a known function of probe position.[3]

The sensitivity of the probe system can be greatly increased by amplifying the output of the crystal or bolometer. If a continuous-wave oscillator or signal generator is used to provide radio-frequency power for the system, a d-c amplifier is called for. It is preferable, however, to modulate the oscillator. In this case the output from the crystal contains the modulation frequency, and an audio amplifier may then be used. If, further, a narrow-band tuned audio-frequency amplifier is employed, a very high signal-to-noise ratio is obtained. It is then possible to employ more amplification than would be useful with an untuned audio amplifier, thereby further reducing the energy the probe must pick up to give a satisfactory indication.

Oscillator Considerations. It is essential that the oscillator which serves as the energy source for the measurement produce an output wave that is free of harmonic frequencies. The presence of harmonics distorts the standing-wave pattern, because each harmonic tends to go through maxima and minima at different locations from the fundamental. When trouble of this sort is encountered, the customary expedient for eliminating harmonics is the insertion of a low-pass filter, or a resonant circuit, between the oscillator and the standing-wave detector.

It is also necessary that the oscillator frequency maintain a constant value. If the probe introduces a slight reflection, there may be slight variations in the loading on the oscillator as the probe position is varied; these can affect the frequency of the oscillator. The customary safeguard against this difficulty is the insertion of an attenuation pad of perhaps 10 db between the oscillator and the standing-wave detector.

[1] The necessity of knowing the crystal characteristic can be avoided by inserting a variable and accurate radio-frequency attenuator between the probe and the crystal, or between the oscillator and the slotted line. In this way, a wide range of input voltages can be measured by always adjusting the attenuator to give the same rectified output from the crystal. The law of the crystal detector is then not important, and the accuracy of the measurement depends only upon the accuracy of the adjustable attenuator.

[2] Another, and somewhat more elaborate, technique for avoiding errors resulting from the fact that a crystal can be depended upon to have a square-law characteristic only when the amplitudes are small is described by A. M. Winzemer, Methods for Obtaining the Voltage Standing-wave Ratio on Transmission Lines Independently of the Detector Characteristics, *Proc. IRE*, vol. 38, p. 275, March, 1950.

[3] See "Microwave Antenna Theory and Design" (Vol. 12, Radiation Laboratory Series), pp. 552–556, McGraw-Hill Book Company, Inc., New York, 1949.

In the usual case where the oscillator is amplitude-modulated, it is necessary that there be no incidental frequency modulation; otherwise the location of the minima will vary during the modulation cycle.   In the case of reflex klystron and magnetron oscillators, this difficulty can be avoided by the use of square-wave or pulse modulation of the "on-off" type (see Secs. 12-11 and 12-12).   In other cases, particularly at ultra-high and very high frequencies, modulated amplifier arrangements may be used, thereby isolating the oscillator from the modulating system.   In this case sine-wave modulation can be employed if desired.

Special Considerations Relating to Very Low and Very High Standing-wave Ratios.   Special problems are encountered when measuring a standing-wave ratio that is either very low or very high.   When the standing-wave ratio is very low, *i.e.*, when it approaches unity, the accuracy of the measurement is limited by residual errors in the standing-wave detector. These errors are of two types, (1) small reflections due to discontinuities at or near the junction where the slotted line is connected to the load, and (2) imperfections in the mechanical design of the standing-wave detector that result in irregular variations in probe voltage as the carriage is moved along the line, even when the line is perfectly terminated.   Small reflections can be detected and allowed for by means of the node-shift technique discussed on page 150, while mechanical imperfections are considered further in Sec. 4-6.

When the standing-wave ratio is very high, errors may result from several sources.   In the first place, energy abstracted from the system by the probe circuit is more of a disturbing factor in the measurement when the standing-wave ratio is high.   The principal effect is to reduce the apparent height of the voltage maxima as a result of loading.   Viewed from the probe circuit, the standing-wave detector is then a source of voltage that has an internal impedance that is very high when the standing ratio is very high.   Since the detector element, either crystal or bolometer, is nonlinear, and draws proportionately more current at larger amplitudes of applied voltage, the extra loading which occurs at the voltage maxima may cause the observed pattern to be seriously distorted when the standing-wave ratio is large.   The effect is accentuated by the fact that with large standing-wave ratios, the voltage minima will be of very small relative amplitude.   Thus, in order to obtain readings at the voltage minima, it becomes necessary for the probe to project quite far into the coaxial line in order to pick up enough voltage for the detector. This in turn further increases the change in amplitude produced at the voltage maxima.   An additional complicating factor occurs when a crystal is used for the detector.   The crystal can be considered a square-law device with fair accuracy only when the applied voltage is small; when the voltage becomes large, a decided departure from square-law behavior can easily occur.

A convenient technique for measuring large standing-wave ratios, say greater than 10, is the "double-minimum" method.[1]   In this method, the distance Δ between the two points designated as A and B in Fig. 4-5 is determined, where the voltage response at A and B is $\sqrt{2}E_{\min}$ (corresponding to a power response double the power response for $E_{\min}$).   The standing-wave ratio is then computed from the following simple relationship,

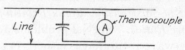

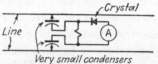

(a) Current in single line (ground return)

$$S = \frac{\lambda_l}{\pi\Delta} \qquad (4\text{-}35)$$

where λ_l is the distance along the line corresponding to one wavelength.

(b) Current in parallel lines

Large standing-wave ratios are perhaps best measured by the use of an attenuator in conjunction with a crystal.   The attenuator is inserted between the probe and the crystal.   For measurement of a voltage minimum, the attenuator is set at zero, thus giving the greatest sensitivity

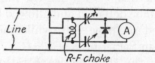

(c) Voltage across parallel lines

(d) Resonant probe for voltage measurement

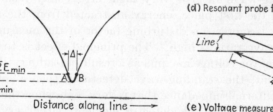

FIG. 4-5. Diagram illustrating notation used in determining standing-wave ratio by the "double-minimum" method.

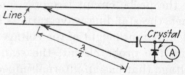

(e) Voltage measured with resonant line section

FIG. 4-6. Various means for observing standing-wave patterns on open-wire transmission lines.

possible, and the probe is inserted only far enough to give an accurate reading.   To measure a voltage maximum, the attenuation is increased until the crystal output produced by the voltage maximum is the same as was obtained from the voltage minimum.   The standing-wave ratio is then the ratio of the two attenuator settings.

Standing-wave Detectors for Two-wire Lines.   Emphasis has been placed on coaxial lines in the above discussion, even though the principles apply equally well to open-wire lines.   Standing waves on two-wire lines can

[1] See "Technique of Microwave Measurements," *op. cit.*, p. 505.

be investigated by the use of indicators such as shown in Fig. 4-6.[1] As the indicating device is moved along the line, the response will vary with either the voltage or the current of the standing-wave pattern, according to the type of coupling between the indicator and the line.

4-6. Miscellaneous Design Features of Coaxial Standing-wave Detectors.[2] Until recent years, it has been necessary for a laboratory to construct its own standing-wave detector. However, there are at present commercial units available, and it is expected that more of these will be on sale in the future. It may still be desirable or necessary in some situations to build rather than to buy a standing-wave detector. A decision to do so when based on economy as the objective is usually disappointing, unless only crude accuracy is required. The high price of commercial units is in general a reflection of the extreme care in design and mechanical precision of fabrication required. While it is beyond the scope of this work to set forth here complete details on the design and construction of a standing-wave detector, certain aspects of the design are so important that they deserve consideration. In addition there are certain tests which can be used to evaluate the effectiveness of design features, whether they be in an instrument that has been built or purchased.

The problem of accuracy in a standing-wave detector has three major elements.[3] The first of these is the line itself; the others concern the traveling probe and the transition or junction to the impedances to be measured. The line must be essentially lossless, and it should have air dielectric. The center conductor can be supported as shown in Fig. 4-4, or in short lines it can be supported by dielectric beads at each end. The center conductor should be very straight, and must be coaxial with the outer conductor. The outer conductor must be accurately round in cross section, a requirement that calls for some care in the machining process inasmuch as ordinary tubing tends to spring outward when a slot is cut as needed in the standing-wave detector. It is helpful if the line can be made as large in diameter as is possible since the use of a large-diameter line increases the tolerances in the motion of the traveling probe.

---

[1] The constructional details of such devices are fairly obvious, and much improvising can be done. Literature references are too numerous to list, although two recent papers may be of interest: W. N. Baker, Standing-wave Indicator for 3-22 Mc/s, *J. IEE* (*Radiocomm. Conv.*) vol. 94, pt. III*A*, p. 328, March–April, 1947; R. J. Lees, C. H. Westcott, and F. Kay, Transmission-line Impedance Measurement, *Wireless Eng.*, vol. 26, p. 78, March, 1949.

[2] For further details see "Technique of Microwave Measurements," *op. cit.*, pp. 480–483, 488–496; R. A. Soderman and W. M. Hague, U-H-F Measurements with the Type 874-LB Slotted Line, *Gen. Rad. Expt.*, vol. 25, p. 1, November, 1950.

[3] Additional discussion of errors in standing-wave detectors is given by H. E. Sorrows, W. E. Ryan, and R. C. Ellenwood, Evaluation of Coaxial Slotted-line Impedance Measurements, *Proc. IRE*, vol. 39, p. 162, February, 1951.

However, the maximum diameter permissible is limited by the fact that higher-order modes can be present in the line if the diameter is too large.

The width of the slot is a compromise between two factors. First, if the slot is too large, there are excessive losses due to radiation. The line will then have appreciable attenuation, and the standing-wave ratio measured near the load will be different from that measured near the generator for a given impedance. On the other hand, if the slot is very narrow, there is a large shunting capacitance between the probe and the outer conductor of the line. This capacitance affects the probe sensitivity, and is moreover subject to large variations if the travel of the probe is the least bit irregular. This latter difficulty can be circumvented to some extent by the use of a shielded probe, as illustrated in Fig. 4-7. Here, the sheath of the probe extends down through the slot at least as far as the inside of the outer conductor of the standing-wave detector. Then if the probe carriage should move sidewise relative to the slot, the capacitance change from inner conductor of the probe to the outer conductor of the line is negligibly small.

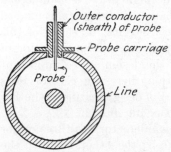

Fig. 4-7. Shielded-probe arrangement.

If the probe moves radially slightly in or out of the slotted line as the probe carriage travels along the line, the relative coupling to the fields in the slotted line varies. As an example, if the probe projects about one-third of the distance to the center conductor in a half-inch coaxial 50-ohm line, a radial movement of 0.001 in. causes a 1 per cent change in the probe voltage.[1]

The effect of relative motion of the probe can be tested by applying an audio-frequency voltage to the slotted line and measuring the probe voltage with a vacuum-tube voltmeter.[2] A constant reading should, of course, be obtained for all positions of the probe. If the reading varies, it is possible to prepare a table or graph of correction factors which can then be applied to radio-frequency observations.[3]

The Parallel Plate or Slab Line. There is an alternative configuration for the standing-wave detector which greatly aids in reducing the prob-

[1] W. R. Thurston, Coaxial Elements and Connectors, *Proc. Natl. Elec. Conf.*, vol. 3, p. 97, 1947.

[2] Soderman and Hague, *op. cit.*

[3] A more complicated procedure capable of obtaining a more precise curve of correction factors is described by R. G. Medhurst and S. D. Pool, Correction Factors for Slotted Measuring Lines at Very High Frequencies, *Proc. IEE*, vol. 97, pt. III, p. 223, July, 1950.

lems of motion of the probe, as well as radiation from the slot.[1] This is illustrated in Fig. 4-8. If the two parallel planes extended ideally in both directions to infinity, and if the center conductor were elliptical instead of round, the geometry would be exactly equivalent to the coaxial line, transition from one to the other being accomplished with mathematical rigor by a conformal transformation. In a typical practical case, the parallel planes are only 6 in. in height compared with a spacing of 0.75 in., and the cross section of the inner conductor is round instead of elliptical.

The effectiveness of this arrangement results from the fact that the field intensity in the region of the slot where the probe is located is changing much more slowly with respect to distance to the center con-

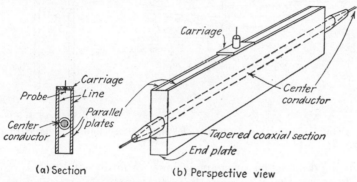

(a) Section   (b) Perspective view

FIG. 4-8. Parallel-plate type of standing-wave detector.

ductor than in the coaxial counterpart. Thus small radial movements of the probe result in much smaller changes in the resulting probe voltage. Moreover, in spite of the fact that the slot in the parallel-plane case appears to be very large, the transformed coaxial equivalent slot is exceedingly small indeed. For instance, for the dimensions quoted above, the equivalent size of the slot is 0.002 radian which in a 1-in. coaxial line would correspond to a slot width of 0.001 in.

Junction and Probe Errors. The output terminals of the standing-wave detector are generally in the form of a coaxial connector of some standard type. The transition between such terminals and the slotted section commonly requires a change in diameter of both the inner and outer conductors, and in some cases also involves a change in the characteristic impedance, *i.e.*, a change in the ratio of the diameters. In the case of the parallel-plate line of Fig. 4-8, there is also a change in the line configuration.

As this latter example deals with the junction problem in a general

[1] W. B. Wholey and W. N. Eldred, A New Type of Slotted Line Section, *Proc. IRE*, vol. 38, p. 244, March, 1950; W. B. Wholey, Greater Reliability in UHF Impedance Measurements, *Hewlett-Packard J.*, vol. 1, p. 1, January, 1950.

way, the manner in which it is handled is worth consideration. A cross section of a junction that has satisfactory characteristics is shown in Fig. 4-9. Looking from left to right, there is seen first the parallel-plate line, then a large-diameter coaxial section (with the outer diameter 0.75 in., which is the same as the plate spacing), followed by a tapered section which gradually reduces the diameter to the desired output size. A

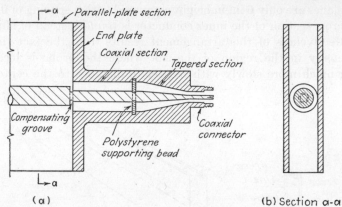

(a)   (b) Section a-a

FIG. 4-9. Details of transition from parallel-plate slotted line to a standard coaxial connector.

change in the dimensions or shape of inner or outer conductors (or both) introduces a discontinuity capacitance even though the characteristic impedance may be the same on both sides of the discontinuity. To compensate for this, a notch (a circular groove around the periphery of the inner conductor) is cut at the point where the parallel-plate line joins the coaxial structure. The equivalent circuit of this notched junction

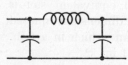

FIG. 4-10. Equivalent circuit of a notched section.

is shown in Fig. 4-10; it is a low-pass structure and is generally of noncritical design except that its high-frequency cutoff must be well above the intended range of operating frequencies. In the case of the parallel-plate line, one dielectric bead at each end of the line is sufficient to support the center conductor.[1] The tapered section provides a smooth, gradual transition at constant Z_0 from the large-diameter coaxial region down to the smaller diameter. When a transition section such as shown in Fig. 4-9 is used, the residual standing-wave ratio can be held to 1.025 or less over a range of 500 to 4000 Mc. This residual standing-wave ratio can be measured by the node-shift method described in Sec. 4-8.

[1] The notch at the bead location is designed to compensate for the dielectric constant of the bead, and also for the resulting discontinuity. The equivalent circuit of this notch and its associated bead is also given by Fig. 4-10.

There is one sort of error in a standing-wave measurement that can occur even when the mechanical design of the standing-wave detector is essentially perfect.   This error results from the fact that the probe projecting into the coaxial line is in itself a discontinuity and will cause reflection.   The effect of these reflections can be computed and a correction applied;[1] however, the corrections are not easy to calculate, and it is much better if they can be made negligible by keeping the probe depth to an absolute minimum.   The presence of such a probe error can be checked by first making a standing-wave measurement with the minimum depth feasible, and then repeating the measurement with a slightly greater depth.   If the results are essentially the same in the two cases, it can be assumed that the probe-reflection error is inconsequential.

Probe reflections cause the observed standing-wave ratio to be less than the correct value.   If the probe is tuned to resonance, its reflections do not change the locations of the maxima and minima of the standing-wave pattern.   However, if the probe is untuned, then the observed location of a maximum will not be midway between the adjacent minima.[2]

4-7. Measurement of Impedance by Use of the Standing-wave Detector.   The standing waves that exist on a transmission line of negligible attenuation when the load or terminating impedance is different from the characteristic impedance of the line, can be used as the basis for measuring this load impedance.   Such a technique is especially valuable at the higher frequencies where bridge measurements of impedance are not feasible.

The arrangement of apparatus used in determining impedance in this way is illustrated in Fig. 4-4a; further details, with particular reference to nomenclature, are to be found in Fig. 4-11.   The unknown impedance is shown directly connected to the receiving end of a slotted section; if a connector is used, it must not introduce a reflection.   Under these conditions, the unknown impedance Z_L in Fig. 4-11a can be determined by observing the magnitude S of the voltage standing-wave ratio, and the distance along the line from Z_L to any convenient voltage minimum or maximum (see d_1 and d_2, respectively, in Fig. 4-11b).[3]   The normalized

---

[1] W. Altar, P. B. Marshall, and L. P. Hunter, Probe Errors in Standing-wave Detectors, *Proc. IRE*, vol. 34, p. 33, January, 1946.   See also K. Tomiyasu, Loading and Coupling Effects of Standing-wave Detectors, *Proc. IRE*, vol. 37, p. 1405, December, 1949.

[2] See "Microwave Antenna Theory and Design," *op. cit.*, p. 556.

[3] It makes no difference which particular minimum is used in determining d_1 (or which maximum is used in obtaining d_2) in Fig. 4-11.   This is because the difference in distances for different minima or different maxima is always an exact multiple of a half wavelength, and because values of d_1 or d_2 differing by multiples of a half wavelength give the same values of Z_L/Z_0 in Eqs. (4-36).

impedance[1] (Z_L/Z_0) is then

$$\frac{Z_L}{Z_0} = \frac{1 - jS \tan (2\pi d_1/\lambda_l)}{S - j \tan (2\pi d_1/\lambda_l)} \tag{4-36a}$$

or

$$\frac{Z_L}{Z_0} = \frac{S - j \tan (2\pi d_2/\lambda_l)}{1 - jS \tan (2\pi d_2/\lambda_l)} \tag{4-36b}$$

Here λ_l is the distance along the slotted line corresponding to one wave-

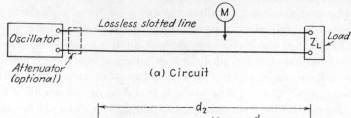

(a) Circuit

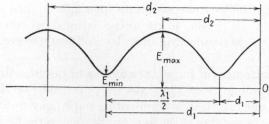

(b) Standing-wave pattern for Z_L moderately different from Z_0

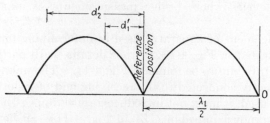

(c) Standing-wave pattern for short circuit ($Z_L=0$)

Fig. 4-11. Circuit arrangement and notation involved in the determination of impedance with the aid of a lossless slotted-line standing-wave detector.

length; the value of λ_l can be determined experimentally from the fact that the distance between adjacent voltage minima (or adjacent maxima) is exactly $\lambda_l/2$ as shown in Fig. 4-11.

[1] The concept of *normalized impedance* is one of great value. Dividing any impedance associated with the line, whether it be the load impedance, the sending-end impedance, etc., by the characteristic impedance Z_0, puts emphasis upon the fact that all reflection phenomena in lines and waveguides depend not upon actual values of impedance, but upon relative values, referred to Z_0. By making use of the concept of normalized impedance, the material in this section will be directly applicable to waveguides as covered in Secs. 4-12 and 4-13.

In measuring distances in connection with a standing-wave pattern it is common practice to use the minima, rather than the maxima. This is because with high or moderately high standing-wave ratios the minima are much more sharply defined than the maxima.

Sometimes it is not convenient to measure the distance from the unknown impedance Z_L to the voltage minimum. In such a case one can establish a reference point by first short-circuiting the line at the point where the load Z_L is to be attached. When the load end of the line is thus short-circuited, there is obviously a voltage minimum at the load, and minima will also exist at intervals of one-half wavelength along the line toward the generator. One of these voltage minima is then used as a reference point, instead of using the load position itself. The next step

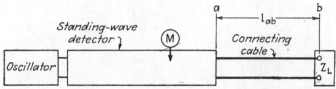

FIG. 4-12. Slotted-line standing-wave detector connected to a load impedance through a connecting cable.

in the procedure is to remove the short circuit and connect the unknown load impedance. Voltage minima will then be present on either side of this reference point at distances of less than one-half wavelength. The distance d_1' from the reference point to the nearest voltage minimum toward the generator (see Fig. 4-11c) can then be used in Eq. (4-36a) in place of d_1. Alternatively, the distance d_1'' from the reference point to the nearest minimum in the direction of the load can be used. In this case one substitutes $-d_1''$ for d_1 in Eq. (4-36a); the negative sign arises from the fact that distance toward the load can be regarded as *negative* distance toward the generator.

Equations (4-36) can be utilized to give the impedance of Z_L with great accuracy. However, for most practical work, where the limitations of the equipment do not justify extreme precision of computation, it is customary to compute the unknown load impedance with the aid of a transmission-line chart. This will be discussed in Sec. 4-9.

Use of Connecting Cable between Load and Standing-wave Detector. In some circumstances it may be convenient or necessary to measure the impedance of a load, such as an antenna, located at some distance from the standing-wave detector. A cable is then used to connect the load to the standing-wave detector as illustrated in Fig. 4-12. When the connecting cable has negligible loss, this introduces no difficulty provided the junction between cable and standing-wave detector introduces no reflection.[1] It is not necessary to know either the exact length of cable, or the length of cable corresponding to one wavelength, as a reference minimum can be established on the slotted section by replacing the load impedance Z_L by a short circuit, as in Fig. 4-11.

When the attenuation of the connecting cable cannot be neglected, as is normally the case if flexible solid-dielectric cable is used, the standing-

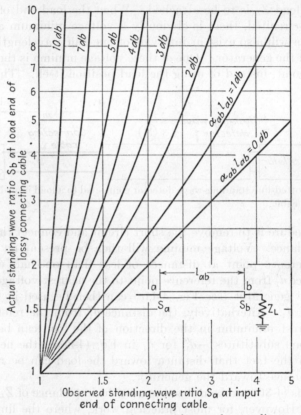

FIG. 4-13. Curves giving effect of attenuation on the standing-wave ratio.

wave ratio observed on the slotted section is less than if there were no attenuation, and so must be corrected before the load impedance is computed by means of Eqs. (4-36).   Assuming that the length l_{ab} of the connecting cable and its attenuation α_{ab} per unit length are known, then

$$S_b = \frac{1}{\tanh\left[\tanh^{-1}\left(1/S_a\right) - \alpha_{ab}l_{ab}\right]} \tag{4-37}$$

[1] The extent to which this condition is realized can be evaluated by the "node-shift" method described below.

where S_b = voltage standing-wave ratio at load end b of cable, *i.e.*, the "true" value of standing-wave ratio which is to be used in calculating the unknown impedance

S_a = voltage standing-wave ratio observed at input end a of the cable by means of the standing-wave detector.

The results of Eq. (4-37) can be presented in convenient graphical form,[1] as in Fig. 4-13.

An alternative method of correcting for the attenuation $\alpha_{ab}l_{ab}$ of the connecting cable ab is as follows: The standing-wave ratios S_a and S_b at the two ends of the cable correspond to reflection coefficients of magnitude $|\rho_a|$ and $|\rho_b|$, respectively, in accordance with Eq. (4-16). These reflection coefficients in turn are related to each other by the equation

$$\frac{|\rho_b|}{|\rho_a|} = \epsilon^{2\alpha_{ab}l_{ab}} \qquad (4\text{-}38)$$

Thus starting with an observed standing-wave ratio S_a, one can calculate $|\rho_a|$ from Eq. (4-16), and then determine $|\rho_b|$ from Eq. (4-38) for a known value of attenuation $\alpha_{ab}l_{ab}$. The standing-wave ratio calculated by Eq. (4-17) for this value of $|\rho_b|$ is then the value S_b of standing-wave ratio that exists at point b in Fig. 4-12, and which would be observed on the slotted line if the attenuation of cable ab were zero. This is also the same value of S_b that would be obtained from Eq. (4-37) or Fig. 4-13.

4-8. Measurement of Reflection Coefficient by Use of the Standing-wave Detector.[2] The reflection coefficient can be readily determined directly from standing-wave data with the aid of the following relations:[3]

---

[1] See E. N. Phillips, W. G. Sterns, and N. J. Gramara, "High Frequency Measuring Techniques Using Transmission Lines," p. 22, J. F. Rider Publ. Co., Inc., New York, 1947.

[2] Several alternative methods for measuring the reflection coefficient find occasional use. Thus a pair of directional couplers can be used to determine directly the relative amplitudes of incident and reflected waves. Another procedure consists in applying a very short pulse to the system under test, and observing the relative magnitude of this pulse, and of any returned echoes; a test set of this type is described by F. F. Roberts, A Pulse Test Set for the Measurement of Small Impedance Irregularities in High-frequency Cables, *Proc. IEE*, vol. 96, pt. III, p. 17, January, 1949. Finally, the reflection coefficient of a load at the end of a long cable can be determined by a frequency-modulated altimeter technique, with visual presentation over a range of frequencies, as described by L. L. Libby, Frequency Scanning VHF Impedance Meter, *Electronics*, vol. 21, p. 94, June, 1948.

[3] These relations are derived as follows: The magnitude of the reflection coefficient is given by Eq. (4-16). The phase angle θ of ρ is then obtained from the fact that at a voltage minimum, the distance d_1 in Fig. 4-11 must be such that the incident and reflected waves are in phase opposition, *i.e.*, differ in phase by $n\pi$ radians, where n is odd. Now the incident wave at the load lags $2\pi d_1/\lambda_l$ radians behind its phase at the minimum. The reflected wave at the load is θ radians advanced in phase compared with the incident wave at the load, but loses $2\pi d_1/\lambda_l$ radians in traveling from the load to the minimum. Hence at the minimum the reflected wave lags the incident

$$\rho = \frac{S-1}{S+1} \left/ \, 4\pi \frac{d_1}{\lambda_l} - n\pi \right. \qquad n \text{ odd} \qquad (4\text{-}39a)$$

$$\rho = \frac{S-1}{S+1} \left/ \, 4\pi \frac{d_2}{\lambda_l} - n\pi \right. \qquad n \text{ even} \qquad (4\text{-}39b)$$

Here d_1 and d_2 are distances in the standing-wave pattern as indicated in Fig. 4-11, S is the voltage standing-wave ratio, n is an integer, and λ_l is the length along the slotted line that represents one wavelength, i.e., twice the distance between adjacent minima. Where only the magnitude of ρ is required, this can be obtained simply by determining S without bothering to determine the location of the minima, and then using Eq. (4-16), which is repeated below

$$|\rho| = \frac{S-1}{S+1} \qquad (4\text{-}39c)$$

Node-shift Method of Evaluating Small Irregularities.[1] Small reflections are difficult to determine by the usual standing-wave type of measurement. Thus when a standing-wave detector constructed from a length of large-diameter rigid coaxial line, is to be used in measurements on small-diameter flexible coaxial cable (see Fig. 4-14), the junction between these two types of line should be as reflectionless as possible. However, the discontinuity capacitance will cause some reflection at the junction even when the two lines have the same characteristic impedance. This reflection could be evaluated by the ordinary standing-wave technique, by terminating line 2 in its characteristic impedance so that there are no reflections in this line, and then measuring the standing-wave ratio present on line 1. However, if the junction is well designed, the standing-wave ratio will be very close to unity, and its exact value will be hard to determine. That is, mechanical irregularities in the traveling probe

---

wave by an amount

$$\left.\begin{array}{l}\text{Phase lag of}\\ \text{reflected wave}\\ \text{at a minimum}\end{array}\right\} = 2\pi \frac{d_1}{\lambda_l} - \theta + 2\pi \frac{d_1}{\lambda_l}$$

$$= 4\pi \frac{d_1}{\lambda_l} - \theta$$

Since the phase lag at a minimum must be $n\pi$, Eq. (4-39a) follows at once. Proof of Eq. (4-39b) can be derived by following an analogous line of reasoning, but noting that to obtain a maximum the incident and reflected waves must be in phase; i.e., n must be even.

[1] E. Feenberg, The Relations between Nodal Positions and Standing-wave Ratio in a Composite Transmission System, *J. Applied Phys.*, vol. 17, p. 530, June, 1946. For alternative methods of measuring small reflections, see M. H. Oliver, Discontinuities in Concentric-line Impedance-measuring Apparatus, *J. IEE*, vol. 97, pt. III, p. 25, January, 1950, discussion p. 242, July, 1950; Roberts, *op. cit.*

may introduce variations in the voltage readings that will be as great as those due to the maxima and minima of the standing-wave pattern.

The node-shift technique is able to overcome these difficulties, by making use of the fact that even though mechanical irregularities may cause fluctuations of the *magnitude* of the probe voltage, they do not in

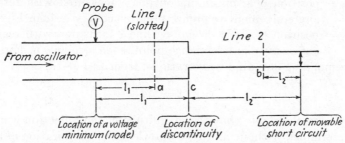

FIG. 4-14. Diagram illustrating notation used in node-shift method of determining small reflection coefficients.

any way influence the *position* of the probe where a voltage node or minimum actually occurs; in contrast, the presence of a small super-imposed reflection does alter the actual observed location of the minimum when a large reflected wave is also present.

To apply the node-shift technique, one first short-circuits line 2 in Fig. 4-14 (an open circuit could equally well be used, the only requirement being complete reflection). The position of the short circuit is then varied, and the change in the position of a voltage node in line 1 is observed.[1] If no reflection is produced at the junction, the position of the node in line 1 would move a distance exactly equal to the movement of the position of the short circuit in line 2. However, if there is a small superimposed reflection, the position of

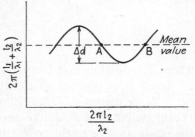

FIG. 4-15. Node-shift behavior when a small reflection is present in a system.

the node in line 1 will vary sinusoidally as shown in Fig. 4-15. On the basis of experimental data obtained and plotted as in Fig. 4-15, the *magnitude* of the reflection coefficient at the junction can be determined from the following equation,

$$|\rho| = \sin \frac{\Delta d}{2} \approx \frac{\Delta d}{2} \tag{4-40}$$

[1] In determining the position of the voltage node in line 1, the proper technique is to move the probe to the left and to the right of the minimum until a small but appreciable voltage reading is obtained of equal amount on either side. An average of these two positions is the correct location of the node.

where Δd = total variation in the quantity $2\pi \left(\dfrac{l_1}{\lambda_1} + \dfrac{l_2}{\lambda_2} \right)$; for small reflection, for $\Delta d \ll 1$

λ_1 = line wavelength for line 1

λ_2 = line wavelength for line 2

l_1 = position of a minimum on line 1 measured with respect to any convenient reference point, such as a or c in Fig. 4-14

l_2 = position of short circuit on line 2 measured with respect to any convenient reference point, such as b or c in Fig. 4-14

The corresponding standing-wave ratio is, from Eq. (4-17)

$$S \approx 1 + \Delta d \qquad (4\text{-}41)$$

It is of interest to note that the magnitude of the reflection coefficient can be determined without an exact knowledge of the location of the discontinuity, since Δd can be determined when l_1 and l_2 are measured from arbitrary fixed reference positions, as for example a and b, respectively, in Fig. 4-14. Thus the presence and magnitude of a discontinuity of unknown origin can be detected and evaluated without a precise knowledge of its location.

The phase angle of the reflection coefficient at the junction can be determined with the aid of data corresponding to the points A and B indicated in Fig. 4-15. The following relationship governs the situation,

$$\phi = \frac{2\pi}{\lambda_1} l_{1_A} = \frac{2\pi}{\lambda_1} l_{1_B} - \frac{\pi}{2} \qquad (4\text{-}42)$$

where l_{1_A} = distance l_1 from junction c to node in line 1 corresponding to point A (Fig. 4-15)

l_{1_B} = distance l_1 from junction c corresponding to point B

It will be noted that unlike the magnitude of the reflection coefficient, the phase angle ϕ of the reflection can be determined only if the location c in Fig. 4-14 of the irregularity producing the reflection is known.

When the reflection coefficient is known both in magnitude and phase, it is possible to derive an equivalent circuit representing the discontinuity. This may be useful in computing the characteristics of the discontinuity over a range of frequencies.

Although the above discussion of the node-shift method has been in terms of coaxial transmission lines, the method is completely general, and can be applied to two-wire transmission lines and to waveguides.

4-9. Transmission-line Charts. There are charts available which greatly expedite the solution of problems involving transmission lines (or waveguides) and their terminating impedances. All of these charts consist of a system of impedance coordinates, superimposed upon which is another system of lines representing loci of constant standing-wave ratio, and constant distance along the line.

The Smith Chart.[1] Of all the various transmission-line charts that have been evolved, the one in most common use is the Smith chart.

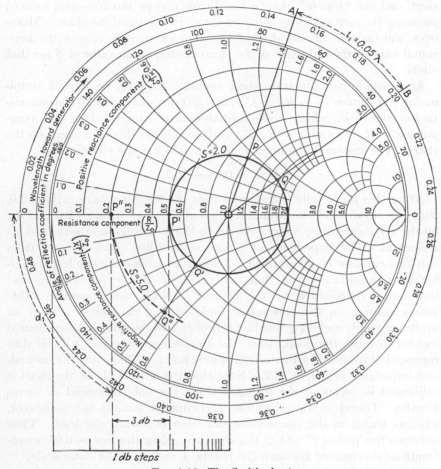

FIG. 4-16. The Smith chart.

This is illustrated in Fig. 4-16, and is derived by a conformal transformation of Eq. (4-14), such that in a circle corresponding to unity reflection coefficient there is contained all possible values of the resistive

[1] P. H. Smith, Transmission Line Calculator, *Electronics*, vol. 12, p. 29, January, 1939; P. H. Smith, An Improved Transmission Line Calculator, *Electronics*, vol. 17, p. 130, January, 1944. Graph paper and a plastic calculator are commercially available. A paper covering the theoretical foundations of the Smith chart, and its relation to the rectangular chart, is H. L. Krauss, Transmission Line Charts, *Elec. Eng.*, vol. 68, p. 767, September, 1949.

and reactive components r and x, respectively, of the normalized imped-ance $Z/Z_0 = r + jx$ that have positive resistance components. *For a lossless line, loci of constant standing-wave ratio (or of constant reflection coefficient) in the Smith chart are circles concentric about the center of the chart, and one "travels" along a line having a given standing-wave ratio by following the corresponding standing-wave circle around the chart.* More-over, the ratio R_L/Z_0 at which a standing-wave circle crosses the hori-zontal axis on the right side of the chart center, is the value of S for that circle.[1]

An example will illustrate these points. Suppose we have a termi-nating impedance $Z_L = R_L + jX_L$, and a transmission line of characteris-tic impedance Z_0, which is assumed to be a resistance. One then com-putes $r = R_L/Z_0$ and $x = X_L/Z_0$, and establishes this as a point on the chart. For instance, the point P in Fig. 4-16 has the coordinates

$$r + jx = 0.98 + j0.7$$

Plotting this point tells one at once that the standing-wave ratio is 2.0, since a concentric circle through the point P passes through 2.0 and 0.5 on the resistance axis, corresponding to the standing-wave ratio and its reciprocal. The impedance at points on the line some distance from this load can now be determined as follows (assuming the line has negligi-ble attenuation): Suppose that one travels from the terminating load impedance, represented by the point P, toward the generator. This means staying on the concentric circle passing through P. If at an arbitrary point, such as Q, the line is broken and the impedance measured looking toward the load, then the impedance observed will be that represented by the coordinates of the new point. Thus, at Q the normal-ized impedance is $1.56 + j0.7$. Note that the outer scale on the chart is calibrated in terms of the distance along the line, measured in wave-lengths. Travel in the clockwise direction is toward the generator, whereas travel in the counterwise direction is toward the load. Thus between the points P and Q the distance along the line is 0.05 wave-length as determined between the points A and B on the outer scale.

The Smith Chart and Standing-wave Measurements. In traversing a standing-wave circle such as the one with a standing-wave ratio of 2.0, the resistance axis is crossed at two points, one giving a very high resist-ance and the other a very low resistance. These correspond to the volt-age maxima and minima, respectively, observed in the standing-wave detector. On the basis of this, we can then use the Smith chart in connection with the standing-wave detector to determine unknown impedances.

[1] This can be proved by substituting Eq. (4-14) into Eq. (4-17), and assuming that Z_L/Z_0 is entirely resistive.

Suppose for example that a standing-wave ratio of 2.0 is observed, and that the first voltage minima is 0.08 wavelength from the load. We enter the chart at the point P', corresponding to the voltage minimum and a standing-wave ratio that is 2.0, and then travel around this circle of constant standing-wave ratio toward the load by a distance d_1 corresponding to 0.08 wavelength, thus arriving at the point Q'. At this point we read the coordinates of the load impedance, namely, $0.6 - j0.38$. Multiplying these numbers by the Z_0 of the standing-wave detector gives the actual impedance of the terminating load.

For another example, suppose that once again the standing-wave ratio is observed to be 2.0. In this case, however, assume that it is not convenient to measure the actual distance from the load to the first voltage minimum. Instead the terminals to which the load is to be connected are first short-circuited, and the position on the standing-wave detector of a voltage minimum is observed. The short circuit is then removed, and the load impedance connected. Assume the voltage minimum is now observed to have moved a distance of 0.15 wavelength from its previous position, and in a direction toward the load. The original position of the minimum corresponds to the position of the load, but removed from it by an integral number of half wavelengths. Thus when the observed minimum moves toward the load by 0.15 wavelength, it is as though the new minimum were at a negative distance beyond the load; hence on the Smith chart one travels 0.15 wavelength from the point P', in a clockwise direction to the point P, there reading the coordinates $0.98 + j0.7$, which when multiplied by Z_0 give the load impedance. Another way of interpreting this maneuver is that the voltage minimum when the load is connected lies in the positive direction, but a distance from the load of one half wavelength minus 0.15 wavelength, or 0.35 wavelength. Thus going from the point P' toward the load a distance of 0.35 wavelength brings one again to the point P.

Effect of Cable Interposed between Load and Standing-wave Detector. The Smith chart can also be of assistance in cases where it is impossible to connect the unknown impedance directly to the terminals of the standing-wave detector (or to the terminals of one of the measuring devices described in Sec. 4-10), but rather it must be separated from the standing-wave detector by a length ab of transmission line, as shown in Fig. 4-12. If the distance d_1 (or d_2) used in the standing-wave measurement is then the distance from the junction a at the end of the standing-wave detector, the impedance measured is the impedance at a looking toward b. Knowing this impedance Z_a, and the characteristic impedance Z_{ab} and length l_{ab} of the line ab, one can readily obtain the unknown impedance Z_L by the use of the Smith chart. This is done by locating Z_a on the chart, and then traveling around the circle of constant standing-wave ratio thus defined by a distance equal to the length l_{ab}. The resulting position on the chart then gives Z_L on the assumption that the attenuation of the cable ab is negligible.

If the total attenuation of the cable is not negligible, the effect of attenuation can be taken into account by correcting the value of standing-wave ratio in the manner discussed in connection with Fig. 4-13 and Eqs.

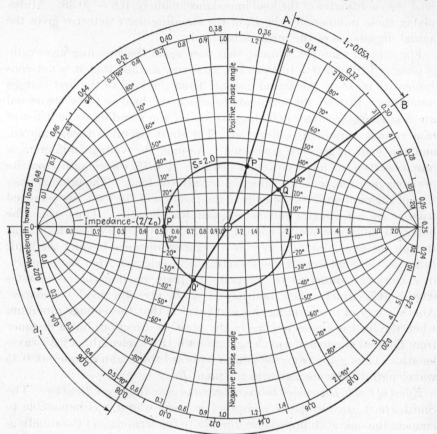

FIG. 4-17. The Z-θ chart.

(4-37) and (4-38). Thus in the example above, in which the observed standing-wave ratio was 2.0 with the minimum 0.08 wavelength toward the generator from the reference minimum, assume that a connecting cable is used which has an attenuation of 3 db (that is, $\alpha_{ab}l_{ab} = 0.345$ neper). Then from Fig. 4-13 the standing-wave ratio S_b at the load is 5.0. One then enters the chart at the point P'', corresponding to a voltage minimum and a standing-wave ratio 5.0 because it lies on the axis at the reciprocal of 5.0, and then travels around this circle of constant standing-wave ratio (shown dotted in Fig. 4-16) toward the load a distance of 0.08 wavelength, thus arriving at the point Q''.   The coordinates of this point, namely, $0.26 - j0.52$, are then the normalized components of the load impedance, and when multiplied by Z_0 give the actual terminating impedance.

Smith charts are sometimes provided with an auxiliary decibel scale that can be used to determine the radius of the circle corresponding to the standing-wave ratio S_b, knowing S_a and the attenuation of the connecting cable.   Such a scale is shown in Fig. 4-16, and is calibrated so that each unit on the auxiliary scale represents the increase in circle radius associated with 1 db attenuation.   Thus starting with a standing-wave circle of radius OP' in Fig. 4-16, the circle of radius OP'', which is 3 units longer on the decibel scale than OP', represents the standing-wave ratio before reduction by passage through a length of cable having 3 db attenuation.

Z-θ Chart.   In the Smith chart, impedances are expressed in rectangular form $R + jX$.   It is possible, however, to devise an analogous chart in which the impedances are in polar form $R + jX = Z\underline{/\theta}$.   Such a Z-θ chart is illustrated in Fig. 4-17, and is utilized in exactly the same way as the Smith chart.   That is, a circle centered on the origin represents a constant standing-wave ratio, while travel around such a circle represents movement along the line, etc.   For purposes of comparison, conditions corresponding to P, Q, P', and Q' in Fig. 4-16 are also shown in Fig. 4-17.

4-10. Special Impedance Measuring Methods.   Measurements with a standing-wave detector are difficult and time-consuming, as well as requiring expensive equipment.   Various techniques have been devised as alternatives for measuring impedances in coaxial-line systems.

Null-type Impedance Meters—Byrne Bridge.[1]   This device, illustrated in Fig. 4-18, is direct-reading in impedance or admittance, and has the advantage of being a null-type instrument like a bridge.   Here power from an oscillator is delivered to the unknown impedance through a coaxial line.   At a point on this line as close as practical to the load, two sampling elements are introduced that are responsive, respectively, to the voltage and current flowing into the load.   The element responsive to voltage consists of a capacitive probe, and the element responsive to current is a loop, as shown.   The amount of pickup by each sampling probe can be adjusted by moving the probe with respect to the coaxial line.   In practice the two probes are joined together so that when one probe moves in toward the center conductor of the line, the other moves away from it. These two sampling probes are connected together by an auxiliary line, as shown, that is slotted.   The voltage induced in each sampling probe initiates a wave which starts from the probe and travels around the

---

[1] J. F. Byrne, A Null-method for the Determination of Impedance in the 100–400 Mc Range, *Proc. Natl. Elec. Conf.*, vol. 3, p. 603, 1947.

auxiliary line, where it is entirely absorbed in the terminating resistance at the opposite end.   In the auxiliary line there is a movable probe which measures the net voltage in the line resulting from the superposition of the two waves traveling in opposite directions.   The relative magnitudes of these two waves induced in the auxiliary line will depend (1) upon the vector ratio of voltage to current in the unknown impedance, and (2) upon the relative positions of the sampling probes.

The procedure by which this arrangement is used to determine the unknown impedance Z_x is as follows: The position of the movable probe is adjusted with one hand, while the sampling-probe control is varied with the other hand, until the detector output is zero.   Under these conditions,

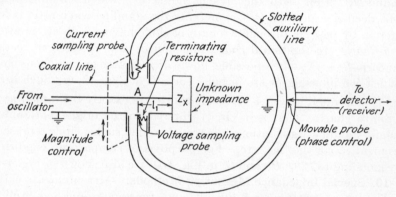

Fig. 4-18. Schematic diagram of Byrne bridge.

the two waves induced on the auxiliary line are equal in magnitude, and are in phase opposition at the position of the movable probe.   The setting of the sampling-probe-control dial required to achieve this result is determined by the ratio of voltage to current flowing into the unknown impedance, *i.e.*, by the *magnitude* of the impedance to be determined, and is independent of the frequency.   This dial can accordingly be calibrated to read impedance directly.   At the same time, the phase angle of the unknown impedance is determined by the position of the movable probe corresponding to the null condition.   If the load is resistive, this null position will be midway between the two sampling probes; for other null positions of the movable probe, the phase angle of the impedance being measured will be proportional to displacement from the reference position corresponding to a resistive load, and will also be proportional to frequency.   Thus the indicator giving the position of the movable probe can be calibrated directly in phase angle at some convenient frequency, say 100 Mc; at other frequencies one multiplies the scale reading by the relative frequency.

The impedance actually measured corresponds to the voltage and currents existing at the sampling probes; *i.e.*, it is the impedance at point A looking toward Z_x in Fig. 4-18.   If the length of the line l_1 is not a negligible fraction of a wavelength at the frequency of measurement (or what is the same thing, if the capacitance of l_1 in shunt with the load cannot be neglected), then one has a situation analogous to that illustrated in Fig. 4-12, where a length of line is interposed between the measuring point and the impedance to be determined.   The unknown impedance is then the measured value as corrected by the use of the Smith or Z-θ charts; the latter is particularly convenient in this case as it utilizes impedances in polar form.

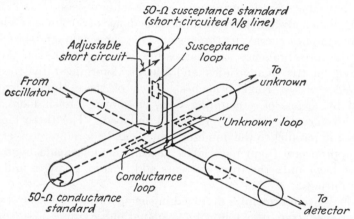

FIG. 4-19. Schematic diagram of the admittance comparator.

The device of Fig. 4-18 is equivalent to an a-c bridge, and gives the vector value of the unknown impedance.   As in the standing-wave detector, there are critical tolerances in the machining work required in the building of this device.   Nevertheless, when it has been built and calibrated, good accuracy can be obtained over a large frequency range. One commercial model has a frequency range of 50 to 500 Mc, and can measure impedances of 2 to 2000 ohms with accuracy of impedance magnitude to within 5 per cent, and phase angle to within 3°.[1]   The ease of operation of such a device in contrast to the standing-wave detector is very considerable.

Admittance Comparator.   Another type of null device is illustrated in Fig. 4-19, and is known as an "admittance comparator."[2]   Here a coaxial

[1] A. Fong, Direct Measurement of Impedance in the 50–500 Mc Range, *Hewlett-Packard J.*, vol. 1, p. 1, April, 1950.

[2] W. R. Thurston, A Direct-reading Impedance-measuring Instrument, for the U-H-F Range, *Gen. Rad. Expt.*, vol. 24, p. 1, May, 1950.   An earlier form of such a device was described by O. M. Woodward, Jr., Comparator for Coaxial Line Adjustment, *Electronics*, vol. 20, p. 116, April, 1947.

line receiving power from an oscillator branches into three coaxial lines as shown.   One of these branch lines is terminated by the unknown impedance (or admittance) as shown; this branch is kept as short as possible so that its input impedance at the junction point is very closely equal to the unknown impedance.   The second, or susceptance, branch is arranged to offer a susceptance corresponding to 50 ohms inductive reactance at the junction of the three lines.   This is achieved by making this branch have a characteristic impedance of 50 ohms, and then adjusting the length of the branch to be exactly one-eighth wavelength at the frequency being used.   The third, or conductance, branch likewise has a 50-ohm characteristic impedance, but is terminated by a 50-ohm resistance as shown, so that this branch always offers an input impedance of 50 ohms.   When the oscillator supplies energy to the system, the same voltage is applied to each of the three branches; this causes branch currents that at the junction have relative magnitudes and phases determined by the input admittances of the three branches.   Each of these three currents is sampled by means of a coupling loop, as shown.   Each loop can be rotated to vary the amount of current induced.   The three loops are connected in parallel to the detector, which can be a radio receiver tuned to the appropriate frequency.   The measurement is made by rotating the three loops until the three currents add to zero, giving a null in the receiver output.

The qualitative principles involved in the operation of this system can be understood from the following explanation: Assume first that the loop in the unknown impedance arm is kept fixed at the position of maximum coupling (parallel to the center conductor).   Then rotating the "conductance" loop varies the amount of inphase current available from the conductance standard to balance the inphase current obtained from the "unknown" loop.   Similarly, rotating the "susceptance" loop varies the amount of reactive current (either positive or negative, the reversal being accomplished by rotating the loop 180°) that is available to balance out the reactive current induced in the "unknown" loop.   Thus, for a given setting of the "unknown" loop, the conductance and susceptance components of the unknown impedance are determined by the settings of the conductance and susceptance loops, respectively, which correspond to a null.   The controls for these two loops may therefore be directly calibrated in mhos, on the assumption that the "unknown" loop is at a standard reference position.   Rotation of the "unknown" loop away from the standard reference position changes the magnitude of the induced current that must be balanced out by the other two loops; hence the control for the "unknown" loop may be calibrated to give a multiplying factor.

The calibration of the admittance comparator is independent of frequency to the extent that the distances from the junction to each of the three loops are small compared with a wavelength.[1]   This sets an upper limit to the useful frequency range.   At low frequencies the only limiting factor is the length of the susceptance stub, which becomes impractically long if the frequency is quite low. .

A commercial form of the admittance comparator has the T junction and coupling loop contained within a cube about 2 in. on a side, and gives accuracy on the order of 5 per cent up to a frequency of around 1000 Mc when measuring admittances of the order of 0.02 mho.   This device is designed to have a low-frequency limit of 70 Mc, and has a working range

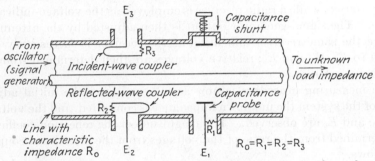

Fig. 4-20. Impedance measurements using directional couplers and supplementary capacitance probe.

of 0.004 to 0.1 mhos (250 to 10 ohms) with an accuracy of the order of 10 per cent or better.

Directional-coupler Method.   The two devices described above have difficult machining requirements on the component parts, particularly those which must move during the measurement.   A device more suitable from the standpoint of construction in a laboratory not equipped for precision machine work is illustrated in Fig. 4-20.[2]   The principal components of the device are two directional couplers, one which responds to the forward wave, and the other to the reflected wave.   If the two couplers are identical, the ratio of their output voltages is the magnitude of the reflection coefficient of the unknown load impedance.   In order to determine the phase angle of the reflection coefficient, and thus obtain the complete specification of the unknown load impedance, some addi-

[1] At high frequencies, the length of the branch line from the "unknown" loop to the unknown admittance can introduce an error unless the length of this line is negligible compared with a wavelength.   Ordinarily the system can be designed so as to realize this condition; if not, a correction can be made using either the Smith or Z-θ charts as discussed on p. 155.

[2] B. Parzen, Impedance Measurements with Directional Couplers and Supplementary Voltage Probe, *Proc. IRE*, vol. 37, p. 1208, October, 1949.

tional information is required. This is provided by the capacitance voltage probe shown in the figure.

The complete calculation of impedance is based upon the three voltages E_1, E_2, and E_3, measured at the points shown in Fig. 4-20. In order to simplify the calculations, the two directional couplers are made as nearly identical as possible, so that when the load is a short circuit or open circuit (*i.e.*, complete reflection) then $E_3 = E_2$. In addition, the coupling of the capacitance probe is adjusted so that in the presence of a load impedance equal to the characteristic impedance of the line (no reflection), $E_1 = E_3$. The relative magnitude of the voltages is determined by using a signal generator with a calibrated output attenuator as the energy source, while a radio receiver is employed as the voltage-indicating device. The signal-generator output is then adjusted by the attenuator to give the same receiver indication as the receiver is successively connected to E_1, E_2, and E_3; relative voltages are then determined from the attenuator settings.

The measuring procedure is now as follows: After the initial adjustment of the system the unknown impedance is connected, and the voltages E_1, E_2, and E_3 are observed. The magnitude of the reflection coefficient is determined from the ratio of the voltages from the directional couplers as follows,

$$|\rho| = \frac{E_2}{E_3} \tag{4-43}$$

where E_2 = voltage at directional coupler for reflected wave

E_3 = voltage at directional coupler for incident wave

The phase angle ϕ_1 of the reflection coefficient at the point on the line corresponding to the location of the capacitance probe is determined from the following relationship:

$$\cos \phi_1 = \frac{(E_1/E_3)^2 - (E_2/E_3)^2 - 1}{2(E_2/E_3)} \tag{4-44}$$

In order to determine the sign of the phase angle given by Eq. (4-44), one additional step in the measurement is required. This is carried out with the aid of the capacitance shunt shown in Fig. 4-20 which is simply a probe with a small end plate to increase its capacitance. When this shunt is pushed part way into the line, the resulting small capacitance added across the line alters the voltage readings. In particular, if the phase angle of the reflection coefficient is *positive*, then the added capacitance increases E_1/E_3 and decreases the ratio E_2/E_3.

In order to compute the load impedance, it is necessary to know the phase angle of the reflection coefficient at the load rather than at the capacitance probe. If the distance l_1 from the load to the probe is

known, the phase angle ϕ_L of the reflection coefficient at the load can
be computed as follows:

$$\phi_L = \phi_1 + \frac{4\pi l_1}{\lambda_l} \qquad (4\text{-}45)$$

Here λ_l is the distance along the line corresponding to one wavelength.
Knowing the magnitude $|\rho|$ and the phase ϕ_1 of the reflection coefficient ρ
at the capacitance probe, the load impedance can then be obtained by
solving Eq. (4-14) for the unknown impedance Z_L. This gives

$$Z_L = R_0 \frac{1 + \rho}{1 - \rho} \qquad (4\text{-}46)$$

where R_0 is the characteristic resistance of the line, typically 50 ohms.

This arrangement for measuring impedance has the advantage of
simple and compact construction. It is especially useful in the frequency
range 50 to 500 Mc, where standing-wave detectors are physically long
and cumbersome, and will give an accuracy of the order of 5 per cent over
wide frequency ranges. The disadvantages are that the system cannot
be made direct-reading, and that considerable calculation is required with
each measurement.

Probe Methods. Various arrangements of fixed capacitance probes
may be used in place of the standing-wave detector. The voltages
induced on these probes are then used to calculate the standing-wave
ratio or reflection coefficient, and from this the load impedance is
determined.

One arrangement consists of three probes spaced along the line at one-
eighth wavelength separation.[1] From the radio-frequency voltages
observed at the three probes, it is possible to compute the magnitude and
phase of the impedance terminating the line. An alternative arrangement uses four probes, and yields two voltages, respectively proportional
to the real and imaginary part of the reflection coefficient.[2] The probes
are used in pairs, each pair having one-quarter wavelength separation, and
one pair being one-eighth wavelength nearer the load than the other.
The radio-frequency voltage at each probe is rectified by a crystal
detector, which must have a square-law characteristic for proper results.
The difference in rectified outputs of the two detectors associated with
one pair of probes then goes to the vertical-deflection plates of an oscilloscope, and the corresponding output of the other pair goes similarly to
the horizontal-deflection plates. The resulting oscilloscope display pre-

[1] W. L. Barrow, Measurement of Radio-frequency Impedance with Networks
Simulating Lines, *Proc. IRE*, vol. 23, p. 807, July, 1935.

[2] A. L. Samuel, An Oscillographic Method of Presenting Impedances on the Reflection-coefficient Plane, *Proc. IRE*, vol. 35, p. 1279, November, 1947.

sents both the magnitude and phase of the reflection coefficient, and the method is accordingly particularly convenient for rapid measurements on resonant cavities and other terminations.

Both of these techniques using fixed probes are essentially single-frequency systems; at most they cannot be used over a frequency band exceeding 10 per cent of the frequency at which the probe spacing is exactly one-eighth wavelength.

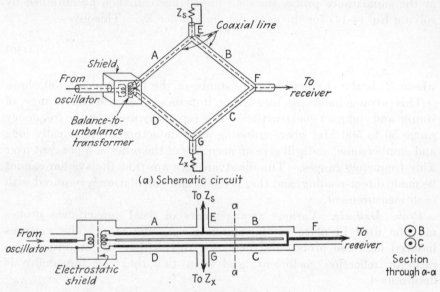

(a) Schematic circuit

(b) Schematic diagram indicating physical layout

FIG. 4-21. Simple transmission-line impedance bridge for comparing impedances.

Impedance Comparators—Transmission-line Bridges. In some cases it is sufficient to compare an unknown impedance (both in magnitude and phase), with a known impedance. Thus one may desire to detect small differences between an impedance under study and an impedance it is supposed to match. Again, if the known impedance is adjustable, then one can determine the unknown impedance in terms of the adjustable known impedance. At frequencies so high that ordinary bridges or null networks such as described in Chap. 3 cannot be used, it is possible to resort to hybrid or magic-T junctions (see Sec. 4-14), or bridges involving transmission links. An example of a transmission-line bridge is illustrated in Fig. 4-21.[1] Here voltages exactly equal in magnitude and

[1] Other bridge arrangements making use of transmission-line elements are described by D. D. King, Two Simple Bridges for Very-high-frequency Use, *Proc. IRE*, vol. 38, p. 37, January, 1950; C. H. Westcott, Transmission-line Bridge, *Wireless Eng.*, vol. 25, p. 215, July, 1948.

opposite in phase are applied to coaxial lines A and D, respectively, while the two impedances Z_s and Z_x that are to be compared are connected to coaxial side arms E and G as shown.   If the system is perfectly symmetrical electrically, a result relatively easy to achieve, then if $Z_s = Z_x$ there will be no output at arm F.   Electrical symmetry can be readily checked by making $Z_s = Z_x$ by the expedient of either open-circuiting or short-circuiting side arms E and G, and observing whether or not the output at F is zero.   If it is not zero, the balance of the input transformer may be adjusted to give a null-output condition, after which Z_s and Z_x may be connected in place and compared.   The bridge arrangement circuit of Fig. 4-21a can be realized practically by a very simple and convenient mechanical arrangement, consisting of two coaxial lines side by side as illustrated in Fig. 4-21b.

4-11. Use of Resonant Lines in the Measurement of Impedance.[1] A resonant length of transmission line can be used as a basis for impedance measurement by associating the unknown impedance with the line and observing the resulting effect on the resonant line.   The principles involved are the same as for the substitution and variation methods described in Sec. 3-9, except that the resonant line replaces the lumped resonant circuit.   Using a transmission line as a resonant circuit gives the possibility of high values of Q in the ultra-high-frequency range, as well as permitting one or two novel techniques.

Typical resonant transmission-line systems for measuring impedance are illustrated in Fig. 4-22.   Here the line is indicated as being of the parallel-line type, although at the higher frequencies a coaxial line would be used because of the higher Q obtainable owing to the absence of radiation loss.   The oscillator is loosely coupled to the line through a capacitance probe or small coupling loop.   Similarly, the detector, which would normally be a vacuum-tube voltmeter, crystal detector, or radio receiver, is likewise loosely coupled to the line in such a way as to respond either to the voltage or to the current in the resonant system.

Arrangements Involving Lines of Fixed Length.   The susceptance of an unknown admittance can be found with the arrangement a.   The technique is first to resonate the line by means of the variable capacitor C with the unknown admittance disconnected.   Next the unknown admittance Y_x is connected, and the system is resonated again by readjusting the capacitor.   The capacitor susceptance change is then equal to the susceptance component B_x of the unknown admittance.   The conductance component G_x of the unknown admittance can be readily obtained by measuring the Q values Q_2 and Q_1 of the resonant system with and without

[1] L. S. Nergaard, A Survey of Ultra-high-frequency Measurements, *RCA Rev.*, vol. 3, p. 156, October, 1938.

the unknown admittance connected. Then

$$\frac{G_1}{G_1 + G_x} = \frac{Q_2}{Q_1} \tag{4-47a}$$

Here G_1 is the parallel resonant conductance (i.e., reciprocal of the parallel resonant impedance) across which G_x is connected. Solving Eq. (4-47a)

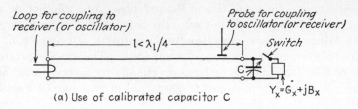

(a) Use of calibrated capacitor C

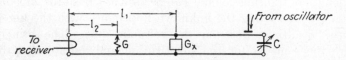

(b) Use of movable conductance standard G

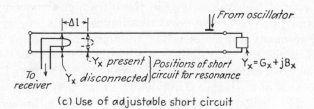

(c) Use of adjustable short circuit

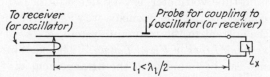

(d) Use of half-wave resonance in measuring low values of Z_x

FIG. 4-22. Methods of using a resonant line to determine impedance.

for G_x gives

$$G_x = G_1\left(\frac{Q_1}{Q_2} - 1\right) \tag{4-47b}$$

The value of G_1 in Eqs. (4-47) that is applicable to the system in use can be most easily obtained by substituting a known conductance for G_x.

The value of Q applicable to a resonant-line system may be readily determined by the frequency-variation method, using Eq. (3-22). Alternatively, the ratio Q_1/Q_2 may be determined in several ways. One method consists in observing the relative voltage (or current) response D_2 and D_1 of the system at resonance with and without the unknown conductance connected, respectively, while keeping constant the input to the system from the oscillator. Then

$$\frac{Q_1}{Q_2} = \frac{D_1}{D_2} \qquad (4\text{-}48)$$

Somewhat greater accuracy may be obtained by varying the input to the system from the oscillator by means of an attenuator, in such a manner as to maintain the response of the system unchanged when the unknown is connected. In this case

$$\frac{Q_1}{Q_2} = \frac{E_2}{E_1} \qquad (4\text{-}49)$$

where E_2 and E_1 are the attenuator output voltages with and without the unknown conductance G_x connected.[1] Finally, Q_1/Q_2 may be determined by detuning the resonant-line system by means of a calibrated standard capacitor, and observing the relative change in capacitance required for a given reduction in response. Assume that a difference ΔC in tuning capacitance is required to change the tuning of the system from one side of resonance, where the response is D_2, to the other side of resonance, where it is likewise D_2. Then if ΔC_2 and ΔC_1 are the values of this capacitance change with and without the unknown conductance connected, one has, from Eq. (3-21),

$$\frac{Q_1}{Q_2} = \frac{\Delta C_2}{\Delta C_1} \qquad (4\text{-}50)$$

An unknown conductance (or resistance) can be determined in terms of a known conductance by the arrangement of Fig. 4-22b.[2] First, with the known conductance G disconnected, the level of the detector is noted when the unknown conductance G_x is connected, and the line is tuned to resonance by capacitance C. Next, the unknown G_x is disconnected, and the conductance G placed across the transmission line. The position of the known conductance G is then moved along the line until the same detector output is obtained as before, while keeping the line tuned to

---

[1] The application of this procedure is discussed in detail by W. H. Ward, A Direct Reading Instrument for Measuring Unbalanced Impedances at Decimetric Wavelengths, *J. IEE*, vol. 97, pt. III, p. 199, May, 1950.

[2] J. M. Miller and B. Salzberg, Measurement of Admittances at Ultra-high Frequencies, *RCA Rev.*, vol. 3, p. 486, April, 1939.

resonance at all times by use of capacitor C. The conductance component of the load admittance can then be computed from the following equation,

$$G_x = G \left[\frac{\sin (2\pi l_2/\lambda_l)}{\sin (2\pi l_1/\lambda_l)} \right]^2 \qquad (4\text{-}51)$$

where G = known conductance

l_1 = length of line from short circuit to position of conductance G_x

l_2 = length from short circuit to position of conductance G

λ_l = length along line corresponding to one wavelength

In this arrangement, the line acts essentially as an autotransformer of variable ratio, so that a fixed standard of conductance can function as a variable standard. The method is especially useful when it is desired to determine the value of a large conductance in terms of a known small conductance, or vice versa (by making $l_1 < l_2$).

Methods Utilizing Lines of Adjustable Length. A different method of utilizing a resonant line is illustrated in Fig. 4-22c and consists in varying the line length to maintain resonance,[1] instead of employing a variable tuning capacitance as in Fig. 4-22a. Here the position of the short circuit is adjusted to give resonance first with Y_x disconnected, and second with it connected as shown in the figure. The unknown susceptance B_x is then related to the movement Δl of the short circuit by the equation

$$B_x = \frac{1}{Z_0} \tan \frac{2\pi \Delta l}{\lambda_l} \qquad (4\text{-}52)$$

where Z_0 is the characteristic impedance of the line, and λ_l is the length along the line corresponding to a wavelength. The sign of Δl is positive if the short circuit is closer to Y_x when Y_x is connected. Alternatively, the unknown susceptance may be determined from the length of line required to give resonance when the unknown impedance is connected, according to the relation

$$B_x = \frac{1}{Z_0} \cot \frac{2\pi l_1}{\lambda_l} \qquad (4\text{-}53)$$

A positive value of B_x denotes capacitive susceptance. Here the notation is as in Eq. (4-52), with the addition that l_1 is the *equivalent* line length for resonance with the load connected, as defined below.

The conductance G_x associated with B_x in Eq. (4-52) or (4-53) can be determined by noting the equivalent length l_1 at which the system is

---

[1] The practical use of this method is discussed by Nergaard, *op. cit.*, and by F. Hamburger, Jr., and C. F. Miller, The Measurement of Coil Reactance in the 100-megacycle Region, *Proc. IRE*, vol. 28, p. 475, October, 1940; R. A. Chipman, A Resonance Curve Method for the Absolute Measurement of Impedance at Frequencies of the Order of 300 Mc/s, *J. Applied Phys.*, vol. 10, p. 27, January, 1939.

resonant, and then determining the equivalent length l_2 at which the voltage (or current) response of the system for constant oscillator input is reduced to 70.7 per cent of the resonant value. Then if $l_1 - l_2$ is small,[1]

$$G_x = \frac{1}{Z_0} \frac{2\pi(l_1 - l_2)}{\lambda_l} \csc^2 \frac{2\pi l_1}{\lambda_l} - G_0 \qquad (4\text{-}54a)$$

Here G_0 is the parallel resonant conductance of the line itself when the unknown admittance is disconnected. When the line conductance G_0 is so small as to be negligible compared with G_x, then Eq. (4-54a) can be written as

$$G_x = \frac{1}{Z_0} \left(\cot \frac{2\pi l_1}{\lambda_l} - \cot \frac{2\pi l_2}{\lambda_l} \right) \qquad (4\text{-}54b)$$

In Eqs. (4-52) to (4-54) it is assumed that (1) the short circuit is perfect, and (2) there is negligible influence due to the idle section of line beyond the short circuit. These are not always safe assumptions. However, if the idle section contains another movable short circuit that is kept one-quarter wavelength from the first one, then there will be little or no current induced in the idle section. In the case of a parallel-wire line, it may be desirable for the first short circuit to be a rather large copper sheet in a plane at right angles to the line axis; such a sheet acts as a shield that tends to eliminate stray couplings to the idle line.

The reactance of the short-circuiting element prevents it from acting as a perfect short circuit. This effect can be allowed for if l_1 and l_2 are interpreted to be *equivalent* lengths, which are the actual lengths plus a correction Δl_{eq} such that

$$\Delta l_{eq} = \frac{\lambda_l}{4} - l' \qquad (4\text{-}55)$$

where l' is the actual length required for resonance when the unknown admittance Y_x is disconnected. The equivalent value of l_1 with Y_x connected is then the observed length l_1 plus Δl_{eq}; similarly the equivalent value of l_2 is the observed length l_2 plus Δl_{eq}. It will be noted that this correction does not affect the value of $\Delta l = l_1 - l_2$ appearing in Eqs. (4-53) and (4-54b).

Measurement of Low Values of Impedance. All of the methods of measurement described above except that of Fig. 4-22b require that the unknown admittance, and particularly its conductance component, be relatively small. When the unknown impedance $Z_x = R_x + jX_x$ to be determined is relatively low, the arrangement of Fig. 4-22d can be used. Here the unknown is connected across the line as in b, but the short circuit is adjusted to give half-wave resonance. Under these conditions

[1] See Nergaard, *op. cit.*

the reactance component X_x of the unknown impedance can be determined by rewriting Eq. (4-52) to give

$$X_x = Z_0 \tan \frac{2\pi l_1}{\lambda_l} \qquad (4\text{-}56)$$

Here l_1 is the equivalent length of line, corrected if necessary by Δl_{eq} as explained in connection with Eq. (4-55), while λ_l and Z_0 have the same meaning as before. A positive value of X_x denotes an inductive reactance. Alternatively, one may determine the line lengths that give half-wave resonance, first with Z_x in place, and then with Z_x replaced by a short circuit similar to that on the other end of the line. Then,

$$X_x = Z_0 \tan 2\pi \, \Delta l \qquad (4\text{-}57)$$

where Δl is the actual change of line length plus the equivalent length Δl_{eq} of the added short circuit as defined by Eq. (4-55). The change Δl is positive if the line is longer when z_x is replaced by the short circuit.

The resistance component R_x in Fig. 4-22d can be obtained by observing the Q's of the resonant system with Z_x in the system, and Z_x replaced by a short circuit. By analogy with Eqs. (4-47) one then can write

$$\frac{R_1}{R_x + R_1} = \frac{Q_2}{Q_1} \qquad (4\text{-}58a)$$

or

$$R_x = R_1 \left(\frac{Q_1}{Q_2} - 1 \right) \qquad (4\text{-}58b)$$

where $Q_1 = Q$ of system with Z_x replaced by a short circuit

$Q_2 = Q$ of system with Z_x in place

R_1 = equivalent lumped series resistance of the resonant system referred to the point where Z_x is connected

The values of Q involved can be determined experimentally by the frequency-variation method, or by the use of Eq. (4-48) or (4-49). It is also possible to determine Q in a manner analogous to Eq. (4-50) by noting the change in line length required to detune the system sufficiently to reduce the response some specified amount, such as 70.7 per cent of the response at resonance. In this case

$$\frac{Q_1}{Q_2} = \frac{\Delta l_2}{\Delta l_1} \qquad (4\text{-}59)$$

Here Δl_2 is the change in length required to give the specified reduction in response below resonance when the unknown impedance Z_x is connected as in Fig. 4-22d. Similarly Δl_1 is the change in length that gives the same reduction in response below resonance when Z_x is replaced by a short circuit. The value of R_1 can be most easily determined experimentally by substituting a known resistance for R_x.

4-12. Waveguide and Waveguide Impedance.   At frequencies above 1000 Mc the waveguide is an important transmission element.   It is rather different from the two-conductor transmission line in some respects, particularly in the distribution of electric and magnetic fields, but on the other hand it has many properties in common with the line.   The discussion here will emphasize the similarities of the waveguide and two-conductor line, because once these similarities have been set forth it is possible to utilize many of the same measurement techniques for both waveguides and lines.   Specifically, all measurements based upon reflection coefficients, or standing-wave ratio, which have been described in detail for coaxial lines, can be used for waveguides if, in the equations, one uses normalized impedances Z/Z_0, and replaces line wavelength λ_l by guide wavelength λ_g.

The general principles of waveguides are set forth in numerous places, and in the brief discussion here it will not be possible to go over all the details, such as field distribution in the various possible modes, etc.   It is important to point out, however, that the waveguide is a transmission system along which a wave travels with a given phase velocity and a given attenuation per unit length.   There is a guide wavelength λ_g, which is the counterpart of the line wavelength, and is the distance traveled by the wave (at its phase velocity) in a time corresponding to one cycle.   The guide wavelength can be determined experimentally with a standing-wave detector, being twice the distance between two successive voltage minima of a standing-wave pattern, or it can be computed with the aid of the following equation,

$$\lambda_g = \frac{\lambda}{\sqrt{1 - (\lambda/\lambda_c)^2}} \tag{4-60}$$

where λ = free-space wavelength in meters = $3 \times 10^8/f$

$\qquad f$ = frequency, cycles per sec

$\qquad \lambda_c$ = cutoff wavelength for the particular waveguide mode[1]

The guide wavelength, expressed in Eq. (4-60), is exactly analogous to the line wavelength for two-conductor lines, and can be used in all the equations in which the latter appears.

In common with all types of transmission lines, the waveguide will have both a direct and a reflected wave if there is a discontinuity in the guide, or if the termination or load does not match the impedance of the waveguide.   There is associated with the reflected wave a reflection coefficient which relates the relative magnitude and phase of the reflected wave to that of the incident wave.   From this reflection coefficient there can be computed a normalized resistance and reactance at the load end of the

---

[1] For example, in the commonly used rectangular guide of width a and height b ($b \leq a$), operating in the customary TE_{10} mode, $\lambda_c = 2a$ for an air-filled guide.

line; these are properties of the load, and are similar to the components of a load impedance connected to a transmission line.

Measurement of this waveguide normalized load impedance, or of the reflection coefficient, can be accomplished with a standing-wave detector (see Sec. 4-13), or by the use of directional couplers and supplementary voltage probes, exactly as described in Secs. 4-7 and 4-10. Also, the transmission-line charts described in Sec. 4-9 are fully applicable to the waveguide case.

Reflected waves can be eliminated in a waveguide system by avoiding irregularities, and then terminating the guide in such a manner that the incident wave is completely absorbed. Load arrangements capable of providing a nonreflecting termination for waveguides are described in Sec. 14-7.

Definitions of Waveguide Impedance.[1] When the normalized impedance in a waveguide system has been measured, it is possible to convert the results into actual impedances. How this is done depends upon the use to which the data will be put. In marked contrast to the two-conductor line, it is not possible to define uniquely a characteristic impedance for a waveguide. In a two-wire line, one defines a characteristic impedance which is determined by the geometry of line and holds for all frequencies. For the waveguide case, however, the impedance will be a function of frequency even for a given guide. Moreover, the characteristic impedance can be defined in at least three ways, each of which gives a different numerical result.

One way to define waveguide impedance is to consider it to be the ratio of the maximum value of the transverse voltage developed across the guide[2] to the total longitudinal current flowing in the guide walls, for a traveling wave when no reflected wave is present. On this basis, the waveguide impedance Z_0 for the TE_{10} mode in a rectangular guide is

$$Z_0 = 377 \sqrt{\frac{\mu}{\varepsilon}} \frac{\lambda_g}{\lambda} \frac{\pi}{2} \frac{a}{b} \qquad (4\text{-}61)$$

where μ = magnetic permeability of any material filling guide ($\mu = 1$ for air)

ε = dielectric constant of any material filling guide ($\varepsilon = 1$ for air)

λ_g = guide wavelength

λ = free-space wavelength

a = width of guide (long dimension)

b = height of guide (short dimension)

[1] For further discussion see S. A. Schelkunoff, "Electromagnetic Waves," pp. 319, 490, D. Van Nostrand Company, Inc., New York, 1943; "Very High Frequency Techniques," p. 674, McGraw-Hill Book Company, Inc., New York, 1947.

[2] Thus for the TE_{10} mode, this would be the transverse voltage existing midway between the two sides, where the transverse electric field is maximum.

A second definition of waveguide impedance is to regard it as the ratio of the power transmitted along the guide to the square of the longitudinal current.   On this basis the waveguide impedance is twice the value given in Eq. (4-61).

A third definition of characteristic impedance of the waveguide is the so-called *wave impedance*.   This is the ratio of transverse components of electric to magnetic field strength.   The appropriate formulas for the transverse electric, or *TE*, modes and the transverse magnetic, or *TM*, modes, are

For TE waves:

$$\text{Wave impedance} = 377 \sqrt{\frac{\mu}{\varepsilon}} \frac{\lambda_g}{\lambda} \qquad (4\text{-}62a)$$

For TM waves:

$$\text{Wave impedance} = 377 \sqrt{\frac{\mu}{\varepsilon}} \frac{\lambda}{\lambda_g} \qquad (4\text{-}62b)$$

The notation is the same as used in Eq. (4-61).   Unlike the first two kinds of guide impedance, the wave impedance is independent of the guide proportions or shape, except in so far as these affect the guide wavelength λ_g.   For comparison with Eqs. (4-62), the wave impedance of free space has the value

$$\text{Wave impedance of free space} = 377 \sqrt{\frac{\mu}{\varepsilon}} \qquad (4\text{-}63)$$

This is also the wave impedance of a coaxial line, and of a two-wire line. It is to be noted that the wave impedance of such lines is quite different from their characteristic impedance.   In particular, the wave impedance of a two-conductor line is independent of the dimensions of the line.

The wave impedance has the desirable feature that it is uniquely defined for a given mode of transmission, and it can be conveniently used as the basis of a study of waveguide discontinuities and loads.   On the other hand, the impedance defined by Eq. (4-61) is more closely related to the characteristic impedance of coaxial and two-wire lines, and hence is useful in connection with the design of transformers between waveguides and coaxial lines.   It must be used with some caution, however, because the currents and voltages are not uniformly distributed over the cross section of a guide as they are over the cross section of a two-conductor line.

4-13. Waveguide Standing-wave Detectors.[1]   The standing-wave pattern existing in a waveguide may be investigated in the same manner

[1] Further discussion will be found in "Technique of Microwave Measurements," *op. cit.*; Barlow and Cullen, *op. cit.*; D. Hirst and R. W. Hogg, The Design of Precision Standing-wave Indicators for Measurements in Waveguides, *J. IEE (Radiocommuni-*

as for the case of a coaxial line. That is to say, an axial slot is provided in the top of the guide, through which projects a probe that rides on a movable carriage, as shown in Fig. 4-23. The electric field existing within the guide induces a voltage on the probe, just as in the corresponding coaxial case. The probe itself may be an arrangement such as illustrated in Fig. 4-5*b*, or it may be a coaxial line that leads to a bolometer or crystal detector as in Fig. 4-23.

The slot in the waveguide is preferably located in a region where the electric field is strongest, and where at the same time the transverse current which would be interrupted by the slot is zero. In the common case of the TE_{10} mode in a rectangular guide, this requirement is met by locating the slot in the middle of the long side, as shown in Fig. 4-23.

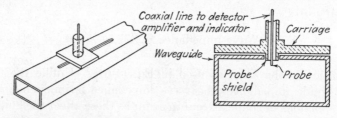

(a) Slotted waveguide with carriage   (b) Details of probe

FIG. 4-23. Slotted-waveguide type of standing-wave detector.

Waveguide standing-wave detectors are typically used at frequencies higher than those customary with coaxial lines, just as waveguides are ordinarily used instead of coaxial lines at the higher microwave frequencies. This fact introduces special problems in waveguide standing-wave detectors. Thus, because the wavelength is small, special refinements, such as micrometer elements, may be needed to measure with sufficient accuracy the distance traveled by the carriage. Again, to prevent radiation when the frequency is very high, the slot must be correspondingly narrow. This requires that the clearance between the probe and the sides of the slot be very small, which in turn makes necessary the use of a shielded probe,[1] as indicated in Fig. 4-23, to prevent minute transverse motions of the probe from affecting the probe impedance. Finally, tolerances relating to permissible variations in the depth of penetration of the probe as the carriage moves are correspondingly severe.

---

cations Conv.), vol. 94, pt. III*A* p. 489, March–April, 1947; S. A. Johnson, Microwave Slotted Sections, *Proc. Natl. Elec. Conf.*, vol. 4, p. 22, 1948.

[1] A shielded probe also prevents stray fields outside of the guide from affecting the probe output. This is important at the higher microwave frequencies where the wavelength is so small that even the narrowest practical slot will allow leakage of some energy, thus giving rise to fields external to the guide.

The reflection coefficient associated with a load impedance or with an irregularity in a waveguide system can be readily determined from standing waves by the methods discussed in connection with Eqs. (4-39); the only difference is that the guide wavelength λ_g is substituted for the line wavelength λ_l. Similarly, the node-shift method (see Sec. 4-8) may be used to evaluate small irregularities.

To the extent that a waveguide system is free of irregularities, the observed standing-wave ratio is a measure of the ratio of the load impedance to the waveguide impedance, exactly as in the case of the coaxial line (Sec. 4-7). The only difference is that the guide wavelength λ_g replaces the line wavelength λ_l in all the equations and figures applying to coaxial systems, including the Smith chart. The load impedance obtained in this way is the normalized value referred to the waveguide impedance as defined above; one may use whichever of the three possible definitions of waveguide impedance is most convenient, as the standing-wave measurement gives only *relative* impedances.

4-14. Special Waveguide Techniques. Although the waveguide standing-wave detector can be considered the basic measuring tool for determining reflection coefficients and impedances in waveguide systems, there are numerous situations in which alternative techniques permit simpler apparatus or faster reduction of data. Thus, some of the special methods described in Sec. 4-10 for coaxial lines can be applied to waveguides, particularly those techniques involving directional couplers[1] or fixed probes. Null-type waveguide impedance bridges are not readily available, although at least one successful device has been built, and it can be expected that more research will be done along these lines in the future.[2] Two additional techniques which are not commonly used with coaxial systems, but which are especially adapted to waveguides, are described below.

Fixed Probe and Phase Shifter. The difficulties arising from slot radiation in guides operating at very short wavelengths can be avoided by associating a fixed probe with a phase shifter. Such an arrangement is illustrated in Fig. 4-24, and can be regarded as a standing-wave detector where the electrical length of the system between the probe and the unknown impedance is varied by means of a phase shifter instead of by mechanical movement of the probe. The effect is exactly as though the probe were moved along the line; in particular, as the phase shift is varied the probe voltage will be found to go through maxima and minima from

---

[1] A directional-coupler system specifically for waveguides is described by H. J. Riblett, A Swept-frequency 3-centimeter Impedance Indicator, *Proc. IRE*, vol. 36, p. 1493, December, 1948.

[2] M. Chodorow, E. L. Ginzton, and F. Kane, A Microwave Impedance Bridge, *Proc. IRE*, vol. 37, p. 634, June, 1949.

which the standing-wave ratio can be determined. That is to say, introducing an additional phase shift of ϕ radians between probe and load is equivalent to moving the probe a distance d_1 farther from the load, where

$$d_1 = \frac{\phi}{2\pi}\lambda_g \qquad (4\text{-}64)$$

Here λ_g is the guide wavelength as given by Eq. (4-60). Any convenient type of phase shifter may be used in Fig. 4-24. Typical arrangements suitable for waveguide systems are the "wave-squeezer," movable-vane, and rotary phase shifters illustrated in Figs. 6-35 and 6-36.

In a system such as illustrated in Fig. 4-24, the magnitude of the standing-wave ratio existing in the guide can be determined without knowing

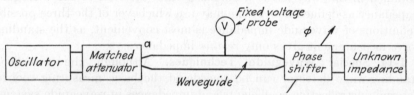

Fig. 4-24. Schematic diagram of phase-shifter and fixed-probe arrangement for measuring an unknown impedance.

the actual phase shift that is introduced. All that need be done is to observe the maximum and minimum values of probe response as the phase shifter is continuously varied, and then substitute the results into Eq. (4-15) to obtain the standing-wave ratio S.

From the standing-wave ratio, one can also calculate the magnitude of the reflection coefficient, using Eq. (4-16). However, if the phase angle of the reflection coefficient is desired, or if the magnitude and phase of the load impedance are to be determined, then it is necessary that there be available a calibration giving accurately the phase shift as a function of the setting of the phase-shifter control.

To calibrate the phase shifter in Fig. 4-24 one first replaces the load impedance by a short circuit. Under these conditions the relation between the voltage induced on the probe, and the adjustable phase shift ϕ introduced by the phase shifter is[1]

$$\left.\begin{array}{l}\text{Voltage induced}\\\text{on probe}\end{array}\right\} = A|\sin{(\phi + \alpha)}| \qquad (4\text{-}65)$$

Here A is a proportionality constant determined by the design of the probe system, while α is the total electrical phase shift existing between

[1] Note that if a square-law probe system is used, the response actually observed is proportional to the square of the induced voltage; i.e., to get relative induced voltage, one must then take the square root of the observed probe output voltage.

the probe position and the load point when $\phi = 0$.   The value of α is determined by the distance in guide wavelengths from probe to load, augmented by any insertion phase shift introduced by the phase shifter when the phase-shifter control dial reads $\phi = 0$.   A calibration of the phase shifter is then obtained by observing the relative voltage induced on the probe as a function of the setting of the phase-shifter dial.   Settings that make the induced voltage a minimum then correspond to $\phi + \alpha = n\pi$, where n can be any integer (including zero), while the settings that make the induced voltage a maximum correspond to $\phi + \alpha = m\pi/2$, where m is an odd integer.   The phase shift corresponding to intermediate settings of the phase shifter can then be determined by introducing the observed variations in probe response into Eq. (4-65).   Thus, when the probe voltage is 70.7 per cent of the maximum voltage (*i.e.*, half the maximum response if a square-law probe is used), then ϕ has a value that differs by 45° from the value that makes the response a minimum.   From Eq. (4-64) the introduction of such a phase shift has the effect of moving the probe a distance $\lambda_g/8$.

In measuring standing-wave ratios with a phase shifter and fixed probe it is necessary that a matched impedance be seen looking from the probe along the waveguide toward the oscillator.   This can be accomplished by the use of an attenuation pad, as indicated in Fig. 4-24, with an impedance that matches the guide.   This attenuator absorbs the wave reflected by the load impedance, thereby making the amplitude of incident wave independent of the presence or absence of a reflected wave.   The attenuator also isolates the oscillator from the measuring system; this prevents the oscillator frequency from changing as variations in the phase-shifter setting alter the input impedance at the point a in Fig. 4-24.

Hybrid Junction (Magic-T) Techniques.[1,2]   A technique widely used in waveguide systems for determining the magnitude of the standing-wave ratio, or the magnitude of the reflection coefficient, is based upon the "magic-T," or hybrid, junction.   The geometry of such a device is shown in Fig. 4-25.   This device has the property that a wave entering A cannot pass directly to the output B, but rather splits into two equal parts that travel down the side arms C and D.   Reflected waves in arms C and D reaching the junction will, however, enter arm B as shown, to produce a resultant wave in B that is the *difference* between the reflected

---

[1] The term "magic T" is here used synonymously with "hybrid."   More properly a magic T is a hybrid such as in Fig. 4-25 with the addition of posts and irises that compensate for discontinuity effects so that when matched loads are connected to any three branches the impedance seen looking in at the fourth is a perfect match.   Such compensation is not usually needed for the measurements described here.

[2] For more information see "Technique of Microwave Measurements," *op. cit.*, pp. 525–543.

wave in arm C and the reflected wave in arm D. It is therefore apparent that if arms C and D are of equal length and are terminated identically, then no output will appear in arm B. However, output will appear in B to the extent that the terminating impedances are not identical.

A measuring system making use of the hybrid junction of Fig. 4-25 is shown schematically in Fig. 4-26. Here a reference termination Z_0 is

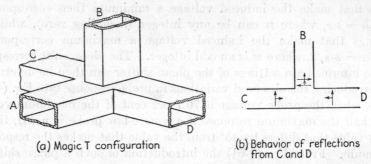

(a) Magic T configuration

(b) Behavior of reflections from C and D

FIG. 4-25. "Magic-T" arrangement.

connected at D while the unknown impedance Z_x is used as the termination for arm C. Arms C and D are further made identical in every respect, including particularly length. Power from an oscillator is supplied to arm A through an isolating attenuator, while output in arm B is observed by a crystal detector, preferably operated on the square-law part of its characteristics. Alternatively, a bolometer may replace the crystal detector. When the unknown impedance Z_x in Fig. 4-26 is the

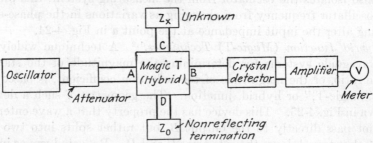

FIG. 4-26. Block diagram of system for making impedance or reflection-coefficient measurements using a magic-T (hybrid junction) arrangement.

same as the known reference impedance Z_0, then zero output will be observed in arm B. Thus if Z_0 has a value that provides a nonreflecting termination for arm D, then zero output indicates Z_x is a nonreflecting termination for arm C. However, if output is present in arm B when D is terminated to be nonreflecting, then the magnitude of the reflection coefficient introduced by Z_x is directly proportional to the magnitude of this output. The quantitative relation involved can be readily obtained experimentally from the fact that when Z_x is replaced by a short circuit, the output magnitude present in B corresponds to a reflection coefficient of 1.0.

The hybrid-junction system of Fig. 4-26 is not frequency-sensitive,[1] and so is particularly useful where impedances must be compared over a wide frequency range. This introduces the possibility of using an oscilloscope screen to present the reflections existing on a waveguide system as a function of frequency. The apparatus arrangement is shown

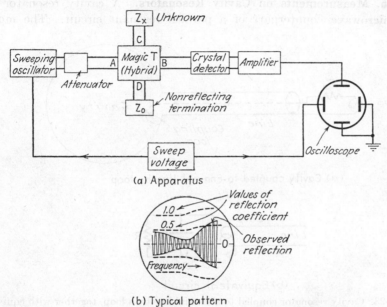

(a) Apparatus

(b) Typical pattern

Fig. 4-27. Impedance-measuring system of Fig. 4-26 modified to present on a cathode-ray screen the behavior of the reflection coefficient over a band of frequencies.

in Fig. 4-27, and differs from Fig. 4-26 in that the carrier frequency of the exciting oscillator is swept electronically by a voltage that also provides the horizontal deflection of the oscilloscope. Thus the horizontal position on the presentation represents frequency, while vertical deflection represents reflection coefficient. A scale of reference for interpreting vertical deflections can be obtained by placing a short circuit across arm C in place of Z_x, thus producing a reflection coefficient of 1.0 for all frequencies. This can be sketched on the oscilloscope face as shown in Fig. 4-27b, using a grease pencil. The line will not necessarily be straight because the oscillator output may vary over the frequency range. In a typical situation the unknown impedance Z_x would be the input of a

[1] This implies that the termination Z_0 is nonreflecting over the frequency range involved. Such a termination can be obtained by the methods illustrated in Fig. 14-21.

waveguide transmission system, and the object of the measurement would be to determine the reflections existing in this system over a band of frequencies.

The hybrid-junction technique is a convenient one, requiring relatively simple equipment. It will very precisely compare two terminations that are almost identical. Also, when a good nonreflecting termination is available, the hybrid device accurately determines very small values of reflection coefficient.[1]

4-15. Measurements on Cavity Resonators. A cavity resonator is the microwave counterpart of a parallel resonant circuit. The most

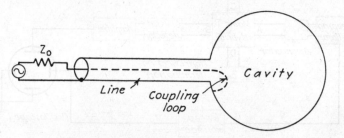

(a) Cavity coupled to coaxial line by loop

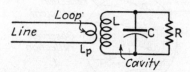

(b) Equivalent circuit

Fig. 4-28. Cavity resonator coupled to a coaxial line by a loop, together with equivalent circuits.

important properties of a cavity are the resonant frequency and the Q. In many cases the impedance that the cavity presents to associated circuits is also of significance.

When making use of cavities, it is necessary to provide some means of coupling the cavity to other electrical circuits. Coupling to a coaxial line can be obtained by terminating the line with a loop that projects into the cavity as illustrated in Fig. 4-28a; alternatively one may employ a probe formed by an extension of the center conductor that projects into the cavity. In the case of a waveguide, the coupling can be supplied by a suitably located hole (iris) that connects the interior of the waveguide with the interior of the cavity.

[1] A. F. Pomeroy, Precision Measurement of Impedance Mismatches in Waveguide, *Bell System Tech. J.*, vol. 26, p. 446, July, 1947.

Determination of Resonant Frequency and Q of a Cavity by Impedance Measurements. In practice one very commonly encounters a cavity in a system such as illustrated in Fig. 4-28a, and then desires to determine the characteristics that the cavity possesses when in this environment. This arrangement is equivalent to a circuit of the form shown in Fig. 4-28b, in which the cavity is represented by a parallel resonant circuit *RLC* coupled to the inductance L_p of the coupling loop.

When an attempt is made to determine the cavity properties in the system of Fig. 4-28, a practical difficulty arises from the fact that one

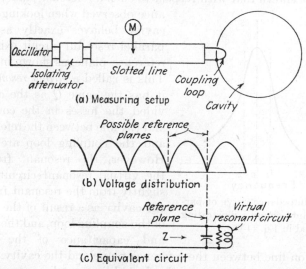

(a) Measuring setup

(b) Voltage distribution

(c) Equivalent circuit

Fig. 4-29. Measurement of cavity characteristics by means of a slotted-line standing-wave detector.

has access to the cavity only indirectly at some point external to the cavity. Between this point and the interior of the cavity is interposed a short section of line, and also the coupling loop. This introduces complications.

A number of methods have been devised for determining the cavity properties under this situation. One of these will now be described; it is typical, but is by no means the only procedure possible.[1] The apparatus arrangement used is illustrated in Fig. 4-29a; it involves the insertion of a slotted-line standing-wave detector into the system as shown. The first step in the measuring procedure is then to establish a plane of refer-

[1] For other methods see "Technique of Microwave Measurements," *op. cit.*, pp. 286–289, 330–340; L. Malter and G. R. Brewer, Microwave *Q* Measurements in the Presence of Series Losses, *J. Applied Phys.*, vol. 20, p. 918, October, 1949; "Very High Frequency Techniques," *op. cit.*, pp. 610–626.

ence on the slotted transmission line.   This is always chosen as the location of a voltage minimum on the slotted line either when the cavity is detuned, or when the frequency is far enough off resonance so that the resonant circuit in Fig. 4-28b couples negligible impedance into the loop inductance L_p.   There are a succession of such voltage minima along the transmission line, separated by a half wavelength, as shown in Fig. 4-29b. One should choose one of the minima near the cavity as the reference, although it is not necessary to use the particular minimum that is the nearest to the cavity.

It can be shown that with respect to such a reference plane, the imped-

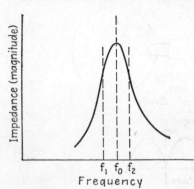

FIG. 4-30.   Impedance curve of parallel resonant circuit, illustrating notation used in Eq. (4-65).

ance observed when looking toward the cavity behaves exactly as though a parallel resonant circuit existed at the reference plane, as shown in Fig. 4-29c. This is called a *virtual resonant circuit;* it has the same Q as the cavity, provided the losses in the coupling loop and the line between the reference plane and the coupling loop are negligible. However, the resonant frequency of the virtual resonant circuit will differ slightly from the resonant frequency of the cavity as a result of the inductance of the coupling loop, and the inductance and capacitance of the connecting transmission line between the reference plane and the cavity.

The next steps are to employ the slotted-line standing-wave detector to measure the impedance Z of the virtual circuit for a succession of frequencies,[1] and then plot the results as shown in Fig. 4-30.   The resonant frequency f_0 of the virtual circuit is the frequency of maximum impedance, while the Q of the virtual circuit, and hence of the cavity, is given by the relation

$$Q = \frac{f_0}{f_2 - f_1} \tag{4-66}$$

Here f_2 and f_1 are the frequencies above and below resonance, respectively, at which the impedance has a magnitude that is 70.7 per cent of the magnitude at resonance.   Knowing f_2 and f_1, the most accurate

[1] Strictly speaking, the position of the reference plane shifts with frequency.   However, the frequency range necessary to cover the resonance curve of a cavity is such a small percentage variation that the position of the reference plane can be regarded as independent of frequency in measurements on cavities, provided the reference plane corresponds to a minimum near the cavity.

means of determining the exact resonant frequency is to use the relation

$$f_0 \approx \frac{f_2 + f_1}{2} \tag{4-67}$$

Instead of plotting the resonance curve as in Fig. 4-30, it is commonly more convenient to plot the standing-wave data directly on a Smith chart as shown in Fig. 4-31. The resonant frequency is then the frequency at which the right-hand side of the impedance curve intersects the horizontal

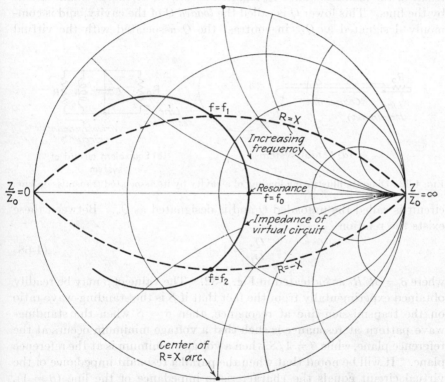

FIG. 4-31. Impedance curve of Fig. 4-30 plotted on a Smith chart, upon which arcs are superimposed showing the loci where the phase angle of the impedance is 45°.

axis; this is the frequency at which the standing-wave ratio is a maximum. The frequencies f_1 and f_2 required to determine the Q of the virtual resonant circuit according to Eq. (4-66) are the two frequencies on the impedance curve at which the resistive component of the impedance equals the reactive component. To facilitate location of these two points, it is convenient to draw lines on the Smith chart corresponding to points where the resistive and reactive components are equal; such loci are shown in Fig. 4-31, and are arcs of circles centered at the normalized impedance components $0 \pm j1.0$, and passing through zero and infinity, as shown.

When dealing with a system such as shown in Fig. 4-28a, one is some-times interested in the Q of the complete system comprising both virtual resonant circuit and the associated transmission line terminated at the sending end, rather than only the Q of the virtual circuit. This complete system can be represented by the equivalent circuit shown in Fig. 4-32; it will have a lower Q than the Q of the cavity (or virtual circuit) as a result of the load resistance R_0 shunted across the virtual resonant circuit by the line. This lower Q is called the *loaded Q* of the cavity, and is com-monly designated as Q_L; in contrast the Q associated with the virtual

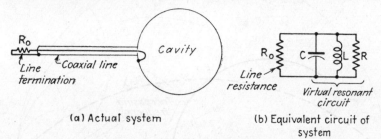

(a) Actual system   (b) Equivalent circuit of system

Fig. 4-32. Diagram illustrating loading of a cavity by its associated transmission line.

circuit is called the unloaded Q and is designated as Q_u. Between these exists the relation

$$\frac{Q_u}{Q_L} = 1 + \beta \tag{4-68}$$

where $\beta = R/R_0$ as indicated in Fig. 4-32. The value of β may be readily obtained experimentally from the fact that if S is the standing-wave ratio on the transmission line at resonance, then $\beta = S$ when the standing-wave pattern at resonance is such that a voltage minimum occurs at the reference plane, while $\beta = 1/S$ when a voltage minimum is at the reference plane. It will be noted that when the parallel resonant impedance of the virtual circuit equals the characteristic impedance of the line ($\beta = 1$), then the loaded Q of the system is exactly half the unloaded Q of the cavity.

Determination of cavity properties as outlined above has the advantage that it is necessary to have access to the cavity only at one coupling point, and that the only equipment required is a slotted line. However, the method gives the resonant frequency of the virtual circuit, rather than of the unloaded cavity.

Determination of Resonant Frequency and Q of Unloaded Cavities from Transmission Measurements. The characteristics of an unloaded cavity can be determined with the arrangement of apparatus illustrated in

Fig. 4-33.   Here oscillations are excited in the cavity by coupling element A, which is so designed as to provide only very slight coupling between the oscillator system and the cavity.   The response of the cavity is indicated by means of a crystal detector, bolometer, or simple radio receiver that is likewise very loosely coupled to the cavity by a second coupling element B.   Probe coupling is shown in Fig. 4-33, although loop or iris coupling could also be used.

A typical measuring procedure for determining the resonant frequency of the cavity then consists in varying the frequency of the oscillator and observing the frequency at which the output detector indicates maximum cavity response.   Alternatively, somewhat greater accuracy can be

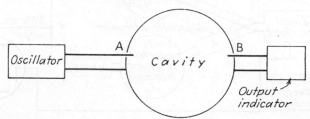

Fig. 4-33. Arrangement of apparatus for measuring the characteristics of a cavity by the transmission method.

obtained by considering the resonant frequency to be the mean of the two frequencies on either side of resonance at which the response is less than at resonance by some specified amount, such as 3 db; this procedure has the possibility of greater accuracy since the response on the side of the resonance curve varies more rapidly with frequency than does the response in the immediate vicinity of resonance.   When the cavity is tunable, one may instead start with a fixed oscillator frequency and determine the cavity setting corresponding to resonance, by observing the point of maximum response, or by taking the mean value of the settings corresponding to equal reductions in response on the two sides of resonance.   The Q of the resonant cavity may be measured by modifying the procedure to determine the frequencies f_1 and f_2 on either side of resonance at which the response of the system is reduced 3 db below the response at resonance.   One then has

$$Q = \frac{f_0}{f_2 - f_1} \qquad (4\text{-}69)$$

where $f_0 \approx (f_1 + f_2)/2$ is the resonant frequency.   It is possible in this way to determine the Q with high precision if means are provided for *directly* determining the frequency difference $f_2 - f_1$, rather than attempting to obtain this rather small difference by the independent measurement of the much larger quantities f_1 and f_2.

The resonant frequency and Q obtained in this way correspond to the values for the *unloaded* cavity to the extent that the couplings at the input and output points are *individually* so small that the resulting loading of the cavity is negligible. It is not sufficient merely that there be negligible direct transmission between the two coupling elements. In view of the small couplings involved, it is necessary either that the oscillator be relatively powerful or that the output indicator be unusually sensitive.

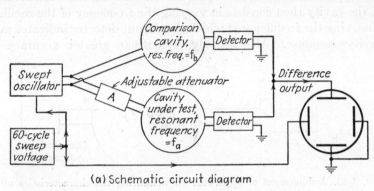

(a) Schematic circuit diagram

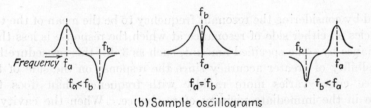

(b) Sample oscillograms

Fig. 4-34. Method of making a precise comparison between the resonant frequency of a standard cavity and of an unknown cavity. The diagram indicates iris (hole) coupling to the cavities, although other methods could be employed equally well.

The resonant frequency of a cavity under investigation can be very precisely determined in terms of the resonant frequency of a tunable calibrated cavity using the arrangement of apparatus illustrated in Fig. 4-34.[1] Here, the two cavities are excited from a common oscillator that is frequency-modulated at 60 cycles. The same 60 cycles is used to provide horizontal deflection of the oscilloscope, so that the horizontal position of the cathode-ray spot is a function of frequency. Vertical deflection of the oscilloscope is supplied by the difference in outputs of the output systems associated with the two cavities. An adjustable attenuator, indicated by A in Fig. 4-34, is provided so that the outputs of the two

[1] For additional information see R. L. Sproull and E. G. Linder, Resonant Cavity Measurements, *Proc. IRE*, vol. 34, p. 305, May, 1946.

cavities can be adjusted to be approximately equal, although there is no particular advantage in exact equality. Typical oscilloscope patterns produced by this arrangement for different frequency settings of the tunable calibrated cavity are shown for the case where the comparison cavity has a higher Q than the cavity under test. It is apparent that the condition corresponding to identical resonant frequencies can be rather precisely determined.

4-16. Measurement of Insertion Loss in Coaxial and Waveguide Systems. In coaxial systems operating at the higher frequencies, par-

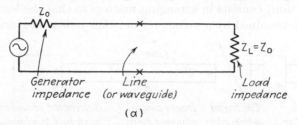

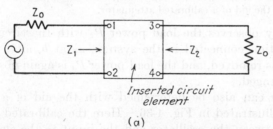

Fig. 4-35. Schematic diagram illustrating situation resulting from insertion of a circuit element in a transmission-line or waveguide system operating with matched terminal impedances.

ticularly microwaves, and in waveguide systems, it is often important to know the reduction in power reaching the load that results from the insertion of some circuit element into the system. The element in question might be a connector, a length of cable, a rotating joint, bend, etc. The reduction in power output resulting from the presence of such a circuit element is termed the *insertion loss*. That is, referring to Fig. 4-35,

$$\text{Insertion loss in db} = L = 10 \log_{10} \frac{P_1}{P_2} \qquad (4\text{-}70)$$

Here P_2 is the power delivered to the load when the circuit element under study is present in the system as in Fig. 4-35b, while P_1 is the power delivered to the load when this circuit element is removed (Fig. 4-35a).

It is important to note in Fig. 4-35 that when the circuit element under investigation is not present, as at *a*, one then has a matched system in which the load and generator impedances both equal the characteristic impedance of the coaxial line.[1,2] This is the case of practical importance in dealing with ultra-high-frequency and microwave systems, and the discussion in this section is limited to the effect of inserting a circuit element into such a matched system. The insertion loss under these conditions is commonly termed *insertion attenuation*, or simply *attenuation*.

Determination of Insertion Loss by Power-ratio Measurements and by Calibrated Attenuators.[3] An obvious method of determining insertion loss (attenuation) consists in arranging matters so that the load power in Fig. 4-35 is determined by a bolometer or other power-measuring means.

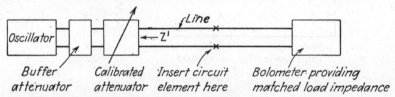

Buffer   Calibrated   'Insert circuit   Bolometer-providing
attenuator   attenuator   element here   matched load impedance

Fig. 4-36. Schematic diagram illustrating arrangement of apparatus for measuring insertion loss with the aid of a calibrated attenuator.

One then simply observes the load power P_2 with the circuit element under investigation connected in the system, as at *b*, after which this circuit element is removed, and the load power P_1 is again observed with nothing else changed.

Insertion loss can also be determined with the aid of a calibrated attenuator, as illustrated in Fig. 4-36. Here the calibrated attenuator is introduced between the oscillator and the input to the system under test, while some means is provided for determining the relative value of output power or voltage developed in the load (a bolometer is indicated in Fig. 4-36). The measuring procedure consists in setting the attenuation to some convenient low reference value, and observing the output indication at the load when the circuit element under test is present in the system. The circuit element being investigated is then removed, and the attenuator setting readjusted to restore the original output indica-

[1] In the case of a waveguide, the wave impedances [see Eqs. (4-62)] take the place of the characteristic impedance.

[2] It is, however, permissible for a transformation in characteristic impedance to occur; *i.e.*, the system to the right of terminals 3-4 in Fig. 4-35b may have a characteristic impedance differing from that of the system to the left of 1-2. Such a situation can exist when a tapered section, or a coaxial-line-to-waveguide transformer, is involved. In this case P_1 in Eq. (4-70) is the load power when an ideal impedance-transforming network is present.

[3] Details of systems making use of power-ratio measurements or calibrated attenuators are described by Fleming, *loc. cit.;* "Technique of Microwave Measurements," *op. cit.*, pp. 805–816.

tion.   The change in attenuator setting gives the insertion loss (or attenuation) desired.   In this arrangement of apparatus, it is essential that
the impedance Z' looking toward the oscillator from the system under
test be equal to the characteristic impedance of the transmission system;
otherwise reflections from the inserted impedance will cause the insertion loss to depend upon the extent of the impedance mismatch at the
sending end of the line.   The desired result can be assured by proper
design of the calibrated attenuator.

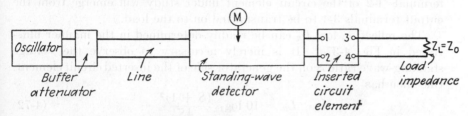

(a) Determination of reflection attenuation L_R

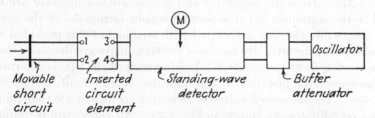

(b) Determination of dissipation attenuation L_D

Fig. 4-37.   Determination of reflection attenuation and dissipation attenuation by
standing-wave measurements.

Both of the above methods of measuring insertion loss have the disadvantage of requiring that the circuit element under test be alternately
physically added and subtracted from the system.   In some cases, as for
example when dealing with a rotating joint, this is mechanically impossible.   This difficulty can be overcome by determining the insertion loss
from impedance measurements.

*Determination of Insertion Loss by Impedance and Standing-wave Meas-
urements.*[1]   When using impedance measurements to determine insertion
loss, it is convenient to divide the total loss L into two parts, which can
be considered as due, respectively, to reflection and dissipation introduced
by the presence of the circuit element under study.   That is

$$L = L_R + L_D \qquad \text{decibels} \qquad (4\text{-}71)$$

[1] For further information see R. W. Beatty, Determination of Attenuation from
Impedance Measurements, *Proc. IRE*, vol. 38, p. 895, August, 1950.

Here the insertion reflection loss L_R takes into account the fact that if the impedance Z_1 looking into terminals 1-2 in Fig. 4-35b does not equal the characteristic impedance Z_0, then reflection occurs, and some of the power transmitted toward the load by the incident wave is returned to the generator, and absorbed in the generator impedance. In the special case where Z_1 equals the characteristic impedance Z_0 of the system, the reflection loss will be zero. The insertion dissipation loss L_D takes into account the fact that only a portion of the power actually entering the input terminals 1-2 of the circuit element under study will emerge from the output terminals 3-4 to be transmitted on to the load.

The reflection loss L_R can be readily determined in the manner illustrated in Fig. 4-37a. It is merely necessary to observe the voltage standing-wave ratio S on the generator side of the inserted circuit element. One then has[1]

$$L_R = 10 \log_{10} \frac{(S + 1)^2}{4S} \qquad (4\text{-}72)$$

To determine the dissipation loss L_D, the system is connected as shown in Fig. 4-37b. Here the oscillator and standing-wave detector are connected to the terminals 3-4 (the normal output terminals) of the system under test, while the line associated with terminals 1-2 is provided with a movable short circuit. By means of the standing-wave detector, the reflection coefficient at terminals 3-4, looking toward the left, is determined for a succession of positions of the movable short circuit, as described in Sec. 4-8. The measured values of reflection coefficient are then plotted on polar coordinates, as shown in Fig. 4-38. All values will be found to lie on a circular locus, the radius r of which is related to the dissipation attenuation according to the relation[2]

$$L_D = 10 \log_{10} \frac{1}{r} \qquad \text{decibels} \qquad (4\text{-}73)$$

Theoretically the reflection coefficient need be measured for only three positions on the movable short circuit, since three points determine a circle; however, it is safer to make additional measurements and use the circle as a means for averaging the data.

It is to be noted that Eqs. (4-71), (4-72), and (4-73) apply irrespective of whether or not an impedance transformation exists between the two

[1] This relation follows from the fact that when the reflection coefficient has the value ρ, a fraction ρ^2 of the power of the incident wave is reflected. Thus the power entering terminals 1-2 in Fig. 4-35b is reduced by the factor $1 - \rho^2$ because of reflection at these terminals. Substituting for ρ from Eq. (4-16), this fraction becomes $1 - \left(\dfrac{S - 1}{S + 1}\right)^2 = \dfrac{4S}{(S + 1)^2}$, from which Eq. (4-71) follows immediately.

[2] This equation is derived by A. L. Cullen, Measurement of Microwave Transmission Efficiency, *Wireless Eng.*, vol. 26, p. 255, August, 1949.

sides of the inserted circuit element in Figs. 4-35b and 4-37.   Hence the impedance method of determining L is particularly suitable when an impedance transformation is involved.   The one special consideration involved is that the standing-wave detector shown in Fig. 4-37a must have a characteristic impedance that matches the system looking from the standing-wave detector toward 1-2, while the standing-wave detector in Fig. 4-37b must have a characteristic impedance that corresponds to the system looking toward terminals 3-4.

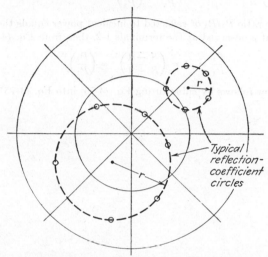

Typical reflection-coefficient circles

FIG. 4-38. Polar-coordinate plot of reflection coefficient obtained in Fig. 4-37b for a succession of frequencies, showing two typical reflection-coefficient circles.

A special case of importance occurs when the inserted circuit element possesses input and output impedances equal to the characteristic impedance of the associated transmission system; in Fig. 4-35b this means that Z_1 and Z_2 will both equal the characteristic impedance Z_0.   Under these conditions the insertion reflection loss L_R is zero, and the insertion dissipation loss (*i.e.*, the attenuation) can be determined by short circuiting the terminals 3-4 in Fig. 4-37a and observing the voltage standing-wave ratio S.   Then[1]

$$L_D = 10 \log_{10} \frac{S+1}{S-1} \qquad \text{decibels} \qquad (4\text{-}74)$$

[1] This relation is derived as follows: Call P_1 the power of an incident wave entering terminals 1-2 in Fig. 4-37a, and P_2 the power of this wave after passage through the circuit element under study.   Then

$$L_D = 10 \log_{10} \frac{P_1}{P_2} \qquad (4\text{-}75)$$

However, if terminals 3-4 are short-circuited, then P_2 is totally reflected.   When this reflected wave emerges from terminals 1-2 after a return passage through the network,

Equation (4-74) provides a very useful result, in that it enables the attenuation of a matched attenuator to be determined experimentally by a standing-wave measurement.

ts power P_3 satisfies the relation

$$\frac{P_3}{P_2} = \frac{P_2}{P_1}$$

or

$$\frac{P_1}{P_3} = \left(\frac{P_1}{P_2}\right)^2$$

However, since the ratio P_3/P_1 of reflected to incident power equals the square of the reflection coefficient ρ observed at the terminals 1-2, then from Eq. (4-16)

$$\frac{P_3}{P_1} = \rho^2 = \left(\frac{S-1}{S+1}\right)^2 = \left(\frac{P_2}{P_1}\right)^2 \tag{4-76}$$

Equation (4-74) now follows by substituting Eq. (4-76) into Eq. (4-75).

CHAPTER 5

MEASUREMENT OF FREQUENCY

5-1. Standards of Frequency.[1] The fundamental standard of frequency is the period of rotation of the earth. This can be measured with great accuracy by astronomical methods, and might be thought of as a standard frequency of one cycle per day. All standards of frequency must ultimately be referred to this fundamental source of frequency for calibration purposes.

Practical frequency standards can be classified as either primary or secondary standards. A primary standard of frequency is an oscillator which generates a frequency that is very constant over long periods of time, and which is checked against the earth's rotation at regular intervals. Secondary standards of frequency are very stable oscillators which have their frequency checked periodically against a primary standard. The essential difference between primary and secondary standards is not necessarily in the degree of frequency stability, which is sometimes the same and sometimes quite different, but in the fact that the primary standard is directly referred to the period of the earth's rotation.

Recent developments in microwave spectroscopy have introduced the possibility of using spectrum lines as frequency standards.[2] For example, ammonia gas has an absorption line at a frequency of 23,870.1 Mc. It has been found possible to employ this spectrum line as a reference for controlling the frequency of an oscillator by means of an automatic-frequency-control system that operates to keep the frequency of the oscillator from departing appreciably from the frequency corresponding to the spectrum line. While arrangements of this type have not yet been

[1] A comprehensive survey of the subject of frequency measurements is given by J. E. Thwaites and F. J. M. Laver, The Technique of Frequency Measurement, and Its Application to Telecommunications, *J. IEE*, vol. 89, pt. III, p. 139, September, 1942.

[2] For further information see W. V. Smith, J. L. Garcia de Quevedo, R. L. Carter, and W. S. Bennett, Frequency Stabilization of Microwave Oscillators by Spectrum Lines, *J. Applied Phys.*, vol. 18, p. 1112, December, 1947; J. L. Garcia de Quevedo and W. V. Smith, Frequency Stabilization of Microwave Oscillators by Spectrum Lines, II, *J. Applied Phys.*, vol. 19, p. 831, September, 1948; W. D. Hershberger and L. E. Norton, Frequency Stabilization with Microwave Spectral Lines, *RCA Rev.*, vol. 9, p. 38, March, 1948; F. H. Rockett, Stable Time and Frequency Standard, *Electronics*, vol. 22, p. 82, April, 1949.

fully perfected, they offer intriguing possibilities as primary frequency standards in view of the inherent stability of spectrum lines.

Primary Standards of Frequency.[1]   Present-day standards of frequency are based on a very carefully designed quartz crystal oscillator.   Typical features include a quartz crystal operating in the range 50 to 100 kc and having a low temperature coefficient of frequency, thermostat control of the crystal temperature, an oscillator circuit that maintains constant amplitude of oscillations at a frequency that is relatively little affected by the electrical circuits and the tube associated with the crystal, voltage-regulated power supplies, etc.   Such a crystal oscillator that is well designed and properly operated will have a long-time frequency stability of a few parts in a hundred million over a period of several months; over short periods of time it will generate a frequency that is constant to within a few parts in a billion.   The extent of this precision is indicated by the fact that 1 part in 50,000,000 of the distance across the United States from New York to San Francisco is about 3 in.

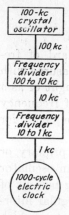

FIG. 5-1. Schematic diagram illustrating electric clock operated from a crystal oscillator.

A typical arrangement for comparing the frequency of a primary standard with the period of rotation of the earth is shown schematically in Fig. 5-1.   Here the frequency of the crystal oscillator, shown as 100 kc in this instance, is reduced by a chain of frequency dividers to 1000 cycles that is employed to operate an electric clock. This clock is so designed that it will keep correct time when supplied with exactly 1000 cycles; the correctness of the frequency of the primary standard is then obtained by comparing the time indicated by this clock with observatory time as made available by wire transmission or radio time signals.   The primary standard must be provided with very accurate means for making this comparison, since 0.01 sec in one day represents slightly more than 1 part in 10,000,000, and is somewhat greater

---

[1] An excellent summary of the many techniques made use of in primary frequency standards is given by W. A. Marrison, The Evolution of the Quartz Crystal Clock, *Bell System Tech. J.*, vol. 27, p. 510, July, 1948; also see C. F. Booth and F. J. M. Laver, A Standard of Frequency and Its Application, *J. IEE*, vol. 93, pt. III, p. 223, July, 1946; John M. Shaull, Adjustment of High-precision Frequency and Time Standards, *Proc. IRE*, vol. 38, p. 6, January, 1950; C. F. Booth, The Evolution of Frequency Control, *Proc. IEE*, vol. 98, pt. III, p. 1, January, 1951; L. Essen, Frequency Standardization, *Proc. IEE*, vol. 98, pt II., p. 154, April, 1951; Humphrey M. Smith, The Determination of Time and Frequency, *Proc. IEE.*, vol. 98, pt II, p. 143, April, 1951.

A discussion of considerations involved in the crystal oscillator of a primary frequency standard is also given by J. K. Clapp, Bridge-controlled Oscillator, *Gen. Rad. Expt.*, vol. 18, p. 1, April, 1944, p. 6, May, 1944.

than the error in time developed by a good primary standard in a single 24-hr period.[1]

Secondary Standards of Frequency.   Secondary frequency standards are ordinarily based on carefully designed crystal oscillators.[2,3]   The very best secondary standards of frequency differ from primary standards only in the omission of the clock, and associated means for accurately comparing the time registered by the clock with observatory time signals. Where the utmost in frequency precision is not required of the secondary standard, it is possible to relax the design in certain respects, as, for example, less precise temperature control of the crystal, use of crystals at frequencies lying outside the optimum range 50 to 100 kc, etc.   In any case, a properly designed secondary standard of frequency using a crystal oscillator can ordinarily be expected to maintain its frequency constant to within a few parts in a million for long periods of time without readjustment.

Radio Signals as Frequency Standards.   Certain classes of radio signals are very useful as frequency standards.   In particular, the National Bureau of Standards conducts a regular schedule of transmissions that include continuous operation on several carrier frequencies, and operation for a portion of each day or night on other frequencies as well.   The carrier frequencies employed are so chosen as to ensure reliable coverage of the entire United States at all times.   These signals are provided with

[1] In large laboratories, which attempt to maintain the very best in primary-standard frequencies, it has been found desirable simultaneously to operate two to four primary standards, the instantaneous frequencies of which are continuously intercompared with each other, as well as periodically being compared against astronomical time information.   Means have been devised whereby the instantaneous frequencies of two such oscillators can be compared with an accuracy of about 1 part in 10^{10}; for further information see L. A. Meacham, High-precision Frequency Comparison, *Bell Labs. Record*, vol. 20, p. 179, March, 1942; H. B. Law, An Instrument for Short-period Frequency Comparisons of Great Accuracy, *J. IEE*, vol. 94, pt. III, p. 38, January, 1947; Marrison, *loc. cit.*; Booth and Laver, *loc. cit.*; L. Hartshorn and L. Essen, Radio Standards, *Proc. IEE*, vol. 96, pt. III, p. 37, January, 1949; J. M. Shaull and C. M. Kortman, Comparing Outputs from Precision Time Standards, *Electronics*, vol. 14, p. 102, April, 1951.

[2] When the secondary standard need operate only in the audio-frequency range, an electrically driven tuning fork is sometimes used.   By careful design and temperature control, it is possible to obtain a constancy of frequency within a few parts in a million in this way; see Marrison, *loc. cit.*; D. W. Dye and L. Essen, The Valve Maintained Tuning Fork as a Primary Standard of Frequency, *Proc. Royal Soc. (London)*, vol. 143, p. 285, 1943; E. Norrman, A Precision Tuning Fork Frequency Standard, *Proc. IRE*, vol. 20, p. 1715, November, 1932.

[3] It is not required that the crystal be incorporated in an oscillator.   Instead, the secondary standard of frequency may make use of a crystal as a fixed-frequency wavemeter having a stable high-Q resonant circuit of low temperature coefficient.   Methods of utilizing such a wavemeter are described by F. J. M. Laver, Crystal Resonators as Frequency Substandards, *Proc. IEE*, vol. 97, pt. III, p. 93, March, 1950.

modulations of various types, such as 440 cycles and 4000 cycles, and are interrupted precisely on the hour, and at successive 5-min intervals. The carrier frequencies, modulation frequencies, and time intervals associated with these signals are derived from a primary standard of frequency that has an accuracy that is better than 1 part in 50,000,000.[1] The signals as received may, however, at any particular instant have a frequency that is somewhat less precise.   This arises from the fact that when the ionosphere is involved, a shifting in the height of the ionosphere will introduce Doppler effects that will cause the received frequency to differ from the transmitted frequency.   However, the maximum error that can be thus introduced is very, very slight; also if the received frequency is averaged over an extended time interval, the Doppler effects will cancel out and the precision becomes that of the transmitted signal.

Signals from commercial radio stations, particularly broadcast stations, are often found useful as secondary frequency standards for checking heterodyne frequency meters, wavemeters, etc.   Broadcast stations are particularly good sources of standard frequencies since they are in operation nearly continuously, are required to maintain their assigned frequency to within 20 cycles, and as a practical matter commonly maintain their frequencies to within a few parts in a million.   Signals of other classes ordinarily have somewhat lower frequency stability, but nevertheless maintain assigned frequencies to a much closer percentage than represented by the accuracy of such equipment as heterodyne frequency meters.

5-2. Derivation of Additional Frequencies from a Single-frequency Source.   A primary or secondary standard of frequency produces oscillations of only a single frequency.   In making practical use of such frequency standards it is commonly desirable to have available other frequencies, both higher and lower, which are derived from the standard frequency and have the same accuracy.

Additional frequencies can be derived from a given standard frequency by means of harmonic and subharmonic generators.   One example of this is illustrated in Fig. 5-1, where a 1000-cycle oscillation is derived from the 100-kc standard for the purpose of operating the electric clock. A more general example is illustrated in Fig. 5-2.   Here by means of a chain of subharmonic generators (frequency dividers), one obtains frequencies of 10,000 cycles, 1000 cycles, and 100 cycles which have the same degree of precision as the standard frequency.   It is also possible to employ harmonic generators to extend the series upward to 1000 kc, and even further if desired.

---

[1] Details as to these signals are summarized in the paper, WWV Schedules, *Electronics*, vol. 20, p. 87, May, 1947.

Frequency division in arrangements such as illustrated in Fig. 5-2, is commonly carried out by means of a multivibrator, a regenerative frequency divider, or a counter-type frequency divider.[1] The regenerative and counter types of subharmonic generators are commonly preferred to

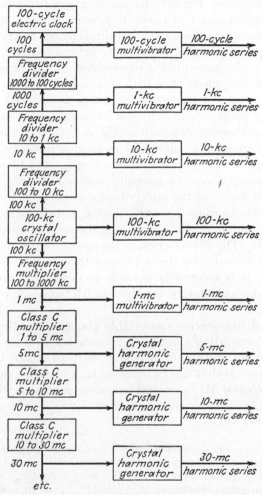

FIG. 5-2. Frequency standard provided with harmonic and subharmonic generators for deriving a large number of frequencies from the original standard frequency.

the multivibrator, particularly for high ratios, because their behavior is less affected by tube aging and changes in electrode voltages.

The harmonic generators used in arrangements as illustrated in Fig. 5-2 for extending the frequency chain to frequencies higher than the standard

[1] For further discussion of subharmonic generators see F. E. Terman, "Radio Engineering," 3d ed., p. 594, McGraw-Hill Book Company, Inc., New York, 1947.

can be of a variety of types.   At fundamental frequencies up to about 1 Mc, harmonic generation is commonly carried out with the aid of multivibrators.   However, at frequencies higher than this, tube and circuit capacitances cause multivibrators to lose most of their advantages.   At these higher frequencies, Class C harmonic generators are customary; they are also sometimes used at lower frequencies where a multivibrator would be a satisfactory alternative.   Multiplications ranging from two to five per stage are practical in Class C arrangements.   The highest frequency that can be generated is determined by the upper frequency limit of the triode amplifier; thus with close-spaced triodes it is possible to extend the chain of frequencies in Fig. 5-2 to about 3000 Mc.[1]

Each frequency made available by the frequency chain can be used to generate a harmonic series as shown in Fig. 5-2, thus further increasing the number of frequencies available for measuring purposes.   When the fundamental frequency is of the order of a megacycle or less, the multivibrator is customarily used to generate such a harmonic series.   The irregularly shaped waves of the multivibrator are very rich in high-order harmonics, particularly when the multivibrator is designed as a wide-band amplifier so that rounding of the corners of the multivibrator wave form will be minimized.   The effectiveness of the multivibrator in generating a harmonic series is indicated by the fact that with a fundamental frequency of 100 kc or less, it is commonly possible to detect the presence of all harmonics up to approximately the thousandth harmonic using a sensitive radio receiver.

At fundamental frequencies appreciably above 1 Mc, the most satisfactory means of generating a harmonic series is a silicon (or germanium) crystal rectifier.   Harmonics up to about the fiftieth can be generated in this way in amounts that can be detected by a sensitive radio receiver. Thus starting with 500 Mc, a crystal harmonic generator will produce a harmonic series based on a fundamental frequency of 500 Mc, and extending to about 25,000 Mc.[2]

---

[1] At the higher frequencies a klystron frequency multiplier is an alternative possibility.   Multiplication of frequencies by ratios of 5:1 or 10:1 is readily possible with a single klystron tube designed to operate as a frequency multiplier.   See D. L. Webster, The Theory of Klystron Oscillations, *J. Applied Phys.*, vol. 10, p. 864, December, 1939; A. E. Harrison, "Klystron Tubes," Chap. 5, McGraw-Hill Book Company, Inc., New York, 1947, "Klystrons and Microwave Triodes" (Vol. 7, Radiation Laboratory Series), pp. 285–294, McGraw-Hill Book Company, Inc., New York, 1948.

[2] The extension of the frequency-multiplier chain and harmonic-generator system associated with a frequency standard to cover the microwave region is discussed in further detail in "Technique of Microwave Measurements" (Vol. 11, Radiation Laboratory Series), pp. 343–375, McGraw-Hill Book Company, Inc., New York, 1947; also see B. F. Husten and Harold Lyons, Microwave Frequency Standards, *Elec. Eng.*, vol. 67, p. 436, May, 1948, and *Trans. AIEE*, vol. 67, p. 321, 1948; Richard

The variety of frequencies available from a system such as indicated in Fig. 5-2 may be still further increased by modulating the output of one of the lower frequency harmonic series upon a higher frequency harmonic series. For example, if the distorted 1000-cycle output wave is modulated upon the 100-kc harmonic series by means of a pentagrid mixer or other equivalent arrangement, then each frequency component (100 kc, 200 kc, etc.) of the 100-kc series possesses sidebands spaced at 1000-cycle intervals on either side of this component. In this way one obtains 99 and 101 kc, 98 and 102 kc, etc., also 199 and 201 kc, 198 and 202 kc, etc.

5-3. Wavemeters. A wavemeter is an adjustable resonant circuit provided with a calibration that gives the resonant frequency in terms of the setting of the tuning adjustment. Wavemeters are used to measure frequency when the higher accuracy of a primary or secondary standard is not required, and where simplicity and portability are important. A wavemeter may employ any type of resonant circuit that is convenient for the frequency range to be covered: thus resonant circuits based on lumped constants, including butterfly circuits, coaxial two-wire lines, and cavities, all find use in wavemeter applications.

Wavemeters may be utilized as absorption, reaction, or transmission devices. In the absorption arrangement, the wavemeter is equipped with means for indicating the current induced in it. The wavemeter is then *loosely* coupled to the oscillation whose frequency is to be determined, and is adjusted for maximum response. In the reaction method, the adjustment of the wavemeter corresponding to the frequency being measured is determined from the reaction produced by the wavemeter upon the system being investigated; for example, the resonant frequency of a low-power oscillator may be readily measured by taking advantage of the fact that when a wavemeter is loosely coupled to the tank circuit of the oscillator, the d-c grid current will drop abruptly when the coupled wavemeter is tuned through resonance with the frequency being generated by the oscillator. In the transmission type of wavemeter, the wavemeter is used as a coupling device in a system that transmits power from a generator to a load or indicator. Such a system is so proportioned that appreciable transmission of energy to the load occurs only when the wavemeter is tuned to the frequency of the energy involved; transmission wavemeters find considerable use at microwave frequencies.

The accuracy with which frequency may be determined by a wavemeter is limited by the fact that a resonance curve is flat on top. As a result, in the immediate vicinity of resonance the reaction of the wave-

G. Talpey and H. Goldberg, A Microwave Frequency Standard, *Proc. IRE*, vol. 35, p. 965, September, 1947.

meter is insensitive to the exact wavemeter setting. This difficulty can be partially overcome by using the two sides of the resonance curve; thus the wavemeter setting corresponding to resonance is almost precisely the average between the two settings corresponding to the same reduction in response on either side of resonance, such as 50 per cent response points on either side of resonance. In any case, *the accuracy with which one may determine the desired frequency by means of a wavemeter is greater the higher the Q of the resonant circuit.* This arises from the fact that the sharpness of the resonance curve is directly proportional to the circuit Q. In general, the accuracy with which one can determine frequency is less than the accuracy with which the dial setting may be read.

The extent to which a wavemeter maintains its calibration over a period of time is determined by the temperature coefficient and aging of the resonant system. Thus good mechanical design is important, and considerable benefit results from using a resonant system that has a low temperature coefficient. Also, if the wavemeter behaves cyclically with temperature variation, it is possible to include a temperature correction in the calibration.

When accuracy is important, the coupling between the resonant circuit of the wavemeter and other circuits must be very small. Otherwise coupled reactance effects will modify the relation between frequency and wavemeter calibration; this is true for transmission as well as absorption and reaction arrangements.

Wavemeters with Lumped Circuit Elements. Wavemeters can be constructed with lumped circuit elements up to about 1200 Mc. Such arrangements are normally employed either as absorption or as reaction devices. The response of the wavemeter is commonly indicated by a crystal detector that is loosely coupled to the resonant circuit and associated with a microammeter that indicates the rectified current. Alternative indicators that are sometimes used include an incandescent lamp connected in series with the resonant circuit, a thermocouple in series with the circuit, or a diode vacuum-tube voltmeter connected across the circuit. The indicating system must be so designed that it does not seriously lower the Q of the resonant system.

Arrangements employing a fixed inductance and variable capacitance are suitable for use from the lowest radio frequencies up to about 100 Mc; this entire range can be covered by a single variable condenser provided with a suitable set of plug-in coils. A convenient way to associate a crystal detector indicator with such a wavemeter is illustrated in Fig. 5-3, in which the coupling between the crystal and the resonant circuit is made small by making capacitance C_1 small and C_2 large.

In the frequency range above 100 Mc the butterfly is the most nearly

ideal form of resonant circuit having lumped constants.[1] The frequency
range covered by an individual resonant circuit of this type can be made
as great as 5:1 by appropriate design.

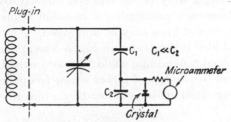

FIG. 5-3. Tuned-circuit type of wavemeter showing plug-in coil and means for
coupling a crystal indicator to the resonant circuit.

A variation of the inductance-capacitance wavemeter that is useful at
very high frequencies consists in varying both the coil and condenser
simultaneously, as shown in Fig. 5-4.[2] This increases the frequency
range that can be covered with a single coil and condenser combination,
and is particularly useful at fre-
quencies on the order of 50 to
400 Mc.

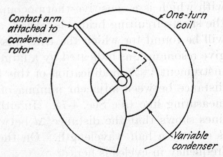

The accuracy obtainable with
wavemeters using tuned circuits
composed of lumped elements
depends upon the circuit Q and
upon details of construction. In
general, accuracies of the order
of 1 per cent or better are readily
obtained, but it is quite difficult
to make the accuracy as great as
0.1 per cent.

FIG. 5-4. Wavemeter for use at ultra-high
frequencies, in which both the circuit
inductance and capacitance are varied
simultaneously.

The law of frequency variation
with angular rotation of the variable condenser depends upon the shape of
the plates of the variable condenser, and upon the distributed capacitance
of the associated coil. By careful attention to details it is possible to
obtain a uniform scale in which the frequency is linearly proportional

[1] Wavemeters using butterfly resonant circuits are described by E. Karplus, A
Wavemeter for 240 to 1200 Megacycles, *Gen. Rad. Expt.*, vol. 20, October, 1945; R. G.
Hibberd, An Absorption Wavemeter for 250–800 Mc/s, *J. IEE (Radiolocation Conv.)*,
vol. 93, pt. IIIA, p. 1303, March–May, 1946.

[2] E. Karplus, Direct-reading Wavemeter for Ultra-high Frequencies, *Gen. Rad.
Expt.*, vol. 15, p. 1, August, 1940.

to the angle of rotation; when this is done interpolation becomes very easy.[1]

Frequency Measurements Using Resonant Lines. At very high frequencies the wavelength may be determined directly by measurements made of the standing-wave pattern on a resonant transmission system. Either two-wire or coaxial lines may be employed.[2]

The fundamental idea is illustrated in Fig. 5-5 as applied to a two-wire line, although a slotted coaxial line could be used instead. Here the line is coupled at one end to a source of power whose frequency is to be measured, and is short-circuited at the other end by a movable bridge in series

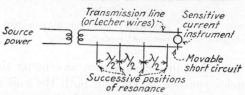

FIG. 5-5. Lecher-wire arrangement for directly measuring wavelength at very high frequencies.

with which is a sensitive thermocouple instrument. As the position of the short-circuiting bridge is varied, a series of sharply defined positions will be found for which the transmission line is of the proper length to give resonance, as indicated by a large current through the thermocouple instrument.[3] A modification of this technique consists in observing the distance between adjacent minima of the standing-wave pattern on the measuring line (see Sec. 4-7). In either case, the theory of transmission lines shows that the distance Δl between successive maxima or minima is exactly a half wavelength. On the assumption of air dielectric, the frequency in cycles is hence[4]

---

[1] A discussion of the problems involved in obtaining such a linear scale when plug-in coils are used is given by W. H. F. Griffiths, Direct Reading of the Frequency of Resonant Circuits, *Wireless Eng.*, vol. 20, p. 254, November, 1943.

[2] A two-wire resonant line used for the measurement of frequency is commonly called a Lecher wire.

[3] In making measurements of frequency in this way it is sometimes found that the expected sharp maximum of current is replaced by a broad maximum or even a double-humped maximum. This behavior results from coupling between the parts of the transmission line on the two sides of the short-circuiting bridge, and can be avoided by terminating the unused portion of the line by its characteristic impedance, by associating a shield of considerable diameter with the movable bridge, or by placing additional short circuits across the unused portion of the wires in order to prevent resonance in them. See Eijiro Takagishi, On a Double Hump Phenomenon of Current through a Bridge across Parallel Lines, *Proc. IRE*, vol. 18, p. 513, March, 1930.

[4] Theoretically a slight correction should be made in Eq. (5-1) to take into account the effect of losses in the line. However, as a practical matter this correction is ordinarily smaller than the inaccuracy inherent in the measurement; for further details

$$f = \frac{150,000,000}{\Delta l} \qquad (5\text{-}1)$$

where Δl is in meters.   It will be noted that the frequency determined in this way is referred to a measurement of length.   It is thus not necessary to calibrate a Lecher wire against a frequency standard; also end effects cancel out since Δl is the *change* in length, or is the observed distance between adjacent minima of the standing wave pattern.   In any case, however, Eq. (5–1) is true only if the line has no solid dielectric whatsoever in the length Δl.

Lecher wire arrangements are particularly suitable for wavelengths ranging from a few meters to a fraction of a meter.   Since resonant

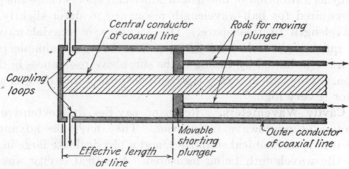

Fig. 5-6. Coaxial wavemeter, showing input and output coupling loops and movable plunger for adjusting the cavity length.

lines have a relatively high Q, the accuracy is quite good, and may reach 0.1 per cent if care is employed.   The chief disadvantage of the arrangement is the large amount of space occupied by the resonant line, and the rather inconvenient nature of the manipulations required to make a determination of frequency.[1]

Resonant Coaxial Lines.   A coaxial line such as illustrated in Fig. 5-6 and operating as a resonant system can be used to measure frequency in the range 600 to 10,000 Mc.[2]   At lower frequencies the cavity becomes excessively long; at higher frequencies the dimensions become impractically small.   The arrangement illustrated is said to be of the *transmission type;* it has two coupling loops, one for feeding power into the line

see August Hund, Correction Factor for the Parallel Wire System Used in Absolute Radio Frequency Standardization, *Proc. IRE*, vol. 12, p. 817, December, 1924.

[1] For further discussion of Lecher wire arrangements, see F. W. Dunmore and F. H. Engels, A Method of Measuring Very Short Radio Wave Lengths and Their Use in Frequency Standardization, *Proc. IRE*, vol. 11, p. 467, October, 1923.

[2] More information on coaxial wavemeters is found in "Technique of Microwave Measurements," *op. cit.*, pp. 320–322.

through a coaxial cable, and one for coupling a crystal rectifier indicator to the oscillations in the cavity. Alternatively, the coaxial wavemeter may be used as a *reaction* device (see page 199), in which case the second coupling loop is omitted. Tuning is accomplished by varying the position of the short-circuiting plunger, using a lead screw. Provision is made for accurately measuring the resulting displacement of the plunger.

At the shorter wavelengths, where the total line length available is one wavelength or more, frequency can be measured by determining the displacement Δl between adjacent maxima, using Eq. (5-1). At lower frequencies, the coaxial line is ordinarily adjusted to be exactly a half wavelength long. In this case, it is necessary to make a calibration of frequency as a function of line length, since end effects cause the physical length required for half-wavelength resonance to differ slightly from a half wavelength in free space. The accuracy of coaxial wavemeters can be quite high, values of 0.05 per cent being obtainable provided backlash is eliminated by tuning to the successive resonances in the same direction. This high accuracy is a result of the fact that the Q of a coaxial resonator is very high.[1]

5-4. Cavity Wavemeters.[2] Resonant cavities find extensive use as wavemeters at microwave frequencies. They have the advantages of high accuracy, mechanical simplicity, and a physical size large in proportion to the wavelength being measured. Practical cavity wavemeters are always in the form of cylinders which are tunable either by means of a piston that varies the length of the cavity as in Fig. 5-7a, or by means of a plunger which projects into the cavity, as in Fig. 5-7b and c.

Mode Considerations and Tuning Arrangements. In making use of a cylindrical cavity to measure frequency it is necessary to take into account the fact that for any given position of the piston, such a cavity has many resonant frequencies as a result of the fact that many field configurations or modes are possible. Furthermore, the resonant frequency of each mode varies according to a different law with the length of the cavity. The resulting situation is illustrated by the "mode chart" of

---

[1] See F. E. Terman, Resonant Lines in Radio Circuits, *Elec. Eng.*, vol. 53, p. 1046, July, 1934, or "Radio Engineering," 3d ed., p. 98, McGraw-Hill Book Company, Inc., New York, 1947.

[2] For further information of a general character on cavity wavemeters, see "Technique of Microwave Measurement," *op. cit.*, pp. 286–384; L. Essen, The Design, Calibration, and Performance of Resonance Wavemeters for Frequencies between 1,000 and 25,000 Mc/s, *J. IEE (Radiolocation Conv.)*, vol. 93, pt. IIIA, p. 1413, March–May, 1946; E. I. Green, H. J. Fisher, and J. G. Ferguson, Techniques and Facilities for Microwave Radar Testing, *Bell System Tech. J.*, vol. 25, p. 435, July, 1946; Husten and Lyons, *loc. cit.*; H. R. Allen and C. D. Curling, The Design and Use of Resonant Cavity Wavemeters for Spectrum Measurements of Pulsed Transmitters at Wavelengths near 10 Cm, *J. IEE*, vol. 95, pt. III, p. 473, November, 1948.

Fig. 5-8, and is seen to be very complicated.[1,2]   The existence of various modes limits the tuning range that is possible without introducing ambiguities such as resonance at the same frequency occurring with two different cavity lengths within the tuning range.

Practical wavemeters of the simple cylindrical type shown in Fig. 5-7a normally use either the TE_{111} or the TE_{011} mode (see Fig. 5-9).   The

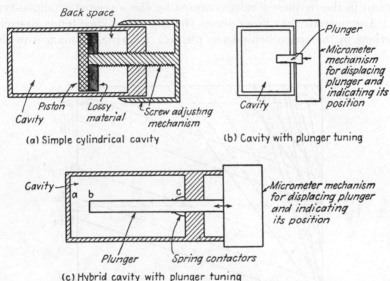

(a) Simple cylindrical cavity

(b) Cavity with plunger tuning

(c) Hybrid cavity with plunger tuning

FIG. 5-7. Various forms of cavity wavemeters.

TE_{111} mode is often preferred because it has the lowest resonant frequency that it is possible to obtain for a given diameter.   Thus mode troubles are minimized by employing this mode, particularly if the cavity is so arranged that the TM modes are not excited.   The TE_{011} mode has the advantage that for a given frequency it has a Q about twice that of the TE_{111} mode.

[1] An extensive discussion of cavity properties, including suppression of undesired modes and also further details of the mode chart, is given by I. G. Wilson, C. W. Schramm, and J. P. Kinzer, High Q Resonant Cavities for Microwave Testing, *Bell System Tech. J.*, vol. 25, p. 408, July, 1946; see "Technique of Microwave Measurements," *op. cit.*, pp. 293–308.

[2] The notation for designating cavity modes can be explained as follows: All cavity modes in a cylinder can be divided into two types in which either all electric flux lines or all the magnetic flux lines are transverse to the axis of the cylinder; these are designated, respectively, as TE and TM modes.   Subscripts l, m, and n are then used to denote, respectively, the number of wavelengths in the configuration of this transverse field around any concentric circle, the number of wavelengths in the field configuration across a diameter, and the number of half wavelengths along the length of the cylinder.   Some typical field configurations are shown in Fig. 5-9.

The tuning piston is ordinarily arranged so that it does not touch the side walls of the cylinder.   With the TE_{011} mode, no current flows from the walls to the ends of the cylinder, so that a relatively large gap can be allowed to exist.   With the TE_{111} mode a noncontact piston can also be employed, but since a considerable current must flow from the sides to the ends, the gap must be so proportioned that it offers a low impedance to current in the frequency range covered by the wavemeter (choke-type gap).   Any current that flows across the gap impedance tends to excite oscillations in the space behind the piston.   Parasite resonances in this

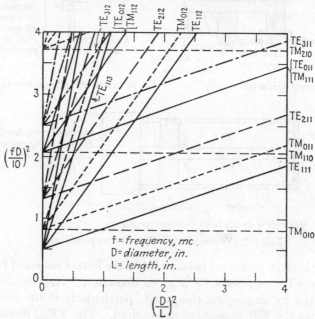

Fig. 5-8. Mode chart for cylindrical cavity.

back space affect the calibration and Q, and so must be suppressed; this can be readily done by placing polyiron or lossy bakelite on the back of the piston to absorb energy and thus give the back space a low Q (see Fig. 5-7a).

Tuning arrangements such as shown in Fig. 5-7b, consisting of a short plunger projecting into the cavity, are commonly used where the resonant frequency of the wavemeter is to be varied over only a very limited range. Such wavemeters commonly employ the TM_{010} mode; by proportioning the cavity so that the diameter is appreciably greater than the length, it is seen from Fig. 5-8 that mode interference is minimized.[1]   By employing

[1] Alternatively, the TE_{011} is sometimes employed.   The use of a tuning plunger with this mode causes the frequency to vary only slightly with a relatively large axial

a tuning plunger of relatively small diameter, the change of resonant frequency for a given mechanical displacement is much less than when a piston is employed; this is important when fine control of the frequency setting is required, and is particularly useful at the higher frequencies.

A wide tuning range, as for example 3:1, can be obtained by making

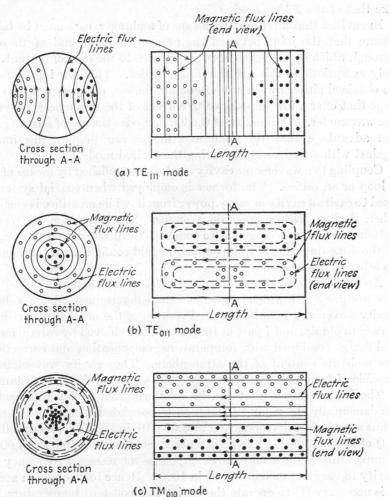

Fig. 5-9. Field configurations for cavity modes most frequently used in wavemeters.

displacement of the plunger, which is sometimes an advantage. Because the plunger has very little effect on the fields in this mode, the high Q of the TE_{011} mode is retained; also no current flows between the plunger and the associated end wall of the cylinder, so that the plunger may be fitted loosely in its hole and, if desired, make no contact at all. For further information see "Technique of Microwave Measurements," *op. cit.*, pp. 328, 382.

the length of the cylinder much larger than the diameter, and designing the plunger so that it can be inserted for nearly the entire length of the cavity,[1] as in Fig. 5-7c. Such an arrangement is often referred to as a hybrid cavity, since in the region bc the field configuration corresponds to that in a coaxial line, while in the region ab the field configuration is more like that of the TM_{010} mode.

In cavities that are tuned by means of a plunger, care must be taken to ensure that the joint between the plunger and the end of the cavity through which it passes has a low impedance to the flow of current. The only exceptions to this are the TE_{01n} modes. This low impedance can be obtained either by the use of contact fingers, or by gaps of the choke type that offer a low impedance to current of the frequencies covered by the wavemeter. In the case of the TE_{01n} modes the use of a large gap has the advantage that the undesired modes are thereby discriminated against without adversely affecting the desired mode.

Coupling to a wavemeter cavity can be accomplished by means of either a loop or an orifice. The former is employed when coaxial systems are used to excite a cavity or carry power from it, while an orifice is customary when dealing with waveguide systems. In either case the coupling system must be so arranged as to couple to the desired cavity mode, while at the same time minimizing coupling to field configuration corresponding to other modes.

Accuracy of Cavity Wavemeters and Relation to Coaxial-line Wavemeters. The accuracy with which frequency can be determined using a well-made cavity wavemeter is quite high. Precision of the order of 1 part in 1000 is easy to obtain, and 1 part in 100,000 can be achieved by careful mechanical design combined with temperature compensation and correction for the moisture content of the atmosphere. Thus cavity wavemeters are capable of functioning as relatively good secondary frequency standards.

The high accuracy that can be obtained from cavity wavemeters is fundamentally the result of the high Q associated with such resonators. Thus a typical cavity operating at 3,000 Mc in the TE_{111} mode will have a Q of about 25,000, while values above 8000 are possible at 24,000 Mc. Temperature changes may, however, cause the resonant frequency of the cavity to vary as much as 1 part in 1000. Hence for maximum accuracy it is necessary (1) to operate the cavity at a constant temperature, or (2) to design the cavity so that it is compensated against temperature

---

[1] For further discussion of such cavities, including a description of practical examples, see L. Essen, Cavity-resonator Wavemeters, *Wireless Eng.*, vol. 23, p. 126, May, 1946; G. E. Feiker and H. R. Meahl, Direct-reading Wavemeter Design, *Electronics*, vol. 21, p. 103, March, 1948; L. W. Shawe and C. M. Burrell, Direct-reading Centimetre Wavemeters, *J. IEE (Radiolocation Conv.)*, vol. 93, pt. IIIA, p. 1479, March–May, 1946; W. L. Barrow and W. W. Mieher, Natural Oscillations of Electrical Cavity Resonators, *Proc. IRE*, vol. 28, p. 184, April, 1940.

changes, or (3) to apply an experimentally determined correction for the temperature.   The water-vapor content of the atmosphere in the cavity also affects the frequency through its contribution to the dielectric constant of the gas within the cavity.[1]   This effect can amount to as much as several parts in 10,000.   Hence if highest precision is required, the cavity must be sealed, or alternatively a correction can be applied for the effect of a known humidity.   For purposes of standardization, cavities are sometimes referred to a standard condition corresponding to 25°C and 60 per cent relative humidity.

Reactance coupled into the cavity by the coupling loop or orifice will affect the resonant frequency obtained.   For the cavity wavemeter to realize the full accuracy of which it is capable, it is accordingly important that the coupled reactance be constant, and preferably small.   This result is aided by the use of small coupling loops (or orifices) that give the equivalent of "loose" coupling to the resonant cavity.   In addition, it is essential that a matched impedance attenuator introducing 5 to 10 db be placed in every cable (or guide) connecting to the cavity.   Such attenuators effectively isolate the cavity from changes in the associated circuits, and also tend to make the coupled impedance resistive rather than reactive.

The high precision that is potentially available in cavity wavemeters, has led to the development of special techniques for calibrating the resonant frequency of wavemeter cavities against a standard frequency, and for comparing the resonant frequencies of two cavities.   While these procedures are too specialized to be discussed in any detail here,[2] they make it possible to calibrate a cavity with a precision of approximately 1 part in $100Q$, and also make it possible to compare the calibration of one cavity against another cavity to about this same accuracy.   In comparison, calibration by determining the condition of maximum response of the cavity gives a result that is accurate to about 1 part in $10Q$.   Since a Q of the order of 10,000 or more is obtainable, these techniques for comparing and calibrating cavities possess a resolving power somewhat greater than the accuracy with which the best cavity is able to maintain its calibration unchanged over a substantial period of time.

[1] This situation is summarized in "Technique of Microwave Measurements," *op. cit.*, pp. 390–392.

[2] For information on these procedures, see "Technique of Microwave Measurements," *op. cit.*, pp. 392–407; F. J. Gaffney, Microwave Measurements and Test Equipments, *Proc. IRE* (*Waves & Electrons*), vol. 34, p. 775, October, 1946; Loyd E. Hunt, A Method for Calibrating Microwave Wavemeters, *Proc. IRE*, vol. 35, p. 979, September, 1947; R. L. Sproull and E. G. Linder, Resonant Cavity Measurements, *Proc. IRE*, vol. 34, p. 305, May, 1946.   This last paper is particularly recommended because of the simplicity of the method it describes, which is briefly summarized in Sec. 4–15.

Both cavity and coaxial wavemeters find extensive use for measuring frequency in the microwave range. Cavity wavemeters have the advantage of considerably higher accuracy, a result in part due to the higher Q, and in part due to the fact that cavities are mechanically simpler than coaxial lines and therefore can be made more stable from a mechanical point of view. At the same time the cavity has the disadvantage of much greater susceptibility to ambiguity from higher order modes. As a result, coaxial wavemeters, and also coaxial slotted-line arrangements, have a definite field of usefulness, included in which is checking the more precise cavity wavemeters to detect mode errors.

5-5. Heterodyne Frequency Meters. A heterodyne frequency meter is an oscillator in which the tuning control is calibrated in terms of fre-

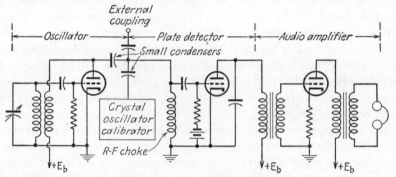

Fig. 5-10. Schematic diagram of a heterodyne frequency meter.

quency, and which is intended to be of service in connection with frequency measurements. Heterodyne frequency meters are employed for such purposes as producing known frequencies, measuring an unknown frequency by comparison with the controllable and known frequency of the heterodyne frequency meter, and for interpolation between known fixed frequencies.

The basis of a heterodyne meter is a stable and tunable oscillator. The details will depend upon the frequency range to be covered, and moreover can be varied greatly according to the personal preferences of the designer; a typical example is shown in Fig. 5-10. It is desirable that the oscillator have a low temperature coefficient of frequency, and that its frequency be insensitive to changes in supply voltage, and to variations in tube characteristics such as those which result from normal aging or from tube replacements. Good mechanical construction is also desirable. The oscillator of the heterodyne frequency meter must be isolated by a buffer tube or suitable circuit arrangements so that its frequency is not affected by either the energy or the impedance of the circuits into which the frequency meter is connected when making measurements. When a heterodyne frequency meter is to be used for interpolation purposes, it is desirable that the frequency be linearly proportional to the angle of rotation of the tuning dial to a high degree of precision.

Heterodyne frequency meters are commonly provided with a detector, audio amplifier, and headphones. Energy from the oscillator is supplied to the detector by internal coupling, and in addition provision is made whereby energy from an external source may be superimposed upon the detector input. The frequency of the heterodyne meter can then be made the same as the unknown frequency by adjusting so that the difference (or "beat") frequency between the two oscillations as observed on the headphones is reduced to zero.[1] Alternatively, harmonics of the oscillator in the heterodyne frequency meter may also be adjusted to zero beat with the unknown frequency, thus extending the range of the heterodyne meter. Such harmonic action is aided by the fact that if a relatively large voltage from the heterodyne meter is applied to the detector, harmonics are generated in the detector in addition to the harmonics already contained in the output of the oscillator itself. Similarly, when the amplitude of the unknown frequency is relatively large, harmonics of its frequency are generated in the detector, and the fundamental frequency of the heterodyne oscillator can then be adjusted to zero beat with these harmonics of the unknown. In this way it is possible to extend the useful range of the heterodyne frequency meter considerably below, and considerable above, the actual range of frequencies generated by the instrument; harmonic ratios as great as fifteen can be usefully employed in this manner.

Heterodyne frequency meters are sometimes provided with a crystal-oscillator calibrator. This is a simple but well-designed crystal oscillator utilizing a low-temperature-coefficient crystal to ensure good frequency stability. The crystal oscillator produces a known frequency (and harmonics thereof) which can be used to check one or more points on the frequency calibration of the heterodyne meter with the aid of the detector and audio amplifier.

The accuracy of the frequency indicated by a heterodyne frequency

[1] The accuracy with which the exact zero-beat condition can be determined in this way is limited by the fact that very low difference frequencies are below audibility, and so cannot be heard in the head phones. The zero-beat adjustment can be made very precisely, however, by superimposing upon the unknown frequency an additional oscillation differing by about 1000 cycles from the frequency of the heterodyne meter. When this is done, a very low-frequency beat note such as a few cycles per second, causes a flutter in the amplitude of the 1000-cycle note; the frequency of this flutter is the beat frequency produced by the interaction of the heterodyne oscillator and the unknown frequency in the detector.

An alternative way to determine when two frequencies are in precise harmonic relation is with the aid of a cathode-ray tube, as discussed in Sec. 5-4.

meter is ordinarily greater than the accuracy of the corresponding lumped-circuit wavemeter. This is because an oscillator generates a definite frequency for any particular setting of its resonant tank circuit, while in the case of a wavemeter using the same resonant circuit there is an uncertainty as to exactly what setting corresponds to resonance in view of the flat-top character of the resonance curve. By careful design, the short-time frequency stability of a heterodyne frequency meter can be made very high, often a few parts in a million for periods of a few minutes to an hour. The long-time frequency stability is of course much poorer, as it is affected by aging of the circuits and tubes. It is, however, a relatively simple matter to obtain a long-time frequency precision of approxi-

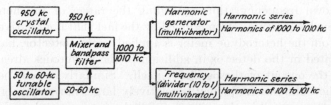

Fig. 5-11. Block diagram of interpolation oscillator having unusually great frequency stability.

mately 1 part in 1000. Where a crystal calibrator is included, the frequency calibration can be considered as dependable to somewhat better than 100 parts in 1,000,000 over indefinitely long periods of time.

An interpolation oscillator system having unusually great frequency stability for both short and long periods of time can be obtained by the expedient illustrated schematically in Fig. 5-11.[1] Here the output frequency consists of the upper side band obtained by modulating the output of a crystal oscillator by the output of a tunable oscillator adjustable over the required range of frequencies. By arranging so that the tunable oscillator operates at a much lower frequency than does the crystal oscillator, the stability of the output frequency tends to approach the stability of the crystal oscillator, so is much greater than that of the usual tunable oscillator. Multivibrators can be used as frequency dividers and harmonic generators, as they will remain controlled over the 1 per cent variation in frequency shown in Fig. 5-11. For such a 1 per cent variation, continuous coverage is obtained for frequencies exceeding the 100th harmonic of the fundamental frequency of the lowest harmonic sequence. Thus in Fig. 5-11 continuous interpolation is possible above 10 Mc; if a 10-kc multivibrator were added to the system, the interpolation would be continuous above 1 Mc.

[1] Such an arrangement is discussed further by J. K. Clapp, Frequency Measurement by Sliding Harmonics, *Proc. IRE*, vol. 36, p. 1285, October, 1948.

5-6. Comparison of Frequencies by Interpolation Methods.[1]   While a wavemeter or a heterodyne oscillator will give an approximate determination of an unknown frequency, a precise measurement requires the use of a frequency standard such as illustrated in Fig. 5-2.   Since such a standard develops a series of fixed frequencies, the measuring problem becomes that of comparing the unknown frequency with known frequencies that are slightly different.   This situation is illustrated schematically in Fig. 5-12, where f_x is the unknown frequency, nf_s is the nth harmonic of a harmonic series obtained from the standard and having a fundamental frequency f_s (as for example 10 kc), while $(n + 1)f_s$ represents the next higher harmonic in this series.   There are two principal methods of carrying out this comparison, (1) direct interpolation between the two nearest known frequencies, and (2) direct measurement of the difference between the unknown and a not greatly different known frequency.

Direct interpolation in a situation such as illustrated in Fig. 5-12 can be carried out with the aid of a heterodyne frequency meter.   The procedure consists in successively adjusting the heterodyne frequency meter so that its frequency equals (or is a harmonic or a subharmonic of) the frequencies nf_s, f_x, and $(n + 1)f_s$.   From these three scale readings, one can determine the frequency f_x by interpolation between the adjacent known frequencies.   The accuracy of the resulting interpolation is greater the more nearly linear the relation between frequency and dial setting of the heterodyne frequency meter, the smaller the ratio of the interval f_s in Fig. 5-12 to the unknown frequency f_x, and the more open the scale of the interpolation oscillator (*i.e.*, the smaller the number of cycles per division).   Also unless f_s is an appreciable fraction of the total tuning range of the interpolation oscillator, the interpolation loses accuracy.   The absolute accuracy of the frequency calibration of the heterodyne frequency meter does not enter into the results; the heterodyne meter merely need be sufficiently accurate to identify the particular harmonics of the standard frequency f_s that are adjacent to the unknown frequency.   That is to say, it is merely necessary that the frequency error of the heterodyne frequency meter be less than $f_s/2$.

Direct measurement of the difference between the unknown frequency

[1] For further details see J. K. Clapp, Continuous Interpolation Methods, *Gen. Rad. Expt.*, vol. 18, p. 4, January, 1944, p. 3, February, 1944; Interpolation Methods for Use with Harmonic Frequency Standards, *Proc. IRE*, vol. 18, p. 1575, September, 1930.   Typical equipment for carrying out the interpolation procedure is described by George J. Kent, Production-line Frequency Measurements, *Electronics*, vol. 24, p. 97, February, 1951.   Modified procedures suitable for use when the frequency to be determined is the frequency of a radio signal are described by H. A. Taylor and E. C. Rundquist, *Electronics*, vol. 24, p. 98, March, 1951.

An interpolation system for microwave frequencies is described by W. F. Brown, Accurate Frequency Measurement, *Wireless Eng.*, vol. 26, p. 218, July, 1949.

and an adjacent known frequency can be carried out in several ways. The simplest procedure is simultaneously to impress the three frequencies nf_s, f_x, and $(n + 1)f_x$ upon a detector to obtain the difference frequency between f_x and the *nearest* known frequency. This will lie in the range 0 to $f_s/2$, and is then measured directly. Thus when the fundamental frequency f_s of the harmonic series is 10 kc, the measurement of the difference could be carried out by comparison with an audio-frequency oscillator covering the range 0 to 5000 cycles. This difference frequency is either added to nf_s or subtracted from $(n + 1)f_s$ to obtain the unknown frequency f_x, according to which of these two known frequencies is closest to the unknown frequency.

A modification[1] of this procedure consists in utilizing the component of the detector output representing the difference in frequency between f_x

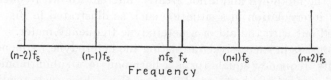

$(n-2)f_s$ $(n-1)f_s$ nf_s f_x $(n+1)f_s$ $(n+2)f_s$
Frequency

Fig. 5-12. Illustration showing relationship of an unknown frequency f_x to the various components of a harmonic sequence of a standard frequency f_s.

and the adjacent harmonic that is *not* closest to f_x. This difference frequency lies in the range $0.5f_s$ to f_s, and can be determined by a heterodyne frequency meter or by a wavemeter covering this frequency range. This modified procedure is desirable when f_s is large, such as 100 kc or 1 Mc; the heterodyne frequency meter is then required to cover the range 50 to 100 kc, or 500 to 1000 kc, as the case may be, which is quite practical, whereas a heterodyne frequency meter to cover the range 0 to 50 kc or 0 to 0.5 Mc would be quite impractical. For a range such as 500 to 1000 kc, a calibrated broadcast receiver may be used as an interpolation device instead of a heterodyne frequency meter.

When the difference between the unknown and nearest known frequency is very small, a difficulty arises in all interpolation methods in determining whether the unknown frequency is higher or lower than the nearest known frequency. An analogous difficulty arises when the unknown frequency lies almost exactly midway between the adjacent standard frequencies. Several means can be used to resolve the potential ambiguity that may arise under such circumstances. One possibility is

---

[1] Still another modification is to employ several successive heterodynings between the unknown and known frequencies to reduce the order of magnitude of the difference to a small residual that can be measured to a small fraction of a cycle. This method requires a rather elaborate equipment, however, and so is not extensively used. It is described by F. A. Polkinghorn and A. A. Roetken, A Device for the Precise Measurement of High Frequencies, *Proc. IRE*, vol. 19, p. 937, July, 1931.

to explore the situation with a heterodyne frequency meter. The heterodyne meter is first set to exactly the unknown frequency with the known frequencies turned off. The known frequencies are then turned on, and the unknown frequency is turned off. The frequency of the heterodyne meter is next very slowly increased. If the difference frequency produced by the interaction of the heterodyne meter and the known frequency then increases, the unknown frequency is greater than the nearest known frequency. Alternatively, it is possible in some cases to increase the standard frequency slightly and note whether the difference between the known and unknown frequencies increases or decreases.

When harmonics are employed in making a frequency comparison, it is necessary that the particular harmonics involved be identified with care. This is normally done by means of a wavemeter or heterodyne frequency meter. However, when very high-order harmonics such as the 451st and 452d, for example, are involved, the percentage difference between adjacent harmonics is so small that there may sometimes be doubt as to just which harmonics are being used. In such circumstances the simplest procedure is to provide certain harmonics with a distinguishing feature. Thus when the measuring is done with a 10-kc harmonic sequence, one can provide an auxiliary 100-kc multivibrator controlled from the same source. By modulating the amplifier of this multivibrator output with a distinguishing tone, such as 60 cycles, it is possible to locate every tenth harmonic of the 10-kc sequence with certainty, and intermediate harmonics may then be determined by counting from the nearest harmonic so marked. Thus in the case of uncertainty mentioned above, one would locate the 45th harmonic of the 100-kc multivibrator, which can be readily done without uncertainty. The harmonic in question would then be the 451st or the 452d depending upon whether it was the first or second harmonic of the 10-kc sequence beyond the harmonic marked with the 60-cycle distinguishing tone. In an alternative arrangement, the 10-kc harmonic series is modulated on the 100-kc series. This provides a 10-kc harmonic series with 100-kc marker frequencies that are available merely by removing the 10-kc modulation.

5-7. Cathode-ray-tube Methods for Comparing Frequencies.[1] A cathode-ray tube can be used in a number of ways to determine when two frequencies are identical (or in harmonic relationship) to each other. For such purposes the cathode-ray tube is therefore an alternative to the zero-beat method of determining when two frequencies have an exact relationship. The use of the cathode-ray tube has the advantage that it permits the establishing of a harmonic relationship without the necessity of generating the harmonic. It is also possible to employ a cathode-ray

[1] For more information on this subject see F. J. Rasmussen, Frequency Measurements with the Cathode-ray Oscillograph, *Trans. AIEE*, vol. 45, p. 1256, 1926.

tube as an indicator in interpolation methods, as explained below in connection with Fig. 5-16.

The simplest method of using a cathode-ray tube to determine when two sine-wave voltages are in harmonic relationship to each other is to employ a voltage of one frequency to produce the horizontal deflection of the cathode-ray spot, while obtaining the vertical deflection using a voltage of the other frequency. When the ratio of the two frequencies involved can be expressed by an integer, or by a ratio of integers, the

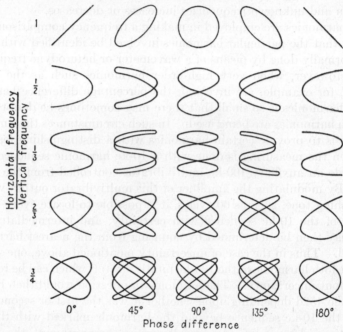

Fig. 5-13. Lissajous figures for several frequency ratios and various phase differences.

result is a pattern called a Lissajous figure. The exact configuration of the pattern depends upon the frequency ratio and upon the relative phase of the two waves, and is shown in Fig. 5-13 for typical cases. When the ratio of frequencies is exactly a ratio of integers, the pattern is stationary and the ratio of horizontal to vertical frequency is the number of times the side of the figure is tangent to a horizontal line divided by the number of times its end is tangent to a vertical line.[1] If the frequency ratio is nearly but not exactly a ratio of integers, then the pattern weaves about as though the relative phase of the two deflecting waves was con-

[1] This assumes that the forward and return traces do not coincide (as they do in the 0 and 180° cases in Fig. 5-13). If they do coincide, the rule does not hold.

tinuously changing.   If the ratio of frequencies differs very much from a simple ratio of integers, the pattern is merely a luminous rectangular area.

Lissajous figures become difficult to interpret when the frequency ratio is large, because of complicated patterns.[1]   Alternative arrangements then become increasingly desirable.   One useful alternative for such conditions is illustrated in Fig. 5-14a.   Here the circuit arrangements are such that the lower frequency is used to produce an elliptical or circular pattern by the use of a resistance-capacitance phase splitter as shown. The electrode controlling the intensity of the beam is biased slightly more

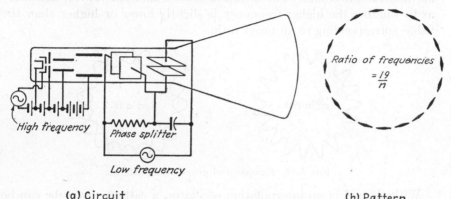

Ratio of frequencies $= \dfrac{19}{n}$

High frequency

Phase splitter

Low frequency

(a) Circuit   (b) Pattern

FIG. 5-14. Diagram showing circuit for producing a spot-wheel pattern and typical pattern.

negative than cutoff, and the higher frequency voltage is superimposed upon this bias.   The pattern that results on the face of the cathode-ray tube is illustrated in Fig. 5-14b, and consists of a circle of spots in which the ratio of the high frequency to the low frequency is equal to the number of spots divided by a suitable integer n that is less than the number of spots.   The pattern is the same for different values of n, so that the proper value of this integer must be determined from other information, such as prior knowledge of the approximate frequency.

An alternative for the spot pattern of Fig. 5-14b is the gear-wheel pattern in Fig. 5-15.   This is obtained by using the low frequency to produce an elliptical or circular path as in Fig. 5-14a, but in this case the high-frequency voltage is applied to a radial-deflecting electrode, causing the spot to move regularly in and out in accordance with the amplitude and polarity of the high-frequency wave applied to the radial deflecting electrode.   In the resulting wheel pattern, the frequency ratio is equal to the number of teeth in the pattern divided by the number of times a radial

[1] Very complicated patterns corresponding to high-frequency ratios such as 201:1 can be used if proper care is taken; thus see discussion by F. R. Stansel in *J. IEE*, vol. 90, pt. III, p. 73, June, 1943.

line from center outward intersects the pattern.   It will be noted that the wheel arrangement avoids the ambiguity in the ratio n that is characteristic of the spot pattern.[1]

When the two frequencies involved are in exact harmonic relationship, the spot or wheel pattern will be stationary.   However, if the frequencies differ slightly from an exact ratio expressible by a ratio of simple integers, the wheel or the spots, as the case may be, appears to rotate at a rate that becomes greater as the frequency departs increasingly from the simple harmonic relationship.   The direction of rotation is, moreover, indicative as to whether the higher frequency is slightly lower or higher than the value corresponding to an exact ratio.

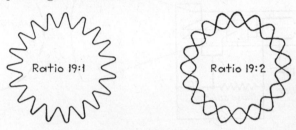

Fig. 5-15.   Examples of gear-wheel patterns.

With the aid of an interpolation oscillator, a cathode-ray tube can be used as an indicator for comparing an unknown frequency with a known frequency that is not in harmonic relationship.[2]   The procedure consists in superimposing the interpolation-oscillator output upon the higher frequency, and applying the combination to the vertical-deflecting electrodes of the cathode-ray tube, while the lower frequency is applied to the horizontal-deflecting electrodes.   The addition of the two waves of different frequencies produces a wave having an envelope that pulsates at the difference frequency $f_2 - f_0$, where f_2 is the higher frequency, and f_0 is the frequency of the interpolation oscillator.[3]   The interpolation-oscillator frequency f_0 is then so adjusted as to satisfy the relationship

$$nf_1 = f_2 - f_0 \tag{5-2}$$

where f_1 is the lower frequency, and n is an integer representing a harmonic ratio.   When Eq. (5-2) is satisfied, one obtains a stationary solid

[1] Another form of wheel pattern is described by G. H. Rawcliffe, A New Frequency-comparison Circuit for the Cathode-ray Tube, *J. IEE*, vol. 89, pt. III, p. 191, December, 1942.

[2] Further information on this topic is given by F. R. Stansel, An Interpolation Method for Setting Laboratory Oscillators, *Bell Labs. Record*, vol. 19, p. 98, November, 1940.

[3] See F. E. Terman, "Radio Engineering," 3d ed., p. 527, McGraw-Hill Book Company, Inc., New York, 1947; "Radio Engineers' Handbook," p. 568, McGraw-Hill Book Company, Inc., New York, 1943.

pattern on the screen of the cathode-ray tube of the character indicated in Fig. 5-16.   In this pattern, n is twice the number of pulsations in the envelope if the forward and return horizontal sweeps are superimposed, or is equal to the total number of pulsations in the envelope counted as the sum of the pulsations undergone as the spot travels first forward and then backward.   If the relationship between the known, unknown, and interpolation frequencies is such as almost but not quite to satisfy Eq. (5-2), then the pulsations in the envelope appear to travel either forward or backward at a rate determined by the extent of the inequality.

When two frequencies that are already known approximately are to be brought into an exact relationship with the aid of the cathode-ray tube,

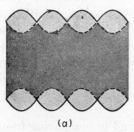 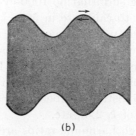

(a)   (b)

Fig. 5-16. Patterns obtained when using a cathode-ray tube with an interpolating oscillator.   The two cases shown differ only in the phase relation of the voltages, and both are for $4f_1 = f_2 - f_0$.

it is not necessary to identify the details of a cathode-ray pattern since the harmonic ratio is already established.   It is merely necessary to make a small adjustment of one of the frequencies involved in order to obtain a pattern on the cathode-ray tube that is completely stationary.   Under such conditions it is possible to make use of complex patterns corresponding to very much higher harmonic ratios than would be permissible under other conditions.   For example, in connection with the comparison of frequencies by the method illustrated in Fig. 5-16, assume that an oscillator whose frequency calibration is already known to a precision of better than 0.1 per cent is to be set to a frequency that is exactly 323,383 cycles, using a 1000-cycle frequency standard and an interpolation oscillator that covers the range 11,000 to 12,000 cycles.   In this situation the unknown frequency would be set to a nominal value of 323,383 cycles as determined by its calibration, while the interpolation oscillator would be set at a frequency of 11,383 cycles.   These latter two frequencies would simultaneously be applied to the vertical electrode, while the 1000-cycle standard frequency would be applied to the horizontal electrode.   The unknown frequency would then be varied slightly back and forth until a stationary pattern was obtained.   This would correspond to a difference frequency of $323,383 - 11,383 = 312,000$ representing a value of n in Eq. (5-2) of 312.

A second example would be if the "unknown" oscillator were to have its frequency calibration in the range 250,000 to 350,000 cycles checked against the 1000-cycle standard. This would be done by producing an ordinary Lissajous figure, first setting the oscillator at a nominal 250,000 cycles and then adjusting slightly about this setting until a stationary pattern was obtained, indicating a harmonic ratio n of 250. The setting would then be increased to nominal value of 351,000 cycles and the process repeated, etc. If desired, one could repeat the process using a 10,000-cycle standard frequency, thereby double checking every tenth interval, and making sure that no 1000-cycle points were omitted. It would also be possible to calibrate in 500-cycle steps by starting with a 1000-cycle standard and using frequency ratios such as 501:2, etc., since such ratios also produce stationary patterns. When complicated harmonic ratios such as this are employed, the Lissajous patterns are correspondingly more complicated; however, with a little experience it is possible for an observer to distinguish between cases where m in the harmonic ratio n/m has values of 1, 2, 3, etc.

When high harmonic ratios are employed in comparing frequencies in the above manner, it is desirable that the pattern be opened up by employing a horizontal-deflecting voltage so great that only a small portion of the pattern appears on the cathode-ray screen. In this way the distinguishing features of the pattern can be more easily observed.

It will be noted that the use of a cathode-ray tube as an indicator permits harmonic comparison of frequencies without the necessity of generating harmonics, as required in other methods of frequency comparison. At the same time, when a cathode-ray tube is employed, it is necessary to have relatively large voltages to compare, especially when one is dealing with frequencies so high that the amplifiers normally included in a cathode-ray oscilloscope do not give full gain.

5-8. Frequency Comparison by Counting Systems. The development of high-speed counting or scaling systems has made available still another means of comparing frequencies, which is coming into increasing use. The basic idea is that a scaler is allowed to count cycles of the unknown frequency for some predetermined length of time such as 10 msec or 1 sec. This time interval is in turn controlled by the known frequency.

One possible arrangement of this type is shown schematically in Fig. 5-17a.[1] Here the known and unknown frequencies f_1 and f_2, respectively,

---

[1] A more detailed description of apparatus performing these functions is given by R. L. Chase, Measuring a Varying Frequency, *Electronics*, vol. 23, p. 110, March, 1950; A. S. Bagley, The High-speed Frequency Counter, *Hewlett-Packard J.*, vol. 2, p. 1, January, 1951.

are passed through pulse-forming circuits P_1 and P_2 that produce one positive output pulse per cycle. These pulses are counted by scalers S_1 and S_2, respectively, except that S_1 counts only when gate G_1 is open and S_2 only when gate G_2 is open. The measuring procedure is as follows: Scaler S_1 is first set so that after it has counted a predetermined number of cycles N_1, it sends out a signal that turns off both gates. Operations are started by pressing the push button, which opens both gates simultaneously. The scalers then count until S_1 reaches a value N_1, at which

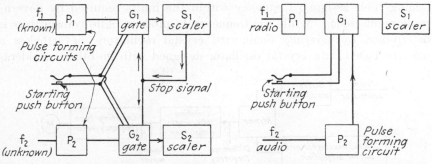

(a) Comparison of radio frequencies   (b) Comparison of an audio frequency with a radio frequency

FIG. 5-17. Block diagram of start-stop counter systems for comparing two frequencies.

point both gates close. The relation between the unknown frequency f_2 and the known frequency f_1 is then

$$f_2 = \frac{N_2 f_1}{N_1} \qquad (5\text{-}3)$$

where N_2 is the count on S_2 after gate G_2 closes. It will be noted that the time interval during which gate G_2 is open and S_2 counts cycles of the unknown frequency is N_1/f_1 seconds.

The accuracy with which frequencies can be compared in this way is determined by the number of cycles of the standard frequency f_1 that are counted on S_1. The accuracy is accordingly greater the longer the time interval involved (*i.e.*, the larger N_1), and the higher the frequency f_1. If f_1 is of the order of 1 to 10 Mc, then comparisons having an accuracy of better than 1 part in 1,000,000 can be obtained in 1 sec.[1]

The highest frequency that can be handled in this type of system is limited by the speed with which the scalers will operate. The highest counting frequency of commercially available scalers is about 10 Mc,[2] which is therefore a practical limit.

[1] With time intervals of the order of 1 hr, accuracies of 1 part in 1,000,000,000 are readily obtainable. Thus, see Hartshorn and Essen, *loc. cit.*

[2] For example, see A. S. Bagley, A 10 Mc Scaler for Nuclear Counting and Frequency Measurement, *Hewlett-Packard J.*, vol. 2, p. 1, October, 1950.

The counting method of determining frequency has the advantage of giving precise results almost instantaneously, without ambiguity, and with almost no manipulation of apparatus. The method is hence particularly attractive when many frequency comparisons must be made.

5-9. Frequency Monitors. Frequency monitors are devices for continuously observing and indicating the frequency of a radio transmitter through comparison with a reference frequency generated by the monitor. Such arrangements are used to ensure that radio transmitters are maintaining their assigned frequency within the limits required by government regulations. While the frequency of modern radio transmitters is determined by carefully engineered crystal oscillators, nevertheless a monitor based on a crystal oscillator designed with no other considera-

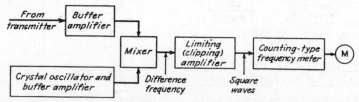

Fig. 5-18. Block diagram of frequency monitor for amplitude-modulated waves.

tion than the highest possible frequency stability, is somewhat more dependable.

Frequency monitors for amplitude-modulated transmitters ordinarily are of the type indicated schematically in Fig. 5-18, and may be operated either as zero-beat or offset devices.[1] In zero-beat operation, the crystal oscillator of the monitor develops a frequency that is either the same or a subharmonic of the frequency assigned to the transmitter. By mixing the transmitter and the monitor frequencies, one hence obtains a difference or beat frequency which is equal to the error in cycles of the transmitter frequency with reference to the standard frequency provided by the monitor. Thus when the difference frequency is zero, the transmitter frequency is exactly correct, while if the difference is 800 cycles, then the transmitter frequency is either greater or less than the reference frequency by 800 cycles. The difference frequency produced by the monitor is indicated by a frequency meter of the type described in connection with Fig. 5-21.

The zero-beat method of operating a frequency monitor has many advantages when maximum flexibility is required for a wide range of

[1] Examples of commercial monitors of these types are described by C. A. Cady, A Versatile Monitor for Use from 1.6 to 150 Megacycles, *Gen. Rad. Expt.*, vol. 21, p. 1, February, 1947; A Frequency Monitor for Television Video Transmitters, *Gen. Rad. Expt.*, vol. 23, p. 1, September, 1948; M. Silver, Monitor for Television Broadcasting Station, *Proc. Natl. Electronics Conf.*, vol. 3, p. 569, November, 1947.

applications.   It has the disadvantage, however, that it does not indicate directly whether the deviation of the frequency being monitored is a result of this frequency being too high or too low; also there is a limited region near zero error frequency where the system becomes inoperative because the usual frequency meter is not able to respond to extremely low frequencies.   These disadvantages are overcome by operating the frequency monitor as an offset device.   Offset operation differs from zero-beat operation in that the frequency of the monitor crystal oscillator is so selected that a convenient beat frequency, such as 1000 cycles, is produced by the mixing action of the monitor when the transmitter frequency has exactly the correct value as compared with the monitor.   By arranging so that the reference frequency generated by the monitor is less than the transmitter frequency, the deviation of the monitor output from 1000 cycles indicates the error in transmitter frequency; thus if the difference frequency is 1000 cycles, the transmitter is operating at exactly the correct frequency (with respect to the monitor as a standard), while if the beat frequency is 600 cycles or 1400 cycles, the transmitter frequency is, respectively, 400 cycles low or 400 cycles high.   The difference frequency obtained from the offset arrangement is indicated by a frequency meter of the type discussed in connection with Fig. 5-21, in which the scale calibration is so arranged that the preassigned beat frequency corresponding to zero error is marked on the scale as zero, while frequencies greater and less are marked as cycles high and low with respect to the zero-error condition.

In monitors of the type discussed above, the effect of amplitude modulation of the carrier is minimized by so severely clipping the difference-frequency oscillations applied to the frequency meter, that these oscillations are converted into square waves that have an amplitude substantially unaffected by the modulation (except, of course, during those very rare moments when the modulation reduces the total amplitude actually to zero).

Frequency-modulated signals present a special problem in frequency monitoring because here the instantaneous frequency is continually varying, while it is the *average* frequency that is of interest.   This situation can be very effectively met by a monitor system of the type illustrated schematically in Fig. 5-19.[1]   Here the frequency of the crystal oscillator in the monitor is so chosen that by mixing with the transmitter output, an intermediate frequency of relatively low value, such as 200 kc, is

---

[1] Such frequency monitors are described by N. B. Schrock and D. Packard, A Pulse-counter Type FM Station Monitor, *Proc. Natl. Electronics Conf.*, vol. 3, p. 630, November, 1947; C. A. Cady, Type 1170-A F-M Monitor for Broadcast and Television Services, *Gen. Rad. Expt.*, vol. 22, p. 1, October, 1947; M. Silver, Monitor for Frequency-modulation Broadcasting, *Elec. Commun.*, vol., 24, p. 428, December, 1947.

obtained. This intermediate frequency possesses the same frequency deviation as does the original signal; thus if the deviation of the signal is 75 kc, the actual intermediate frequency will vary over the range 125 to 275 kc. This intermediate frequency is applied to a counter-type frequency meter, such as discussed in connection with Fig. 5-21. The output current of this counter device varies exactly in proportion to the frequency of the applied wave; the current accordingly contains a d-c component that is exactly proportional to the average or center frequency, while it contains an alternating component varying at audio frequency that reproduces with a high degree of precision the frequency modulation of the wave. For frequency indication, the d-c component is separated out and applied to a zero-center d-c instrument, after first being com-

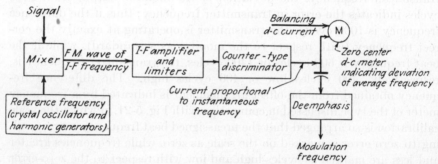

FIG. 5-19. Block diagram of frequency and modulation monitor for frequency-modulated waves.

bined with a balancing current of such magnitude as to give zero resultant amplitude when the average frequency of the transmitter is exactly the correct value. The precision of such an arrangement is determined not only by the frequency stability of the crystal oscillator of the monitor, but also by the balancing voltage. By deriving this balancing voltage from the amplitude of the wave applied to the counter system, it is possible to obtain a balancing effect that is exactly correct irrespective of ordinary changes in amplitude of the incoming signal, or of changes in tube constants or supply voltages. High accuracy is further ensured by periodically lining up the counter system, using a crystal oscillator of intermediate frequency provided as part of the monitor. This is done by applying output from such an oscillator to the counter system, and adjusting the latter to indicate zero frequency deviation.

5-10. Measurement of Audio Frequencies. Audio frequencies can be measured by comparing the unknown frequency with a known frequency, by balancing a bridge of a type in which the conditions of balance depend upon frequency, or by some form of cycle-counting device.

Audio frequencies are somewhat more difficult to measure with high accuracy than are radio frequencies.   If a frequency of 100 cycles is to be measured with a precision of 1 part in 10,000,000, this is equivalent to one cycle error every 28 hr.   It thus takes a long time to make an accurate determination unless a high harmonic of the audio frequency is compared with a radio-frequency standard.   The accuracy normally required in audio-frequency measurements is, however, much less than the precision commonly necessary at radio frequencies.

Comparison Method of Measuring Audio Frequencies.   Standard frequencies for use in audio-frequency measurements may be obtained in a number of ways.   One possibility is by frequency division of the radio-frequency generated by a standard, as illustrated in Fig. 5-2.   Electrically driven tuning forks represent another source of standard audio frequencies.[1]   Where known radio frequencies are available, it is always possible to adjust a low-frequency oscillator in a known relation to the high frequency by the use of harmonics, etc.

When one or more known audio frequencies are available, it is possible to calibrate completely an audio-frequency oscillator by the usual frequency-comparison methods.   Thus, if the known frequency is 100 cycles, one can obtain a calibration point for every harmonic of 100 cycles either by comparing the known and unknown frequencies directly with a cathode-ray tube, as described in Sec. 5-4, or by zero beating harmonics of the standard with the unknown.   Other calibration points, such as 50 cycles, 150 cycles, 133.3 cycles, etc., can similarly be obtained by employing the Lissajous figures corresponding to ratios of 1:2, 3:2, and 4:3, respectively.   If the standard frequency has a higher value, such as 1000-cycles, and a 100 cycle standard would be preferable, one can set up an auxiliary oscillator operating at exactly 100 cycles by adjustment to the appropriate harmonic relation.   Many modifications of these harmonic methods are possible, and can be readily worked out to fit any particular set of circumstances.

In adjusting two audio frequencies to exactly the same value, one may employ a Lissajous figure, or may combine the outputs in a telephone receiver to give aural beats.   Alternatively, the two frequencies may be simultaneously applied to a vacuum-tube voltmeter, and the resulting vibration of the meter pointer used to indicate the difference frequency. The particular method preferred in any individual case depends upon the circumstances involved, and is purely one of convenience.

The accurate comparison of an unknown audio frequency with known fixed audio frequencies involves special problems.   The usual procedure is to obtain beats representing the difference between the unknown frequency and the nearest available known frequency.   The difference fre-

[1] See footnote 2, p. 195.

quency so obtained can then be determined by counting the beats by visual or aural methods if the frequency does not exceed a few cycles per second, and either by mechanical or by electrical counting for higher frequency beats, as discussed below.

Bridge Method of Measuring Audio Frequencies. An unknown frequency can be determined by applying it to a bridge in which the balance depends upon frequency, and then calculating the frequency from the circuit constants required to give balance. Such arrangements find considerable use for measuring audio frequencies. Any type of bridge or null network in which the balance depends upon frequency can be used.

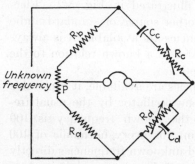

Typical examples are the Wien, Hay,[1] and resonance bridges, and the null network of Fig. 3-15*b*.

The Wien bridge is particularly satisfactory for measuring audio frequencies because it can be brought into balance merely by varying resistance elements, contains no inductances, and can be conveniently proportioned to cover a wide frequency range. The absence of inductances in the bridge arms is important since the large inductances that would be

FIG. 5-20. Wien bridge arranged for the measurement of frequency.

required at audio frequencies could readily pick up energy from stray fields, and either introduce errors or obscure the balance.

A Wien bridge arranged for measuring frequency is shown in Fig. 5-20. Balance in such a bridge is obtained by simultaneously satisfying the two equations.

$$f = \frac{1}{2\pi \sqrt{R_c R_d C_c C_d}} \qquad (5\text{-}4a)$$

and

$$\frac{C_d}{C_c} = \frac{R_b}{R_a} - \frac{R_c}{R_d} \qquad (5\text{-}4b)$$

By making $C_c = C_d$, $R_c = R_d$, and $R_b/R_a = 2$, the second condition of balance is always satisfied, and one has

$$f = \frac{1}{2\pi R_c C_c} \qquad (5\text{-}5)$$

Thus by making R_c and R_d identical slide-wire resistances, and mounting them on a common shaft, the dial can be calibrated directly in frequency.

[1] The use of the Hay bridge for frequency measurements is discussed in detail by Chester I. Soucy and B. de F. Bayly, A Direct Reading Frequency Bridge for the Audio Range Based on Hay's Bridge Circuit, *Proc. IRE*, vol. 17, p. 834, May, 1929.

Furthermore, convenient multiplying factors, such as decimal values, can be obtained by merely changing the capacitances of the condensers C_c and C_d by the appropriate amounts. A frequency range of 10 to 1 can be readily covered with a single condenser value, so that by the use of three pairs of condensers one can cover the complete audio range from 20 to 20,000 cycles. In practical construction it is impossible to maintain equality between R_c and R_d with the accuracy required to maintain a perfect balance, so that the potentiometer P having a total resistance of perhaps 1 to 2 per cent of R_a is used to sharpen the balance. This has negligible effect upon the frequency calibration.

An accuracy in the order of $\frac{1}{2}$ to 1 per cent can be readily obtained in frequency bridges. In the frequency range 300 to 5000 cycles, balance can be most easily made by the use of telephone receivers. At frequencies outside this range some indicating arrangement, such as an amplifier and vacuum-tube-voltmeter combination, is normally required. The principal difficulty involved in making accurate frequency measurements by bridge methods arises from harmonics of the frequency being measured. The bridge is unbalanced for these harmonics, which are thus very prominent in the bridge output even though only a small percentage in the bridge input current. When telephone receivers are used in the middle audio range, it is usually possible to balance the bridge for the fundamental in spite of the presence of harmonics; but when indicating instruments are employed, appropriate filters must be placed in the output of the neutral arm to prevent spurious voltages from reaching the indicating device.

Measurement of Audio Frequencies by Cycle-counting Methods. One method of measuring an audio frequency is to use current of this frequency to operate an electric clock. Such a clock is essentially a cycle-counting device, since each minute recorded by the clock requires the passage of a definite number of cycles. Clocks can be made for audio frequencies up to several thousand cycles. In this connection it is to be noted that many ordinary electric clocks designed for use at 60 cycles will operate synchronously over a considerable frequency range, commonly from about 30 cycles to over 100 cycles.

Very low frequencies can be measured by a simple cycle counter operated from a polarized relay. The number of cycles that occur in a given length of time, as indicated by a stop watch, are recorded and the frequency calculated from the resulting data.

When the frequency is too high for the mechanical counting of cycles, the procedure is to charge a condenser on one half of each cycle, and then to discharge the condenser through a different path during the other half of the cycle. By making the voltage to which the condenser is charged independent of frequency, the average current flowing into (or out of) the condenser is proportional to the number of charges per second, and hence to the frequency. A d-c meter placed in either the charge or the discharge circuit will accordingly give a deflection proportional to the number of cycles per second, and so can be calibrated to read frequency directly.

A typical circuit arrangement[1] for carrying out the necessary details is illustrated in Fig. 5-21. Here the wave that is to have its frequency measured is passed through a succession of tubes that limit and clip in

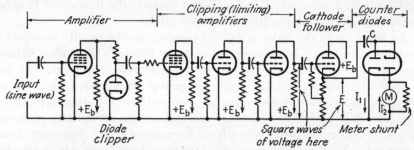

FIG. 5-21. Schematic diagram of counting-type frequency meter.

such a manner as to develop an output that is a square wave. This square wave is then applied to a condenser C in series with a double-diode rectifier, in which the two rectifier sections are connected back to back as shown. In this wave the current that charges the condenser passes through one diode, while the current discharging the condenser passes through the other. Thus the charge (or discharge) current can be recorded separately by means of a d-c meter M as shown. This direct current is proportional to the amplitude of the square wave and to the number of times the condenser is charged per second (i.e., to the frequency of the wave). The amplitude is determined by the final clipping and limiting level, and so may be made constant by using a regulated power supply. The indication of the d-c instrument then becomes

[1] For further discussion of details see H. H. Scott, The Constant Waveform Frequency Meter, *Gen. Rad. Expt.*, vol. 20, February, 1946. An earlier frequency meter of this type used an electronic switching arrangement employing thyratrons in place of the square-wave generator and double-diode arrangement; thus see Frederick V. Hunt, A Direct-reading Frequency Meter Suitable for High Speed Recording, *Rev. Sci. Instruments*, vol. 6, p. 43, February, 1935. The use of gas tubes has the disadvantage, however, that the life of such tubes is less the higher the frequency, and becomes excessively short at the higher audio and at the low radio frequencies.

For frequencies up to several hundred cycles one can employ a polarized relay as a mechanical switch, that on alternate half cycles connects the condenser to a battery, and then discharges it through a resistance, respectively. For details see N. P. Case, A Precise and Rapid Method of Measuring Frequencies from Five to Five Hundred Cycles per Second, *Proc. IRE*, vol. 18, p. 1586, September, 1930.

dependent only upon frequency, and the meter M can be calibrated accordingly. In a frequency meter of this type the frequency corresponding to full-scale deflection of the indicating instrument is determined by the sensitivity of the meter M and the size of the condenser C in Fig. 5-21. By changing the meter shunt and/or the capacitance of this condenser, full-scale deflection can be made to correspond to different values of frequency. The maximum frequency range that can be obtained with this type of arrangement is limited only by the maximum frequency at which a square wave may be generated, and so when desired can be made much higher than the highest audible frequency. Accuracies on the order of ± 2 per cent are readily obtained if the supply voltage is closely regulated. With special care it would be theoretically possible to improve this accuracy very considerably.

Comparison of an Audio Frequency with a Known Radio Frequency by Cycle Counting. A start-stop cycle-counting system for comparing frequencies, such as shown schematically in Fig. 5-17b, can be used to measure an audio frequency precisely in terms of a known radio frequency. Here pulse-forming circuit P_2 produces a pulse once each cycle of the audio frequency f_2; at the same time gate G_1 is of a type such that with the starting switch open the gate is closed. However, when the switch is held closed, then the first incoming pulse from P_2 opens G_1, and the second pulse closes it, after which G_1 stays closed until the push button is released and again pressed. Thus, pushing the button and holding it on causes G_1 to be open for exactly one cycle of f_2. The number of cycles counted by S_1 during this time then gives the exact ratio of the known radio frequency f_1 to the unknown audio frequency f_2, with an error less than one cycle of the radio frequency.

CHAPTER 6

WAVEFORM, PHASE, AND
TIME-INTERVAL MEASUREMENTS

6-1. Oscillographic Representation of Wave Shapes—Cathode-ray Oscillograph.[1,2] Wave shape is ordinarily determined either by means of a cathode-ray or a magnetic oscillograph. Cathode-ray tubes can be used in many ways to delineate wave shape. The most common arrangement employs electrostatic deflection, with the unknown wave applied to the vertical deflectors. A horizontal left-to-right deflection proportional

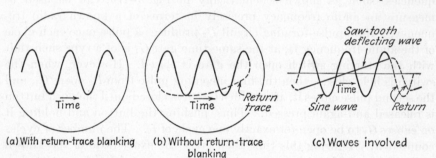

(a) With return-trace blanking   (b) Without return-trace blanking   (c) Waves involved

Fig. 6-1. Representation of a sine-wave oscillation using a cathode-ray oscillograph with a saw-tooth-wave deflecting voltage to provide the horizontal time axis.

to time is then provided by a saw-tooth wave. This wave is ordinarily synchronized at a subharmonic of the unknown wave, either by manual adjustment, or by injecting a voltage derived from the unknown wave into the circuits of the relaxation oscillator producing the saw-tooth wave.

[1] For descriptions of typical cathode-ray oscilloscopes of relatively sophisticated design, see R. P. Affenhouse, General Purpose Precision Oscilloscope, *Electronics*, vol. 22, p. 106, August, 1947; Ellsworth D. Cook, A Wide-band Oscilloscope, *Proc. IRE*, vol. 31, p. 410, August, 1943; E. H. Bartelink, Wide-band Oscilloscope, *Electronics*, vol. 17, p. 122, February, 1944; J. G. Barlett and G. T. Davies, The Design of Highspeed Oscillographs, *J. IEE* (*Radiolocation Conv.*), vol. 93, pt. IIIA, p. 1304, 1946; W. L. Gaines, High-frequency Oscilloscopes for Pulses and Other Transients, *Bell Labs. Record*, vol. 26, p. 68, February, 1948; Y. P. Yu, H. E. Kallman, and P. S. Christaldi, Millimicrosecond Oscillography, *Electronics*, vol. 24, p. 106, July, 1951.

The simple, inexpensive, laboratory oscilloscope incorporates most of the same features, but to a less refined degree.

[2] The terms oscillo*scope* and oscillo*graph* are commonly used interchangeably as applied to systems involving cathode-ray tubes.

In many cases provision is made for turning off the electron beam during the time the cathode-ray spot is returning from right to left; this is accomplished by circuit arrangements that cause a negative bias voltage greater than cutoff to be applied to the control electrode of the cathode-ray tube when the saw-tooth timing wave is decreasing in amplitude. In other cases a return trace is displayed on the cathode-ray screen. An example showing a sine wave represented with and without blanking of the return trace is shown in Fig. 6-1.

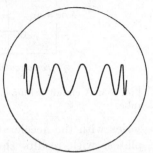

FIG. 6-2. Representation of a sine-wave oscillation using a synchronized sinusoidal sweep voltage. The cathode-ray spot is blanked out during the interval it is moving from right to left.

Time Axes. The cathode-ray tube possesses great flexibility. This is particularly true with respect to the time axis. Thus it is sometimes convenient to employ a sinusoidal deflecting wave; however, this has the disadvantage that the time scale is then a sinusoidal function of time rather than being proportional to the time, producing a result of the type shown in Fig. 6-2. Still another possibility is the circular sweep in Fig. 6-3. Here, two sinusoidal deflecting voltages of equal magnitude, but 90° out of phase, are produced by a phase-splitting arrangement, commonly a resistor-capacitor combination as shown.[1] These voltages are applied respectively to the vertical- and horizontal-deflecting electrodes, producing a circular trace[2] in which the angle of rotation of the spot is

[1] A simple resistance-capacitance phase splitter as shown in Fig. 6-3 gives the desired behavior only at one frequency. However, by means of more complicated resistance-capacitance networks it is possible to obtain two voltages that over a wide frequency band, such as the speech range, are substantially equal in magnitude and are almost exactly 90° out of phase; thus a circular sweep that is not sensitive to frequency can be achieved when necessary. For details of such networks see R. B. Dome, Wide-band Phase-shift Networks, *Electronics*, vol. 19, p. 112, December, 1946; D.G.C. Luck, Properties of Some Wide-band Phase Splitting Networks, *Proc. IRE*, Vol. 37, p. 147, February, 1949; Sidney Darlington, Realization of a Constant Phase Difference, *Bell System Tech. J.*, vol. 29, p. 94, January, 1950; H. J. Orchard, Synthesis of Wideband Two-phase Networks, *Wireless Eng.*, vol. 27, p. 72, March, 1950; W. Saraga, The Design of Wide-band Phase Splitting Networks, *Proc. IRE*, vol. 38, p. 754, July, 1950.

Oscillators which directly generate two equal voltages that are 90° out of phase are described in Sec. 12-7.

[2] Equal voltages 90° out of phase applied respectively to the vertical (x) and horizontal (y) deflectors cause the spot to deflect according to the parametric equations

$$x = A \sin \omega t$$
$$y = \pm A \cos \omega t \qquad (6\text{-}1)$$

where A is a constant proportional to amplitude. Combining these equations by

proportional to time, with a complete revolution corresponding to the time represented by one cycle of the deflecting wave. The unknown wave to be depicted is then applied to a radial-deflecting electrode, or in

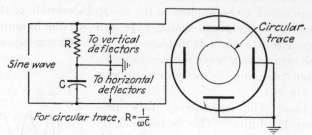

Fig. 6-3. A circuit arrangement for producing a circular time base on a cathode-ray tube.

series with the accelerating voltage, or to one of the pairs of deflecting plates, with results shown in Fig. 6-4. The circular sweep has the advantage that there is no time lost due to the return of the trace; it is also particularly convenient for presenting phase relations.

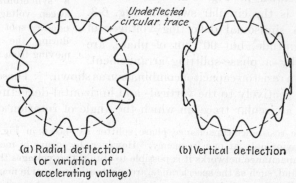

(a) Radial deflection
(or variation of
accelerating voltage)

(b) Vertical deflection

Fig. 6-4. A cathode-ray tube with circular time base, showing the pattern produced by a sinusoidal deflecting voltage applied in different ways. In this particular example, the sweep frequency is synchronized so that it is exactly a subharmonic of the deflecting frequency.

Modulation of the voltages producing a circular trace by a saw-toothed wave synchronized at a subharmonic, results in the spiral trace shown in Fig. 6-5.[1] This has the advantage of giving a very long time base. It is

squaring and adding, and noting that $\sin^2 \omega t + \cos^2 \omega t = 1$, gives

$$x^2 + y^2 = A^2 \qquad (6\text{-}2)$$

This is the equation of a circle.

When the two voltages are unequal, or are not exactly 90° out of phase, then the spot traverses an elliptical path. The direction in which the spot moves is determined by the sign in Eq. (6-1).

[1] Such a sweep system is described by R. B. Moran, Jr., Spiral Sweep Oscilloscope

customarily used with a type of tube that has a radial-deflecting electrode, to which the wave to be depicted is applied. The spot is preferably blanked out during the return stroke of the saw-tooth wave, as in Fig. 6-5, to avoid confusing the presentation.

A further example of the versatility of the cathode-ray tube as an oscilloscope is illustrated by the ease with which timing markers may be introduced in the presentation. For example, by applying positive pulses to the electrode controlling the beam current (or to an intensifier

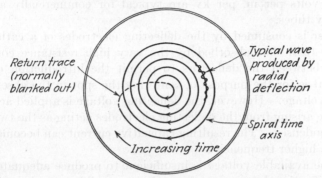

Fig. 6-5. A spiral sweep, showing a transient applied to a radial-deflecting electrode.

electrode), bright spots will appear on the trace; thus if these pulses are generated by a 1-Mc wave, then the bright spots will be spaced along the time axis at intervals of 1 μsec. This provides an accurate time scale irrespective of imperfections that may be present in the tube, or in saw-tooth, circular, or spiral sweeps. Further discussion of time-marking systems is given in Sec. 6-8.

Deflection of Cathode-ray Beams. The deflection of the beam of a cathode-ray tube employing electrostatic deflection is directly proportional to the deflecting voltage, and is inversely proportional to the anode voltage of the beam, according to the relation

$$\text{Deflection on screen} = \frac{LbE_d}{2aE_a} \qquad (6\text{-}3)$$

where L = length along beam from center of deflecting plates to fluorescent screen
   b = effective length of deflecting plates in direction of beam
   a = spacing of deflecting plates at right angles to the beam
   E_d = deflecting voltage between plates
   E_a = beam voltage

Timer, *Electronics*, vol. 20, p. 120, October, 1947. Another method of producing a spiral-sweep voltage is described by G. H. Rawcliffe, Shock-impulsed Spiral Time Base, *Wireless Eng.*, vol. 26, p. 243, July, 1949; also see Spiral Time Base, *Wireless Eng.*, vol. 17, p. 224, August–September, 1950.

Any convenient units of length may be used.   This expression is approximate in that fringing flux is neglected.   Actually the behavior is as though the effective value of b were greater than the actual length by roughly the spacing between deflecting electrodes.[1]   The deflection sensitivity is commonly expressed in terms of the deflecting voltage required to produce a deflection of 1 in. (or 1 cm) for an anode potential of 1000 volts; for other anode voltages the deflection sensitivity will be inversely proportional to anode potential.   Deflection sensitivities of the order of 50 to 200 volts per in. per kv are typical for commercially available cathode-ray tubes.

No power is consumed by the deflecting electrodes of a cathode-ray tube other than that absorbed by the very high resistance commonly connected between the deflectors to permit the introduction of a d-c voltage that is for the purpose of centering the spot in the absence of a deflecting voltage.   However, the deflecting voltage is applied across the capacitance arising from the deflecting electrodes acting as the two plates of an air condenser.   The resulting capacitive current can become important at the higher frequencies.

When the available voltage is insufficient to produce adequate deflection, amplification by means of a voltage amplifier can be employed. Such amplifiers should have constant amplification and negligible phase distortion over the frequency range of interest.   To achieve this result, video amplifier techniques for compensating the high- and low-frequency ends of the response range are commonly used; it is also frequently helpful to employ negative feedback.   Amplifiers employing video techniques can be designed to give a satisfactory performance up to a top frequency of 10 Mc or even higher; by the use of the distributed amplifier, it is possible to meet the severe requirements of the cathode-ray oscillograph up to frequencies of 200 Mc and higher.[2]   Oscillograph amplifiers are ideally push-pull, thereby exciting the pair of deflecting electrodes with a voltage that is symmetrical with respect to ground.   It is ordinarily permissible, however, to ground one of the deflecting plates and to employ a deflecting voltage generated by a single-ended amplifier.

Frequency Characteristics.   The cathode-ray tube is able to depict waves of all frequencies, from direct current up to a frequency so high that the time required for the electrons in the beam to travel the length of the deflecting plates becomes an appreciable fraction of a cycle.   For frequencies such that this transit time of the beam in traveling the length of the deflecting plate is not a negligible part of the cycle, the deflection

[1] See Hans E. Hollmann, The Dynamic Sensitivity and Calibration of Cathode-ray Oscilloscopes at Very-high Frequencies, *Proc. IRE*, vol. 38, p. 32, January, 1950.

[2] See E. L. Ginzton, W. R. Hewlett, J. H. Jasberg, and J. D. Noe, Distributed Amplification, *Proc. IRE*, vol. 36, p. 956, August, 1948.

that is produced by a given deflecting voltage is less than at low frequencies, according to the equation

$$\frac{\text{Deflection at high frequency}}{\text{Deflection at low frequencies}} = \frac{\sin (\omega T/2)}{\omega T/2} \qquad (6\text{-}4)$$

Here T is the time in seconds required for an electron in the beam to travel a distance equal to the length of the deflecting plate,[1] and ω is 2π times the frequency of the deflecting voltage in cycles per second. It will be noted that ωT is the transit time, measured in radians at the applied frequency, that is required by an electron to travel the length of the plate. The results of Eq. (6-4) are plotted in Fig. 6-6, which shows that the high-frequency sensitivity has dropped to 0.9 times the sensitivity at low frequencies when the transit angle along the deflecting plate is 90°, that is, when the time required for an electron to travel the length of the deflecting plate is one-fourth of a cycle.[2]

It is apparent that the high-frequency limit of a cathode-ray oscillograph can be increased by reducing the length of the deflecting

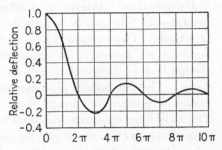

FIG. 6-6. Relative deflection of a cathode-ray tube as a function of the time required by the electron to travel the length of the deflecting plate, measured in radians at the frequency of the deflecting voltage.

electrodes and increasing the anode voltage.[3] With commercial cathode-ray tubes, it is found that the 90 per cent point will typically occur at frequencies in the order of 100 Mc or higher; thus with deflecting plates 1 in. long and an anode potential of 2500 volts, 90 per cent response occurs

[1] At ordinary anode voltages, where relativistic effects can be neglected, the value of T is given by the relation

$$T = \frac{b}{\text{electron velocity}} = \frac{0.0168 \times 10^{-6} b}{\sqrt{E}} \qquad (6\text{-}4a)$$

where b is the electrode length in centimeters, and E is the anode voltage in volts.

[2] Actually Fig. 6-6 and Eq. (6-4a) represent an idealized situation where the spacing between the deflecting plates is small compared with their length, so that the fringing flux is of negligible importance. When this is not the case, the transit-time effect is somewhat greater than given by Eq. (6-4) even when the value of b used in the calculation is an effective length greater than the actual length by the spacing of the plates. This matter is excellently covered by Hollmann, *loc. cit.*

[3] The performance can also be improved at high frequencies by using a traveling wave to deflect the cathode-ray beam; see J. R. Pierce, Traveling Wave Oscilloscope, *Electronics*, vol. 22, p. 97, November, 1949.

at about 290 Mc. By using very high anode voltages and very short plates, this frequency limit can be raised well above 1000 Mc.[1]

At frequencies near the upper limit at which a cathode-ray tube will operate satisfactorily, another type of frequency effect must also be taken into account. This is the fact that the voltage existing between the deflecting electrodes may differ from the voltage applied to the leads associated with these electrodes. In particular, the capacitance between the electrodes may resonate with the inductance of the leads to produce an effect that is exactly analogous to that present in a vacuum-tube voltmeter, as discussed on page 25.

Miscellaneous Aspects of Cathode-ray Oscillographs. The ordinary cathode-ray tube is able to present for observation only one voltage wave at a time. Two or more waves of the same fundamental frequency may be observed, however, by arranging matters so that the different waves are applied to the vertical deflectors on successive sweeps of the timing wave. The persistence of vision and of the screen phosphorescence then makes it appear as though these waves were simultaneously present. The switching operation required to apply different waves during alternate sweep cycles can be carried out electronically, as illustrated in Fig. 6-7. Here the two waves to be observed are applied to the inputs of pentagrid mixer-amplifiers A_1 and A_2, respectively. The plate circuits of these amplifier tubes are in parallel so that any output from either tube produces vertical deflection. A square-wave generator synchronized to operate at half the frequency of the sweep voltage then produces "gate" pulses that turn each individual amplifier on during successive half cycles. By making bias E_c sufficient to cut off the plate current in the absence of the square wave, then at any particular time only one amplifier is active.

Cathode-ray tubes are often used to observe transient voltages. One method of doing this is to repeat the transient at regular intervals so that it may be observed as a steady-state phenomenon. Alternatively, the transient can be displayed on a single sweep of the timing wave, and then photographed;[2] fairly satisfactory visual observation is also possible if the screen of the cathode-ray tube has persistence. The single sweep is commonly produced by a one-shot multivibrator; the transient to be observed then triggers off this multivibrator, causing it to execute one

[1] The upper frequency limit that has been reached at the present time has been attained by Gordon M. Lee, A Three-beam Oscillograph for Recording at Frequencies up to 10,000 Megacycles, *Proc. IRE*, vol. 34, p. 121, March, 1946.

[2] Details of oscillograph techniques that are used in recording high voltage transients of brief duration, such as the output of an impulse generator, are described by H. P. Kuehni and Simon Ramo, A New High-speed Cathode-ray Oscillograph, *Trans. AIEE*, vol. 56, p. 721, June 1937; N. Rohats, High Speed Oscillograph, *Electronics*, vol. 19, p. 135, April, 1946.

cycle of oscillation that produces a single cycle of the saw-tooth deflecting wave, after which the system becomes quiescent.   In such an arrangement the control electrode of the cathode-ray tube is normally biased more negative than cutoff, thus turning the beam off.   A square wave is then derived from the saw-tooth wave and used to reduce the bias on the control electrode for the duration of the single sweep of the timing wave. In this way the spot is turned on only when needed, and for this brief interval can be made more intense than would be permissible for continuous operation.   In many cases it is desirable to delay the application of the transient to the vertical-deflecting electrode in order to permit the

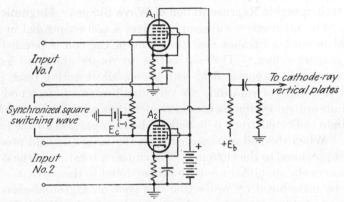

FIG. 6-7. Electronic switching arrangement for presenting two different waves on the same cathode-ray screen.

sweep circuit to get started first.   This can be achieved by introducing a time delay by means of a cable or network inserted in the circuit leading to the deflecting electrode.   These techniques are discussed further in Sec. 6-7.

Cathode-ray-tube traces are frequently photographed.[1]   The photographic effect produced by a cathode-ray spot is greater as the beam power for a given spot size is increased.   The photographic effectiveness also depends upon the spectral distribution of the light produced by the fluorescent screen, and will accordingly differ for different types of phosphors.   In photographing recurrent traces, the maximum permissible exposure time is limited only by the fogging due to stray light, and

[1] For further information on this topic see H. G. Hopkinson, The Photography of Cathode-ray Tube Traces, *Jour. IEE (Radiolocation Conv.)*, vol. 93, pt. IIIA, p. 808, 1946; N. Hendry, Photography of Cathode-ray Tube Traces, *Electronic Eng.*, p. 234, January, 1944; R. Feldt, Photographing Patterns on Cathode-ray Tubes, *Electronics*, vol. 17, p. 130, February, 1944; Norman Fulmer, Improved C-R Photographs, *Electronics*, vol. 23, p. 86, March, 1950; Kodak Recording Materials, a booklet available from Eastman Kodak Company, Rochester, N.Y.

can be determined experimentally. In case of transient phenomena, the densities produced on the film are determined by the speed of the trace, the beam power of the cathode-ray tube, the lens stop, etc. Again, suitable combinations can be determined experimentally. The photographic effect for transients is commonly expressed in terms of "writing speed," which is the maximum rate at which the fluorescent spot can move while being satisfactorily photographed when the spot does not retrace its path. With anode potentials on the order of 2.5 kv, writing speeds such as 10 to 100 km per sec are typical, while writing speeds exceeding 1000 km per sec can be obtained with some commercial cathode-ray tubes, at an anode potential of 10 kv.

6-2. Oscillographic Representation of Wave Shapes—Magnetic Oscillograph. The magnetic oscillograph utilizes a coil suspended in a magnetic field in such a manner that the plane of the coil is parallel to the lines of magnetic flux.[1] The coil is free to rotate about an axis perpendicular to the magnetic field with an elastic restoring force proportional to the angle of rotation. A very small mirror is fastened on the coil, and an optical system is provided such that as the mirror rotates, a spot of light reflected from it is deflected in proportion to the angle of rotation. When the coil carries a current, the magnetic field produces a torque proportional to the current. This causes a rotation of the coil, and a deflection of the spot, that are both proportional to the current. A time axis can be introduced by projecting this spot on a ground-glass screen with the aid of a rotating mirror that is synchronized with the frequency of the wave being observed. Alternatively, the wave being observed can be photographed using photographic film or paper wrapped around a rotating drum, on which the light spot is allowed to fall for exactly one revolution by the action of a synchronized shutter.

The variation of the response of a magnetic oscillograph with frequency depends upon the mass, resonant frequency, and damping of the moving-coil system. This vibrating system behaves like a series resonant circuit in which the mass corresponds to inductance, the elastic compliance corresponds to capacitance, and damping corresponds to resistance. The applied force is equivalent to applied voltage, the velocity with which the coil moves is equivalent to current flowing in the analogous series circuit, and the displacement or amplitude of deflection is proportional to the

---

[1] An alternative form of magnetic oscillograph has recently found considerable use at low frequencies. This utilizes a driving unit consisting of a moving coil mounted in a magnetic field, and similar to the driving unit of a dynamic loudspeaker. A light-weight pen, or stylus, is attached to this moving coil, and records on a moving paper chart, using sensitive paper or instantaneous-drying ink fed by capillary action. With proper compensation in the associated amplifier, it is possible to obtain in this way a response substantially independent of frequency up to slightly over 100 cycles, with adequate amplitude of the pen motion.

integral of current, *i.e.*, to the charge.   The equation governing motion is accordingly as follows:

$$\text{Torque (or force) on coil} = BIN \times \text{constant} \qquad (6\text{-}5)$$

where B is the flux density of the magnetic field in which the coil is placed, I is the current in the coil, and N the number of turns in the coil. The effective impedance against which this force is exerted is

$$\text{Impedance} = R + j\left(\omega m - \frac{1}{\omega C}\right) \qquad (6\text{-}6)$$

where R is the equivalent resistance or friction in appropriate units, m is the equivalent mass, and C is the equivalent compliance ($1/C$ is the equivalent stiffness) of the vibrating system, with ω being 2π times the frequency.   The velocity of the coil vibration is then, in appropriate units,

$$\text{Velocity} = \frac{\text{force}}{\text{impedance}} \times \text{constant} \qquad (6\text{-}7)$$

while

$$\text{Amplitude of vibration} = \frac{\text{velocity}}{\omega} \qquad (6\text{-}8a)$$

$$\text{Amplitude of vibration} = \frac{\text{force}}{\omega\left[R + j\left(\omega m - \dfrac{1}{\omega C}\right)\right]} \times \text{constant} \qquad (6\text{-}8b)$$

$$\text{Amplitude of vibration} = \frac{BIN \times \text{constant}}{\omega\left[R + j\left(\omega m - \dfrac{1}{\omega C}\right)\right]} \qquad (6\text{-}8c)$$

At frequencies appreciably below resonance the impedance to motion is almost entirely that arising from the elastic impedance $1/\omega C$.   To the extent that this is the case, the amplitude of the deflection is seen from Eqs. (6-8) to be independent of frequency.   At resonance, where $\omega m = 1/\omega C$, the amplitude of the deflection depends on the damping R; when R is properly chosen, the response at resonance will then be substantially the same as at lower frequencies.   At frequencies appreciably above resonance the impedance to motion is largely supplied by the mechanical inertia ωm, and the response drops off with increasing frequency almost inversely proportional to the square of frequency.   It is thus apparent that with proper damping[1] the response of a magnetic oscillograph can be made substantially constant, independent of frequency, up to the region of resonance, but for higher frequencies will fall

[1] The damping can be controlled by immersing the moving coil in a liquid of suitable viscosity, by means of eddy currents induced by coil motion, and by the impedance of the source supplying current to the moving coil.

off rapidly.   It is, however, possible to extend the useful frequency range of a magnetic oscillograph somewhat beyond resonance by suitable equalizing circuits that cause the current passed through the coil to be greater at frequencies above resonance than at the lower frequencies; in this way an extension of perhaps 50 per cent in useful frequency range is practical.

The frequency range of magnetic oscillographs depends upon the design.   It is possible to obtain resonant frequencies as high as 5000 to 10,000 cycles with practical oscillograph elements.   On the other hand, when such a high upper frequency limit is not required, lower resonant frequencies are preferred since this results in increased sensitivity. Depending on the application, the resonant frequency may be made as low as 50 cycles or even less.   With any particular coil the resonant frequency can be controlled by adjusting the stiffness of the elastic suspension.

The sensitivity of a magnetic oscillograph, $i.e.$, the amplitude of deflection obtained for a given current, is seen from Eq. (6-8c) to be directly proportional to the strength of the magnetic field and to the number of turns in the coil.   However, for a given resonant frequency the sensitivity is inversely proportional to the mass of the coil, so that increasing the number of turns does not help unless the size of the wire can be reduced at the same time.   With a given coil mass, the sensitivity is inversely proportional to the square of the resonant frequency, since a lowering of the resonant frequency under these conditions is accomplished by reducing the elastic stiffness directly as the square of the resonant frequency. Thus to halve the resonant frequency, the stiffness $1/C$ is reduced by a factor of 4, and from Eq. (6-8c) the amplitude at low frequencies is increased four times.   The resonant frequency accordingly should be no greater than the circumstances require.

The phase relation between the current passing through the coil, and the resulting deflections, is constant and is independent of frequency at the lower frequencies where the elastic stiffness controls the motion.   At the resonant frequency of the moving-coil system a phase shift of 90° is present with respect to the phase at low frequencies; at appreciably higher frequencies where the mechanical inertia controls the motion of the coil, the phase is shifted 180° with respect to the phase at low frequencies.   Thus, if preservation of phase relations is important in reproducing the wave to be observed, the upper frequency limit of the magnetic oscillograph is considerably less than the resonant frequency of the mechanical system unless an appropriate phase-compensating electrical network is introduced into the system.

The impedance level at which the magnetic oscillograph operates depends upon the design.   In arrangements where the coil consists of a single-turn bifilar loop, the impedance is only a few ohms, and relatively large deflecting currents are required.   The present tendency is increasingly to use multiturn coils wound with extremely fine wire. The impedance of these is much greater, but is still generally appreciably less than the optimum load impedance for the plate circuit of a vacuum-tube amplifier. Transformers are accordingly frequently used in association with magnetic oscillographs, to improve the impedance match.

6-3. Harmonic Analysis of Oscillograms. Periodic electrical waves can always be expressed as the sum of a d-c component plus a series of components that are all harmonics of the fundamental frequency of the wave. That is, if E is a periodic function, one can then write

$$E = D_0 + C_1 \sin (\omega t + \Phi_1) + C_2 \sin (2\omega t + \Phi_2)$$
$$+ C_3 \sin (3\omega t + \Phi_3) + \cdots \quad (6\text{-}9a)$$

where D_0 = amplitude of d-c component
C_1, C_2, etc. = amplitudes of corresponding a-c components
Φ_1, Φ_2, etc. = phase angle of corresponding a-c components
   $\omega = 2\pi$ times the fundamental frequency of the wave.

Equation (6-9a) is often rearranged as

$$E = A_1 \sin \omega t + A_2 \sin 2\omega t + A_3 \sin 3\omega t + \cdots$$
$$+ D_0 + B_1 \cos \omega t + B_2 \cos 2\omega t + B_3 \cos 3\omega t + \cdots \quad (6\text{-}9b)$$

where

$$\sqrt{A_n{}^2 + B_n{}^2} = C_n$$
$$\frac{B_n}{A_n} = \tan \Phi_n$$

Fourier Method of Determining the Coefficients of an Arbitrary Curve. The A coefficients appearing in Eq. (6-9b) can be evaluated by making use of the fact that, when a periodic curve is multiplied by $\sin n\omega t$ and the resulting area summed up over one complete cycle of the fundamental frequency, the result is determined only by the coefficient A_n in Eq. (6-9b). This coefficient is equal to twice the average height of the area. Likewise, when the curve is multiplied by $\cos n\omega t$ and the resulting area summed up over a complete cycle, the result is determined solely by the coefficient B_n. By making use of this principle one obtains the following formulas:[1]

$$A_n = \frac{1}{\pi} \int_{\omega t = 0}^{\omega t = 2\pi} E \sin n\omega t \, d(\omega t) \quad (6\text{-}10a)$$

$$B_n = \frac{1}{\pi} \int_{\omega t = 0}^{\omega t = 2\pi} E \cos n\omega t \, d(\omega t) \quad (6\text{-}10b)$$

$$D_0 = \frac{1}{2\pi} \int_{\omega t = 0}^{\omega t = 2\pi} E \, d(\omega t) \quad (6\text{-}10c)$$

where E represents the curve being analyzed.

[1] The development of these equations is to be found in every mathematical discussion of Fourier series, but is beyond the scope of this book.

The integration indicated in Eqs. (6-10) can be carried out mathematically when the wave being analyzed follows some known law, as, for example, when the wave analyzed is the voltage output wave of a rectifier. In other cases the product under the integral sign can be calculated point by point, plotted, and the resulting net area (positive minus negative areas) determined by counting squares, by use of a planimeter, or with the aid of Simpson's rule. The Fourier method gives directly the correct amplitude of any particular component irrespective of the presence or absence of other components.

Schedule Method. In the schedule method one cycle of the arbitrary curve which is to be analyzed is divided up into a number of equally spaced ordinates as shown in Fig. 6-8. As many coefficients as there are

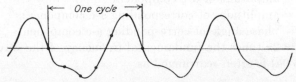

Fig. 6-8. Arbitrary curve with six equally spaced ordinates. A six-point schedule will give a curve that will pass through the six selected points.

ordinates are then evaluated so that the resulting curve will pass through the selected points. Thus in Fig. 6-8 it is possible to obtain an equation that will pass through the selected ordinates by assigning proper values to A_1, A_2, D_0, B_1, B_2, and B_3 while making all other coefficients in Eq. (6-9b) equal to zero. Evaluating the coefficients to accomplish this result involves solving as many simultaneous equations as there are coefficients to be evaluated. By taking advantage of the fact that the ordinates are evenly spaced, the solution of these simultaneous equations can be simplified to the point where it involves performing only a few simple multiplications, and carrying out a series of simple additions and subtractions. These operations are commonly indicated by a form or schedule—hence the name "schedule method."[1] A simple schedule for the case of six ordinates is given in the accompanying table. Schedules for 8-, 12-, 18-, and 36-point analyses are available for both the general case where there is a d-c component and both even and odd harmonics, and also where only

---

[1] The method of deriving schedules is described by F. W. Grover, Analysis of Alternating-current Waves by the Method of Fourier, with Special Reference to Methods of Facilitating Computations, *Reprint* 203, *Natl. Bur. Standards (U.S.) Bull.*, vol. 9, 1913. This publication gives a number of schedules. Schedules for 6, 8, and 12 points are also given by Larry S. Cole, Graphical Analysis of Complex Waves, *Electronics*, vol. 18, p. 142, October, 1945, while 36- and 72-point schedules are contained in the paper by R. P. G. Denham, Harmonic Analysis Schedules, *Electronics*, vol. 15, p. 44, September, 1945.

odd harmonics are present.[1]   These schedules with more ordinates are naturally more complicated than the one shown in Table 6-1, but will likewise evaluate a greater number of coefficients.

The schedule method evaluates the coefficients so that the resulting curve is correct for the selected ordinates.   Between these points the computed and actual curves will not agree, however, unless the coefficients evaluated are the only coefficients actually present in the wave. Thus in Fig. 6-8 the schedule method will not give the correct result if there is some fourth harmonic present.   It is therefore necessary to use

TABLE 6-1.

SIX-POINT SCHEDULE INVOLVING BOTH EVEN AND ODD HARMONICS
AND A DIRECT-CURRENT COMPONENT

Measured ordinates	Sums	Differences		Sine terms		Cosine and constant terms			
				A_1 and A_2		B_1 and B_2		B_0 and B_3	
y_0	s_0	d_0							
$y_1 \quad y_5$	s_1	d_1	sin 30°	. . . .		$-s_2$	s_1		
$y_2 \quad y_4$	s_2	d_2	sin 60°	d_1	d_2				
y_3	s_3	d_3	sin 90°	. . . .		s_0	$-s_3$	$s_0 + s_2$	$s_1 + s_3$
Sums.				S_0'	S_e'	S_0''	S_e''	S_0'''	S_e'''
				$A_1 = \dfrac{S_0' + S_e'}{3}$		$B_1 = \dfrac{S_0'' + S_e''}{3}$		$B_0 = \dfrac{S_0''' + S_e'''}{6}$	
				$A_2 = \dfrac{S_0' - S_e'}{3}$		$B_2 = \dfrac{S_0'' - S_e''}{3}$		$B_3 = \dfrac{S_0''' - S_e'''}{6}$	

CHECKS

$$s_0 = (B_0 + B_3) + (B_1 + B_2)$$
$$s_2 = 2(B_0 + B_3) - (B_1 + B_2)$$
$$s_0 + s_2 = 3(B_0 + B_3) \qquad 2s_0 - s_2 = 3(B_1 + B_2)$$
$$s_1 = 2(B_0 - B_3) + (B_1 - B_2)$$
$$s_3 = (B_0 - B_3) - (B_1 - B_2)$$
$$s_1 + s_3 = 3(B_0 + B_3) \qquad s_1 - 2s_3 = 3(B_1 - B_2)$$
$$d_1 = 2(A_1 + A_2) \sin 60°$$
$$d_2 = 2(A_1 - A_2) \sin 60°$$

Procedure.   The measured ordinates are first written down in two columns in the order indicated.   In the next two columns appear the sums s_m of the ordinates, found by adding those in the same row, and the differences d_m of the same ordinates.   In the fifth column are indicated the trigonometric functions which enter into the calculation. The rest of the schedule indicates in an abbreviated form what products are to be formed, the convention being adopted that each quantity s_m or d_m is to be multiplied

[1] The commonly used formulas for determining amplifier distortion based on points determined from a load line are equivalent to simple schedules for the case where it is known in advance that all the A coefficients in Eqs. (6-9) are zero.

by the sine of the angle which appears in the same row at the left. Thus one forms the product $d_1 \sin 60°$ in one case, of $-s_2 \sin 30°$ in another case, and $(s_1 + s_3) \sin 90°$ in still another.

enough ordinates to permit the evaluation of all important frequency components present in the wave.

6-4. Wave and Distortion Analyzers for Audio-frequency Waves. Several methods are available for experimentally determining the frequency components of a periodic audio-frequency wave. These include wave analyzers, which may be either of the tunable-selective-circuit or of the heterodyne type, and distortion-measuring equipment, which suppresses the fundamental frequency and measures the *rms* value of the distortion components.

Wave Analyzers Employing Tunable Selective Circuits. A schematic diagram of this type of analyzer is illustrated in Fig. 6-9. Here the com-

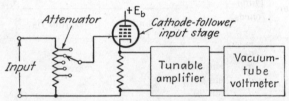

Fig. 6-9. Schematic diagram of wave analyzer employing a tunable selective circuit.

plex wave to be analyzed is passed through an adjustable attenuator, and is then applied to the selective amplifier, which is tuned to the frequency component to be determined. The amplifier output is indicated[1] by a suitable meter, such as a diode vacuum-tube voltmeter, or an average-reading rectifier of the type discussed in Sec. 1-7. The attenuator serves as a range multiplier, and thus permits a large range of signal amplitudes to be analyzed without overloading the amplifier. The system can be calibrated by means of an auxiliary signal generator that applies a known voltage to the input. Alternatively, if the amplifier has constant gain for all adjustments of the tuning control, one can set the attenuator so that the output indication produced by the fundamental frequency is full-scale (or 100 per cent) and can then read the harmonic components of a wave directly as a fraction of the fundamental amplitude.

The tuned amplifier in a wave analyzer is ordinarily of the resistance-tuned type.[2] Such an arrangement has the advantage that by the use

[1] A visual display of a complete amplitude versus frequency characteristic can be obtained by rapidly sweeping over the frequency band involved and presenting the wave analyzer output on a cathode-ray tube. See A. E. Hastings, Electronic Indicator for Low Audio Frequencies, *Proc. IRE*, vol. 35, p. 821, August, 1947.

[2] See H. H. Scott, A New Type of Selective Circuit and Some Applicators, *Proc. IRE*, vol. 26, p. 226, February, 1938; The Degenerative Sound Analyzer, *J. Acous. Soc. Am.*, vol. 11, p. 225, October, 1939; Oswald G. Villard, Jr., Tunable A-F Amplifier,

of negative feedback, the gain at the frequency of maximum response can be stabilized and made substantially independent of the value of this frequency. Also, the arrangement lends itself to achieving a very wide tuning range, and avoids the use of audio-frequency coils, which are not only expensive and cumbersome to tune over a wide range, but which in addition are susceptible to pickup from stray magnetic fields.

The bandwidth of the response characteristic of a resistance-tuned amplifier is a substantially constant percentage of frequency throughout the tuning range. Thus the bandwidth in cycles is greater, the higher the frequency being selected. The selectivity obtainable depends upon the design of the system, but in a typical case is such as to correspond to

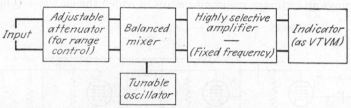

FIG. 6-10. Schematic diagram of heterodyne wave analyzer.

a 3-db reduction in response at a frequency that differs by 1 per cent from the resonant frequency, and 35-db for a frequency differing by one octave.

Heterodyne Wave Analyzers. A schematic diagram of a heterodyne wave analyzer is shown in Fig. 6-10. Here the wave to be analyzed is combined with a tunable local oscillator in a balanced mixer. The output of the mixer passes through a very highly selective multistage amplifier having a predetermined fixed response frequency that is somewhat higher than any of the frequencies contained in the unknown wave. The output of this selective amplifier is indicated by means of a vacuum-tube voltmeter, or equivalent instrument. In operation, the frequency of the local oscillator is adjusted so that the difference (or heterodyne) frequency produced by interacting with the desired component of the complex unknown wave is equal to the resonant frequency of the selective amplifier. Thus the component to be determined has its frequency transformed to the predetermined value, and is amplified and measured at this fixed frequency. Other frequency components present in the unknown wave transform to frequencies that are rejected by the selective amplifier. The amplitude of the unknown component is obtained from the measured output by means of a suitable calibration, which can conveniently take the form of adjusting the gain of the fixed-frequency amplifier until a calibrating signal of known amplitude gives a standard output when applied to the input; the calibrating signal can conveniently be 60 cycles. The frequency of the unknown component is determined from the local oscillator frequency that must be used to change the unknown component to the known fixed frequency.

Two types of selective amplifiers find use in heterodyne wave analyzers. The first type employs a crystal filter, typically having a center frequency of approximately 50 kc.[1] By employing two crystals in a band-pass arrangement, it is possible to obtain a relatively flat passband over a 4-cycle range with a response about 15 db down at 5 cycles off the center frequency.

An alternative frequency-selective system that also finds commercial use employs an ordinary resonant circuit in which the effective Q has been

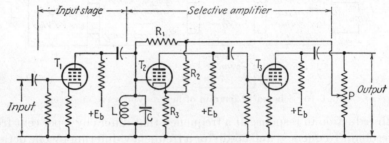

Fig. 6-11. Method of obtaining high and controllable selectivity by the use of a combination of negative and positive feedback in conjunction with tuned circuit LC.

made high and controllable by the use of negative feedback.[2] The method of doing this is shown in Fig. 6-11. The tuned circuit LC, typically resonant at 20 kc, is associated with resistors R_1, R_2, R_3, and the two-stage amplifier $T_2 T_3$ in such a manner that at the resonant frequency, the negative feedback through $R_2 R_3$ is balanced by positive feedback through $R_1 LC$. However, at frequencies off resonance the positive feedback becomes less, and there is a net negative feedback that reduces the output. This reduction in output is in addition to that arising from the ordinary selectivity of the tuned circuit LC, and so increases the effective selectivity of the resonant circuit by reducing the response off resonance without changing the response at resonance. The increase in selectivity obtained in this way over the selectivity of the tuned circuit LC becomes greater the larger the positive- and negative-feedback effects that are balanced against each other, and so can be varied by the potentiometer P. A wave analyzer using four such units connected in cascade, each of which has a resonant frequency of 20 kc, has a selectivity that compares

[1] See L. B. Arguimbau, Wave Analysis, *Gen. Rad. Expt.*, vol. 7, p. 12, June, 1933.

[2] F. E. Terman, R. R. Buss, W. R. Hewlett, and F. C. Cahill, Some Applications of Negative Feedback with Particular Reference to Laboratory Equipment, *Proc. IRE*, vol. 27, p. 649, October, 1939.

favorably with that of a band-pass crystal filter, and there is the added flexibility of being able to control the selectivity.

The heterodyne wave analyzer has excellent frequency resolution, can be built to cover the entire audio-frequency range conveniently, and by the use of appropriate input attenuators can cover a very wide range of input voltages from quite small to very large values.   The chief limiting feature of the heterodyne wave analyzer is that the mixer introduces spurious cross-modulation products that cannot be depended upon to be less than about 60 or 70 db below the largest frequency component of the wave being analyzed.[1]   This sets a lower limit to the amplitude that can be measured in the presence of a large voltage of another frequency.

Fundamental Suppression Method of Distortion Measurement.[2]   The rms distortion of a wave is conveniently defined as the effective value of the harmonics divided by the rms amplitude of the wave.   That is,

$$\text{rms distortion} = \frac{\sqrt{I_2{}^2 + I_3{}^2 + I_4{}^2 + \cdots}}{I_0} \qquad (6\text{-}11)$$

where I_2, I_3, etc., are the effective values of the various distortion components, and I_0 is the effective value of the wave, including *both* harmonics and fundamental.

The rms distortion can be conveniently measured by suppressing the fundamental-frequency component, and then measuring the part of the wave that remains.   When this measurement is made by means of a thermocouple or square-wave vacuum-tube voltmeter, the effective value is obtained without error; however, an average-reading meter of the type illustrated in Fig. 1-23 will give an indication sufficiently close to the effective value to be satisfactory under most circumstances.   Peak-reading diode voltmeters cannot be used without introducing a large error.

Suppression of the fundamental can be accomplished by the use of a high-pass filter which is so designed that the harmonics lie in the pass-band, while the fundamental frequency is severely attenuated.   An alternative arrangement is to employ a bridge, or a bridged-T network, that is balanced for the fundamental frequency but is decidedly unbalanced for the harmonics.   Examples of suitable networks are shown in

---

[1] The problem of spurious products is treated in considerable detail by C. R. Moore and A. S. Curtis, An Analyzer for the Voice Frequency Range, *Bell System Tech. J.*, vol. 6, p. 217, April, 1927.

[2] For further information see I. Wolff, The Alternating-current Bridge as a Harmonic Analyzer, *J. Optical Soc. Am.*, vol. 15, p. 163, 1927; H. M. Wagner, A Note on the Fundamental Suppression in Harmonic Measurements, *Proc. IRE*, vol. 23, p. 85, January, 1935; R. R. Freeland, Distortion and Noise Meter, *Electronics*, vol. 22, p. 86, January, 1949.   The latter paper gives constructional details of an instrument based on the network of Fig. 6-12*b*.

Fig. 6-12.   The circuit arrangements at *a* and *b*, which involve coils and condensers, are preferably used only for fixed values of the fundamental frequency.[1]   When a continuous adjustment of the fundamental frequency is desired, it is usually preferable to employ the Wien-bridge arrangement of Fig. 6-12c, which is seen to be equivalent to the tunable Wien bridge of Fig. 5-20 used to measure frequency.   In those arrange-

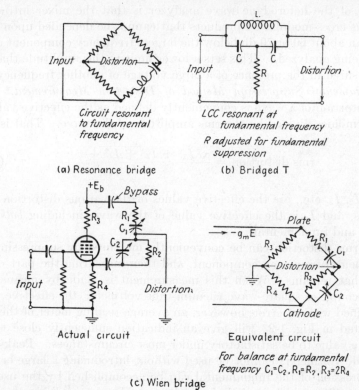

(a) Resonance bridge

Circuit resonant to fundamental frequency

(b) Bridged T

LCC resonant at fundamental frequency
R adjusted for fundamental suppression

(c) Wien bridge

For balance at fundamental frequency $C_1 = C_2$, $R_1 = R_2$, $R_3 = 2R_4$

FIG. 6-12. Typical null networks used in measuring distortion by suppression of the fundamental frequency.

ments having resonant circuits, a Q of 3 will result in the harmonics being transmitted to the output with practically no attenuation while the fundamental frequency is completely suppressed; thus in Fig. 6-12b, when $Q = 3$ the second harmonic suffers only 0.5 db attenuation.   The resistance-capacitance-tuned arrangement of Fig. 6-12c is not quite as good in this respect, but still the second harmonic will be attenuated by less than 1.0 db.

[1] An ingenious method of overcoming the disadvantage of a coil is described by J. E. Hayes, A New Type of Practical Distortion Meter, *Proc. IRE*, vol. 31, p. 112, March, 1943, and consists in using a reactance tube to develop a variable inductance.

A schematic diagram illustrating a possible form of distortion meter utilizing the circuit of Fig. 6-12b is shown in Fig. 6-13. Here switch S is at first thrown to A, thus by-passing the attenuator, and the output indication is observed after condenser C and resistance R of the bridged-T network have been adjusted for suppression of the fundamental (which is indicated by minimum output). Switch S is next thrown to B, and the attenuation is adjusted to give the same reading as before. The attenuator reading is then the rms distortion as expressed by Eq. (6–11) and defined in decibels.

Distortion-measuring instruments based on the suppression of the fundamental frequency are simpler, less expensive, and easier to build than are wave analyzers. However, they give only the total distortion,

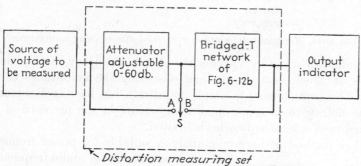

Fig. 6-13. Schematic diagram of a practical distortion meter based on the network of Fig. 6-12b.

and not the amplitude of the individual distortion components. In particular, they are useful only in dealing with a fundamental wave and its harmonics, and cannot be employed in situations involving two independent waves which have fundamental frequencies unrelated to each other, and which may differ much less in frequency than do a fundamental and its harmonic.

Miscellaneous Types of Wave Analyzers. A simple method of analyzing a complex wave is illustrated schematically in Fig. 6-14.[1] Here a search voltage of variable frequency is superimposed upon the voltage to be analyzed, and the combination is applied to a full-wave square-law vacuum-tube voltmeter.[2] In such an arrangement the vacuum-tube voltmeter will give an average deflection that depends only upon the effective value of the combined wave. However, when the frequency of

[1] C. G. Suits, A Thermionic Voltmeter Method for the Harmonic Analysis of Electrical Waves, *Proc. IRE*, vol. 18, p. 178, January, 1930.

[2] If care is taken to make the search voltage considerably larger than the voltage to be analyzed, it is permissible to use an average-reading voltmeter, such as illustrated in Fig. 1-23. A peak-reading vacuum-tube voltmeter is, however, to be avoided.

the search voltage is within a fraction of a cycle of a frequency component contained in the unknown wave, then pulsations (beats) are superimposed upon this steady deflection. These pulsations (beats) have an amplitude proportional to the crest amplitude of the component of the unknown wave that differs from the search frequency by only a fraction of a cycle. One can thus measure the amplitude and frequency of each component

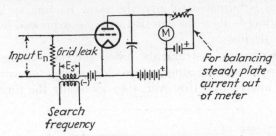

FIG. 6-14. Vacuum-tube-voltmeter method of analyzing waveform.

of the unknown wave by varying the search frequency, noting the frequencies at which beats occur, and observing the amplitudes of these beats. This arrangement is simple and direct, but has the disadvantage that the ability to measure small components in the presence of large components of other frequencies is limited.

Another method of harmonic analysis suitable for power frequencies and the lower audio frequencies is illustrated in Fig. 6-15.[1] Here a dynamometer instrument is employed, through one coil of which is passed a current representing the wave to be analyzed, while through the other coil there is passed a search current of controllable frequency. The operation of the device depends upon the fact that the instrument pointer

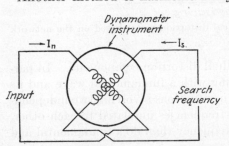

FIG. 6-15. Dynamometer method of analyzing waveform.

will not be deflected unless the frequency of the search current is very close to the frequency of a component contained in the wave being analyzed. When the difference between the two frequencies is a fraction of a cycle per second, the pointer will pulsate at the difference frequency. The amplitude of pulsation is equal to $I_n I_s$, where I_n is the effective amplitude of the unknown component, and I_s is the effective amplitude of the search current. Thus to analyze a wave one varies the frequency of the search current, notes the frequencies at which beats occur, and

[1] M. G. Nicholson and William M. Perkins, A Simple Harmonic Analyzer, *Proc. IRE*, vol. 20, p. 734, April, 1932.

observes the amplitudes of these beats.   The dynamometer method of analyzing a complex wave has the advantage of simplicity and directness. However, the ability of the method to measure accurately small components in the presence of large components of other frequencies is limited by the allowable power dissipation in the dynamometer coil.   This is because the dissipation limits the current that can be passed through the coil, and hence the amplitude of the beat.   The method is also limited to the lower audio frequencies, where dynamometer instruments operate satisfactorily.

6-5. Spectrum Analyzers.[1]   When a radio-frequency carrier wave is modulated, whether by telegraphic keying, by speech or music signals, or by radar pulses, the resulting waveform comprises not only the original carrier frequency but also two groups of side-band components displaced in frequency above and below the carrier.   The distribution of these frequency components, plotted as a graph of amplitude (voltage or power) versus frequency, is termed the spectrum.   The problem of determining these side-band components is somewhat related to that of determining the frequency components of audio-frequency signals by means of the wave analyzer of Sec. 6-4.   The frequency components now occur at radio frequencies, including especially the microwave region, where spectrum analyzers have proved particularly valuable.

As in the case of the wave analyzer, the radio-frequency spectrum analyzer operates on the principle of exploring the desired frequency region with a narrow-band-selective voltmeter or receiver.[2]   There are two possible circuit arrangements, the one most commonly used being shown in Fig. 6-16.   The device provides a plot on the screen of a cathode-ray tube, portraying a graph of amplitude versus frequency.   The pattern in Fig. 6-16 is that which would occur from a pulse-modulated magnetron under proper operating conditions.

The upper portion of the block diagram in Fig. 6-16 is seen to be essentially that of a superheterodyne receiver, except that the local oscillator is

[1] See "Technique of Microwave Measurements" (Vol. 11, Radiation Laboratory Series), Chap. 7, pp. 408–468, McGraw-Hill Book Company, Inc., New York, 1947; C. W. Oatley, Ultra-high Frequency Measurements, *Jour. IEE (Radiolocation Convention)*, vol. 93, pt. IIIA, p. 204, March–May, 1946; Everard M. Williams, Radio-frequency Spectrum Analyzers, *Proc. IRE*, vol. 34, p. 18, January, 1946; L. Apker, J. Kahnke, E. Taft, and R. Watters, Wide-range Double-heterodyne Spectrum Analyzers, *Proc. IRE*, vol. 35, p. 1068, October, 1947; E. Kettlewell, W. A. Bourne, and C. Chilton, A 3-cm R.F. Spectrometer and Mismatching Impedance Unit, *J. IEE (Radiolocation Conv.)*, vol. 93, pt. IIIA, pp. 224 (abstract), 1491, March–May, 1946.

[2] The special problems involved in measuring the radiation produced by radiotelephone transmitters in adjacent channels are discussed by Nean Lund, Methods of Measuring Adjacent-band Radiation from Radio Transmitters, *Proc, IRE*, vol. 39, p. 653, June, 1951.

electronically swept back and forth between two frequency limits at a linear rate.   At the same time, the spot on the cathode-ray tube is caused to move horizontally across the face of the tube in synchronism, so that the horizontal position is a function of the frequency of the local oscillator. As the spot moves horizontally, it is deflected vertically upward in proportion to the amplitude of the voltage delivered by the detector and video amplifier.   The sweep-voltage waveform is usually a saw tooth, providing essentially zero "flyback" time, although a sine wave could be used with a suitable means for phase adjustment to provide overlapping of the forward and return traces on the cathode-ray tube.   A suitable

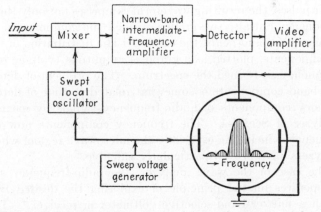

Fig. 6-16. Schematic diagram of one form of spectrum analyzer.

local oscillator tube at microwave frequencies is the reflex klystron; the frequency of such a tube is readily controlled over a small range by applying the sweep voltage to the repeller electrode.   At lower frequencies a triode oscillator can be used in conjunction with a reactance-tube modulator, or even mechanical means for sweeping the frequency can be used.[1]

In order to secure proper operation of the spectrum analyzer, attention must be given to certain design considerations.   These include the rate and range of the frequency sweep, together with the bandwidth and center frequency of the intermediate-frequency amplifier.   Ideally, one would wish the bandwidth to be as narrow as possible, in order to provide the highest resolution.   However, if carried to the limit, this would require a very low sweep speed in order to allow time to build up the voltage in the receiver circuits, and would also ultimately lead to unsatisfactory flicker of the cathode-ray image.   The range of frequencies to be covered should

[1] For a compilation of several means of securing a frequency sweep, see C. B. Clark and F. J. Kamphoefner, Panoramic Sweep Circuits, *Electronics*, vol. 22, p. 111, November, 1949.

be as small as possible.   The intermediate frequency should be chosen high enough to avoid the image response associated with superheterodyne reception.

One of the principal applications of spectrum analyzers has been in the study of the radio-frequency spectrum produced in the pulse modulation of microwave oscillator tubes.   Examination of the spectrum by an experienced observer facilitates a diagnosis of maladjustments of the system, including such things as unwanted frequency modulation.   For the examination of a carrier that is amplitude-modulated by a succession of rectangular pulses, the characteristic pattern of the pulse spectrum is that shown in Fig. 6-16, with the envelope going through zero amplitude at frequency intervals above and below the carrier frequency equal to $1/T$, where T is the duration in seconds of the rectangular pulse.   To give a sufficiently complete picture of the spectrum, the frequency band presented on the screen of the cathode-ray tube should be at least $6/T$, thus including at least three of these points of zero amplitude above and below the carrier.   This would require a 6-Mc band for pulses of 1 μsec duration. Thus is set the optimum range to be swept by the electronically tuned local oscillator in the analyzer.

The rate at which this frequency range must be swept is a function of the pulse recurrence frequency.   The analyzer presents a picture in which the spectrum is determined from the envelope of the succession of pulses that are received during the time the spots travel across the screen. Obviously, the greatest detail will be obtained with the largest number of pulses received during this time.   Since the pulse-recurrence frequency is usually predetermined, this means that the best definition occurs if the sweep interval is made as long as possible.   Actually, if at least 50 pulses are present on the screen, the envelope can be determined sufficiently well, and hence we can say that the sweep speed should be no greater than one-fiftieth of the pulse-recurrence frequency.   If this turns out to require such a low sweep speed that flicker results, it may be necessary to use a long-persistence cathode-ray screen.

The bandwidth, and hence the resolution, of the analyzer is determined primarily by the bandwidth of the intermediate-frequency amplifier.   If the resolution is to be adequate, there is a maximum permissible bandwidth, which is related to the pulse duration.   The evaluation of this relationship is too complicated to derive here, primarily because it also involves the shape of the band-pass characteristic as well as the width of the passband between the 3-db points.   For simple intermediate-frequency amplifiers, however, using a large number of single-tuned stages, it can be shown that the bandwidth of the amplifier should be no greater than one-tenth of the reciprocal of the pulse duration, namely, $0.1/T$.   If the bandwidth is greater than this, the envelope does not go entirely to zero at the frequencies where it theoretically would with perfect pulse modulation.

The final design consideration is the determination of the center frequency for the intermediate-frequency amplifier. Here it must be pointed out that the analyzer is essentially a superheterodyne receiver without any selectivity ahead of the mixer, and accordingly, will have an image response which must not appear on the screen. Thus if the total bandwidth presented on the screen is $6/T$ as suggested above, the center of the intermediate-frequency band should have a frequency that is at least $4/T$. Under these conditions the image action is to superimpose on the presentation the side band frequencies from $5/T$ to $11/T$ cycles on one side of the carrier. The relative magnitude of such frequencies will normally be negligibly small.

Sometimes the requirements on center frequency and bandwidth of the intermediate-frequency amplifier are somewhat incompatible, particularly in requiring an impossibly narrow bandwidth for a very high-frequency amplifier. Here the problem is solved by using a double superheterodyne circuit in which the first intermediate-frequency amplifier is at a high frequency and determines the image spacing. This first amplifier is followed by the second mixer and a low-frequency, very narrow-band amplifier which determines the over-all bandwidth of the analyzer.

There is an alternative form of the radio-frequency spectrum analyzer which provides certain advantages over that indicated in Fig. 6-16.[1,2] The arrangement in this second type is shown in Fig. 6-17. It is a form of a double superheterodyne, with the over-all bandwidth being determined by the amplifier following the second mixer. The first local oscillator is not electronically swept, but is arranged to be manually tunable over a wide frequency range, for instance, 300 to 1,000 Mc. For the case shown in Fig. 6-17, where the bandwidth of the first intermediate-frequency amplifier is 20 Mc, the second mixer is presented with a 20-Mc portion of the original high-frequency spectrum, but moved downward in frequency so that it lies between 20 and 40 Mc. This spectrum, 20 Mc wide, is now swept with the aid of a mechanically or electronically tuned local oscillator associated with the sweep generator; the resolution in Fig. 6-17 taking into account the image response of the second mixer, corresponds to a response band 100 kc wide with a 10-kc hole in the center.

[1] This analyzer is described in "Very High Frequency Techniques," Radio Research Laboratory Staff, p. 608, McGraw-Hill Book Company, Inc., New York, 1947.

[2] Still another method of making a spectrum analysis that finds occasional use at microwave frequencies, consists in loosely coupling a very high-Q cavity wavemeter to the wave being investigated, and observing the variation in cavity output as the resonant frequency of the cavity is varied. This method lacks resolution, but requires little equipment. For further details see P. Andrews, A 10-cm Mechanically Swept Spectrometer, *Proc. IEE* (*Radio & Comm.*), vol. 96, pt. III, p. 254, May, 1949.

This circuit has the advantage that frequency calibration marks can be placed upon the cathode-ray screen, and they will not be changed by the frequency of the input and the tuning of the first local oscillator.   In contrast, in the spectrum analyzer of Fig. 6-16 a given sweep voltage from the sweep generator varies the frequency through a range that is approximately proportional to the center frequency of the swept local oscillator. Thus the calibration in Fig. 6-16 will change whenever the center frequency of the local oscillator is retuned to accommodate an input signal of different frequency.   In Fig. 6-17 is shown an auxiliary feature whereby a manually obtained analysis can also be obtained with the aid

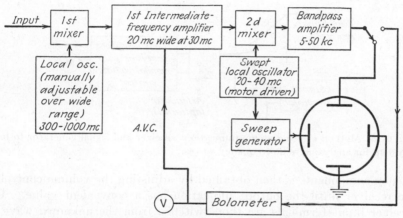

FIG. 6-17. Schematic diagram of second form of spectrum analyzer.

of a bolometer voltmeter.   The AVC connection serves to increase the amplitude range of the manual measurement.

The spectrum analyzer can, of course, be used for examining modulated signals of types other than those modulated with rectangular pulses.   An example might be frequency modulation with sine waves of different amplitudes and different modulation frequencies.

When dealing with pulses, a spectrum analyzer used in conjunction with an envelope viewer such as discussed in connection with Fig. 6-21, not only gives complete information regarding the pulse, but also frequently enables an experienced experimenter to deduce the cause of pulse distortion.

6-6. Wave Analyzers for Radio Frequencies. Spectrum-analyzer techniques are applicable only where the various frequency components contained in the wave under investigation lie within a relatively narrow frequency band.   In other cases, as, for example, in the determination of the harmonic content of a radio-frequency wave, it is customary to improvise a wave analyzer as illustrated in Fig. 6-18.[1]   Here, a sample of the wave to be investigated is applied to the input terminals of a radio receiver provided with an output meter, and arranged for manual rather than automatic volume control.   Provision is made whereby the receiver input terminals may be switched to the output of a signal generator capable of producing a known output in the frequency range that is being investigated.

The experimental procedure is as follows: Frequency components that are present in the wave being investigated are detected by tuning the receiver over the appropriate frequency range, and noting the frequencies at which output is indicated.   The amplitude of any one of these fre-

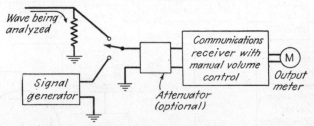

FIG. 6-18. Method of using a communications receiver and signal generator to form a system for analyzing radio-frequency waves.

quency components is then obtained by adjusting the volume control of the receiver until the output indication has a convenient value.   The receiver input terminals are then switched from the unknown wave to the signal generator.   The frequency of the signal generator is adjusted to be identical with the frequency of the component under measurement; this is done by adjusting the signal-generator frequency to give maximum receiver output.   Next, the amplitude of the signal-generator output is varied until the receiver indicates the same output as was produced by the wave being investigated.   The amplitude of the unknown component being determined is then obviously equal to the known signal-generator output.

When the wave under investigation has a large amplitude, it is necessary to place an attenuator in the input of the radio receiver as illustrated in Fig. 6-18, in order to prevent overloading of the receiver input with consequent danger of harmonic generation and cross-modulation effects occurring within the receiver.   Under these conditions, the receiver should be adequately shielded in order to prevent direct pickup of energy that by-passes the attenuator.   When an attenuator is used with the receiver, one may apply the signal-generator voltage on the input side of

[1] See Arnold Peterson, The Communications Receiver as a Wave Analyzer, *Gen. Rad. Expt.*, vol. 18, January, 1944.

the attenuator as illustrated in Fig. 6-18; in this case the amount of attenuation need not be known.   However, it is sometimes inconvenient to obtain a signal-generator output equal in amplitude to the magnitude of the frequency component being measured, as for example with high-power radio transmitters.   One can then use a known attenuation, and connect the signal generator directly to the receiver input terminals instead of to the input of the attenuator.   In this case, the actual amplitude of the unknown is greater than the output of the signal generator by the known attenuation.

The amplitudes of the harmonics and cross-modulation terms encountered in radio-frequency circuits are usually quite small because these circuits generally represent highly resonant systems.   Thus in analyzing a radio-frequency wave, one is very frequently faced with the problem of measuring a small harmonic component in the presence of a very large fundamental-frequency component.   This fact must be taken into account when determining the amount of voltage that it is permissible to apply to the receiver input in Fig. 6-18 without creating spurious frequency components within the receiver.   In particular, if one is measuring small harmonics in the presence of a large fundamental, it is desirable that the receiver be well shielded so that energy can enter the receiver only at the normal input terminals; the selectivity between the input terminals and the first tube should also be adequate to provide considerable discrimination against the fundamental frequency when tuned to a harmonic.

At frequencies in the video range, a heterodyne type of wave analyzer analogous to Fig. 6-10 is sometimes used.   In some cases the fixed amplifier operates at a lower frequency than any frequency contained in the wave being investigated, and is either a low-frequency tuned system,[1] or is an audio amplifier.   In other cases a double-heterodyne system is employed; the latter arrangement is especially suitable for determining frequency spectra, such as noise, that extend into the audio range.[2]

6-7. Pulse Shape.   Measurement of the shape and duration of rectangular pulses is common in many fields of activity, including radar[3] and television,[4] and is a problem closely related to that of observing and

[1] See A. G. Landeen, Analyzer for Complex Waves, *Bell System Tech. J.*, vol. 6, p. 230, April, 1927.

[2] See Philip S. Jastram and Gordon P. McCouch, A Video-frequency Noise-spectrum Analyzer, *Proc. IRE*, vol. 37, p. 1127, October, 1949.

[3] Oscilloscopic techniques developed specifically for radar, but generally useful, are described in detail in "Electronic Instruments" (Vol. 21, Radiation Laboratory Series), Part IV, Pulse Test Equipment, pp. 573–663, McGraw-Hill Book Company, Inc., New York, 1948.

[4] See, for instance, R. D. Kell, A. V. Bedford, and H. N. Kozanowski, A Portable High-frequency Square-wave Oscillograph for Television, *Proc. IRE*, vol. 30, p. 458. October, 1942; H. E. Kallman, Portable Equipment for Observing Transient Response

measuring transient voltages by means of the cathode-ray oscillograph, as described in Sec. 6-1. A general-purpose cathode-ray oscillograph can be used for viewing pulses if their duration is not too short, and if they repeat at a constant frequency.[1] For single pulses, or for pulses recurring at an irregular rate, and for accurate measurements upon pulses of very short duration, the oscilloscope must possess special features. Oscilloscopes designed for this purpose are commonly known as *synchroscopes*, for reasons that will become apparent in the discussion that follows.

Shape Definitions. The two most common measurements on pulses are the *amplitude*, usually in volts,[2] and the *time duration*. The latter

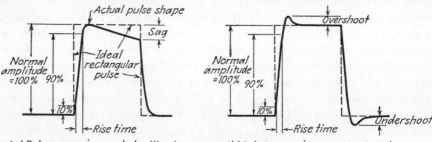

(a) Pulse possessing sag but without overshoot or undershoot

(b) Pulse possessing overshoot and undershoot but without sag

Fig. 6-19. Definition of terms used in describing the characteristics of a pulse.

quantity may range from a small fraction of a microsecond to several milliseconds. In addition, since most electronic systems fail to transmit a rectangular pulse with perfect fidelity, it is usually desired to measure certain quantities, shown in Fig. 6-19, which have been found most useful in describing the waveform distortion. These quantities are the *rise time*, measured in microseconds, the *overshoot*, *sag*, and *undershoot*, usually measured in per cent of the nominal pulse amplitude. The definition of rise time that is indicated in the figure, *i.e.*, the time required to increase from 10 to 90 per cent amplitude, is the one most commonly used. Other

---

of Television Apparatus, *Proc. IRE*, vol. 28, p. 351, August, 1940; R. A. Montfort and F. J. Somers, Measurement of the Slope and Duration of Television Synchronizing Impulses, *RCA Rev.*, vol. 6, p. 370, January, 1942; H. L. Morrison, Precision Device for Measurement of Pulse Width and Pulse Slope, *RCA Rev.*, vol. 8, p. 276, June 1947; see also footnotes, Sec. 6-1.

[1] Thus see A. Easton, Measuring Pulse Characteristics, *Electronics*, vol. 19, p. 150, February, 1946.

[2] Occasionally the amplitude of current pulses is required; this is easily obtained by amplifying and observing the voltage drop across a small resistor inserted in the current path. If the addition of even a small resistance is precluded by considerations of damping in the test circuit, it is possible to use a small inductance; see N. Rochester and D. L. Stevens, The Measurement of Large Pulse Currents, *Sylvania Technologist*, vol. 1, p. 17, October, 1948.

ways occasionally used to express rise time are to define it as (1) the maximum amplitude divided by the maximum rate of rise, or (2) the maximum amplitude divided by the rate of rise at half amplitude.[1]

Oscilloscope Characteristics.   In making measurements of the above characteristics it is apparent that calibration of the oscilloscope both in amplitude and in time is required.   In addition, the time base should be linear if the waveform is to appear in proper proportions.

A first requirement of the oscilloscope amplifier is that the amplitude of the observed pulse be a linear function of the actual pulse voltage.   This requires simply that the oscilloscope amplifiers be not overloaded beyond their linear operating range.   Such overloading may easily go undetected because the characteristic flattening of the top of the waveform that accompanies overloading looks normal with rectangular pulses.   The amplitude of the input to the oscilloscope should be made small at first, and then increased to the desired level; overloading can then be detected by observing whether or not the height of the cathode-ray trace continues to increase uniformly.

It is even more apparent that the oscilloscope amplifiers must introduce as little waveform distortion as possible; this may be a very stringent requirement if an almost rectangular pulse is to be examined for distortion.   The oscilloscope amplifiers will introduce small amounts of the same kinds of distortion as are shown in Fig. 6-19, and it is important that this added distortion be substantially less than that in the original waveform.   Occasionally the manufacturer of an oscilloscope will specify the amplifier distortion in terms of the quantities of Fig. 6-19.   More commonly, only the steady-state amplitude response is given.   This is indirectly related to the transient performance, which can then be inferred from Eq. (6-13).

If the rise time of the oscilloscope amplifiers is less than one-fifth of the rise time to be observed and measured, the rise-time distortion of the pulse introduced by the amplifiers can be regarded as negligible.   If the oscilloscope amplifiers are not this fast, an approximate correction, good to about 10 per cent, can be made when the overshoot is small.   If t_1 is the pulse rise time observed on the cathode-ray tube, and t_2 is the known rise time of the amplifiers,[2] then the actual pulse rise time t_0 of the pulse

---

[1] A discussion of these is given by D. G. Tucker, Bandwidth and Speed of Build-up as a Performance Criteria for Pulse and Television Amplifiers, *J. IEE*, vol. 94, pt. III, p. 218, May, 1947.

[2] For an actual measurement, t_2 should include the finite rise time of the test generator.   This combined t_2 is found by connecting the generator directly to the oscilloscope and measuring the rise time on the cathode-ray tube.

The general rule for the total rise time t of cascaded circuits is

$$t = \sqrt{t_1^2 + t_2^2 + t_3^2 + \cdots} \qquad (6\text{-}12a)$$

is given by

$$t_0 = \sqrt{t_1^2 - t_2^2}$$ (6-12)

As an aid in evaluating whether or not the rise time of a given oscilloscope is fast enough when only the bandwidth of the oscilloscope amplifier is specified, the following approximate relationship is helpful,

$$T = \frac{0.35}{B}$$ (6-13)

where T is the amplifier rise time in microseconds, and B is the bandwidth[1] in megacycles. This relationship assumes that the transient response has no overshoot. If the overshoot is greater than about 5 per cent, the constant 0.35 should be more nearly 0.45.

In measurement of the *sag* (see Fig. 6-19) of long pulses, the sag introduced by the oscilloscope amplifier may be important. This distortion is related to the low-frequency response of the amplifier, but not in a simple manner analogous to Eq. (6-13). There is, however, a simple rule for combining the effects of the sag introduced by the amplifier with that present in the pulse to be measured. The top of the pulse is a portion of an exponentially decreasing curve, but in well-designed amplifiers it represents only the initial portion of the exponential, and is therefore approximately a straight line with a negative slope. The rule is that these slopes add directly as a rectangular pulse passes through successive amplifier circuits. Therefore, if an oscilloscope amplifier is known to introduce a slope of a particular magnitude, then this slope is to be subtracted from the observed slope when a pulse is displayed on the oscilloscope. The net slope resulting after the subtraction is that present in the original pulse. Amplifiers with d-c couplings do not have this distortion, and may be advantageous for work with long pulses. Amplifiers with a-c couplings must be tested with square waves of known precision in order to determine their sag.

Sweep Provisions. The viewing of extremely short pulses calls for higher sweep speeds than are normally included in general-purpose oscilloscopes. Sweep speeds of 4 or 5 in. per μsec are common in oscilloscopes for pulse use, and may go as high as several hundred in. per μsec.

Since pulses frequently occur with large intervals between them, and also at intervals that do not repeat precisely, it is almost universal practice to use a driven (also known as "servo," "start-stop," or "single-shot") sweep. This sweep wave is a saw-tooth wave of the character shown in Fig. 6-20c, in which the duration of each sweep is small compared with the time interval between sweeps. The sweep may be initiated by the signal pulse itself, as in Fig. 6-20a, or may be triggered by a separate

---

[1] Essentially, B is equal to the high-frequency limit corresponding to the frequency for which the amplitude response has fallen off 3 db from midrange.

timing or synchronizing generator, as in Fig. 6-20b.   In the latter case, the synchronizing source also initiates the pulse generator that provides the pulses being observed.   In either case, a delay provision is normally

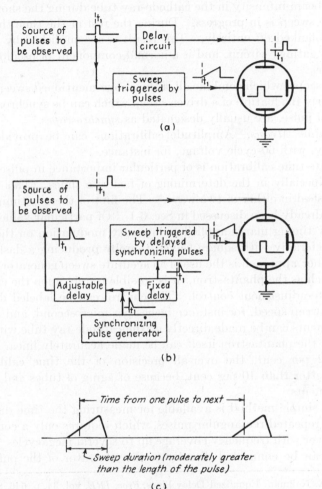

(a)

(b)

(c)

FIG. 6-20. Typical sweep arrangement of the synchroscope type for viewing short pulses, showing wave shapes present in various parts of the system in relation to a common reference time t_1.

included as shown, whereby the sweep is initiated prior to the advent of the pulse;[1] this permits the viewing of the entire pulse, including the important leading edge.

[1] Delay lines for this purpose can consist of a half dozen or more T or π sections; thus see J. B. Trevor, Jr., Artificial Delay-line Design, *Electronics*, vol. 18, p. 135, June, 1945.   Alternatively, one can use an artificial line with distributed constants;

When very fast sweeps are used, and when they are initiated by pulses occurring at long intervals, the average light intensity of the cathode-ray screen tends to be low. This can be compensated for by increasing the electron-beam intensity in the cathode-ray tube during the short interval while the sweep is in progress. During the rest of the time the electron beam is blanked off entirely. This result is accomplished by a "blanking" or "gating" circuit, and is a normal component of oscilloscopes for pulse work.

Oscilloscopes which combine all of the above-mentioned sweep features, particularly the feature of a driven sweep which can be synchronized with the signal pulse, are usually designated as *synchroscopes*.[1]

Calibration Means. Amplitude calibrations can be provided in the usual way, with 60-cycle voltage, for instance.

Accurate time calibration is of particular importance in pulse measurements, especially in the determining of fast rise times. This is usually accomplished in either of two ways.[2] The first of these is timing marks, and has already been discussed in Sec. 6-1. Of particular value are high-frequency timing marks applied as intensity modulation on the electron beam, preferably with square waves, thereby producing a dashed trace.

The other approach is the use of an accurate sweep generator. With a circuit such as the phantastron,[3] it is possible to rely upon the calibration of the rate-adjustment control. The control can be labeled directly in units of sweep speed, for instance inches per microsecond, and thus time measurements can be made directly on the cathode-ray tube with a ruler. Although the phantastron itself can be made accurately linear to within about 0.2 per cent, the over-all precision of the time calibration is seldom better than 10 per cent, because of aging of tubes and variation in components.

A very simple method is available for measuring the time duration of regularly repeated rectangular pulses, which requires only a communication receiver with frequency coverage up to several megacycles.[4] Such a receiver can be connected directly to the generator of the pulses to be

---

see Heinz E. Kallman, Equalized Delay Lines, *Proc. IRE*, vol. 34, p. 646, September, 1946; J. P. Blewett and J. H. Rubel, Video Delay Lines, *Proc. IRE*, vol. 35, p. 1580, December, 1947; A. H. Turner, Artificial Lines for Video Distribution and Delay, *RCA Rev.*, vol. 10, p. 447, December, 1949; K. H. Zimmerman, Spiral Delay Lines, *Elec. Comm.*, vol. 23, p. 327, September, 1946.

[1] For descriptions of several synchroscopes, see "Electronic Instruments," *op. cit.*, p. 594. Synchroscopes for very high-speed operation are described in the following: G. G. Kelley, A High-speed Synchroscope, *Rev. Sci. Instruments*, vol. 21, p. 71, January, 1950; Pierce, *loc. cit.*

[2] See Sec. 6-8 for further details.

[3] See Sec. 13-15.

[4] See Peterson, *loc. cit.*

measured, and used essentially as a spectrum analyzer. As the receiver is tuned across the frequency range, starting at the low end, a frequency component is encountered at intervals equal to the pulse-recurrence frequency. The amplitude of these components goes through minima at frequencies that are multiples of the reciprocal of the pulse duration. Thus if the pulse were 1 μsec long, nulls would be encountered at 1 Mc, 2 Mc, etc. Correction factors for pulses that have other shapes, such as a trapezoid, are available.[1]

Another simple method for determining the time duration of rectangular pulses involves the use of a conventional oscilloscope, together with a sine-wave oscillator used to provide a circular sweep.[2] The pulse to be measured is passed through a shunt-R series-C differentiating circuit (see Sec. 13-2), giving a short positive pulse coincident with the leading edge

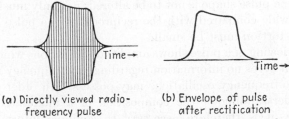

(a) Directly viewed radio-
frequency pulse

(b) Envelope of pulse
after rectification

Fig. 6-21. Methods of presenting the envelope of a pulse-modulated radio-frequency wave.

and a negative pulse at the trailing edge. These new pulses are applied to the vertical-deflection plates of the oscilloscope, and the sweep frequency adjusted until they are coincident; i.e., when exactly one period of the sweep frequency transpires between the positive and the negative pulses. This period is thus equal to the time duration of the original pulse.

Pulse Envelope Viewers. When dealing with pulse-modulated radio-frequency waves, the actual shape of the radio-frequency envelope is fully as important as the shape of the pulse used to modulate the radio-frequency oscillator. When the carrier frequency is not too high, and the amplitude is large, one can observe this envelope shape by applying the pulse-modulated radio-frequency wave directly to the vertical-deflector electrodes of a cathode-ray synchroscope, as shown in Fig. 6-21a. The horizontal timing wave can be synchronized with the envelope by triggering the sweep with a video-frequency pulse obtained either from the modulating pulse, or by rectification of a portion of the radio-frequency wave. Direct viewing in this manner has the advantage that it presents the modulated pulse as it actually is, without any possibility of

[1] *Ibid.*

[2] Easton, *op. cit.* See Sec. 6-1 for circular sweeps.

distortion by accessory equipment such as rectifiers or amplifiers; the method has the disadvantage, however, that sufficient voltage must be available to produce reasonable vertical deflection. Furthermore, the carrier frequency must not be so great that the transit time of the electrons in passing the deflecting electrode is such a large fraction of a cycle that the oscilloscope has little or no sensitivity (see Fig. 6-6). This upper limit is typically of the order 500 to 1000 Mc with most oscilloscopes.

When direct viewing of the radio-frequency wave is not practical for any reason, one can rectify the pulse-modulated wave, amplify the resulting video pulse if necessary, and apply to the vertical deflectors of a cathode-ray synchroscope (see Fig. 6-21b). The rectifier may be either a diode or a crystal; in either case it must be chosen with due regard to the carrier frequency involved. Great care must be taken with pulse amplifiers if the pulse shape is not to be altered; not only must the amplifier band be wide compared with the reciprocal of the pulse length, but also phase distortion must be small.

Envelope viewing of a pulse shows amplitude variations which the pulse undergoes, but gives no information regarding any frequency modulation that the radio-frequency oscillations may possess. In order to obtain a complete understanding of the composition of a modulated radio-frequency pulse, it is therefore necessary to combine information from envelope viewing with the type of information derived from a spectrum analyzer (see Sec. 6-5).

6-8. Time-interval Measurements. The measurement of time intervals, particularly short intervals as small as $\frac{1}{10}$ μsec, can be performed readily by electronic means.[1] Not only are such measurements often needed in connection with radio engineering, but they find wide usefulness in all types of instrumentation.

Time-interval measurements are closely associated with pulse techniques, for the events to be timed are usually of short duration and can be converted by some means to electrical pulses. Time measurements involving sinusoidal quantities are essentially phase measurements, and are discussed in Sec. 6-9.

The precise measurement of short time intervals has been highly developed in connection with radar systems, navigational systems such as loran, radio altimeters for aircraft, primary standards of frequency, and nuclear-physics instrumentation. A substantial body of literature exists describing the many and varied techniques which have been found useful. The reader is referred to these for details beyond the elementary principles set forth here.

[1] A comprehensive treatment with applications primarily to radar and electronic navigation systems, will be found in "Electronic Time Measurements" (Vol. 20, Radiation Laboratory Series), McGraw-Hill Book Company, Inc., New York, 1949.

Oscillographic Methods.   Although it is possible to construct complicated circuits which will measure time intervals automatically and present the result on an indicating meter,[1] most measurements can be made with the aid of a cathode-ray-tube display.   Generally, a sweep is used that is initiated by the event or pulse which is to serve as the time reference.   The length or duration of this "driven" sweep is adjusted so that both of the events or pulses are visible on the screen.   If the approximate sweep speed is known, a rough measurement of the time interval separating the two pulses can be determined from the linear distance separating the pulses on the cathode-ray tube.

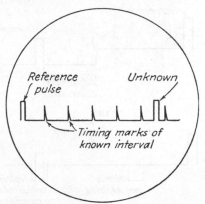

For greater accuracy, a set of fixed markers or indices can be superimposed upon the cathode-ray trace. These markers usually have their origin in a sine-wave oscillator of accurately known frequency. The waveform from this oscillator is then modified by amplifying, clipping, and differentiating, until a series of sharp pulses is obtained as shown in Fig. 6-22.   To obtain greater precision

FIG. 6-22. Measurement of time interval between two pulses with the aid of timing marks.

with fixed markers, an expanded sweep can be used, which displays only the interval between the two markers that bracket the pulse.   In Fig. 6-22, the markers are shown as deflections; they could equally well be applied as intensity modulations, thus giving brightened spots for the time markers.

Instead of fixed markers, it is possible to use a movable index, or cursor. The operator adjusts the position of the marker until it coincides with the observed pulse; the time interval is then given by the setting of the position control.   The nature of the index, or cursor, can be a step, a

[1] This is particularly so when the time interval repeats at a regular recurrence frequency.   Thus the phase-measuring system of Fig. 6-30 is essentially an arrangement that gives a meter indication of the time interval between two sets of pulses having regular rates of repetition.

A method of obtaining a meter indication of a nonrepeating time interval, the beginning and end of which can be defined by electrical pulses, is described by M. E. Krom, Electronic Timing Test Set, *Bell Labs. Record*, vol. **27**, p. 176, May, 1949.   In this system, a condenser is charged from a constant-current source during the desired time interval, which is then given by the final voltage built up across the condenser as observed on a vacuum-tube voltmeter.   The constant charging current is turned on and off at the beginning and end of the desired time interval by a flip-flop or gate circuit operated by the pulses associated with the two ends of the time interval.

notch, or a pulse, as shown in Fig. 6-23. Fundamental to the operation of a movable-index arrangement is a circuit which is triggered by the reference pulse, and then after a time interval determined by the setting of a control, a second pulse is generated which provides the marker pulse. Two suitable circuits for this application are the delay multivibrator and the phantastron, which are discussed in Sec. 13-18. Each of these gives a sharply rising (or falling) voltage at the end of a time interval determined

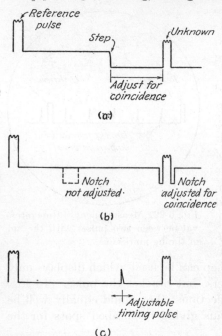

by the setting of a control voltage. Thus the time adjustment is made by means of a source of fixed voltage and a potentiometer. The sharp voltage transition that indicates the end of the interval can be passed through a differentiating circuit to give a simple pulse as in Fig. 6-23c, or it can trigger a pulse generator, which is used to produce a notch as in Fig. 6-23b. Simplest of all, the delay-circuit output voltage can be used directly to produce the step of Fig. 6-23a.

Counting Methods.[1] When the time interval to be measured is not too short, and can have its beginning and end marked by pulses, then counting methods are particularly satisfactory. The idea is that a known frequency is applied to a high-speed counting system through a gate. The gate is turned on and off by the pulses that define

Fig. 6-23. Various types of adjustable time markers used in cathode-ray presentations.

the time interval under investigation; if this time interval repeats over and over, the gate is so arranged that after being open for one interval it stays closed until manually reset by a push button. In such a system the counter registers the number of cycles of the known frequency generated during the period the gate is open, *i.e.*, during the time interval to be determined. Thus, if the known frequency is 1 Mc, then the count shows the time interval in microseconds with an error that will always be less than ± 1 μsec. The absolute error is less the higher the known frequency, and hence is limited by the maximum speed with which a dependable counter will operate, while the percentage accuracy will always be less the shorter the time interval being measured.

[1] See Sec. 5-8 for details of counting systems.

6-9. Measurement of Phase Difference.[1] *Cathode-ray-tube Methods.*
A cathode-ray tube is commonly used to determine the phase difference
between two voltages of the same frequency.   Thus, if one of these
voltages is applied to the horizontal-deflecting electrodes, while the other
is applied to the vertical deflectors, an elliptical pattern results, the exact
character of which depends upon the relative phase and amplitude of the

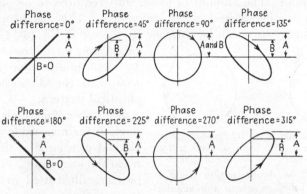

Equal amplitudes and varying phase differences

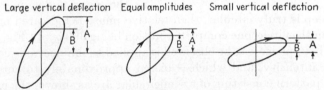

Constant phase difference of 45° but varying
amplitude on vertical deflection

Fig. 6-24. Typical patterns produced by a cathode-ray tube when sinusoidal voltages
of the same frequency, but differing in phase and amplitude, are applied to the horizontal and vertical deflectors.

two voltages concerned.   Patterns in typical cases are shown in Fig. 6-24.
The phase difference θ between the two waves is given by the formula

$$\sin \theta = \pm \frac{B}{A} \tag{6-14}$$

where A and B have the significance shown in Fig. 6-24.   The quadrant
must be worked out from the orientation of the major axis of the ellipse
and the direction in which the spot travels.   Uncertainty as to the direc-

[1] Excellent general discussions of the subject are given by M. Levy, Method and
Apparatus for Measuring Phase Distortion, *Elec. Commun.*, vol. 18, p. 206, January,
1940; H. Nyquist and S. Brand, Measurement of Phase Distortion, *Bell System Tech.
J.*, vol. 9, p. 522, July, 1930.

tion in which the spot travels can be eliminated by shifting the phase of one of the deflecting voltages in a known direction and noting the effect on the pattern.[1]

A variation of the above procedure consists in inserting an adjustable phase shifter in series with one of the deflecting plates, and then varying the phase shift thus introduced until the pattern on the cathode-ray tube becomes a line. The amount of phase shift required to accomplish this result then is the desired phase difference. This arrangement gives greater accuracy than can be obtained by the use of Eq. (6-14), since the phase shift introduced can usually be determined more accurately than can the dimensions of an elliptical pattern.

(a) Phase indication by position of semicircular arc

(b) Phase indication by blank spot on circular trace

FIG. 6-25. Phase determination using a cathode-ray tube, in which the angular scale corresponds to position on a circular trace.

A number of methods have been devised for measuring phase with the aid of a circular time base on a cathode-ray tube. Two examples are illustrated in Fig. 6-25. In each of these cases the circular time base has the same frequency as the wave under investigation; if this sweep is truly circular, then relative phase is indicated by angular position on the circle, one complete rotation being 360°. In Fig. 6-25a the voltage whose phase is to be observed is applied to the electrode controlling the beam intensity, and which is biased approximately to cutoff. The result is a pattern consisting of a semicircular arc as shown, the position of which is a function of phase. If the relative phase of two voltages is to be determined, these voltages are applied successively to the control electrode while leaving the sweep unchanged; the angular shift in the position of the arc is then equal to the phase difference between these voltages. An alternative procedure[2] is to derive short pulses from a specified part of the waves under investigation (as the instants when the amplitudes are zero going positive). The bias on the control electrode is then adjusted to be less than cutoff, and these pulses are applied to the control electrode with negative polarity. The result is that each pulse momentarily interrupts the trace as shown in Fig. 6-25b, with the interruptions corresponding to the relative phases of the waves from which the pulses were derived.[3]

[1] Other methods of determining the direction of travel of the spot are described by E. R. Mann, A Device for Showing the Direction of Motion of the Oscillograph Spot, *Rev. Sci. Instruments*, vol. 5, p. 214, June, 1934; J. R. Haynes, Direction of Motion of Oscilloscope Spot, *Bell Labs. Record*, vol. 14, p. 224, March, 1936.

[2] This method is due to B. D. Loughlin, Vector-response Indicator, *Trans. AIEE*, vol. 59, p. 335, June, 1940.

[3] A variation of this arrangement, in which the control electrode is biased beyond cutoff, and the pulses are applied with positive polarity so that each pulse produces a

Markers indicating a reference phase may be added to the ordinary oscillograph presentation of a wave shape by the expedient illustrated schematically in Fig. 6-26. Here, pulses derived from a definite part of the cycle of a reference voltage (as when the voltage is passing through zero going positive) are applied to the control electrode of the cathode-ray tube with such polarity as to increase the trace intensity. Each such pulse then produces a bright spot on the wave being shown on the face of the tube. The position of these spots with respect to the wave being shown then gives the phase relation of this wave with respect to the reference wave; thus in Fig. 6-26, the wave shown lags the reference wave by approximately 45°, assuming that the pulse corresponds to the reference wave going through zero and becoming positive.

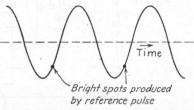

FIG. 6-26. Phase determination by employing pulses derived from a definite part of a reference voltage to brighten the cathode-ray trace and thereby indicate a reference-phase position.

Phase Determination by Voltage Addition. A very widely used method of measuring phase difference consists in superimposing the two voltages involved, and then varying the amplitude and phase of one of the voltages until the sum is zero. The details involved in carrying out this principle can take a variety of forms. An arrangement suitable for all except microwave frequencies is illustrated in Fig. 6-27.[1] Here the two voltages whose relative phase is to be determined are applied to the inputs of separate amplifier tubes, the plate circuits of which are common to each other. A vacuum-tube voltmeter indicates the sum of these two voltages as developed across the resistance R. A null indication[2] of the vacuum-

bright spot, is described by Peter G. Sulzer, Vector Voltage Indicator, *Electronics*, vol. 22, p. 107, June, 1949. The angular direction of a radial line drawn from this spot to the center of the cathode-ray screen gives the relative phase of the wave from which the spot was derived.

A system in which the length of this radial can be made proportional to amplitude, so that the position of the spot represents both magnitude and phase of the vector corresponding to the wave, is described by E. A. Walker, A. H. Waynick, and P. G. Sulzer, Polar Vector Indicator, *Trans. AIEE*, vol. 68, pt. I, p. 154, 1949 (also *Elec. Eng.*, vol. 68, p. 489, June, 1949.

[1] Another arrangement that is both simple and effective is described by Joseph A. Vanous, Single-tube Audio Phasemeter, *Electronics*, vol. 23, p. 226, October, 1950; also see Y.P.Yu, Measuring Vector Relationships, *Electronics*, vol. 24, p. 124, July, 1951.

[2] A modification of this procedure consists in dispensing with the phase shifter and using the vacuum-tube voltmeter to measure the amplified output under three conditions, (1) when both voltages are applied to their respective tubes, (2) when the input is removed from tube T_1, and (3) when the input is removed from T_2. Calling these

tube voltmeter is obtained by varying the transconductance of one of the tubes through bias adjustment to obtain equality of the two amplitudes,[1] while simultaneously adjusting the phase shifter to produce a phase difference of 180°.[2]

An alternative arrangement suitable for use at microwave frequencies is illustrated schematically in Fig. 6-28.[3,4] Here samples of the two

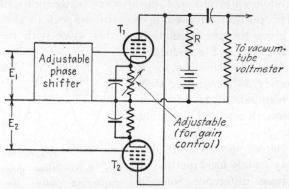

FIG. 6-27. Schematic diagram showing phase-measuring system that involves varying the phase and amplitude of one voltage until it is equal and opposite to the reference voltage.

waves involved are obtained by means of directional couplers D_1 and D_2 (or other sampling means). The couplers are each terminated so as to be nonreflecting in one direction, while the unterminated ends are connected together through a slotted section provided with pickup probe, and an adjustable attenuator, as shown. The attenuator is adjusted so that the

---

respective voltages E_s, E_1, E_2, the phase angle θ between the two waves is then given by the relation

$$E_s = \sqrt{E_1^2 + E_2^2 + 2\overline{E_1E_2} \cos \theta} \tag{6-15}$$

This is the familiar equation giving the third side E_s of a triangle in terms of the other two sides E_1 and E_2, and the angle θ between E_1 and E_2. This technique is described by E. E. Wright and G. E. G. Graham, Measurement of Amplification and Phase Shift in Amplifiers, *Wireless Eng. and Expt. Wireless*, vol. 13, p. 259, May, 1936.

[1] The gain adjustment must not vary the phase shift; hence the arrangement shown would be suitable only at frequencies high enough for the cathode bypass capacitor to be a virtually perfect short circuit. Alternatively, a capacitance-compensated voltage divider or a resistive attenuator can be inserted in the circuit ahead of the phase shifter (see Sec. 15-2).

[2] A variation of this sytem is described by J. R. Ragazzini and L. A. Zadeh, A Wideband Audio Phasemeter, *Rev. Sci. Instruments*, vol. 21, p. 145, February, 1950.

[3] See A. L. Samuel and C. F. Crandell, A Wave-guide Bridge for Measuring Gain at 4000 Mc., *Proc. IRE*, vol. 36, p. 1414, November, 1948.

[4] Another example of phase-measuring equipment for microwaves is described by Sloan D. Robertson, A Method of Measuring Phase at Microwave Frequencies, *Bell System Tech. J.*, vol. 28, p. 99, January, 1949.

minima of the standing-wave pattern observed in the slotted section are quite deep. The position of the minima as observed by the probe is then an indication of the relative phase of the two waves existing at the points D_1 and D_2. A change in the position of the null by a distance x corresponds to a phase change of $360\,(x/\lambda)$ degrees, where λ is the wavelength in the slotted section, in the same units as x.

Phasemeters. A number of arrangements have been devised whereby the phase difference between two waves is indicated directly on a meter. One such arrangement is shown in Fig. 6-29.[1] Here the voltages whose

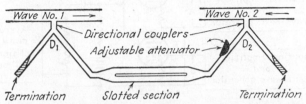

FIG. 6-28. Phase determination at microwave frequencies by observation of the position of the minima in a standing-wave pattern that results from the combination of the two waves whose phases are to be compared.

phase difference is to be determined are applied to separate amplifier channels so designed and operated as to develop square-wave outputs. By using the same clipping level in both channels, the square waves thus produced not only have amplitudes independent of the strength of the applied voltages, but also have the same amplitude in each of the two channels. These two square waves are applied to the grids of separate Class A amplifier tubes T_1 and T_2, which have a common plate load resistance R. The output voltage developed across R is accordingly the algebraic sum of the two square waves, and will have a character that depends upon the relative phase of these square waves. Thus, if the voltages were originally 180° out of phase, the sum of the two square waves is zero, while if the two voltages are in phase, their sum is a square wave having twice the amplitude of the square wave of an individual channel. Intermediate phase relations give intermediate results, in which the area under the wave depends upon the phase, as shown in Fig. 6-29*b*. The combined output is rectified by an average-reading diode, such as shown in Fig. 1-23, and the resulting rectified current is indicated by a d-c instrument which can be calibrated directly in degrees. It will be noted that the indication is independent of frequency. However, there is an ambiguity of the phase indication with respect to 180°; thus $180 + 30 = 210°$ gives the same indication as does $180 - 30 = 150°$.[2]

[1] This is due to Edward L. Ginzton, Electronic Phase-angle Meter, *Electronics*, vol. 15, p. 60, May, 1942.

[2] A modification that removes this ambiguity is described by E. F. Florman and A. Tait, An Electronic Phasemeter, *Proc. IRE*, vol. 37, p. 207, February, 1949.

Another type of phasemeter is shown schematically in Fig. 6-30.[1]
Here, the two waves whose phase difference is to be determined are used
to generate trains of positive pulses by squaring, differentiating, and
rectifying, as shown.   The time displacement between these pulse trains
is a measure of the phase difference.   The two pulse trains are simultaneously fed to both grids of an Eccles-Jordan trigger circuit (often
called flip-flop circuit).   At any one time in such a circuit one tube carries

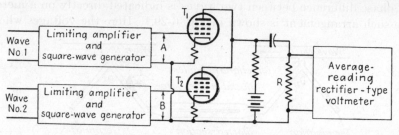

(a) Schematic circuit

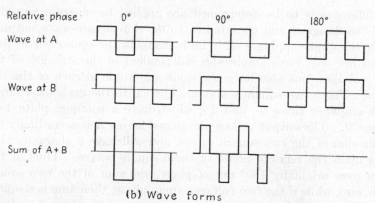

(b) Wave forms

FIG. 6-29. Phasemeter based on the addition of square waves.

current while the other tube is nonconducting; moreover, each time a
positive pulse is applied to the two grids simultaneously, the tubes interchange functions.   Thus the fraction of the time one of the tubes is
carrying current is proportional to the time displacement of the two
pulse trains and hence to the phase angle; a d-c meter indicating the
average plate current of this tube can hence be calibrated to read degrees,
independent of frequency.

A balanced modulator arrangement such as illustrated in Fig. 6-31a

[1] See Ernest R. Kretzmer, Measuring Phase at Audio and Ultrasonic Frequencies,
Electronics, vol. 22, p. 114, October, 1949.

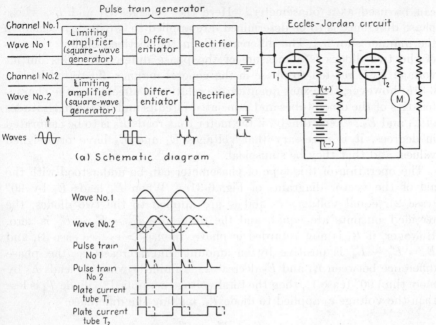

FIG. 6-30. Phasemeter based on a trigger (flip-flop) circuit actuated by pulse trains.

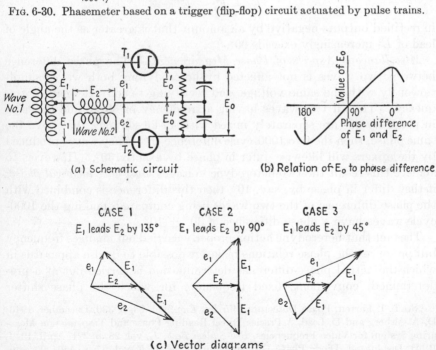

FIG. 6-31. Balanced modulator type of phasemeter.

can be used as a phasemeter.[1] Here the voltages E_1 and E_2, whose phase difference is to be determined, are applied to two diode rectifiers in the manner shown. The difference E_0 in the rectified output voltages of the two diodes is a measure of the phase difference. This output voltage E_0 is related to phase in the general manner illustrated in Fig. 6-31b; however, the exact quantitative relation is affected by the characteristics of the diode tubes and associated circuits and by the magnitudes of E_1 and E_2. Accordingly, if the meter that reads E_0 is to be calibrated in degrees, it is necessary that voltages E_1 and E_2 have preassigned values, and that they be sinusoidal.

The operation of this type of phasemeter can be understood with the aid of the vector diagrams of Fig. 6-31c. When E_1 leads E_2 by 90° (case 2), equal voltages e_1 and e_2 are applied to the two diodes, the rectified outputs are equal, and the difference $E_0 = E_0' - E_0''$ is zero. However, if E_1 is now retarded in phase, then $e_1 > e_2$ (see case 3), and $E_0 = E_0' - E_0''$ is positive by an amount that increases as the phase difference between E_1 and E_2 decreases. Similarly when E_1 leads E_2 by more than 90° (case 1), then the total voltage e_1 applied to diode T_1 is less than the voltage e_2 applied to diode T_2, making the difference

$$E_0 = E_0' - E_0''$$

in rectified outputs negative by an amount that is greater as the angle of lead of E_1 increasingly exceeds 90°.

Miscellaneous Aspects of Phase Measurements. The phase difference between two waves is not affected by heterodyning both waves simultaneously with the same voltage, and rectifying to convert to a new frequency. Thus if two waves having a frequency of 50 kc and differing in phase by 30° are separately mixed with 49-kc voltages that have the same phase, then the two 1000-cycle difference-frequency waves produced by the mixers will likewise differ in phase by exactly 30°. However, to achieve this result the two heterodyne voltages *must have identical phase;* if they differ in phase by, say, 10°, then this difference is combined with the phase difference of the two waves being compared, making the 1000-cycle waves have a phase difference of 30° ± 10°.

The fact that heterodyne action properly carried out changes frequency but preserves the phase relations makes it possible to devise apparatus in which the actual phase-difference determination is carried out at a predetermined, convenient, fixed frequency, for which the phase shifter

[1] See L. I. Farren, Phase Detectors, *Wireless Eng.*, vol. 23, p. 330, December, 1946; D. A. Alsberg and D. Leed, A Precise Direct Reading Phase and Transmission Measuring System for Video Frequencies, *Bell System Tech. J.*, vol. 28, p. 221, April, 1949; R. H. Dishington, Diode Phase Discriminators, *Proc. IRE*, vol. 37, p. 1401, December, 1949.

or other phase-measuring equipment is designed to operate.   To measure phase, one then converts the waves under investigation to the predetermined frequency by heterodyne action by adjusting the mixer oscillator frequency to the value required to achieve this result.   It thus is possible to make phase measurements over a wide frequency range, while handling only one frequency in the phase-measuring equipment.[1]

When the accuracy with which the phase difference is required is greater than the inherent accuracy of the measuring method that would ordinarily be used, harmonic generation may be used to increase the phase difference.   This takes advantage of the fact that the phase difference between two voltages is increased in proportion to frequency multiplication; thus the tenth harmonics of two voltages that differ by 0.5° will differ in phase by 5°.   Alternatively, one can mix the $(n - 1)$st harmonic of wave A with the nth harmonic of wave B; the resulting difference-frequency wave then has a phase difference with respect to wave A that is n times the phase difference of B with respect to A.*

6-10. Delay Time, Phase Distortion, and Envelope Delay.[2] The phase shift that a current undergoes when being transmitted through a circuit is related to the time of transmission through the circuit according to the equation

$$\text{Phase shift (lag) in radians} = \beta = \omega\tau + n\pi \qquad (6\text{-}16)$$

where τ is called the *delay time*, and is expressed in seconds, ω is 2π times the frequency, and n is an integer which represents the numbers of phase reversals that are inherent in the circuit involved (thus each stage of amplification ordinarily introduces one phase reversal).   Equation (6-16) comes about since a phase shift at a particular frequency may be directly expressed in time.   Thus, a 90° phase shift of a 1000-cycle wave corresponds to a quarter of a cycle, or 0.00025 sec, since each cycle represents 0.001 sec.

When the wave applied to the input of an electrical circuit contains several frequency components having some particular initial phase rela-

---

[1] Phase-measuring instruments using this principle are described by Alsberg and Leed, *loc. cit.;* Levy, *loc. cit.*; H. T. Friis, Oscillographic Observations on the Direction of Propagation and Fading of Short Waves, *Proc. IRE*, vol. 16, p. 658, May, 1928; R. R. Law, A New Radio-frequency Phase Meter, *Rev. Sci. Instruments*, vol. 4, p. 537, October, 1933; Bernard D. Loughlin, A Phase Curve Tracer for Television, *Proc. IRE*, vol. 29, p. 107, March, 1941.

* Further discussion of the use of harmonic methods to increase the accuracy of phase measurements is given by R. A. Glaser, The Accurate Measurement of Relative Phase, *Proc. Natl. Electronic Conf.*, vol. 3, p. 593, November, 1947; S. Bagno and A. Barnett, Cathode-ray Phasemeter, *Electronics*, vol. 11, p. 24, January, 1938.

[2] For further discussion of these subjects see Nyquist and Brand, *loc. cit.;* C. E. Lane, Phase Distortion in Telephone Apparatus, *Bell System Tech. J.*, vol. 9, p. 493, July, 1930: Levy, *loc. cit.*

tionship, it is necessary that the delay times of all the frequency components of the complex wave be the same if this phase relationship is not to be disturbed. If the delay time τ is different for the different frequency components, phase distortion is said to exist. In order to avoid phase distortion, it is apparent that the curve of phase shift as a function of frequency, *when plotted on a linear frequency scale*, must be a straight line passing through an integral multiple of π at zero frequency.

The delay time can be obtained at any frequency by determining the phase shift for that frequency, and then substituting in Eq. (6-16). Typi-

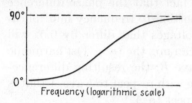

Frequency (logarithmic scale)

cal phase-shift and delay-time curves, showing the relationship between the two, are shown in Fig. 6-32.

The slope of the phase curve at a particular frequency defines a time called the *group delay time*, or *envelope delay time*, according to the equation

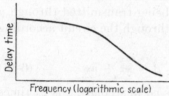

Frequency (logarithmic scale)

FIG. 6-32. Curves showing relation between phase shift and delay time.

$$\frac{d\beta}{d\omega} = \tau_0 \qquad (6-17)$$

The envelope delay τ_0 is important in dealing with modulated waves. For example, a carrier wave having an angular velocity of ω_0 and modulated at a frequency $f_s = \omega_s/2\pi$, possesses side-band components having angular velocities $\omega_0 + \omega_s$ and $\omega_0 - \omega_s$. When passed through a circuit having an envelope delay of τ_0 seconds, the upper and lower side bands are then symmetrically shifted in phase in opposite direction with respect to the carrier by $\omega_s\tau_0$ radians. This produces a phase shift in the modulation envelope of $\omega_s\tau_0$ radians, where these radians are now radians at the modulation frequency. Thus, if the radio frequency side bands of an amplitude-modulated wave are shifted symmetrically 30° with respect to the carrier frequency, then the modulation envelope of the wave at the output of the circuit is likewise shifted in phase by 30°. After detection this envelope delay appears as a 30° phase delay of the modulation frequency output of the detector.

Envelope delay can be determined in several ways.[1] An obvious procedure is to determine the phase shift as a function of frequency, plot the relationship, and determine the slope of the curve about the frequency at which one desires the envelope delay. An alternative procedure consists in modulating a test signal with a modulating voltage of suitable fre-

[1] Also see D. H. Ring, The Measurement of Delay Distortion in Microwave Repeaters, *Bell System Tech. J.*, vol. 27, p. 247, April, 1948.

quency, and passing this modulated wave through the circuit whose envelope delay is to be determined. Samples of the modulated wave at the input and output of this circuit are separately rectified, and the phase difference between the modulation-frequency components of the two rectified currents is measured, and used to calculate the envelope delay. Still another procedure consists in applying two test voltages of slightly different frequency to the input of the circuit. A sample of the combined wave applied to the input terminals is rectified to produce a difference-frequency component, and a sample of the complex output wave is similarly treated. If the two difference-frequency waves derived from the

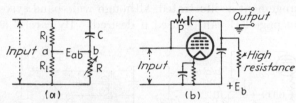

FIG. 6-33. Phase-shifter arrangements operating from a single-phase source.

input and output terminals in this way differ in phase by an angle $\Delta\Phi$ radians, then the envelope delay τ_0 is

$$\tau_0 = \frac{\Delta\Phi}{2\pi \,\Delta f} \qquad (6\text{-}18)$$

where Δf is the difference frequency.[1]

6-11. Phase Shifters. Phase-shifting devices find use in the measurement of phase, and also have other applications in measurement work. A great many arrangements for shifting phase have been devised, of which a few of the more common are shown in Figs. 6-33 and 6-34. At Fig. 6.33a, varying the resistance R from 0 to infinity causes the phase of the voltage E_{ab} to vary continuously over a 180° range with no change in amplitude.[2] The circuit of Fig. 6-33b employs a capacitive load in the plate circuit of a pentode, causing the voltage between plate and control grid to differ in phase by 90°. The voltage between the sliding contact on potentiometer P and ground can accordingly be varied continuously through a 90° range by means of this slider.[3] The amplitude of this volt-

[1] A modification of this procedure that is used to determine variations in the delay time of television signals transmitted over coaxial and other circuits in which the two terminals of the system are far apart is described by O. D. Engstrom, Transmission Measuring System, *Bell Lab. Record*, vol. 24, p. 264, June, 1951.

[2] This arrangement, and variations of it, are described by F. Alton Everest, Phase Shifting Up to 360 Degrees, *Electronics*, vol. 14, p. 46, November, 1941; K. Kreielsheimer, Phase Adjuster, *Wireless Eng.*, vol. 17, p. 439, October, 1940.

[3] J. P. Taylor, Cathode-ray Antenna Phasemeter, *Electronics*, vol. 12, p. 62, April, 1939.

age is not constant with varying phase shift, although it can be made the same at the two extreme positions if the transconductance of the tube is adjusted so that the amplification is exactly unity.

The phase shifters of Fig. 6-34 employ a polyphase source of energy to excite them, and produce a continuous variation of phase through 360° by merely rotating a pickup coil or condenser rotor. At a, a rotating magnetic field is produced by two crossed coils carrying currents differing in phase by 90°. The output is derived from a pickup coil that can be rotated in this field. The required 90° phase shift between the two field coil currents is normally obtained by a resistance-capacitance phase-splitting arrangement as illustrated, although wide-band systems such as referred to on page 231 can be used if desired. By careful attention to

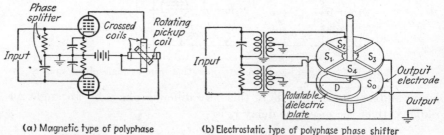

(a) Magnetic type of polyphase phase shifter   (b) Electrostatic type of polyphase phase shifter

FIG. 6-34. Phase shifters involving two-phase arrangements.

design details, an arrangement of this type will develop an output voltage, the magnitude of which is almost completely independent of angular position of the pickup coil, while the phase will be directly proportional to the angle of rotation to a high degree of accuracy.[1]

An electrostatic equivalent of the crossed-coil phase shifter is shown in Fig. 6-34b.[2] Here the two pairs of segments S_1S_3, and S_2S_4, correspond to the two crossed coils of Fig. 6-34a, and are excited by voltages differing in phase by 90°. These four segments are placed parallel to an output plate electrode S_0. The phase of the voltage induced in the output plate is controlled by rotation of an appropriately shaped dielectric disk D.

---

[1] This arrangement is essentially a radiogoniometer such as is used in direction finding, and so involves the same design considerations. These are discussed at some length by J. H. Moon, The Design of Electromagnetic Radiogoniometers for Use in Medium-frequency Direction Finding, *J. IEE*, vol. 94, pt. III, p. 69, January, 1947; B. G. Pressey, Radiogoniometers for High and Very-high-frequency Direction Finding, *J. IEE*, vol. 95, pt. III, p. 210, July, 1948.

[2] Design details of capacitive phase shifters of this type, and also of corresponding three-phase devices, are given in "Components Handbook" (Vol. 17, Radiation Laboratory Series), p. 288, McGraw-Hill Book Company, Inc., New York, 1949; also see John F. Morrison, Simple Methods for Observing Current Amplitude and Phase Relations in Antenna Arrays, *Proc. IRE*, vol. 25, p. 1310, October, 1937.

The dielectric constant of this disk increases the coupling between the output electrode and the segments which are adjacent to the disk, so that by rotation of the disk one can control the relative contributions that each of the four electrodes S_1, S_2, S_3, and S_4 makes to the output. Thus rotation of the disk varies the phase of the output voltage from 0 to 360° without requiring moving contacts. When the disk is properly shaped, the output voltage will be substantially constant irrespective of the angular position of the dielectric disk, while the phase of the output voltage will be almost exactly linearly proportional to the angle of rotation of the disk.[1]

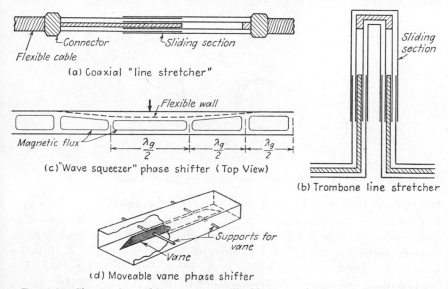

(a) Coaxial "line stretcher"

(c) "Wave squeezer" phase shifter (Top View)

(b) Trombone line stretcher

(d) Moveable vane phase shifter

Fig. 6-35. Simple phase-shift systems applicable to coaxial lines and waveguides.

At microwave frequencies it is possible to use methods of phase shifting that would not be practical at lower frequencies. Examples are shown in Figs. 6-35 and 6-36. The arrangement of Fig. 6-35a is termed a "line stretcher," and consists of a section of coaxial line that can be varied in length by means of a sliding arrangement as shown. The change in total length of the system is taken care of by means of the flexible cables in the system. Since the phase shift of a wave traveling along a line is proportional to length, an increase in length of one wavelength corresponds to an added phase shift of 360°. A form of line stretcher that does not require the use of a flexible cable to take care of the changes in length is illus-

[1] In the four-segment arrangement illustrated in Fig. 6-34b, it is satisfactory to make the disk circular in shape, with its axis offset from the center of the circle by a distance that is 0.53 times the disk radius.

trated in Fig. 6-35b, and involves a trombonelike slide, the position of which determines the line length.[1]

The phase shift of a wave transmitted through a waveguide can be reduced by reducing the guide dimension in the direction perpendicular to the electric field of the TE_{10} mode (see Fig. 6-35c). Such a "squeezing" of the wave increases the guide wavelength λ_g, thus reducing the phase shift per unit length. An alternative arrangement[2] is illustrated in Fig. 6-35d, and consists in moving a long, thin dielectric vane laterally across the interior of the waveguide. This vane is oriented so that it is parallel to the electric field. The effect of the dielectric is accordingly to increase

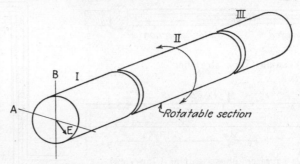

FIG. 6-36. Rotating-waveguide phase changer.

the electric flux, and hence reduce the effective velocity of the wave; this increases the phase shift per unit length. Moving the dielectric vane from the edge toward the center where the electric field is more intense, increases the effect and thereby causes the phase shift to be increased. The vane is preferably a material, such as polystyrene, that has low dielectric losses. It is customary to taper the ends of the vane in order to minimize reflection.

A form of phase shifter that has found many uses in microwave work is shown schematically in Fig. 6-36.[3] Here I is a section of circular waveguide so modified that a wave polarized along the axis B has a lower phase velocity than a wave of the same mode polarized at right angles along axis A. The length of this section is such that the wave polarized along B undergoes a phase shift that is 90° more than the wave polarized along A. Now, when section I is oriented so its axis A is 45° with respect to the

[1] Details of such a phase shifter are given in "Microwave Transmission Circuits" (Vol. 9, Radiation Laboratory Series), p. 478, McGraw-Hill Book Company, Inc., New York, 1948.

[2] These waveguide arrangements are discussed further in "Microwave Transmission Circuits," op. cit., p. 513.

[3] An excellent discussion of this arrangement and some of its practical applications is given by A. Gardner Fox, An Adjustable Wave-guide Phase Changer, Proc. IRE, vol. 35, p. 1489, December, 1947.

polarization E of a linearly polarized input wave, this wave has equal components along the axes A and B at the input to section I.   The wave that emerges from section I is accordingly circularly polarized.   This circularly polarized wave enters section II, which is the same as I except that it is twice as long, and so produces a differential difference in phase with respect to the two components that is now $2 \times 90° = 180°$.   It can be shown that when a circularly polarized wave enters such a section, the wave that emerges is likewise circularly polarized, but rotates in the opposite direction.   This effect exists irrespective of the orientation of the axes of section II.   However, it can be shown that the phase of the circularly polarized wave that emerges from II has a phase that is shifted with respect to the circularly polarized wave entering this section by an amount determined by the orientation of the axes of section II with respect to the axes of section I.   Thus, by rotating II one rotates the

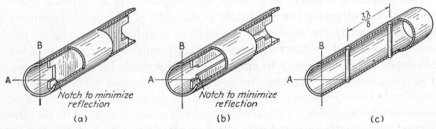

Notch to minimize reflection

(a)

Notch to minimize reflection

(b)

(c)

Fig. 6-37. Methods of obtaining different phase velocities along different perpendicular planes in a circular waveguide.

phase of the output wave.   This phase rotation in degrees is twice the angle of rotation of section II.   Finally, the circularly polarized output wave emerging from section II, with its phase shift determined by the orientation of the axis of II, now enters section III, which is similar to I. This final section converts the circularly polarized wave back to a linearly polarized wave that possesses a phase shift with respect to the input wave that is determined by the orientation of II.

The difference in phase velocity between axis A and axis B in sections I, II, III, can be achieved in a number of ways, the more common of which are illustrated in Fig. 6-37.   At a, a low-loss dielectric slab is placed along axis B, as shown, thus increasing the component of electric flux along this axis, while having relatively little effect on the electric flux oriented along axis A.   A similar effect is obtained in b by the metal fins placed parallel to axis B as shown, which reduce the distance across the guide in this direction and hence increase the electric flux.   In both the metal-fin and the dielectric-slab arrangements, the ends are tapered or notched in order to provide a gradual transition that minimizes discontinuities and the reflections that thereby result.   The arrangement at Fig. 6-37c

employs metal rods connected across the guide as shown; these act as inductive shunts to waves polarized in the direction of the rods, while having negligible effect on waves polarized perpendicular to the rods. This method is very desirable from a constructional point of view, although it has a somewhat narrower bandwidth over which it is reasonably effective than do the systems of *a* and *b*. However, none of these three arrangements is highly sensitive with respect to frequency.

6-12. Measurements on Amplitude-modulated Waves. The features of an amplitude-modulated wave of importance from a measurement point of view are the percentage modulation of the positive and negative peaks, and the distortion of the modulation envelope. In the case of amplitude-modulated radio transmitters, modulation measurements are used to aid in adjusting the transmitter, and for monitoring purposes, particularly to warn of overmodulation.

Investigation of Modulation Envelope by Rectification of Modulation Envelope. In investigating the amplitude modulation of a wave, it is common practice to rectify the wave. If the rectifier is distortionless, the output voltage developed by the rectifier will exactly reproduce the modulation envelope. It is customary to employ a diode rectifier for such purposes. The distortion introduced by the detector will be small if (1) the radio-frequency voltage applied to the detector is large (such as 20 volts or more carrier amplitude), (2) the plate-cathode resistance of the diode tube is very, very small compared with the diode load impedance (achieved by using a low-impedance tube, together with a relatively high load impedance), and (3) the load impedance of the diode offers the same impedance to modulation-frequency voltages as to d-c voltages (*i.e.*, the a-c/d-c impedance ratio of the load must approach unity). If this latter requirement is not met, the detector output will have the negative peaks clipped.[1]

The rectified voltage wave produced by the diode output may be utilized in a number of ways. The average, or d-c, value of this voltage is a measure of the carrier amplitude of the wave, while the alternating component of the voltage developed across the output load impedance is a reproduction of the modulation-envelope variations. Thus changes in the d-c rectified current, such as are indicated by a d-c microammeter in series with the diode load impedance, signify a change in carrier amplitude, *i.e.*, a "carrier shift." The relation of the positive peak amplitude of the rectified voltage wave, to the average, or d-c, amplitude, indicates the positive peak modulation, while the relation of the trough, or minimum, of the rectified wave to the average amplitude determines the percentage modulation at the negative peaks (see Fig. 6-38). A frequency analysis of the alternating component of the voltage developed by the

[1] For discussion of this point see F. E. Terman, "Radio Engineering," 3d ed., pp. 502–513, McGraw-Hill Book Company, Inc., New York, 1947.

rectifier output represents a frequency analysis of the modulation envelope, and reveals the presence of distortion. A picture of the modulation envelope can be obtained by oscillographic observation of the voltage developed by the rectifier output, provided both the direct and alternating components of the output voltages are applied to the oscilloscope without change in relative magnitude.

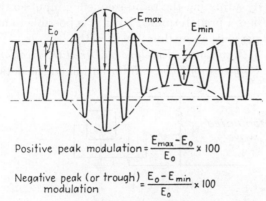

$$\text{Positive peak modulation} = \frac{E_{max} - E_0}{E_0} \times 100$$

$$\text{Negative peak (or trough) modulation} = \frac{E_0 - E_{min}}{E_0} \times 100$$

FIG. 6-38. Modulated wave with equations giving positive and negative peak modulation.

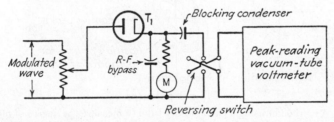

FIG. 6-39. Schematic diagram of modulation meter capable of reading positive and negative peak modulation.

Equipment for accurate measurement of the positive and negative peak modulation is shown schematically in Fig. 6-39.[1] The radio-frequency wave to be investigated is rectified by diode detector T_1 operated as a linear detector with a minimum of distortion. The average value of the rectified output voltage gives the carrier amplitude, and is read by d-c microammeter M. The peak and trough values of modulation are

[1] For further discussion of equipment for measuring the degree of amplitude modulation, see Verne V. Gunsolley, A Differential Modulator Meter, *Electronics*, vol. 13, p. 18, January, 1940; H. D. McD. Ellis, Measurement of Modulation Depth, *Wireless Eng.*, vol. 18, p. 99, March, 1941; F. C. Williams and A. E. Chester, A New Modulation Meter, *Wireless Eng.*, vol. 15, p. 257, May, 1938; L. F. Gaudernack, Some Notes on the Practical Measurement of the Degree of Amplitude Modulation, *Proc. IRE*, vol. 22, p. 819, July, 1934.

obtained by separating the modulation-frequency component of the rectifier output from the d-c component, and then separately measuring positive and negative peaks of this wave by a diode voltmeter provided with a reversing switch as shown. Modulation factors for the positive and negative peaks are then given by a comparison of the peak voltage indicated by the diode voltmeter with the carrier amplitude as indicated by meter M. By adjusting the radio-frequency input so that the carrier indicated by M has a predetermined level, it is possible to make the diode voltmeter read percentage modulation directly.

Investigation of Modulation Envelope by Direct Observation of the Modulated Wave on a Cathode-ray Tube. Information on the details of modula-

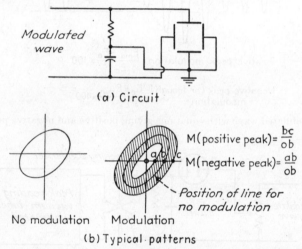

(a) Circuit

$$M(\text{positive peak}) = \frac{bc}{ob}$$

$$M(\text{negative peak}) = \frac{ab}{ob}$$

~ *Position of line for no modulation*

No modulation   Modulation

(b) Typical patterns

Fig. 6-40. A method of using a cathode-ray tube to measure the degree of modulation.

tion can be obtained by directly observing the modulated wave on a cathode-ray tube, without previous rectification. For example, the modulated wave may be applied to a resistance-capacitance phase splitter, and the resulting voltage components used for vertical and horizontal deflection. The result is a circular or elliptical pattern as shown in Fig. 6-40. In the absence of modulation, this pattern consists of a simple line; however, with modulation the magnitude of the ellipse varies during the modulation cycle, causing the line to widen out into a band. The degree of modulation for the positive and negative peaks can then be calculated from distances measured along any convenient radial from the center, as shown. It will be noted that for complete modulation on the negative peaks, the center of the pattern closes completely.

When the modulating voltage is available, one may apply the modulated wave to the vertical deflectors, and use the modulating voltage to produce the horizontal deflection.   When the phase is adjusted so that there is no phase difference between the modulation envelope and the horizontal-deflecting voltage, then, in the absence of amplitude distortion, a trapezoid pattern with straight lines is obtained as in Fig. 6-41b.   The degree of modulation can be readily calculated from this pattern by the equation given in the figure.   The presence of amplitude distortion in the modulation envelope causes the sloping sides of the trapezoid to be curved, as shown in Fig. 6-41d.   A phase difference between the modulation envelope and the sample of the modulating voltage used for horizontal deflection causes the sides of the pattern to be curved, and in most cases also causes a shaded ellipse to appear along the upper and lower edges as

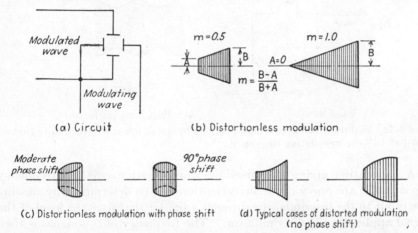

Fig. 6-41. Cathode-ray-tube arrangement for observing amplitude modulation when the time axis is provided by the modulating voltage.

indicated in Fig. 6-41c.   Such a phase shift can be eliminated, when desired, by introducing an appropriate phase-shifting network in the horizontal-deflecting circuit.

If the arrangement of Fig. 6-41 is modified so that the horizontal deflection is obtained by the use of a saw-tooth timing wave synchronized at a subharmonic of the modulation frequency, the result is as shown in Fig. 6-42b if the return trace is blanked out.   The necessary synchronization can be obtained by injecting modulation-frequency voltage into the synchronizing circuits of the cathode-ray oscilloscope.   Such a voltage may be obtained by rectification of the modulation envelope, if not otherwise conveniently available.

6-13. Modulation Characteristics of Frequency- and Phase-modulated Waves.   In frequency-modulated systems, a discriminator may be used to obtain a d-c voltage that varies in magnitude and polarity according to the magnitude and direction of the frequency deviation of a wave.   The output of such a discriminator accordingly reproduces the actual frequency modulation of the wave, and gives a result analogous to rectifying an amplitude-modulated wave.   The discriminator used for this purpose must have the minimum possible distortion.   The preferred arrangement is a counter-type discriminator such as discussed in connection with Fig. 5-19; the distortion of a well-designed discriminator of this type will be less than 0.2 per cent.[1]   The audio output wave obtained from a discriminator can be presented on a cathode-ray oscilloscope, or subjected to harmonic analysis, etc., as desired.

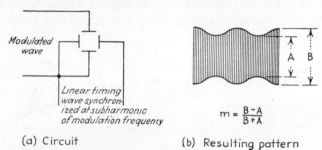

(a) Circuit   (b) Resulting pattern

$$m = \frac{B-A}{B+A}$$

Fig. 6-42. Modulated-wave envelope obtained by use of linear sweep circuit synchronized at half the modulating frequency.

A calibration giving the discriminator output versus the frequency deviation of the wave under investigation can be determined by passing the input to the discriminator through a limiter that fixes the level of the signal applied to the discriminator.   The frequency of this signal is then varied step by step, in the absence of all modulation, and the variation in d-c output of the discriminator observed.   In this way a relationship is obtained between discriminator output and the instantaneous frequency of the applied wave.   This relationship obtained by static measurements is, under all ordinary circumstances, the same as exists under dynamic conditions with alternating modulation.[2]

The modulation index m_f of a frequency-modulated wave for the case of sinusoidal modulation is given by the equation

$$m_f = \frac{\text{frequency deviation } (= \Delta f)}{\text{modulating frequency}} \qquad (6\text{-}19)$$

[1] If the requirements are not too severe, it is also possible to use a Seeley-type discriminator, or a ratio detector, for this purpose, provided such systems are designed with a frequency separation between peaks that is much greater than the frequency deviation to be encountered; in this way operation is confined to the central, highly linear portion of the discriminator characteristic.

[2] The limitations of this "quasi-steady-state" method are discussed by Terman, op. cit., p. 499.

The modulation index may be directly measured by taking advantage of the fact that the carrier amplitude of the wave has zero amplitude whenever the modulation index m_f is such that $J_0(m_f) = 0$, where J_0 is a Bessel function of the zero order.[1]   Values of modulation index for which the carrier amplitude becomes zero are given in Table 6-2.

TABLE 6-2.

VALUES OF MODULATION INDEX FOR WHICH CARRIER WAVE HAS ZERO AMPLITUDE

Order of Carrier Zero	Modulation Index
1	2.40
2	5.52
3	8.65
4	11.79
5	14.93
6	18.07
m ($m > 6$)	$18.07 + \pi(m - 6)$

To use this method of determining the modulation index, one must have available a wave analyzer or spectrum analyzer for which the resolution is somewhat better than twice the modulation frequency.[2]   In this case one can adjust the analyzer equipment to respond only to the carrier, without any effect being produced by the presence of first-order or higher order side-band components.   The amplitude of the audio modulating wave is then increased slowly, starting from zero, and the amplitudes for which the carrier becomes zero are noted.   Since these conditions correspond to modulation indices as tabulated in Table 6-2, one is able to plot a curve showing modulating index as a function of the amplitude of the modulating voltage.

In dealing with frequency-modulated waves, it is sometimes desirable to observe the spectrum of the wave.   This can be done with the aid of a spectrum analyzer,[3] as discussed in Sec. 6-5, or by a point-by-point analysis using a sharply tuned receiver as a wave analyzer.   In either case, if the resolution of the modulating equipment is greater than the modulating frequency, the amplitude of the individual frequency components of the wave may be observed; otherwise one obtains an envelope which at each point is an average of the several side-band components in the immediate vicinity of that point.

[1] See Murray G. Crosby, A Method of Measuring Frequency Deviation, *RCA Rev.*, vol. 4, p. 473, April, 1940.

[2] If the modulating frequency is so low that this degree of resolution cannot be obtained, then the approximate value of the modulation index can be inferred from the width of the spectrum of the modulated wave; see H. P. Thomas, Measurements in F. M. Transmitter, *Electronics*, vol. 14, p. 23, May, 1941.

[3] Thus see Roger J. Pieracci, A Frequency Modulation Monitoring System, *Proc. IRE*, vol. 28, p. 375, August, 1940.

Detection of Phase Modulation in Transmitters. Phase modulation, and to a lesser extent, frequency modulation, often appear as undesired by-products in oscillators and transmitters making use of amplitude modulation. The presence of spurious phase or frequency modulation can be detected by passing the wave through a limiter to remove the amplitude modulation, and then applying the resulting wave that is free of amplitude modulation to a discriminator of some type. Any a-c component that appears in the discriminator output then represents phase or frequency modulation.

When a wave is available which has exactly the same frequency as the carrier of the amplitude-modulated wave, and which is known to be com-

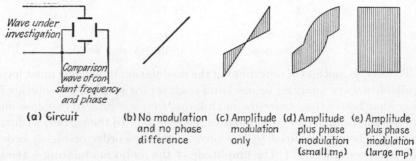

(a) Circuit   (b) No modulation and no phase difference   (c) Amplitude modulation only   (d) Amplitude plus phase modulation (small m_p)   (e) Amplitude plus phase modulation (large m_p)

FIG. 6-43. Detection of phase modulation accompanying amplitude modulation.

pletely free of all modulation of any kind, the presence of spurious frequency or phase modulation can be detected by applying the amplitude-modulated radio-frequency wave directly to one pair of deflectors of a cathode-ray tube, while applying the unmodulated reference wave to the other deflectors. The relative phase of the two voltages is then adjusted so that, with no amplitude modulation, a straight line is produced. Amplitude modulation of one of the waves in the absence of phase shift then produces a pattern as shown in Fig. 6-43c. However, if a small amount of phase modulation is present, such as $\pm 45°$, then the pattern is modified, with one or more of the sides being elliptical rather than straight, as shown in Fig. 6-43d. In case the phase deviation is of the order of a cycle or more (or, with frequency modulation, having a modulation index exceeding about 2π), a shaded rectangular area is produced as shown in Fig. 6-43e.

CHAPTER 7

CHARACTERISTICS OF TRIODES, PENTODES, AND SIMILAR TUBES

7-1. The Coefficients of Vacuum Tubes.[1] Many of the tube character-istics of importance in the practical use of triode, pentode, screen-grid, and beam tubes can be expressed in terms of coefficients. These coeffi-cients describe the properties of the tube in the vicinity of an initial oper-ating condition, and are of three types, designated as mu factors, electrode resistances, and transconductances, respectively.

The term *mu factor* is defined as the relative effect produced by voltage increments applied to some specified pair of tube electrodes on some speci-fied current in the tube. Thus, the mu factor μ_{123} gives the effect of a small increment in the voltage on electrode 1 relative to an increment in the voltage on electrode 2, with respect to the current I_3. That is,

$$\text{Mu factor } \mu_{123} = -\left.\frac{\Delta E_2}{\Delta E_1}\right|_{I_3 \text{ constant}} = -\left.\frac{dE_2}{dE_1}\right|_{I_3 \text{ constant}} \tag{7-1}$$

where ΔE_1 and ΔE_2 are small increments of voltage applied to electrodes 1 and 2, respectively, and of such proportion that when both are applied simultaneously the current I_3 is unchanged. It will be noted that the mu factor is a nondimensional quantity which is defined with respect to a given operating condition or point on the characteristic curves of the tube. It will also be observed that there is a mu factor for every possible pair of electrodes with respect to every current in the tube, so that in general a number of different mu factors can be defined for any particular tube.

The *dynamic resistance* of an electrode is the resistance offered between that electrode and cathode to a small increment in electrode voltage. Thus, when an increment of voltage ΔE produces an increment ΔI in the current to the same electrode, the dynamic resistance is given by relation

$$\left.\begin{array}{c}\text{Dynamic resistance} \\ \text{of electrode}\end{array}\right\} = \frac{\Delta E}{\Delta I} = \left.\frac{dE}{dI}\right|_{\text{other voltages constant}} \tag{7-2}$$

[1] Definitions of tube properties, and methods of testing tubes for many operating characteristics, are to be found in Standards on Electron Tubes, *Proc. IRE*, vol. 38, p. 426, April; p. 917, August; and p. 1079, September, 1950.

The dynamic resistance is expressed in ohms. It will be noted that the dynamic resistance is determined by the *slope* of the curve of electrode current as a function of electrode voltage; it is not the ratio which the total voltage applied to the electrode bears to the total electrode current. The numerical value of the dynamic resistance will in general depend upon the operating point. Each electrode in a tube (other than the cathode) may have a dynamic resistance defined for it.

Transconductance, sometimes also called mutual conductance, g_{12} expresses the change ΔI_2 of current at electrode 2 produced as a result of applying a voltage increment ΔE_1 to electrode 1; that is,

$$\text{Transconductance } g_{12} = \frac{\Delta I_2}{\Delta E_1} = \frac{dI_2}{dE_1}\bigg|_{\text{other voltages constant}} \qquad (7\text{-}3)$$

The transconductance is expressed in mhos. Its numerical value depends upon the operating conditions of the tube, and is determined by the slope of the curve of current I_2 of electrode 2 presented as a function of the total voltage E_1 applied to electrode 1. This transconductance g_{12} is related to the mu factor μ_{122} of electrodes 1 and 2 with respect to current 2, and the dynamic resistance r_2 of electrode 2, according to the relation[1]

$$\text{Transconductance } g_{12} = \frac{\mu_{122}}{r_2} \qquad (7\text{-}4)$$

Other coefficients in addition to mu factors, dynamic resistances, and transconductances can also be defined for tubes. These include particularly those coefficients related to the curvature, and to the rate of change of curvature, of the tube characteristics; such coefficients are sometimes encountered when dealing with modulation (or detection) problems, and with cross-talk, but are not in general use. There is also the conversion transconductance, which is discussed in Sec. 9-8 in connection with receiver measurements.

Triode Coefficients. In the case of triode tubes, three of the possible coefficients are of particular importance. These are the amplification factor, the plate resistance, and the transconductance, designated by the symbols μ, r_p, and g_m, respectively.

The amplification factor of a triode is the mu factor that gives the relative effect produced by increments to the grid and plate voltages on

---

[1] This can be demonstrated as follows: By Eq. (7-3) $g_{12} = \Delta I_2/\Delta E_1$. However, by definition of mu factor, ΔE_1 is μ_{122} times as effective in causing a change in the current of electrode 2 as is ΔE_1. Hence a change ΔE_2 in the voltage of electrode 2 will produce the same increment ΔI_2 in the current of electrode 2 as is produced by ΔE_1 provided $\Delta E_2 = \mu_{122}\,\Delta E_1$. Thus $g_{12} = \Delta I_2/(\Delta E_2/\mu_{122}) = \mu_{122}/(\Delta E_2/\Delta I_2)$. Since by Eq. (7-2), $\Delta E_2/\Delta I_2 = r_2$, then Eq. (7-4) follows at once.

the plate current.   It is accordingly defined by the relation

$$\mu = -\left.\frac{\Delta E_b}{\Delta E_c}\right|_{I_p \text{ constant}} = -\left.\frac{dE_b}{dE_c}\right|_{I_p \text{ constant}} \tag{7-5}$$

where subscripts b and c denote plate and control grid, respectively.   In the usual case where the control-grid current is zero or negligible, the amplification factor of a triode is a measure of the effectiveness with which the control grid shields the cathode from the electrostatic field of the plate. The triode amplification factor is accordingly determined by geometrical considerations, and is largely independent of the electrode voltages. In particular, in the ideal case of perfect geometrical symmetry, the amplification factor is absolutely independent of electrode voltages.   In practical cases, lack of symmetry causes different portions of the tube to have different values of amplification factor.[1] As a result, the measured value of amplification factor for a given plate voltage tends to be lower as plate-current cutoff is approached, as shown in Fig. 7-1.   This is because as the control grid becomes more negative, those parts of the tube having the highest amplification factor will reach cutoff first, leaving only the lower μ portions contributing to the plate current.   Typical values of amplification factor lie in the range 3 to 20; in some cases slightly lower values are encountered, while occasionally values as high as 50 to 100 are used.

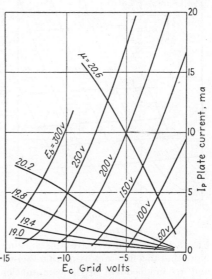

Fig. 7-1. Behavior of amplification factor in a typical triode tube.

The plate resistance of a triode is the dynamic resistance of the plate-cathode circuit of the tube.   Hence

$$r_p = \frac{\Delta E_b}{\Delta I_p} = \left.\frac{dE_b}{dI_b}\right|_{E_c \text{ constant}} \tag{7-6}$$

For a given tube, the plate resistance depends on the operating condition, and is largely determined by the plate current at the operating point, rather than by the combination of electrode voltages used to produce this

[1] F. E. Terman and A. L. Cook, Note on the Variations in the Amplification Factor of Triodes, *Proc. IRE*, vol. 18, p. 1044, June, 1930.

current (see Fig. 7-2a).   In an idealized triode having perfect geometrical symmetry and an equipotential cathode, the plate resistance is inversely

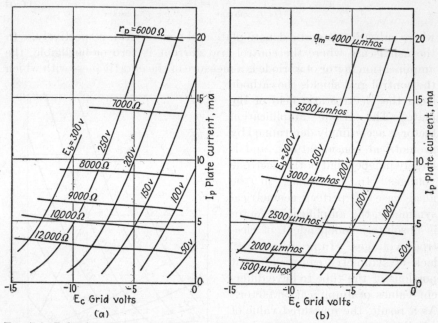

FIG. 7-2. Behavior of plate resistance and transconductance in a typical triode tube. Note that to a first approximation these quantities depend only upon the plate current, and are independent of the combination of electrode voltages that give rise to this current.

proportional to the cube root of the plate current.[1]   Also to the extent that other things are equal, the triode tends to have a plate resistance directly proportional to the amplification factor; this results from the fact

---

[1] This arises from the fact that according to the usual triode theory, one has for an idealized triode

$$I_p = k \left(E_c + \frac{E_b}{\mu} \right)^{\frac{3}{2}} \qquad (7\text{-}7a)$$

where k is a constant depending on the tube dimensions. Solving this expression for E_b, and then differentiating with respect to I_p, while considering E_c and μ constant, gives

$$E_b = \mu \left(\frac{I_p}{k} \right)^{\frac{2}{3}} - \mu E_c \qquad (7\text{-}7b)$$

$$\frac{dE_b}{dI_p} = r_p = \frac{2\mu/3k^{\frac{2}{3}}}{I_p^{\frac{1}{3}}} \qquad (7\text{-}7c)$$

It will be noted that when dissymmetries are present, then the reduction in the value of μ that occurs as cutoff is approached, causes the plate resistance to increase less rapidly than inversely as the cube root of the plate current.

that the extent to which the space charge adjacent to the cathode is shielded from the effect of the voltage on the plate is proportional to the amplification factor.   Typical values of plate resistance for small triode tubes are in the range of 1000 to 20,000 ohms.   Values lower than 1000 ohms are sometimes encountered in small power tubes; likewise, values as high as 100,000 ohms are not unusual when high-amplification-factor tubes are used with small plate currents.

The transconductance of a triode is the rate of change of plate current with respect to change in grid voltage.   Thus, if the grid voltage is changed by an increment ΔE_c, the resulting plate-current change ΔI_p is related to the transconductance g_m by the equation

$$g_m = \frac{\Delta I_p}{\Delta E_c} = \frac{dI_p}{dE_c}\bigg|_{E_b \text{ constant}} \tag{7-8}$$

From Eq. (7-4) it is noted that the transconductance of a triode is also the ratio of amplification factor to plate resistance, i.e.,

$$g_m = \frac{\mu}{r_p} \tag{7-9}$$

Since the amplification factor of a triode approximates a geometrical constant, the transconductance and the plate resistance depend in an inverse way upon the operating conditions of the tube.   In particular, for an idealized triode tube, the value of transconductance is proportional to the cube root of the plate current and is independent of the combination of electrode voltages used to produce this current, as approximated in Fig. 7-2b.   For tubes that are similar except for amplification factor, the transconductance will be approximately independent of μ.   Typical values of transconductances of receiving-type triodes are in the range 1000 to 10,000 μmhos; smaller values occur, however, when tubes are operated with small plate currents.

Coefficients of Pentode, Beam, and Screen-grid Tubes.   In tubes possessing a screen grid, such as pentode, beam, and screen-grid tubes, it is possible to define a very large number of tube coefficients.   Only a few of these are of much practical significance, however.   Most important is the transconductance g_m of the control grid with respect to the plate current; for many purposes this constant alone is sufficient to describe the properties of the tube that are of interest.   It is also customary in tube manuals to list the plate resistance r_p, and the amplification factor μ.   The latter is the mu factor of the control grid and plate electrodes relative to the plate current.

The transconductance g_m of a tube with screen-grid electrodes is only slightly less than the transconductance that would be obtained from the same tube made to operate as a triode by connecting all electrodes except the control grid together to serve as a triode plate electrode. This is because under ordinary operating conditions over 80 per cent of the space current of these tubes flows to the plate; the effect of the control grid on the plate current is accordingly only slightly less than in the equivalent triode.

The amplification factor μ of tubes with screen grids is extremely high, often in excess of 1000. This is because under the usual operating conditions existing in such tubes, the plate current is substantially independent of plate voltage. The exact value of the amplification factor of such tubes also depends very considerably on the electrode voltages, and does not tend to be a geometrical constant, as is the μ of a triode, or as is μ_s (see below). The independence of plate current with respect to plate voltage also causes the plate resistance of tubes with screen grids to be very high under typical operating conditions; thus values of plate resistance in excess of 1 megohm are typical for small receiving pentodes.

Another coefficient of some importance in tubes possessing a screen grid is the amplification factor μ_s, the mu factor of the control grid relative to the screen grid with respect to the *total space current*. This quantity is the amplification factor of the triode tube that is formed by connecting the screen grid and plate together. It is a geometric constant, the same as the triode amplification factor. This coefficient μ_s can be thought of as the "cutoff" amplification factor, since the value of control-grid bias required to reduce the total space current to zero is $-E_s/\mu_s$, where E_s is the screen voltage.

Another amplification factor of occasional importance is μ_s', the mu factor of the control grid relative to the screen grid with respect to the *screen-grid* current. Inasmuch as the ratio of screen-grid current to total space current under most conditions tends to have a fixed value determined largely by the geometry of the tube, the amplification factor μ_s' can usually be taken as identical with μ_s.

When determining the effect that an impedance in the screen-grid circuit has on the behavior of an amplifier, the dynamic screen-grid resistance r_s is of interest. This resistance behaves in the same manner as the plate resistance of a triode; for example, it is determined primarily by the screen current and not by the combination of screen- and control-grid voltages which produces the current. The screen resistance is typically of the order of five to ten times the plate resistance of the same tube connected as a triode.

7-2. Determination of Tube Coefficients from Characteristic Curves, and by Means of Static Increments. *Graphical Methods Utilizing Characteristic Curves of Tubes.* By definition the dynamic resistance is the reciprocal of the slope of the curve of electrode current plotted as a function of electrode voltage, the slope being taken for the operating condition of interest. Thus when the appropriate curves of tube characteristics are available, the dynamic resistance can be obtained by scaling off increments of current and voltage to determine slope, as illustrated in Fig. 7-3a for plate resistance.

In a similar manner, the transconductance is by definition the slope of the curve of current of one electrode plotted as a function of the appropriate voltage. When such curves of tube characteristics are available, the transconductance can hence be obtained by scaling off increments of voltage and current to obtain the slope at the desired operating point. An example is illustrated in Fig. 7-3b for the transconductance of a triode.

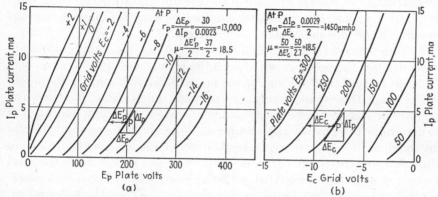

Fig. 7-3. Evaluation of triode plate resistance, transconductance, and amplification factor from the characteristic curves of the tube.

The amplification factor can be determined by scaling off increments on the characteristic curves corresponding to voltage ratios required to keep the reference current constant. Thus, the amplification factor of a triode can be obtained either from a family of E_p-I_p curves, as shown in Fig. 7-3a, or a family of E_c-I_p curves, as in Fig. 7-3b. When using such curves to determine amplification factor, one of the increments represents the voltage displacement of adjacent curves in the family along the horizontal axis, while the other increment is the difference in the fixed voltage assigned to the adjacent curves.

The graphical determination of tube coefficients is often a convenient means of obtaining their approximate value. Tube curves are, however, seldom available with the accuracy and physical size required to give precise values of the coefficients. The method tends also to be unsatisfactory for determining coefficients that are either unusually large or unusually small; under these conditions at least one of the slopes (or increments) involved becomes either too small or too large to be determined with the exactness required to obtain the coefficient with even fair accuracy. For this reason, it is generally unsatisfactory to determine the amplification factor and plate resistance of pentodes and similar tubes by the use of characteristic curves.

Determination of Tube Coefficients Using Experimentally Produced Static Increments. The definitions given for tube coefficients in Eqs. (7-1) to (7-6) all have a form involving increments to the electrode voltages and currents. It is therefore possible to evaluate the tube coefficients by producing these increments experimentally. For example, the transconductance of a triode or a pentode can be determined by altering the control-grid voltage a known amount ΔE_c, and observing the resulting change ΔI_p in plate current. Likewise, the amplification factor μ can be obtained by changing the voltage applied to the control grid by a known amount ΔE_c, and then determining experimentally the change ΔE_b in plate voltage required to restore the original plate current.

The accuracy of this method of determining the tube coefficients depends upon the precision with which the increments in voltage and current can be read, and the size of the increments. By making the increments small they more closely approximate differentials; however, the smaller the change in electrode voltage or current, the more difficult it is to determine this change with accuracy. When only approximate results are required, it is customary to use relatively large increments, which are then observed as the change in readings of meters that indicate the total voltage and current associated with the electrodes involved. In emergencies, tubes may be tested in this way by the "grid-shift" method. This is a rough transconductance test carried out by changing the control-grid bias by a predetermined increment, and noting the change in plate current. A poor tube is indicated by a less than acceptable current change.

Accurate results, however, require that the electrode voltages be changed by small increments which are metered directly without regard to the total voltage or current upon which the increments are superimposed. The required experimental arrangement is illustrated in Fig. 7-4, as applied to a triode. Here the change ΔE_c in control-grid voltage is separately produced and controlled by means of battery E_1 and potentiometer P_1; this increment ΔE_c thus superimposed upon the grid potential is observed directly by voltmeter V_1, which can be chosen to give substantially full-scale deflection for even a very small increment. An analogous arrangement involving battery E_2, potentiometer P_2, and voltmeter V_2 is shown for superimposing an accurately measurable increment ΔE_b on the plate voltage. The change ΔI_p in plate current produced by these voltage increments is determined by associating meter M with an auxiliary battery E_3 in series with a variable resistance R, which is adjusted so that the plate current passing through the meter M before the addition of the increments is exactly balanced by an equal and opposite current supplied by E_3. In this way meter M indicates only the change in plate current, and by using a very sensitive meter even a very small increment in current can be quite accurately determined. In the arrangement illustrated in Fig. 7-4 it is important that the internal resistance of the plate-supply battery E_b be small compared with the plate resistance of the tube, and that the resistance R be large compared with the resistance of meter M.

The use of the incremental method to determine tube coefficients has the advantage that the equipment required is available around any communications laboratory. The disadvantage is that the accuracy is poor

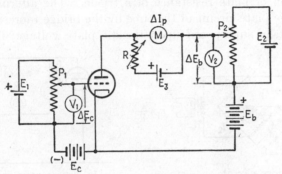

FIG. 7-4. Circuit for accurate measurement of increments to plate and grid voltages, and to plate current, for the purpose of determining tube coefficients.

unless circuit arrangements such as shown in Fig. 7-4 are used, and then the experimental procedure is both slow and cumbersome.

7-3. Measurement of Tube Coefficients by Alternating Increments and Null Balances.[1] The increments of voltage and current appearing in Eqs. (7-1) to (7-8) can be a-c increments instead of d-c (static) increments. Thus in Eq. (7-5), which defines the amplification factor of the triode, one could use alternating voltages ΔE_c and ΔE_b of opposite phase applied to the control grid and plate, respectively, and adjust their ratio until zero alternating current appeared in the plate circuit. This procedure has the advantage that the increments, by being alternating, are not obscured by the large d-c voltages and currents upon which they are

[1] A discussion of the voltage-ratio method of measuring tube constants is given by W. N. Tuttle, Dynamic Measurement of Electron Tube Coefficients, *Proc. IRE*, vol. 21, p. 844, June, 1933. For further information on bridge arrangements such as illustrated in Figs. 7-5a, 7-8, and 7-11 see Roger W. Hickman and Frederick V. Hunt, The Exact Measurement of Electron-tube Coefficients, *Rev. Sci. Instruments*, vol. 6, p. 268, September, 1935; much the same information is given by H. J. Reich, "Theory and Applications of Electron Tubes," 2d ed., pp. 650–656, McGraw-Hill Book Company, Inc., New York, 1944; also see E. L. Chaffee, "Theory of Thermionic Vacuum Tubes," pp. 228–241, McGraw-Hill Book Company, Inc., New York, 1933.

superimposed, as tends to be the case when d-c increments are employed. The use of alternating increments also lends itself to null-balance arrangements for determining the required relation between the increments. The result is high accuracy, such as is commonly associated with bridges. The voltage increments employed should ordinarily be in the range 0.1 to 1.0 volts.

Electrode Resistance (Plate Resistance). The resistance of any electrode of a tube, such as the plate resistance, can be determined by placing the unknown resistance in the X arm of an a-c bridge.[1] An example of such an arrangement is shown in Fig. 7-5a, where the connection is for the determination of plate resistance of a triode. The alternating voltage applied to the plate circuit of the tube by the bridge represents an increment of voltage superposed upon the d-c plate voltage; the resistance

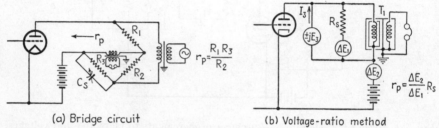

(a) Bridge circuit   (b) Voltage-ratio method

Fig. 7-5. Circuits for measuring electrode resistance, showing application to the measurement of the plate resistance of a triode tube.

measured by the bridge is the resistance which the plate circuit of the tube offers to this superposed alternating voltage. The variable condenser C_s is required to balance the capacitance introduced by the plate-cathode capacitance of the tube. It is important that the bridge be coupled to the oscillator and telephone receivers through appropriately shielded and insulated transformers, since the bridge is at the d-c plate potential with respect to ground. It is also desirable that the bridge be completely shielded, as in Fig. 2-8b, if the electrode resistance being measured is high.

Electrode resistance can be determined with excellent accuracy using a bridge in this manner. Very high plate resistances, such as values above 1 megohm as often encountered in small pentodes, present no more difficulty than when measuring ordinary resistances of similar values on a bridge; they can be readily obtained with precision by using a properly shielded bridge. The principal disadvantage of the bridge circuit for determining plate resistance is that the bridge must carry the d-c electrode current. The bridge resistances accordingly introduce a d-c voltage drop that varies as the bridge is adjusted to balance, and this cor-

[1] For negative resistances, a bridge of the type shown in Fig. 3-36 would be used.

respondingly changes the d-c voltage actually applied to the electrode. This effect can be minimized by so proportioning the bridge that R_1 is small, as 10 ohms; when this is done, then the resistance to the flow of the electrode current is small provided the primary resistance of the output transformer is likewise small.   Another factor to keep in mind in using a bridge to measure electrode resistance is that unless special protection is provided, the bridge may be damaged by excessive current if the tube being tested develops a short circuit between electrodes.

An alternative null arrangement for measuring electrode resistance is provided by the voltage-ratio method, illustrated in Fig. 7-5b as applied to triode plate resistance.   Here alternating voltages ΔE_1 and ΔE_2 are applied as shown, and their ratio adjusted so that a null balance is obtained in the telephone receivers.   The operation of this arrangement can be explained as follows: The voltage ΔE_2 applied to the plate electrode produces an incremental current ΔI_2 which flows through the primary of the transformer T_1.   A null balance is then obtained by neutralizing this current in the primary of the transformer by an equal and opposite current produced by the voltage ΔE_1 acting through the resistance R_s; then[1]

$$\text{Plate resistance} = \frac{\Delta E_2}{\Delta E_1} R_s \qquad (7\text{-}10)$$

Reactive current flowing through T_1 as a result of lead and plate-cathode tube capacitance is balanced by an equal and opposite reactive current I_3 produced by quadrature voltage generator $\pm jE_3$.

The two voltages $\Delta E_2/\Delta E_1$ must be in the same phase,[2] so can be obtained from a transformer with insulated and shielded secondaries as shown in Fig. 7-6.[3]   The ratio $\Delta E_2/\Delta E_1$ can be controlled by attenuators as indicated.   The reactive current I_3 in Figs. 7-5b and 7-7 must be exactly 90° out of phase with respect to voltages ΔE_1 and ΔE_2, and so can be obtained from a third secondary on the same transformer with the aid of a double-stator condenser, as illustrated.   By means of the con-

---

[1] This follows from the fact that according to Eq. (7-2), $r_p = \Delta E_2/\Delta I_2$.   However, the current that neutralizes ΔI_2 has a magnitude $\Delta E_1/R_s$, and substituting this for ΔI_2 gives (7-10).   In making this analysis it can be assumed that the transformer T_1 offers zero impedance to the alternating currents produced by ΔE_1 and ΔE_2.   This is because at balance the voltage drop across this transformer is zero, thus giving an effect equivalent to short-circuiting the primary in so far as the remainder of the circuit is concerned.

[2] Negative resistances can be measured by reversing the polarity of one of these voltages.

[3] A discussion of design details involved in this transformer, and also in T_1, that would be helpful to anyone attempting to construct such transformers himself, is given on pp. 171–173 of the predecessor of this book, "Measurements in Radio Engineering."

denser, the current magnitude can be continuously varied down to a value of zero and can be made either leading or lagging. The transformer T_1 that connects the telephone receivers to the circuit must be fully shielded, as shown, in order to prevent capacitive currents from the transformer primary to ground from producing a voltage across the secondary terminals of the transformer.

The voltage-ratio method of measuring electrode resistance has the

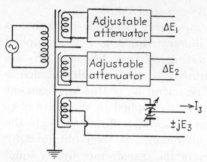

advantage that a very wide range of resistance values can be readily covered with good accuracy. In addition, by using low-resistance attenuators of constant impedance the d-c voltage drop introduced in the plate circuit by the measuring equipment can be made not only quite small, but also constant. The disadvantage of the arrangement is that a special measuring unit is required to produce the voltages ΔE_1 and ΔE_2, and the reactive current I_3; also transformer T_1 is likewise special.

Fig. 7-6. Transformer and attenuator arrangement for producing the voltages and currents required in Figs. 7-5b, 7-7, and 7-10.

However, once available, this same equipment can also be used to measure amplification factor and transconductance.

Amplification Factor (Mu Factor). Null methods of measuring amplification factor (or mu factor) are illustrated in Figs. 7-7 and 7-8. In the voltage-ratio method of Fig. 7-7, alternating increments ΔE_1 and ΔE_2 are applied to the respective electrodes in opposite phase.[1] The ratio of these increments is adjusted until the resulting alternating current produced in the circuit of the reference electrode is zero as determined by a telephone receiver coupled into this circuit through a transformer. Then

$$\text{Amplification factor (or mu factor)} = \frac{\Delta E_2}{\Delta E_1} \qquad (7\text{-}11)$$

The particular mu factor which is determined in this manner depends on where the voltages ΔE_1 and ΔE_2 are inserted, and where the current null is observed; examples for three cases are illustrated in Fig. 7-7.

The sharpness of the null is commonly obscured by reactive current flowing through the primary of transformer T_1. This current arises from the interelectrode capacitances of the tube being tested, lead capacitance, etc. Trouble of this type is eliminated by the reactive-current generator

---

[1] Negative values of mu factor can be measured by making the phase the same instead of opposite.

$\pm jE_3$ shown, which is adjusted to pass an equal and opposite reactive current I_3 through the transformer primary.

The voltages ΔE_1 and ΔE_2, and the adjustable reactive current I_3, required in the voltage-ratio method of measuring mu factor, can be obtained from the transformer-attenuator arrangement of Fig. 7-6.   To change from measurement of electrode resistance to measurement of mu factor, it is merely necessary to switch the connections.

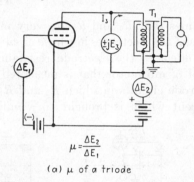

$$\mu = \frac{\Delta E_2}{\Delta E_1}$$

(a) μ of a triode

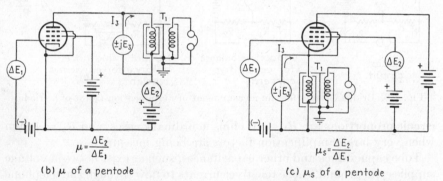

$$\mu = \frac{\Delta E_2}{\Delta E_1}$$

(b) μ of a pentode

$$\mu_s = \frac{\Delta E_2}{\Delta E_1}$$

(c) μ_s of a pentode

FIG. 7-7. Circuits for measurement of mu factor by the voltage-ratio method.

The voltage-ratio method is the most satisfactory means available for measuring mu factor.   It has good accuracy over a wide range of values, even for mu factors as large as 1000; the d-c voltage drop introduced into the tube circuits by the measuring equipment can be made small and independent of the adjustment of the measuring equipment (just as when measuring resistance); and the sources of voltage for the various electrodes involved can be operated with one terminal grounded.   The disadvantage of the voltage-ratio method is the same as when it is used to measure resistance, *viz.*, specially designed transformers and attenuators are required.

Simple bridge arrangements for measuring amplification factor are shown in Fig. 7-8.   Here an oscillator voltage is applied to resistances

R_2 and R_1 in series.   This causes alternating-voltage increments ΔE_2 and ΔE_1 having the ratio R_2/R_1 to be superimposed on the two electrodes. The mu factor is then determined by adjusting one of these resistances until a telephone receiver coupled in series with the current in the reference circuit indicates a null condition.   One then has

$$\text{Amplification factor} = \mu = \frac{R_2}{R_1} \tag{7-12}$$

This equation assumes that R_1 and R_2 are very much smaller than the dynamic resistances of the electrodes in whose circuits they are inserted so that the shunting effect of the electrode resistances can be neglected. The particular kind of mu factor that is measured in this way is determined by the electrode circuits in which R_2 and R_1 are inserted, and by the particular current which is brought to a null condition.   Typical

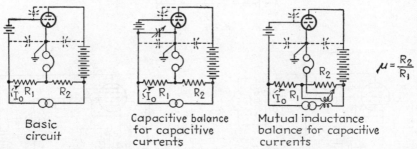

Basic
circuit

Capacitive balance
for capacitive
currents

Mutual inductance
balance for capacitive
currents

$\mu = \dfrac{R_2}{R_1}$

Fig. 7-8. Bridge circuits for the measurement of amplification factor of a triode.

circuit proportions are $R_1 = 10$ ohms in ordinary cases, and $R_1 = 1$ ohm when very large amplification factors are being measured.

Tube capacitance and other capacitances, such as exist between voltage supplies and ground, cause reactive currents to flow through the telephone receiver and thus prevent a sharp null balance from being obtained.   This difficulty can be eliminated by producing a compensating reactive effect by means of a variable condenser or mutual inductance; such reactive balances are shown in Fig. 7-8.

The bridge-circuit method of measuring amplification factor has the advantage that the apparatus can be constructed from equipment commonly available in any laboratory.   The method will give satisfactory results for amplification factors (or mu factors) of moderate value, such as those encountered in triodes, and for μ_s in pentodes and similar tubes. However, the arrangement is generally unsatisfactory for measuring values of amplification factor in excess of 100, such as are encountered in pentodes and similar tubes.   Under these conditions the required value of the ratio R_2/R_1 is so great as to make it difficult to obtain satisfactory per-

formance.   The bridge method of measuring amplification factor also
has the disadvantage that it is not possible to ground the power supplies
associated with the electrodes in series with which the resistances R_1 and
R_2 are inserted.

Null Measurement of Transconductance.   The simplest and most satisfactory null method for determining transconductance is shown in Fig.
7-9a.[1]   Here the alternating current ΔI_2 produced in the plate circuit by

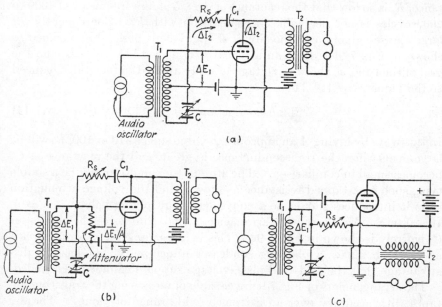

Fig. 7-9. Null circuits for measuring transconductance.

the application of an alternating-voltage increment ΔE_1 to the control
grid is neutralized in the primary of transformer T_2 by an equal and
opposite current produced by the voltage ΔE_1 acting through the variable
resistance R_s.   When the telephone receivers coupled to the plate circuit
indicate zero alternating plate current, one has[2]

$$\text{Transconductance} = \frac{1}{R_s} \qquad (7\text{-}13)$$

The obscuring of balance by reactive current in the primary of T_2 as a
result of grid-cathode tube capacitance and stray circuit capacitances, is
eliminated by means of an equal and opposite reactive current obtained

---

[1] C. B. Aiken and J. F. Bell, A Mutual Conductance Meter, *Communications* (*N.Y.*),
vol. 18, p. 19, September, 1938.

[2] This follows from the fact that by definition, $g_m = \Delta I_2/\Delta E_1$, combined with the
fact that at balance $\Delta I_2 = \Delta E_1/R_s$.

by providing transformer T_1 with a tapped secondary, and a double-stator variable condenser C as shown.

The by-pass condenser C_1 should have a reactance at the frequency of the oscillator that is very small compared with R_s. This condenser can be as large as several microfarads, since considerable capacitance to ground such as is associated with a physically large condenser does not affect the circuit behavior. However, with large values of transconductance, R_s is so low that the reactance of even 5 μf at a frequency of 1000 to 2000 cycles is not negligible in comparison with R_s. Consequently for large transconductances, the circuit of Fig. 7-9a is preferably modified as shown in Fig. 7-9b. Here an attenuator is placed between ΔE_1 and the grid of the tube, so that the voltage actually applied to the grid is reduced to the value $\Delta E_1/A$. Then

$$\text{Transconductance} = \frac{A}{R_s} \qquad (7\text{-}14)$$

In this way, by giving A an appropriate value such as 10 or 100, R_s will be large even when the transconductance is great, and the reactance of C_1 becomes small in comparison. The attenuator can ordinarily be a simple type, such as a tapped resistance as shown, and the voltage attenuation ratio it introduces should be a convenient multiplying value, such as 5, 10, 20, etc. An alternative arrangement that eliminates the condenser C_1 entirely is shown in Fig. 7-9c. This is a rearrangement of the circuit at a, which makes a blocking condenser unnecessary, but has the disadvantage that the grid- and plate-voltage supplies cannot be grounded.

The arrangements of Fig. 7-9 are capable of measuring the transconductance with accuracy over an extremely wide range of values. The d-c voltage drop introduced in the plate circuit by the measuring equipment is independent of the balance adjustment, and also can be made small by using a transformer T_2 having a low resistance primary. The system can, moreover, be put together with parts available in any communication laboratory; thus transformers T_1 and T_2 need not be specially designed, and need not have any shielding whatsoever. Resistance R_s can be a

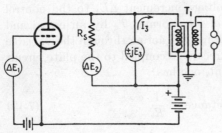

Fig. 7-10. Measurement of transconductance by the voltage-ratio method.

decade resistance box or a calibrated potentiometer, while condenser C can be made by combining two ordinary variable condensers. The power supplies may also have one terminal grounded except in Fig. 7-9c.

Transconductance can also be determined as the ratio of two voltages, as illustrated in Fig. 7-10. The idea is that the alternating current ΔI_2

produced in the plate circuit by the application of the alternating-voltage increment ΔE_1 to the control grid, is canceled in so far as the primary of transformer T_1 is concerned by an equal and opposite current produced by voltage ΔE_2 acting in series with resistance R_s.   For this arrangement[1,2]

$$\text{Transconductance} = \frac{\Delta E_2}{\Delta E_1} \frac{1}{R_s} \qquad (7\text{-}15)$$

The voltage-ratio method of measuring transconductance has the same advantages as when the method is used in determining plate resistance and

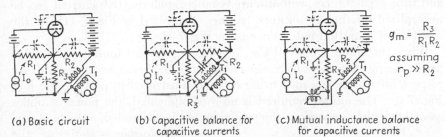

(a) Basic circuit (b) Capacitive balance for capacitive currents (c) Mutual inductance balance for capacitive currents

$$g_m = \frac{R_3}{R_1 R_2}$$
assuming $r_p \gg R_2$

FIG. 7-11. Bridge circuit for measuring transconductance.

amplification factor; *i.e.*, the method enables one to measure a wide range of values with accuracy, introduces a d-c voltage drop that is small and also constant, and permits the power-supply systems associated with the various electrodes to be grounded.   The disadvantage is that a special transformer T_1 and associated attenuators are required; this disadvantage is tempered somewhat, however, by the fact that the same measuring unit reconnected by a proper switching arrangement will also determine amplification factor, and plate resistance.

The bridge circuit of Fig. 7-11 provides another means of measuring transconductance.[3]   Here current from the oscillator produces a voltage drop across the resistance R_1 that is applied to the control grid.   The result is an alternating component of plate current that produces a drop

---

[1] Negative values of transconductance can be measured by reversing either ΔE_1 or ΔE_2.

[2] This follows from the fact that by definition $g_m = \Delta I_2 / \Delta E_1$.   However,

$$\Delta I_2 = \frac{\Delta E_2}{R_s},$$

and substituting this relation gives Eq. (7-15) at once.   The voltages ΔE_1 and ΔE_2 of adjustable ratio are produced by the transformer-attenuator arrangement of Fig. 7-6, as is also the adjustable reactive current $\pm j I_3$, which is for the purpose of neutralizing any reactive current that flows through the primary of transformer T_1 as a result of tube and circuit capacitance.

[3] This circuit, and also variations of it, are described by Chaffee, *loc. cit.*, Reich, *loc. cit.*, and Hickman and Hunt, *loc. cit.*

across R_2, which is then balanced in so far as the telephone receivers are concerned, by an equal and opposite voltage drop produced by the oscillator current flowing through resistance R_3. At balance one has[1]

$$\text{Transconductance} = \frac{R_3}{R_1 R_2} \tag{7-16}$$

Typical values of circuit constants are R_1 either 100 or 1000 ohms, $R_2 = 100$ ohms, R_3 variable up to 100 ohms. Any reactive current flowing through the primary of output transformer T_1 as a result of circuit and tube capacitances, will obscure balance; such reactive current can be neutralized by the capacitance balance illustrated in Fig. 7-11b, or the addition of a mutual inductance as in Fig. 7-11c.

While the bridge circuit of Fig. 7-11 has in the past found considerable use in the measurement of transconductance, the arrangement is in every respect inferior to the measuring method illustrated in parts a and b of Fig. 7-9. The circuit required is more complicated, the power supplies associated with the various electrodes cannot be grounded, a shielded output transformer is desirable, the d-c voltage drop introduced into the plate circuit is usually greater, and finally the accuracy is no better if as good.

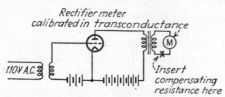

FIG. 7-12. Direct-reading transconductance meter.

Direct-reading Transconductance Meters. In testing tubes, use is frequently made of a direct-reading transconductance meter of the type illustrated in Fig. 7-12. Here the tube under test is operated with d-c electrode voltages corresponding to the desired condition. An alternating-voltage increment derived from the 110-volt 60-cycle power line by means of a transformer is applied to the control grid as shown. The resulting alternating current that flows in the plate or other electrode is

---

[1] This can be shown as follows: Assume the oscillator current is I_0; then the voltage ΔE_1 developed across R_1 and applied to the control grid is $\Delta E_1 = I_0 R_1$. But

$$g_m = \frac{\Delta I_2}{\Delta E_1},$$

where ΔI_2 is the alternating plate current produced by ΔE_1. At balance the voltage drop $\Delta I_2 R_2$ of ΔI_2 flowing through R_2 equals the drop $I_0 R_3$ of the oscillator current I_0 flowing through R_3. Substituting $\Delta I_2 = \Delta E_1 g_m$, and $\Delta E_1 = I_0 R_1$ in the relation $\Delta I_2 R_2 = I_0 R_3$ leads to Eq. (7-16).

It will be noted that this derivation assumes that the resistance R_2 is part of the plate resistance of the tube, and that the control-grid electrode produces no shunting effect across R_1. Thus Eq. (7-16) is accurate only to the extent that R_1 and R_2 are negligible compared with the dynamic resistances of the respective electrodes with which they are associated.

then read by a rectifier meter coupled to this circuit by means of a transformer. The rectifier meter is calibrated directly in transconductance according to the definition of Eq. (7-3). Provision, not shown in Fig. 7-12, is usually made for adjusting the voltage on the transformer to a standard value; this can be done by connecting the rectifier meter across the transformer secondary so that it temporarily serves as a voltmeter, and then adjusting the voltage to the required value by means of a variable resistance in series with the transformer primary.

Direct-reading transconductance meters of this type are particularly useful in the routine checking of tubes. They are convenient, simple to operate, and inexpensive. The accuracy is quite good provided the impedance that the meter inserts in the plate circuit is small compared with the dynamic resistance of this circuit.[1] The accuracy is accordingly excellent with pentode, beam, and similar tubes. With triodes having low plate resistance there is commonly an error that is by no means negligible, although relative results involving a comparison of different tubes of the same type will be significant.[2]

7-4. Special Considerations in Obtaining Characteristic Curves of Tubes. The characteristic curves of tubes are readily obtained with the aid of power supplies in which the d-c voltage is varied by means of a Variac[3] or equivalent device for controlling the alternating voltage applied to the transformer primary. One such power supply must be

---

[1] This is because the transconductance indicated is given by the relation

$$g_m = \frac{\mu}{(r_p + r_m)},$$

where r_m is the meter impedance, whereas the true value of transconductance is μ/r_p.

[2] Accurate results can still be obtained by correcting the meter reading according to the relation

$$\frac{\text{Actual } g_m}{\text{Indicated } g_m} = 1 + \frac{r_m}{r_p} = 1 + \frac{r_m}{\mu}\frac{\mu}{r_p} \tag{7-17}$$

where r_m is the resistance introduced in the plate circuit by the meter. It will be noted that if resistance is added to the meter in such a manner that r_m/μ is maintained constant, then the correction depends only on the true value μ/r_p of the transconductance being measured. The meter scale can then be arranged to include the correction and so directly indicate true transconductance. A transconductance meter based on this principle is described by O. J. Morelock, A Complete Direct Reading G_m Tube Tester, *Weston Eng. Notes*, vol. 1, p. 1, August, 1946. In the case of triodes μ is usually known in advance with adequate accuracy, and an arrangement in which r_m is adjusted to a value determined by an approximately known value of μ is quite practical. With pentode and similar tubes, however, this is not the case, and moreover the correcting resistance required is absurdly large; for testing such tubes an uncorrected scale must be provided.

[3] A Variac is an autotransformer in which the turns ratio is continuously variable by means of a sliding contact.

provided for each electrode to which voltage is applied, *e.g.*, control grid, screen grid, plate, etc.   In order that the voltage applied to an electrode will not change appreciably as the current flowing to this electrode varies it is desirable that these power supplies have good regulation.   This can be achieved by the use of either hot-cathode mercury-vapor or low-impedance high-vacuum rectifier tubes, combined with a choke-input type of filter system having low d-c resistance, and designed to draw sufficient bleeder current to prevent the voltage from soaring at no load. A still better arrangement is a power supply in which the output voltage is regulated electronically.[1]

The meters for reading the voltage and current delivered to the tube by each power supply are preferably multirange types, as in Figs. 1-1 and 1-2, in order to permit a wide range of values to be determined with accuracy.   The meter system should be fused to prevent damage as a result of improper manipulation of controls, or as a result of defective tubes that place unexpected short circuits on the system.   Reversing switches must be provided for plate, screen, and control-grid current meters, and a reversing switch for the control-grid voltage supply is also essential so that both positive and negative voltages may be available. In order that a negative grid bias may not be lost as a result of a burned-out fuse, the current meter in the grid line should have its terminals shunted with a very high resistance, such as 1 megohm.

When characteristic curves of tubes are being frequently obtained it is desirable to assemble the power supplies and meters in a rack mounting. In such cases, it is also sometimes desirable that the assembly include equipment for measuring the amplification factor, plate resistance, and transconductance of the tube.   The voltage-ratio method lends itself most satisfactorily to this application because of its accuracy, and the fact that the different tube coefficients may be readily measured with accuracy over wide ranges of values merely by reconnecting the same basic equipment for the different coefficients as required.

Cathode-ray-tube Methods.   A cathode-ray-tube spot can be used to draw out characteristic curves of a tube.   Thus consider a tube to which there is applied to the plate a constant voltage, while applied to the grid is a bias greater than cutoff upon which a 60-cycle alternating exciting voltage is superimposed (see Fig. 7-13).   The grid-voltage–plate-current $(E_c\text{-}I_p)$ characteristic for the particular plate voltage involved is then

---

[1] Many types of voltage-regulated power supplies in common use are not satisfactory because they are not capable of reducing the output voltage below a certain minimum voltage that is considerably greater than zero.   Special arrangements are required to overcome this difficulty in regulated supply systems; thus see Anthony Abate, Basic Theory and Design of Electronically Regulated Power Supplies, *Proc. IRE*, vol. 33, p. 478, July, 1945.

obtained by making the horizontal-deflecting voltage of the cathode-ray tube proportional to the total voltage applied to the control grid of the tube (*i.e.*, bias plus 60-cycle voltage), while making the vertical-deflecting voltage proportional to plate current.   Similarly the I_p-E_p characteristic can be presented by employing a fixed control-grid bias, and then applying unrectified alternating voltage applied directly to the plate; in such a case the horizontal deflection is made proportional to the voltage between plate and cathode, while the vertical deflection is again derived from the plate current.[1]

Cathode-ray-tube methods make it possible to obtain tube characteristics for combinations of electrode voltages that could not otherwise be

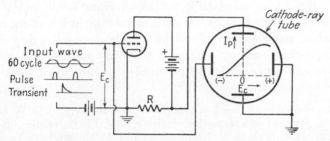

FIG. 7-13. Cathode-ray-oscillograph circuit for obtaining tube characteristics that extend into the positive-grid regions of interest in Class C amplifiers and in pulse operation.

sustained continuously for even a few seconds without permanent damage to the tube.   Thus the arrangement described above makes it a simple matter to extend characteristics into the part of the positive-grid region that is of such importance in Class C amplifier and linear-amplifier operation, but where the dissipation is too high to permit testing by static means.

In the case of pulse applications, tubes frequently reach combinations of control-grid and plate voltages where the instantaneous peak dissipation of power is so high as to require a lower duty cycle than that obtainable with Class C test procedures such as are outlined above.   Tube characteristics in these regions can be obtained by replacing the sinusoidal voltage in Fig. 7-13 by short pulses.   By making the tops of these pulses

[1] Cathode-ray arrangements of this general type have been described by various individuals.   In some cases considerable complexity is involved, as, for example, provision for automatically adding an increment to the fixed voltage after each characteristic curve is traced, so that a complete family of curves is obtained rather than a single curve.   For example, see Henry E. Webking, Producing Tube Curves on an Oscilloscope, *Electronics*, vol. 20, p. 128, November, 1947; Jacob Millman and Sidney Moskowitz, Tracing Tube Characteristics on a Cathode Ray Oscilloscope, *Electronics*, vol. 14, p. 36, March, 1941; Geoffrey Bocking, Tracing Valve Characteristics, *Wireless Eng.*, vol. 19, p. 556, December, 1942.

rounded, or by using triangular or saw-tooth pulses, but otherwise using the same arrangement as in the Class C method of testing, then a satisfactory delineation of the tube characteristic is obtained that extends to the extreme limit of the operating condition covered. Alternatively, characteristics under these conditions may be obtained by one-shot transient methods, as, for example, by precharging a condenser to the desired voltage, and then connecting it by means of a thyratron to one of the tube electrodes in place of the pulse, and recording the results on a cathode-ray tube (see Fig. 7-13).[1]

Oscillographic methods of recording tube characteristics are also useful in detecting and portraying anomalous features of tube behavior that would be difficult or impossible to detect from static point-by-point measurements. For example, in a beam tube in which there is a large space current, space-charge effects in the plate-screen region cause the plate-voltage–plate-current characteristic to possess discontinuities. Such effects can be very clearly pictured with the aid of a cathode-ray tube.

[1] Examples of equipment based on this general idea are given by O. W. Livingston, Oscillographic Method of Measuring Positive Grid Characteristics, *Proc. IRE*, vol. 28, p. 267, June, 1940; H. N. Kozanowski and I. E. Mouromtseff, Vacuum Tube Characteristics in the Positive Grid Region by an Oscillographic Method, *Proc. IRE*, vol. 21, p. 1082, August, 1933; J. Leferson, The Application of Direct-current Resonant-line Pulsers to the Measurement of Vacuum-tube Static Characteristics, *Proc. IRE*, vol. 38, p. 668, June, 1950. A somewhat different approach is described by H. M. Wagner, Tube Characteristic Tracer Using Pulse Techniques, *Electronics*, vol. 24, p. 110, April, 1951.

CHAPTER 8

AMPLIFIER MEASUREMENTS

8-1. Definition of Amplification and Gain. The most important characteristics of an amplifier are the amount of amplification that is developed, and the way in which this amplification varies with frequency. It is common practice to express the amplification, or gain as it is sometimes called, as a ratio of voltages or powers; very frequently this ratio is expressed by its decibel equivalent.

When the details of an amplifier are studied, it is found that there are several ways in which the amplification, or gain, can be defined. Thus consider the situation illustrated in Fig. 8-1a, which shows a multistage amplifier with input and output impedances Z_i and Z_o, respectively. The amplifier is excited by a signal voltage with internal impedance Z_s, and delivers its output to a load impedance Z_L. The numerical value of the ratio representing the amplification of this system then depends upon how one takes into account the impedances associated with the input and output terminals of the amplifier.

Voltage Amplification. The simplest and commonest approach is to define amplification (or gain) as the ratio of the voltages at two appropriate points in the amplifier. Thus the voltage gain of a single stage of amplification would be the ratio of voltages at successive grids, while the over-all voltage gain would be the ratio of the voltages across the output and input terminals. For example, if at a particular frequency in Fig. 8-1a, $E_2/E_1 = 40$, then one could say that the voltage amplification, or gain, between points aa and bb in the amplifier was 40, or 32 db.

This definition of gain as a voltage ratio is particularly convenient in connection with voltage amplifiers intended for use at audio frequencies, and also in voltage amplifiers for low or moderate radio frequencies, as, for example, intermediate-frequency amplifiers. In these cases, the load impedances at successive points in the amplifier consist of the input impedances supplied by the grids of the successive stages; these impedances represent small capacitances which at these frequencies are associated with negligible loss of power. Moreover, at low frequencies these capacitances can be considered as representing open circuits, while at radio frequencies they function as part of the tuning capacitances. Under these conditions, where the load impedances are effectively equivalent to open circuits, the voltage ratio is the important thing, and the concept of voltage amplification is both meaningful and helpful.

Insertion Gain. Consider the situation that would exist in Fig. 8-1a if Z_s represented the output impedance of a telephone line, a line from a microphone, or a radio-frequency transmission line, while Z_L was the input impedance of another line. In such a system the function of the amplifier is to make the power in the output line Z_L greater than would be the case if the two lines were connected directly together. Here one is

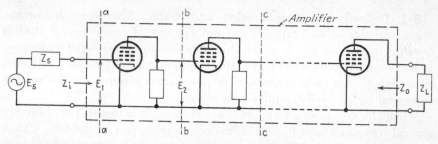

(a) Schematic representation of amplifier

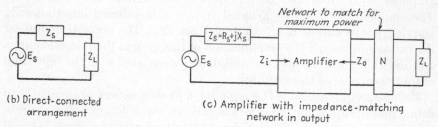

(b) Direct-connected arrangement

(c) Amplifier with impedance-matching network in output

Fig. 8-1. Multistage amplifier with source of excitation E_s and load impedance Z_L, together with circuit arrangements used in tests of amplifier characteristics.

interested in the *insertion gain* of the amplifier, *i.e.*, the increase in power or voltage that results from the insertion of the amplifier into the system.

The *insertion gain* is defined quantitatively as the ratio of the power P_2 (or voltage E_2) delivered to the output load impedance Z_L when the amplifier is inserted in the system as in Fig. 8-1a, to the power P_2' (or voltage E_2') that would be delivered to the load impedance if the generator and load were connected directly together, as in Fig. 8-1b. That is,

$$\text{Insertion power gain} = \frac{P_2}{P_2'} = \frac{|E_2|^2}{|E_2'|^2} \qquad (8\text{-}1a)$$

$$\text{Insertion voltage gain} = \frac{E_2}{E_2'} \qquad (8\text{-}1b)$$

$$\text{Magnitude of insertion voltage gain} = \sqrt{\frac{P_2}{P_2'}} \qquad (8\text{-}1c)$$

The insertion gain of an amplifier is clearly a function of the generator and load impedances, as well as of the actual components of the amplifier itself. A given amplifier will provide different values of insertion gain when connected to different generators, or to different loads. Thus when the insertion gain is specified, the generator and load impedances must also be specified at the same time. This is an unavoidable requirement and must be met squarely. It is, moreover, to be noted that the generator and load impedances may actually be complex impedances, rather than simple resistances. In the case of complex impedances, the load powers must be carefully computed, taking into account the reactive as well as the resistive components of the impedances involved.

Under certain circumstances the insertion voltage gain is equal to the voltage amplification as defined above. This is the case, for example, when the input and load impedances Z_i and Z_L of the amplifier are both large compared with Z_s and Z_o in Fig. 8-1a. This situation also exists in an audio-frequency amplifier, where the input impedance of the tube can be considered as approaching infinity, and in an intermediate-frequency amplifier, where the input capacitance of the tube can be regarded as part of the tuning capacitance that is required by the coupling circuit. Similar circumstances also occur in the case of a chain of identical amplifier stages; here the voltage amplification from the grid of one stage to the grid of the following stage is exactly the same as the insertion voltage gain possessed by the particular amplifier stage considered by itself.

Available Power and Available Power Gain. The definition of available power and available gain can be explained with the aid of Fig. 8-1c. Here the amplifier input is supplied by a source of power having an equivalent voltage E_s and an internal impedance $Z_s = R_s + jX_s$. Next designate by P_o the power that would be delivered by the amplifier output to a load impedance Z_L matched to the output impedance Z_o of the amplifier on a maximum-power-absorption basis with the aid of network N. This is the available output power of the amplifier. The available power gain is then

$$\text{Available power gain} = \frac{P_o}{P_s} \qquad (8\text{-}2)$$

Here P_s is the power that would be delivered by the signal generator with its internal impedance Z_s to a load impedance matched to Z_s on a maximum-power-absorption basis;[1] that is

$$P_s = \frac{E_s{}^2}{4R_s} \qquad (8\text{-}3)$$

---

[1] Impedances are matched for maximum transfer of power by making the load impedance the conjugate of the source impedance; *i.e.*, maximum power is absorbed by the load when the resistance component of the load equals the resistance component

This power P_s is the maximum possible power that E_s with its internal impedance $Z_s = R_s + jX_s$ can deliver to a load impedance, and is termed the *available input power*.

The available gain depends upon the characteristics of the amplifier and on the signal-generator resistance R_s, but is independent of the load impedance actually associated with the amplifier output. The concept of available power gain is of particular use in connection with signal-to-noise-ratio considerations in amplifiers, as discussed in Sec. 8-13.

8-2. Measurement of Amplification. Amplification (gain) is commonly determined with the aid of unmodulated single-frequency signals obtained from a signal generator. Signal generators for this purpose are

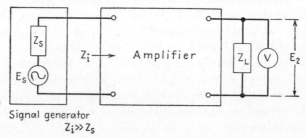

Signal generator
$Z_i \gg Z_s$

Fig. 8-2. Typical circuit arrangement for measuring voltage gain of an amplifier.

described in Sec. 15-7, and consist of a shielded oscillator and attenuator arranged either for producing accurately known adjustable voltages, or alternatively for producing different voltages whose ratios are accurately known.

Measurement of Voltage Gain. A typical arrangement for measuring the voltage gain of an amplifier is illustrated schematically in Fig. 8-2. Here a voltage derived from a signal generator is applied to the amplifier input terminals, and the resulting voltage developed across the output terminals is measured by means of a vacuum-tube voltmeter. The signal-generator voltage is adjusted so that the amplifier output voltage has a value which can be satisfactorily determined by the particular vacuum-tube voltmeter employed, and which at the same time is well above any hum or noise level and yet well below a value that will overload the amplifier. The resulting output voltage is measured, and a compari-

---

of the source impedance, and when simultaneously the reactive component of the load impedance is equal in magnitude and opposite in sign from the reactive component of the source impedance. Thus in Fig. 8-1c, the generator impedance $R_s + jX_s$ is matched on a maximum power-absorption basis when the load impedance is $R_s - jX_s$. Under these conditions the current delivered by the generator to the load is $E_s/2R_s$, and the power P_s dissipated in the load resistance is $P_s = E^2_s/4R_s$, which is Eq. (8-3).

son of this output voltage with the corresponding signal-generator voltage gives the voltage gain.

Where the signal generator is of the type that gives output voltages whose relative rather than absolute values are known, the procedure is first to observe the signal-generator voltage that when applied to the amplifier input gives a convenient reference deflection on the output vacuum-tube voltmeter. The signal generator is next connected directly to the vacuum-tube voltmeter, and is reset to give the same reference deflection. The ratio of the two signal-generator voltages is then obviously the voltage gain.

In measuring voltage gain as illustrated in Fig. 8-2, it is necessary to give some consideration to the impedances Z_s and Z_i associated with the signal generator and the input of the amplifier, respectively. In the very common case where the output impedance Z_s of the signal generator is very much less than the input impedance Z_i of the amplifier, the voltage at the input terminals of the amplifier can be considered as being the open-circuit voltage developed by the signal generator; this situation will be commonly encountered in amplifiers for audio and video frequencies, or for low and moderate radio frequencies. In other situations, it is possible that the amplifier has been designed to operate with a particular value of source impedance Z_s, with the interest being in the voltage gain from the source voltage E_s associated with this impedance, to the output voltage E_2 of the amplifier. In this case the signal generator must accordingly have an internal impedance equal to the particular value called for by the amplifier, or alternatively "padding" impedances must be used as explained in connection with Fig. 8-7. It is also possible to calculate the effect of Z_s and Z_i on the behavior of the system provided the magnitudes and phase angles of these impedances are known; however, if the source impedance used in the gain measurements does not have the design value, feedback effects may be altered.

The voltage gain obtained with the arrangement of Fig. 8-2 will be accurate only if the vacuum-tube voltmeter does not significantly alter the impedance between the terminals with which it is associated. If the vacuum-tube voltmeter does change this impedance, the amplification will obviously be affected, and the results will be in error. When the load impedance Z_L across which the vacuum-tube voltmeter is shunted is low or moderate, no trouble is generally encountered. However, when this load impedance is large, as is the case in audio-frequency and in tuned radio-frequency voltage amplifiers, then the vacuum-tube voltmeter used to measure output voltage will change the characteristics of the system unless (1) its input impedance is extremely high in comparison with the impedance across which it is shunted, or (2) the input impedance of the vacuum-tube voltmeter is incorporated into the load impedance Z_L so that the combination of vacuum-tube voltmeter and load actually present gives the load impedance with which the amplifier is intended to operate.

The first of these approaches can be satisfactorily used in measuring the gain of audio and video voltage amplifiers, provided the vacuum-tube voltmeter is of the diode type, and is arranged to have low input capacitance as discussed on page 18. The second approach to the problem is commonly used in connection with tuned amplifiers. Here the input capacitance of the vacuum-tube voltmeter, even if small, will detune the circuit; however, by readjusting the tuning capacitance one can recreate the same conditions with the vacuum-tube voltmeter present as exist in normal operation with the voltmeter removed. Alternatively, when the output voltage of the amplifier under test is applied to another stage of amplification, this stage can have its electrode voltages readjusted so that

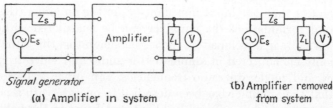

(a) Amplifier in system

(b) Amplifier removed from system

Fig. 8-3. Measurement of insertion gain by means of a signal generator and output voltmeter V.

it serves as a vacuum-tube voltmeter; in this way one is able to determine the output voltage of the amplifier that is under test while not altering the situation under which the amplifier operates.

Measurement of Insertion Gain. Typical methods of measuring insertion gain are illustrated in Figs. 8-3, 8-4, and 8-5. A choice among these will depend upon the frequency range, the power level, and the available equipment.

Considering first the arrangement illustrated in Fig. 8-3, the signal generator must have a source impedance Z_s equal to that with which the amplifier is intended to be used; if the available signal generator does not meet this requirement, its output impedance can be "padded" out to the required value, as discussed in connection with Fig. 8-7. Likewise the load impedance Z_L in combination with voltmeter V must provide the load impedance into which the amplifier is intended to operate. The measuring procedure is then as follows: The amplifier is first connected into the circuit as in Fig. 8-3a, and the signal-generator voltage E_s adjusted to provide a convenient amplifier output voltage which can be accurately indicated by voltmeter V, and which at the same time is well above the hum and noise level, and yet is not sufficiently great to overload the amplifier. The amplifier is next removed from the circuit, and the signal generator connected directly to the load impedance as in Fig. 8-3b, after which the signal-generator voltage is readjusted to a value E'_s that gives the same indication on V as before.   By definition,[1] the insertion voltage gain is then E'_s/E_s.   It will be noted that the accuracy of the result is determined only by the accuracy with which the ratio E'_s/E_s of the two signal-generator voltages is known; errors in the indication of meter V are of no significance, as this instrument merely need maintain constant sensitivity during the time consumed in making the measurement.   Thus, one may use an uncalibrated crystal-detector arrangement, or a diode vacuum-tube voltmeter at frequencies so high that transit-time errors are excessive.

At microwave frequencies it is not feasible to measure the load voltage directly; rather it becomes necessary to employ one of the bolometer power-measuring techniques described in Sec. 2-2.   A typical setup of

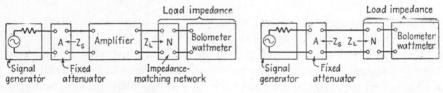

(a) Amplifier in system   (b) Amplifier removed from system

FIG. 8-4. Measurement of insertion gain by means of signal generator, and a bolometer wattmeter.

this type for measuring insertion gain is illustrated in Fig. 8-4.   The input to the amplifier is supplied by a microwave signal generator provided with an attenuator pad A of at least 10 db, as shown.   This attenuator is for the purpose of presenting a known source impedance of the proper value to the amplifier input, and at the same time of ensuring that the signal-generator output always operates into the same load impedance.   The output load impedance of the amplifier is supplied by the bolometer wattmeter in combination with an appropriate impedance-matching network N, such as a stub tuner.   This impedance-matching equipment enables the desired load impedance Z_L to be obtained; Z_L is commonly the impedance that matches the amplifier output on a maximum-power-absorption basis.   The measuring procedure is then analogous to that followed in the system in Fig. 8-3.   With the amplifier connected in the circuit as in Fig. 8-4a, the signal-generator voltage is set at a value E_1 which gives a convenient indication on the bolometer, and which at the same time does not overload the amplifier.   The signal generator and associated attenuator are next connected directly to the

---

[1] The definition in Eq. (8-1b) was stated for a constant generator voltage.   It is equally valid and frequently more convenient to maintain the output voltage constant.

load as in Fig. 8-4b, and the signal-generator output voltage readjusted to a value E_1' that gives the same bolometer reading as obtained before. The insertion voltage gain is then by definition E_1'/E_1.

A variation of the procedures involving Figs. 8-3 and 8-4 consists in maintaining the signal-generator output constant as the connection is changed from a to b, and then observing the resulting change in output voltage (or power). This procedure is entirely satisfactory in principle, but is used only to a limited extent because it is generally more difficult

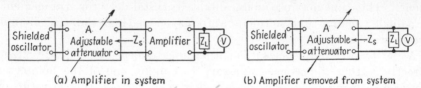

(a) Amplifier in system   (b) Amplifier removed from system

Fig. 8-5. Measurement of insertion gain by means of an adjustable attenuator.

to measure voltage (or power) ratio than it is to produce voltages (or powers) having a known adjustable ratio.

A third system for measuring insertion gain is illustrated in Fig. 8-5; here the signal generator of the previous arrangements is replaced by a well-shielded oscillator associated with an external adjustable attenuator A of constant input impedance. To measure insertion gain the amplifier is connected into the system as at a and the attenuator adjusted until a convenient output is obtained. The circuit is then reconnected with the

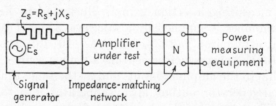

Fig. 8-6. Arrangement of apparatus for determining available power gain of an amplifier.

amplifier removed, as shown at b, and the attenuator readjusted to give the same output indication on V as before. The difference in the attenuator settings obviously represents the insertion gain of the amplifier.

The measurements described above provide only the magnitude component of the insertion voltage gain. The phase shift component is discussed in Sec. 8-5.

Measurement of Available Power Gain. The available power gain can be determined by the arrangement illustrated in Fig. 8-6. Here a signal generator which has a source impedance Z_s with a known resistance component R_s is applied to the amplifier input as shown. The amplifier output is then matched by network N on a maximum-power-absorption basis to a load impedance supplied by the output power-measuring equipment, typically a bolometer.   The available gain is then determined by adjusting the signal-generator voltage E_s to a convenient amplitude, and observing the available power output P_o.   The available input power P_s is next calculated with the aid of Eq. (8-3);[1] the available gain is then given by Eq. (8-2) as P_o/P_s.

Special Considerations Relating to Signal Generators.   The signal generator used in measuring amplification must be well shielded, and must be provided with a suitable attenuator, as discussed in Chap. 15. The signal generator can be calibrated in terms of the *absolute* value of open-circuit voltage, the voltage developed across a matching load resistance, or the available power; alternatively it can indicate *relative* output in terms of voltage, power, or decibels, relative to some arbitrary or perhaps unknown reference value.

The equivalent source impedance Z_s of the signal generator must be properly taken into account if errors are to be avoided.   In some cases, as in the measurement of voltage amplification at short-wave and lower frequencies, the source impedance Z_s is preferably very much lower than the input impedance of the amplifier under test.   In other cases, the source impedance Z_s of the signal generator must represent the impedance with which the amplifier system is designed to work.   Thus, in an amplifier that receives its input from a cable of 50 ohms characteristic impedance, then the source impedance Z_s of the signal generator should be resistive and have a value of 50 ohms.   If the available signal generators do not have the required value of source impedance, one can add a series impedance Z'_s as in Fig. 8-7a if the desired impedance Z is greater than Z_s.

On the other hand, if the desired source impedance Z is less than the impedance Z_s of the signal generator, one can shunt the output terminals by a suitable impedance Z'_s as illustrated in Fig. 8-7b.   In this case it is to be noted that the equivalent series voltage that is effective in the equivalent output circuit is less than the actual voltage E_s, as indicated in Fig. 8-7b.   Still another way of controlling the effective source impedance is to insert a fixed attenuator having 10 to 20 db attenuation in the signal-generator output as in Fig. 8-7c; in this arrangement the effective source impedance is the output impedance of the attenuator.[2]

[1] Some signal generators are calibrated directly in available output power P_s rather than in open-circuit output voltage E_s.   In this case, the signal-generator calibration gives directly the power delivered by the signal generator to a load matched for maximum power absorption.

[2] In this situation, the equivalent open-circuit output voltage of the combination is

$$E_s \frac{Z_A}{Z_s + Z_A} A$$

where Z_A is the input impedance of the attenuator and A is the voltage ratio produced by the attenuation.

At very high frequencies, the inductance and capacitance associated with the leads that connect the signal generator to the amplifier under test will in many circumstances cause the voltage actually applied to the amplifier input to differ from that generated by the signal generator.   It

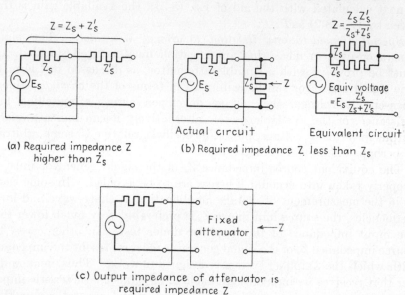

(a) Required impedance Z higher than Z_s (b) Required impedance Z less than Z_s

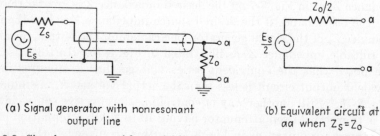

(c) Output impedance of attenuator is required impedance Z

FIG. 8-7. Methods of modifying and controlling the equivalent source impedance Z of a signal generator.

(a) Signal generator with nonresonant output line   (b) Equivalent circuit at aa when $Z_s = Z_0$

FIG. 8-8. Signal generator with coaxial line of characteristic impedance Z_0 for transmitting the signal-generator output voltage to terminals aa, together with equivalent output circuit.

is possible in this way for considerable error to be introduced when absolute rather than relative values of amplifier input voltage are required.   The usual method of avoiding lead errors of this character consists in transmitting the signal-generator output to the amplifier input terminals by means of a coaxial transmission line terminated in its characteristic impedance, as illustrated in Fig. 8-8.   The signal generator is preferably designed so that its source impedance Z_s equals the characteristic impedance Z_0 of this line. The transmission line in such an arrangement may have any reasonable length, and in effect transfers the output terminals of the signal generator to the receiving end of the line. When viewed from the terminals aa associated with the amplifier input, this arrangement (assuming $Z_s = Z_0$) is equivalent to a signal generator having an internal impedance equal to one-half the characteristic impedance of the line. This is because the signal-generator system when viewed from terminals aa consists of the line terminating impedance Z_0 shunted by the input impedance Z_0 of the nonresonant line. At the same time the equivalent output voltage of the system is equal to one-half of the open-circuit voltage of the signal generator, assuming the line to be lossless. The corresponding equivalent circuit is shown in Fig. 8-8b.

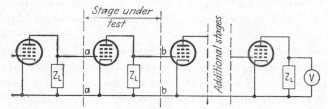

FIG. 8-9. Schematic diagram of multistage amplifier.

8-3. Special Aspects of Gain Measurement in Multistage Amplifiers.

Special problems are presented in the determination of the gain of an individual amplifier stage when this stage is one of a number of stages, comprising, for instance, a high-gain intermediate-frequency amplifier.

The procedure for determining the voltage amplification of an individual stage of a multistage amplifier can be understood with the aid of Fig. 8-9. A known voltage from a signal generator is first applied to the output lead bb of the stage under test by means of a probe that is shielded to minimize stray couplings which might cause regeneration. The signal-generator output is adjusted to a value E'_s such that meter V indicating the amplifier output gives a convenient deflection without overloading the amplifier. The signal-generator leads are then transferred to aa, and the signal-generator voltage readjusted to a value E''_s that causes meter V to give the same indication as before. The voltage gain of this stage is then E'_s/E''_s. When the stage under test has identical impedances associated with its input and output circuits, as would be the case if it were in a chain of identical stages, the voltage amplification obtained in this way is also equal to the insertion voltage gain of the stage.

This process of determining stage gain can be applied in succession to all stages of a multistage amplifier. Normally one would start at the output end of the amplifier, and work back stage by stage toward the input terminals. The results obtained in this way correspond to actual operation, since each stage operates into its normal load impedance and is subject to the same regenerative actions with respect to the stages of higher power level as in normal operation. Also, no shunt impedances are introduced that change the voltage-amplification characteristics. The fact that the signal generator has a low impedance compared with the impedance between terminals aa, bb, etc., across which it is connected has the effect of disabling the previous stages of the amplifier and of causing the signal generator to operate into what is essentially an open-circuit load across its terminals.

In making amplification measurements upon individual stages of a multistage amplifier it is absolutely necessary that no circuits of the amplifier be altered, and that all stages of amplification following the stage under test be in operation. Otherwise, regenerative effects will be changed.

The presence of regeneration in a multistage amplifier will greatly influence the results of the gain measurement, irrespective of whether the regeneration is a direct consequence of the measuring arrangement, or is inherent in the functioning of the amplifier. Regeneration will modify the magnitude of the gain (usually will increase it), and will change the shape of the response curve of amplitude as a function of frequency.

The presence of regeneration can readily be detected in the following manner:[1] A vacuum-tube voltmeter is connected to the output stage of the amplifier; if the amplifier is a complete receiver, the second detector of the receiver can serve as the voltmeter if provided with a meter to indicate the d-c output current. A signal generator is then loosely coupled between the plate of the last amplifier tube and ground, by means of a very small series capacitance that provides a high impedance. The signal-generator output is then set to a large value. If there is no regeneration, the indication on the output meter V (see Fig. 8-9) produced by the signal generator will then be uninfluenced by removing tubes or making other circuit changes in the stages *ahead* of the last one. On the other hand, if such actions cause a change in the vacuum-tube-voltmeter indication, then regeneration is present. The source of the regeneration can be readily isolated by short-circuiting the successive grids and plates to ground, commencing at the amplifier input. Any circuit where a regenerative effect is present can be identified by a change in voltmeter output when the short circuit is applied.

[1] This technique is described by E. C. Freeland, F-M Receiver Design Problems, *Electronics*, vol. 22, p. 107, January, 1949.

8-4. Use of Decibels to Express Relative Amplification. The variation of amplification with frequency in amplifiers is often expressed in decibels referred to some arbitrary level which is taken as zero decibels. The significance of such curves can be understood by considering what a decibel means. The decibel is a unit for expressing a power ratio and is given by the relation

$$\text{Decibels} = \text{db} = 10 \log_{10} \frac{P_2}{P_1} \qquad (8\text{-}4a)$$

The decibel has no other significance; and if it is to be used in expressing relative amplification, it therefore signifies power output as a function of

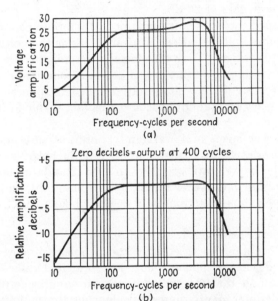

FIG. 8-10. Example showing how relative amplification can be expressed in decibels.

frequency with respect to some arbitrary reference power. Thus if the voltage amplification varies with frequency as shown in Fig. 8-10a, one might replot this curve in decibels by assuming some arbitrary power as the standard. This could, for instance, be the power output obtained at 400 cycles. The power output at any other frequency is then proportional to $(E/E_{400})^2$, where E is the voltage output at the frequency in question and E_{400} is the output voltage at 400 cycles. Since the power output under these conditions is proportional to the square of the voltage, one can rewrite Eq. (8-4a) as follows for this particular case:

$$\text{db} = 10 \log_{10} \frac{P_2}{P_1} = 10 \log_{10} \left(\frac{E}{E_{400}}\right)^2 = 20 \log_{10} \frac{E}{E_{400}} \qquad (8\text{-}4b)$$

It is now possible to plot a curve giving relative amplification in terms of decibels as is done at Fig. 8-10b. The significance of the decibel curve can be seen by considering a specific case. Thus the fact that the amplification in Fig. 8-10b is 5 db lower at 45 cycles than at 400 cycles means that the output power at 45 cycles is 0.316 times the power at 400 cycles.

From the foregoing it is seen that anything which increases or decreases the amplification can have its effect expressed in terms of decibels. Thus if one introduces an extra stage of amplification which increases the output voltage twenty times, then the gain in output power is 20^2, or 400, times, and this power ratio when substituted in Eq. (8-4a) is seen to represent a power gain of 26 db.

It will be noted the decibel is fundamentally a power unit. It cannot be used to express voltage ratios except in so far as the voltage ratios are related to power ratios. If two voltages are applied to identical resistances, then the resulting powers are, of course, proportional to the square of the voltages; but if the voltages are applied to different resistances, then it is necessary to take into account this fact if the decibel unit is to be employed.

Standard power levels of 1 watt and 1 milliwatt are finding popular acceptance, the latter in connection with radio receivers. Numerical values of decibel power ratios relative to these standard levels are designated by the abbreviation dbw for the 1-watt standard, and dbm for the 1 milliwatt level; thus -10 dbm is 10 decibels below 1 milliwatt, that is, 0.1 milliwatt.

8-5. Amplifier Phase Shift. Measurement of the phase shift introduced by an amplifier is essentially the problem of measuring phase difference, as discussed in Sec. 6-9. The principal difficulty involved arises from the fact that the two voltages whose relative phase is to be determined will differ greatly in magnitude when the gain of the amplifier is large. Successful measurement under these conditions depends upon obtaining from the signal-generator system a reference voltage having the same phase as the voltage applied to the amplifier input, but which is much larger in magnitude.

Any of the techniques described in Sec. 6-9 may be employed in the determination of amplifier phase shift; a typical example is illustrated in Fig. 8-11a. Here the combination of a shielded oscillator and resistive attenuator represents a signal-generator system that applies a small voltage E_s to the amplifier input, and simultaneously provides a much larger voltage E'_s for phase comparison. If the attenuator is resistive, it will introduce no phase shift of its own, and E'_s will have the same phase as E_s when the adjustable phase shifter is set at zero.

The relative phase of the reference input voltage E'_s and of the output voltage E_L is determined in Fig. 8-11a by adjusting the calibrated phase shifter S until these two voltages have the same phase. The phase shift introduced by S is then equal in magnitude but opposite in sign to the phase shift of the amplifier between points aa and bb.

The arrangement illustrated in Fig. 8-11a is capable of determining phase with good accuracy provided the two voltages E'_s and E_L to be compared have approximately the same magnitude, and also provided the attenuator introduces no phase shift (or a phase shift which is accurately known). It is not necessary that E'_s exactly equal E_L; neither is it necessary that the phase shifter be of a type that has no attenuation, nor that it possess an attenuation that does not change with phase shift.

The phase shift measured in Fig. 8-11a is the phase shift associated with the voltage amplification E_L/E_s between points aa and bb of the amplifier.

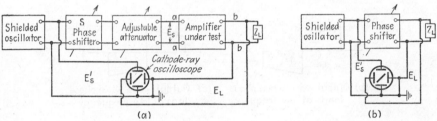

FIG. 8-11. Schematic diagram of arrangement for determining the phase shift of an amplifier.

It is sometimes desired to obtain the insertion phase shift. This can be done by first determining the phase shift ϕ_1 with the amplifier connected in the system as in Fig. 8-11a. Next, a determination is made of the phase difference ϕ_2 existing between E_L and E'_s with the amplifier and attenuator removed, as in Fig. 8-11b. The insertion phase shift is then $\phi_1 - \phi_2$.

8-6. The Use of Square Waves to Detect Low-frequency Deficiencies of Amplifiers. Useful information regarding the characteristics of an audio- or video-frequency amplifier can be gained by applying a low-frequency square wave to the amplifier input and observing the shape of the amplifier output wave that results. Thus phase distortion at low frequencies causes a tilt in a square wave having a low fundamental frequency, as illustrated in Fig. 8-12b and c. A phase error as low as 1° at the fundamental frequency of the square wave can be readily detected in this manner. If the response characteristic of the amplifier rises at low frequencies, then in the absence of phase distortion the output produced by a square wave will have a rounded top as in Fig. 8-12d; conversely if the low-frequency response falls, then the top of the output wave will be concave toward the axis as illustrated at e. When both phase and amplitude response defects are simultaneously present, then the output wave shows both a tilt and a curved top. Square-wave tests of this type are extensively used to check qualitatively the low-frequency characteristics of video amplifiers used in television and similar applications.[1]

When square waves are used to investigate the low-frequency characteristics of an amplifier, it is of course important that the low-frequency deficiencies of the cathode-ray oscilloscope used to observe the output of

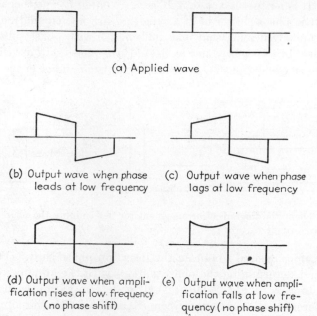

(a) Applied wave

(b) Output wave when phase leads at low frequency   (c) Output wave when phase lags at low frequency

(d) Output wave when amplification rises at low frequency (no phase shift)   (e) Output wave when amplification falls at low frequency (no phase shift)

Fig. 8-12. Effects produced upon a square wave by amplifier imperfections for idealized cases.

the amplifier under study be negligible in comparison with the deficiencies of the amplifier. The behavior of the cathode-ray oscilloscope in this regard can be determined by applying the square-wave directly to the oscilloscope input, and comparing the resulting wave shape with the wave shape of the amplifier output. If the cathode-ray oscilloscope shows significant but quite small amplitude or phase errors, then the true characteristic of the amplifier can be estimated by subtracting the tilts and curves produced by the oscilloscope alone from those observed in the output wave of the amplifier.

[1] A good discussion of the response of typical video amplifiers to a square wave is given by P. M. Seal, Square-wave Analysis of Compensated Amplifiers, *Proc. IRE*, vol. 37, p. 48, January, 1949.

8-7. Transient Response of Audio and Video Amplifiers. The response of an amplifier to a transient applied voltage can be completely formulated in terms of the response of the amplifier to a voltage having a shape corresponding to a step function.[1]   A step function is illustrated in Fig. 8-13a; it is characterized by having an amplitude of zero up to a given time, at which instant there is an abrupt transition to a finite amplitude which is then maintained for an infinite time.

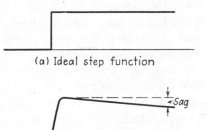

(a) Ideal step function

The deficiencies in the response of an amplifier to a step function can be defined in terms of rise time, sag, and overshoot.   These quantities are discussed and defined in Sec. 6-7, where also will be found a discussion of means for observing the waveform of the response on a cathode-ray oscilloscope. The response of a typical amplifier to a mathematically perfect step wave is illustrated in Fig. 8-13b and c. This response is characterized by an initial rapid but finite rate of change in output, resulting in a

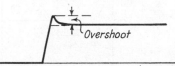

(b) Amplifier response illustrating sag and finite rise time

(c) Amplifier response illustrating overshoot in the absence of sag

Fig. 8-13. Ideal step function, together with responses showing sag, overshoot, and finite rate of rise.

definite rate of rise; thereafter the output drops off, or "sags."   In some cases, the initial response overshoots the proper value and then settles back either with or without oscillation.

The rise time is very nearly inversely proportional to the high-frequency limit of the amplifier.   If B is the amplifier bandwidth, *i.e.*, the frequency at which the response at high frequencies drops 3 db below the midrange response, then if the overshoot is not excessive, one find that

$$\left.\begin{array}{c}\text{Rise time, 10 to 90}\\ \text{per cent, in sec}\end{array}\right\} = \frac{k}{B} \qquad (8\text{-}5)$$

[1] "Vacuum Tube Amplifiers" (Vol. 18, Radiation Laboratory Series), Chap. 2, McGraw-Hill Book Company, Inc., New York, 1948; D. G. Tucker, Bandwidth and Speed of Build-up as Performance Criteria for Pulse and Television Amplifiers, *J. IEE* (*Radio Sec.*), vol. 94, pt. III, p. 218, May, 1947; H. E. Kallman, R. E. Spencer, and C. P. Springer, Transient Response, *Proc. IRE*, vol. 33, p. 169, March, 1945; A. V. Bedford and G. L. Fredendall, Transient Response of Multistage Video-frequency Amplifiers, *Proc. IRE*, vol. 27, p. 277, April, 1939; A. V. Bedford and G. L. Fredendall, Analysis, Synthesis and Evaluation of Transient Response of Television Apparatus, *Proc. IRE*, vol. 30, p. 440, October, 1942; R. D. Kell, A. V. Bedford, and H. N. Kozanowski, A Portable High-frequency Square-wave Oscillograph for Television, *Proc. IRE*, vol. 30, p. 458, October, 1942; P. M. Seal, *op. cit.*

Here k is a constant that depends to a slight extent upon the shape of the gain-frequency curve, but always lies between 0.35 and 0.45; the first of these two values applies when the overshoot is less than 5 per cent.   Sag depends upon the low-frequency response characteristics, and is particularly adversely affected by phase distortion at low frequencies. Overshoot is controlled by the shape of the response band of the amplifier, and particularly the sharpness of the high-frequency cutoff.   A gradual cutoff eliminates overshoot, or at least minimizes it.

The simplest means of producing a step function experimentally is by the use of square waves or pulses.   A square wave can be considered as a succession of equally spaced, alternately positive and negative step functions, as illustrated in Fig. 8-14a.   Similarly, a rectangular pulse may be regarded as an unsymmetrical square wave, and so is equivalent to a suc-

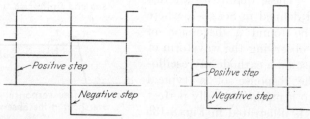

(a) Square wave and equivalent steps   (b) Pulses and equivalent steps

Fig. 8-14.   Diagram illustrating how a square wave and a pulse wave represent a succession of alternating positive and negative steps.

cession of alternately positive and negative step functions with unequal spacing, as illustrated in Fig. 8-14b.

Transient Response by Means of Square Waves.   A straightforward method of determining the transient response of an amplifier consists in applying a square wave to the amplifier input and observing the wave shape of the output on a cathode-ray oscilloscope having an accurately calibrated time axis.   This is equivalent to applying a succession of alternately positive and negative steps.

In order to measure rise time accurately in this way the time interval occupied by the rise of the response to a step must be an accurately measurable distance along the time axis of the oscilloscope.   In practice this requires that the time represented by a cycle of the square wave be not too long in comparison with the rise time of the amplifier, *i.e.*, the square-wave frequency must be relatively high.   Also, it is necessary that both the square-wave generator and the cathode-ray oscilloscope involved have rise times that are much smaller than that of the amplifier under test, *i.e.*, not over 0.2, and preferably less than 0.1 as great.   If the rise times of the square-wave voltage and the cathode-ray oscilloscope are small but not negligible, they can be taken into account by means of the correction given in Eqs. (6-12a).

Overshoot and sag behavior can be determined similarly by scaling off time intervals and amplitudes from the oscilloscope pattern. In investigating overshoot, the time interval represented by the full length of the time axis must be relatively small to observe much detail in most cases of overshoot. In connection with sag, much longer time intervals are usually involved, and a square-wave test signal of lower fundamental frequency is called for.[1] If the determination of sag is to be accurate, it is of course necessary that the sag of the square wave used for testing, and also of the oscilloscope amplifiers, be small compared with the sag of the amplifier under test. If the sag of the square-wave and the oscilloscope is small but not negligible, then an approximate correction may be made by the following rule that when the sag is small all sags add directly. Thus if for a given time interval the total observed sag is 20 per cent, but the sag of the square-wave test voltage is 3 per cent, and that of the oscilloscope amplifier is known to be 5 per cent, then the actual sag introduced by the amplifier in this time interval will be approximately 12 per cent.

A square-wave generator in which the frequency is adjustable and accurately known, is particularly useful for determining the percentage sag in a specified time interval, and also the time of rise.

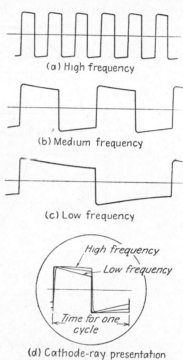

(a) High frequency

(b) Medium frequency

(c) Low frequency

(d) Cathode-ray presentation

Fig. 8-15. Effect upon the sag of decreasing the frequency of a square wave, together with cathode-ray presentations in which the time base representing one cycle is the same for different frequencies.

With such a square-wave generator, the time measurements involved can be obtained in terms of the frequency of the square wave, without requiring calibration of the sweep voltage of the cathode-ray oscilloscope. Thus as the frequency of the square wave is reduced, the amount of sag that takes place per half cycle increases, as shown in Fig. 8-15, because of the greater time interval represented by a half cycle of lower frequency. Accordingly, the time for any specified amount of sag

[1] It is to be noted that the "tilt" indicating a leading low-frequency phase error in Fig. 8-12b is an example of sag.

to occur, as for example 20 per cent, can be determined by adjusting the frequency until the amplitude drops off a corresponding amount by the end of the half cycle.   The time interval in which this amount of sag takes place is then the time for a half cycle, or $1/2f_0$ seconds, where f_0 is the frequency of the square wave.   In carrying out a determination of sag time in this way, it is customary to synchronize the cathode-ray sweep with the square-wave frequency so that the length of the sweep

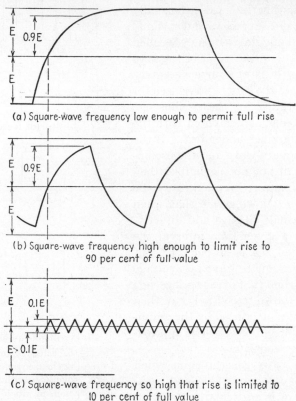

(a) Square-wave frequency low enough to permit full rise

(b) Square-wave frequency high enough to limit rise to 90 per cent of full·value

(c) Square-wave frequency so high that rise is limited to 10 per cent of full value

Fig. 8-16.   Effect of increasing the frequency of a square wave, when the rise time is not negligible compared with the length of time of a half cycle.

represents the same number of cycles, irrespective of the frequency of the sweep.   This causes the cathode-ray presentation of the situation to have the character illustrated in Fig. 8-15d.

In an analogous manner, the rise time can be determined by observing the effect on the output wave of increasing the frequency of the square wave.   If the square-wave frequency is so high that the full output amplitude is not achieved before the end of a half cycle of the square wave, then the peak-to-peak amplitude is less than the value for a low-frequency square wave.   This is illustrated in Fig. 8-16.   When the

square-wave frequency has a value f_{90} such that the peak-to-peak amplitude is 90 per cent of the full amplitude (see Fig. 8-16b), then the time
required for the transient voltage to rise to 90 per cent of the full amplitude is $1/2f_{90}$.   Similarly, at the frequency f_{10} such that the peak-to-peak
amplitude is 10 per cent of the full amplitude (see Fig. 8-16c), then the
time required for the output to reach 10 per cent of its full value is $1/2f_{10}$.
The rise time, when defined as the time required for the amplitude to
rise from 10 per cent to 90 per cent of the full value, is accordingly
$1/2f_{90} - 1/2f_{10}$.

Transient Response by Pulse Testing.   Rectangular-shaped pulses of
short duration are frequently used to determine the transient response
of an amplifier, as an alternative to square waves.   When the signal to be
handled by an amplifier consists of pulses, the response to a rectangular
test pulse then gives directly the characteristics that are of greatest
importance.   Another advantage of pulse testing is that it is often possible
to generate pulses having a short rise time and short duration more easily
than a square wave of the same rise
time.   This is particularly the case
when large amplitudes are desired, as
then the average power required in a
pulse generator can be made substantially smaller than that of a square-
wave generator.

A typical response of an amplifier
to a pulse is illustrated in Fig. 8-17.
Rise time, sag, overshoot, and undershoot can all be obtained from a
cathode-ray presentation of the am-

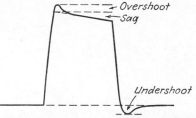

Fig. 8-17. Typical response of an
amplifier to an applied rectangular
pulse, showing finite rate of rise, overshoot, sag, and undershoot.

plifier output by suitable calibration of the time axis.   It is necessary,
of course, that the cathode-ray oscilloscope have a rise time, sag, undershoot, and overshoot that are small compared with those of the amplifier
under test, as discussed in Sec. 6-7.

The pulse used in determining the transient response of an amplifier
must have a shape closely approximating the ideal rectangular pulse, *i.e.*,
the rise time, sag, overshoot, and undershoot of the pulse must be small
compared with those of the amplifier under test.   Pulses for testing purposes are commonly obtained from specially designed pulse generators
that include provision for varying the length and repetition frequency of
the pulse (see Sec. 13-7).   The amplitude of the pulse applied to the
amplifier can be controlled by a suitable attenuator.   In many cases such
an attenuator is provided as an integral part of the pulse generator, thus
giving a pulse signal generator in which the pulse amplitude can be set to a
known value.

Impulse Tests of Amplifiers and Networks.[1] Useful information regard-ing the characteristics of an amplifier or network can be obtained by applying to the input a pulse that is very short compared with the rise time of the system under test, and then observing the resulting output

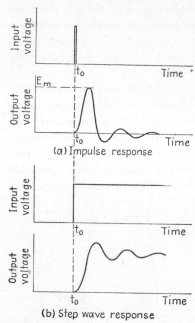

wave on a cathode-ray oscilloscope. If the length of such a test pulse is very small compared with the rise time of the system under investigation, then the shape of the response depends only on the characteristics of the system under test, and is not affected by the exact shape of this pulse. The magni-tude of the response is, however, pro-portional to the area under the pulse, which therefore defines the "equivalent strength" of the pulse. Such an ap-plied wave is often called an *impulse* function.

The response of an amplifier or net-work to an impulse function is the time derivative of the response to a step function. Thus both the impulse and step response contain the same infor-mation, and one can derive the response to a step, square wave, or pulse from the impulse response, and vice versa.

The response of a typical video amplifier to a very short impulse is

(a) Impulse response

(b) Step wave response

Fig. 8-18. Response of a typical video amplifier to a very short im-pulse, and corresponding response to an ideal step function.

shown in Fig. 8-18. Since the output waveform corresponds to the derivative of the step-function response, the maximum height of the impulse response to a pulse of given equivalent strength is proportional to the *maximum rate of rise* of the response to a square wave or pulse. Likewise the area[2] under the impulse curve (when parts below the zero

[1] E. C. Cherry, Pulse Response: A New Approach to A. C. Electric Network Theory and Measurement, *J. IEE*, vol. 92, pt. III, p. 183, September, 1945; D. C. Espley, E. C. Cherry, and M. M. Levy, The Pulse Testing of Wide-band Networks, *J. IEE*, (*Radiolocation Conv.*), vol. 93, pt. IIIA, p. 1176, March–May, 1946, also *Proc. IEE* pt. III, p. 186, May, 1949; M. Levy, The Impulse Response of Electrical Networks, with Special Reference to the Use of Artificial Lines in Network Design, *J. IEE*, vol. 90, pt. III, p. 153, December, 1943; W. W. Hansen, Transient Response of Wide-band Amplifiers, *Proc. Natl. Electronics Conf.*, vol. 1, p. 544, 1944.

[2] If this area is designated as A in units of volts times microseconds, then the quotient A/E_m is the rise time in microseconds according to one possible definition of rise time, where E_m is the peak response to the impulse voltage. The rise time speci-

axis are taken as negative areas) up to a time t is proportional to the amplitude of response to a square wave or to a pulse at time t.   These relations are illustrated in Fig. 8-18.

In practice, square waves or pulses are usually employed in determining the transient response in preference to impulses.   This is because square waves and pulses give the shape of the response wave directly rather than indirectly.   Also, it is often difficult to generate impulses that are short compared with the rise time of the system under test.   However, the impulse method of testing is useful in that it directly determines the maximum rate of rise of the response to a pulse or square wave.

8-8. Nonlinear Distortion in Audio-frequency Amplifiers. *General Considerations.*   In an ideal amplifier, the amplified output is exactly proportional to the input signal; thus if the signal is a sine wave, the output would likewise be a sine wave.   An actual amplifier, however, always departs to some extent from this ideal.   As a result, a sine-wave signal will tend to produce an output that is a distorted sine wave.   This action is termed nonlinear distortion, and sets a practical limit to the output obtainable from an amplifier.

The principal effect of nonlinear distortion is to cause the amplified output to contain frequency components not present in the signal applied to the amplifier.[1]   Thus when the applied signal is a sine wave, nonlinear distortion will cause the output to contain harmonics of this input frequency, particularly the second and third harmonics.   Again, if the applied signal consists of two sine waves of different frequencies f_1 and f_2, then nonlinear distortion will cause the output to contain harmonics of these frequencies (*i.e.*, components having frequencies $2f_1$, $2f_2$, $3f_1$, $3f_2$, etc.), sum- and difference-frequency components $f_1 + f_2$ and $f_1 - f_2$, respectively, and higher order combination frequencies such as $2f_1 \pm f_2$ and $f_1 \pm 2f_2$.   In practical cases the second harmonics, and the sum and difference frequencies, are usually most pronounced; these are sometimes called quadratic effects.   Third harmonics, and second-order combination frequencies such as $2f_1 \pm f_2$, are termed cubic effects, and are next in importance.

Additional consequences of nonlinear distortion are cross modulation and nonproportionality between amplifier input and output voltages.

---

fied in this way corresponds to the time of rise that would be required if the response to a pulse or squarewave rose from zero to maximum amplitude at a steady rate of rise.   This definition of rise time leads to a numerical result that in most cases approximates quite closely to the rise time defined as the time interval between the 10 and 90 per cent levels.

[1] Methods of analyzing the nonlinear distortion introduced by vacuum tubes are considered at some length by F. E. Terman, "Radio Engineering," 3d ed., pp. 268–284, McGraw-Hill Book Company, Inc., New York, 1947.

These phenomena are ordinarily of importance only in tuned amplifiers, and are discussed further in Sec. 8-9.

The ultimate evaluation of the practical significance of nonlinear distortion in audio systems must be based upon listening tests.   This causes the situation to be very complex, as the results of listening tests depend not only upon the nonlinear characteristics of the amplifier, but also upon the character of the sound being reproduced, upon the acoustics of the space in which the sound is observed, and on psychological factors which differ

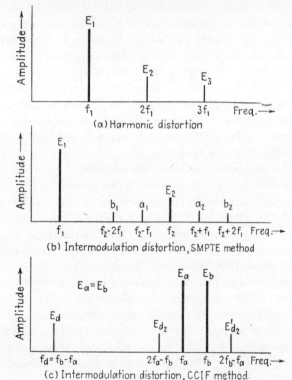

(a) Harmonic distortion

(b) Intermodulation distortion, SMPTE method

(c) Intermodulation distortion, CCIF method

Fig. 8-19. Frequency relations existing in harmonic and intermodulation tests of distortion.

from person to person.   The result is that there is no entirely satisfactory method of objectively defining the nonlinear distortion introduced by an audio amplifier, and several different test methods are in common use.

Harmonic Methods of Determining Nonlinear Distortion.   One method of measuring nonlinear distortion consists in applying a sine wave to the input of the amplifier, and observing the harmonics that are present in the output.   The relationship of the fundamental frequency and the harmonics under such a condition is illustrated in Fig. 8-19a.   In this situation the distortion can be defined by the relation

$$\left.\begin{array}{l} \text{Harmonic distortion,} \\ \text{per cent} \end{array}\right\} = \frac{\sqrt{E_2{}^2 + E_3{}^2 + \cdots}}{E_1} \times 100 \qquad (8\text{-}6)$$

Here E_1 is the amplitude of the fundamental-frequency component of the output, and E_2, E_3, etc., are the amplitudes of the harmonic components (see Fig. 8-19a).[1]   In theory, an infinite number of harmonics are possible, but in practice the second and third usually account for nearly all of the distortion that is present.

The amplitudes of the various frequency components of the output wave can be individually determined with the aid of a wave analyzer such as is described in Sec. 6-4.   Alternatively, the necessary data for determining the harmonic distortion can be obtained by a fundamental-suppression type of distortion meter, as discussed on page 247.

The harmonic distortion of an audio-frequency amplifier will depend upon the frequency of the test voltage.   If this frequency is more than half the high-frequency limit of the amplifier, the observed distortion will tend to be small even though nonlinear effects are present.   This is because under these conditions the harmonics represent frequencies that are not fully reproduced by the amplifier output circuit.   In the middle range of frequencies, the harmonic distortion is usually found to be largely independent of the exact test frequency.   However, when the test frequency is so low as to have a value for which the amplifier response tends to fall off appreciably, the harmonic distortion for a given output voltage will commonly increase.   This is because at low frequencies the load impedance of the amplifier output circuit ordinarily departs from the optimum value; in addition the amplifier does not reproduce a low fundamental frequency as well as it does the harmonics of this low frequency.

Intermodulation Method of Measuring Nonlinear Distortion (SMPTE *Method*).[2]   A second method of measuring nonlinear distortion consists in simultaneously applying two sine-wave voltages of different frequencies to the amplifier input, and observing the sum, difference, and various combination frequencies that are produced by the nonlinearity of the amplifier.   This approach to the problem of evaluating distortion is called the *intermodulation method*.

---

[1] Sometimes it is convenient to replace E_1 in the denominator of Eq. (8-6) with E_0, the rms value of the output voltage [see Eq. (6-11)], particularly when the fundamental suppression type of distortion analyzer is employed.   The resulting effect on the numerical value of the distortion is significant only when the distortion is unusually large.

[2] See John K. Hilliard, Intermodulation Testing, *Electronics*, vól. 21, p. 123, July, 1946; Distortion Tests by the Intermodulation Method, *Proc. IRE*, vol. 29, p. 613, December, 1941; George Daniel, Instrument for Intermodulation Measurements, *Electronics*, vol. 21, p. 134, March, 1948; Arnold Peterson, Measurement of Nonlinear Distortion, *Gen. Rad. Expt.*, vol. 25, March, 1951.

While two signal frequencies may be combined under many different conditions, two cases merit particular attention.   In the first of these, a low-frequency test signal, and a high-frequency test signal of somewhat smaller amplitude, are simultaneously applied to the amplifier.   If non-linear effects are present, then the amplification that the high-frequency component f_2 experiences will vary at the frequency f_1 of the low-frequency signal, as illustrated in Fig. 8-20.   Thus the wave of frequency f_2 in the amplifier output will be modulated at the low frequency f_1.   The amount of distortion is then expressed in terms of this modulation experienced by the high-frequency wave, according to the relation[1]

$$\left.\begin{array}{l}\text{Intermodulation dis-}\\ \text{tortion (SMPTE method),}\\ \text{per cent}\end{array}\right\} = 100\ \sqrt{m_1{}^2 + m_2{}^2 + \cdots} \qquad (8\text{-}7a)$$

Here m_1 is the degree of modulation that the output component of frequency f_2 experiences at frequency f_1, and m_2 is the corresponding modulation of f_2 at frequency $2f_1$.

This particular method of employing two signals to determine nonlinear distortion is widely used in audio-frequency systems associated with sound-picture installations.   It is commonly referred to as the SMPTE intermodulation method, since it has been standardized by the Society of Motion Picture and Television Engineers.[2]

Apparatus for determining intermodulation by the SMPTE method is illustrated schematically in Fig. 8-21.   The system for combining the outputs of the two signal generators may take any one of a number of forms, such as a transformer with center-tapped primary, or two amplifier

---

[1] An alternative method of explaining this situation is to consider that the nonlinear action of the amplifier produces sum and difference frequencies $f_1 + f_2$ and $f_2 - f_1$, respectively.   These frequency components, together with f_2, can be thought of as representing side bands and a carrier, respectively, thus forming a wave of carrier frequency f_2 modulated at the frequency f_1.   If the nonlinear distortion is sufficient also to produce second-order combination frequencies $f_2 + 2f_1$, the modulation envelope then contains a component that is the second harmonic of f_1, that is, the modulation envelope is not sinusoidal.

The relation of these various frequency components is illustrated in Fig. 8-19b. In terms of them the intermodulation distortion can be quantitatively defined as

$$\left.\begin{array}{l}\text{Intermodulation dis-}\\ \text{tortion (SMPTE method),}\\ \text{per cent}\end{array}\right\} = 100\ \frac{\sqrt{(a_1 + a_2)^2 + (b_1 + b_2)^2 + \cdots}}{E_2} \qquad (8\text{-}7b)$$

Here E_2, a_1, a_2, b_1, and b_2 are the amplitudes of the various frequency components, as illustrated in Fig. 8-19b.   Since a_1 and a_2 form one pair of side bands, and $b_1 + b_2$ form a second pair, Eq. (8-7b) is an alternative form of Eq. (8-7a).

[2] American Standard Method of Making Intermodulation Tests on Variable-density 16-millimeter Sound Picture Prints, *J. SMPTE*, vol. 46, p. 303, April, 1946.

tubes with separate inputs and a common output load impedance.   Alternatively, it is possible to use a two-frequency signal generator specially designed for intermodulation tests.[1]   The network N_1 separates the

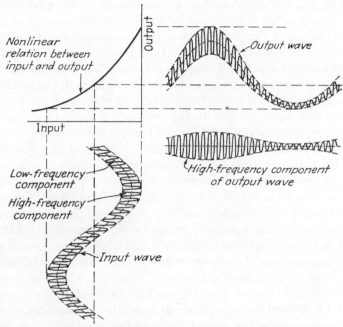

FIG. 8-20. Diagram showing how a nonlinear relationship between input and output will result in modulation of a high-frequency component of the input wave by the low-frequency component of this wave.

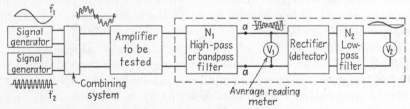

FIG. 8-21. Block diagram of apparatus for determining intermodulation distortion by the SMPTE method, together with waveforms present in different parts of the system.

high frequency f_2 and its side bands from the other frequency components that may be present in the amplifier output.   Voltmeter V_1 measures the *average* amplitude of this resulting modulated wave, *i.e.*, it meas-

[1] Such a signal generator is described by A.P.G. Peterson, An Audio Frequency Signal Generator for Non-linear Distortion Tests, *Gen. Rad. Expt.*, vol. 25, p. 1, August, 1950; H. H. Scott, Audible Audio Distortion, *Electronics*, vol. 18, p. 126, January, 1945.

ures the carrier amplitude E_2 in Fig. 8-19b. The modulation component of the envelope is then determined by rectifying the modulated wave, separating the modulation-frequency component of the envelope by low-pass filter N_2, and determining the amplitude of the modulation component by voltmeter V_2. It will be noted that the apparatus inside the dotted rectangle in Fig. 8-21 represents a system for measuring the characteristics of a modulated wave. Calibration can be carried out by applying known voltages[1] of frequencies f_1 and f_2 to terminals aa.

In a measuring system such as illustrated in Fig. 8-21, the usual practice is to make the low-frequency test signal four times as large as the high-frequency test signal applied to the system. A value of the order of 60 to 100 cycles is ordinarily used for the low frequency, while the high frequency is typically 5000 cycles or higher. Network N_2 should have a bandwidth sufficient to pass second-order side bands, i.e., a cutoff frequency greater than $2f_1$; network N_1 must have a corresponding bandwidth, i.e., a value in excess of $4f_1$. Voltmeter V_1 must be of the average-reading type; a copper-oxide rectifier instrument is quite satisfactory. Voltmeter V_2 is ideally a square-law device, but an average-reading meter such as a copper-oxide rectifier instrument will give results that are accurate enough to meet ordinary requirements. In no case should a peak reading meter be used for V_2, however.

The numerical value of the intermodulation distortion determined by the SMPTE method depends primarily upon the nonlinearity encountered by the low-frequency test signal, because this signal is much the larger under the standard test conditions. The observed intermodulation distortion is largely independent of the value of the higher frequency f_2, but can be expected to depend at least to some extent on the value of f_1, particularly when f_1 is low enough to be in the region where the amplifier response is falling off.

Intermodulation Method of Measuring Nonlinear Distortion (CCIF *Method*).[2] In the second method of carrying out an intermodulation test, the two test signals have equal amplitudes, and relatively high but slightly different frequencies. When nonlinear distortion is present, a difference-frequency component appears in the output and is used as a measure of the amount of distortion present. The situation is illustrated in Fig. 8-19c, where f_a and f_b represent the two test frequencies of amplitudes E_a and E_b, and E_d is the amplitude of the resulting difference frequency component

---

[1] The most direct means of carrying out the calibration procedure consists in giving E_1 the value to be used in the intermodulation test, and then adjusting E_2 with the aid of V_1 so that $E_2 = 0.1E_1$. The resulting deflection of V_2 will then correspond to 10 per cent intermodulation distortion.

[2] A good discussion of intermodulation tests of this type is given by H. H. Scott, *loc. cit.*

f_d.* The intermodulation distortion is expressed quantitatively by the relation

$$\left.\begin{array}{l}\text{Intermodulation distortion} \\ \text{(CCIF method), per cent}\end{array}\right\} = \frac{E_d}{E_a + E_b} \times 100 \qquad (8\text{-}8)$$

This form of intermodulation test has been recommended by the International Telephonic Consultative Committee, and is ordinarily referred to by the initials CCIF.

Apparatus for carrying out intermodulation tests by the CCIF method is illustrated schematically in Fig. 8-22. The difference-frequency component E_d is separated by low-pass filter N, and indicated separately by voltmeter V_2. The amplitudes of the test-frequency signals E_a and E_b

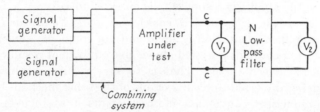

Fig. 8-22. Apparatus for carrying out intermodulation tests by the CCIF method.

appearing in Eq. (8-7) can be determined with the aid of voltmeter V_1; if V_1 is a peak-reading instrument, then the peak voltage observed at terminals cc will approximate very closely the peak value of $E_a + E_b$. Alternatively, E_a and E_b can be determined individually if test voltages of frequencies f_a and f_b are applied one at a time to the input terminals of the amplifier under test, and the resulting values observed on V_1.† In carrying out an intermodulation test by the CCIF method, the test frequencies f_a and f_b are generally centered toward the high-frequency end of the response range, and sometimes are purposely placed in the region where the high-frequency response is beginning to fall off appreciably. The difference $f_d = f_b - f_a$ between the two test frequencies is commonly a moderately low value, such as 60 to 200 cycles. This difference frequency should not be so small as to be below the normal low-frequency response

---

* Second-order combination frequencies E_{d2} and E'_{d2} are also shown in Fig. 8-19c, and are a measure of the cubic type of distortion; however, these components can be detected only by the use of a highly selective wave analyzer, and are generally not made use of in this form of intermodulation test.

† Both of these procedures involve approximations as a result of failing to allow for other frequency components that are simultaneously present at terminals cc as a result of distortion in the amplifier. If an exact determination of E_a and E_b is desired, it is necessary to employ a wave analyzer with good selectivity to measure these components individually. However, the approximate procedure is adequate for most practical applications.

range of the amplifier, as then the amplifier circuits tend to suppress the difference-frequency output.

Values of intermodulation distortion observed by the CCIF method are indicative of the nonlinear distortions present in the system in the frequency region of f_a and f_b. In particular, the CCIF method is able to measure the consequences of the nonlinear distortion present at the upper frequency limit of the amplifier where the high-frequency response is beginning to fall off.

The observed value of intermodulation distortion is substantially independent of the exact value of the difference frequency $f_d = f_b - f_a$ of the two test signals provided this difference is a small fraction of the test frequencies, and provided further that f_d does not fall in the frequency range where the amplifier response falls off substantially.

Comparison of the Different Methods of Measuring Nonlinear Distortion. When the nonlinear distortion is small and not frequency-dependent, all three measuring methods outlined above give equivalent results and there is no choice between them. That is to say, results obtained by one method can be converted to results of one of the other methods by the use of proper numerical conversion factors. Thus if a single-ended (*i.e.,* not push-pull) amplifier is tested under these conditions, and the *same total peak output voltage* is developed by the amplifier in all three test conditions, then the results of Eqs. (8-7) and (8-8), respectively, will be 3.2 and 0.5 times the value obtained from Eq. (8-6).[1]

However, when the nonlinear distortion is different at different frequencies, then the experimental results obtained by the three different methods will no longer be directly related, and the correlation with listening tests will also not be identical. This is because the harmonic method directly observes the extent to which a sine wave of a particular frequency is distorted, whereas in the intermodulation method attention is directed to the distortion that results from the interaction of different frequencies. In the SMPTE intermodulation method, the emphasis is placed on the effects produced on the high-frequency components of the signal by strong low-frequency signals when nonlinear effects are present at low frequencies. In contrast, the CCIF method emphasizes the low-frequency distortion components resulting from nonlinear distortion of the higher frequency components of a complex signal.

These different types of distorting action have different psychological effects upon a listener. Since all three actions are simultaneously present when a complex sound wave is being amplified, no one method can possibly provide a numerical value that will correlate exactly with listening tests under a wide variety of conditions. In general, if a single test is to be

[1] See W. J. Warren and W. R. Hewlett, An Analysis of the Intermodulation Method of Distortion Measurement, *Proc. IRE,* vol. 36, p. 457, April, 1948.

made, an intermodulation test is usually more useful than a harmonic-distortion test. However, to obtain a reasonably complete picture of the nonlinear behavior of a system, it is necessary to make both types of intermodulation tests, and in each case to use several combinations of test frequencies. If a harmonic test is to be made, it should in general be repeated for several different fundamental frequencies, at least one of which should correspond to the low frequency of the intermodulation test by the SMPTE method.

The level of distortion that is tolerable in audio-frequency systems depends on the nature of the audio sounds involved, and upon a variety of psycho-acoustic factors. About 1 per cent harmonic distortion can usually be detected by a listening test, but before harmonic distortion becomes serious it must be greater than about 10 per cent. Even larger values of harmonic distortion can be tolerated if the distortion is mainly at frequencies below 100 cycles or above 4000 cycles. Inter-modulation as determined by the SMPTE method cannot be detected until it has exceeded about 10 per cent provided the low-frequency tone is below 100 cycles; however, if the low-frequency tone is of the order of several hundred cycles, intermodulation distortion as low as 3 to 4 per cent can be detected in a listening test. Intermodulation as determined by the CCIF method can be detected at levels of a small fraction of 1 per cent in a listening test, and becomes objectionable at a value of 3 to 4 per cent when the difference-frequency lies in the range 400 to 5000 cycles, which is where the ear is most sensitive.

8-9. Special Considerations Involved in Tests of Tuned Amplifiers. The term "tuned amplifier" denotes an amplifier in which the load impedance in the plate circuit is supplied by a resonant circuit, or a combination of resonant circuits. A tuned amplifier is characterized by high gain over a limited range of frequencies, combined with a strong discrimination against frequencies lying outside of this range. Tuned amplifiers are used for the amplification of radio-frequency and intermediate-frequency signals, and are an essential part of every radio receiver.

The general discussion on measurement of amplifier gain and phase shift as given in Secs. 8-1 to 8-5 is fully applicable to tuned amplifiers as well as all other types of amplifiers. Also, many of the standard tests commonly made on radio receivers are essentially tests of the characteristics of the tuned amplifiers in the receiver. Accordingly, the discussion in this section will in large measure be limited to presenting a summary of the important features of tuned amplifier tests. Cross references to other portions of this book will be depended upon to provide many of the details.

Gain Characteristics of Tuned Amplifiers. The most important single characteristic of a tuned amplifier is the amplification (gain) as a function of frequency. A typical example of the gain characteristic of a multistage tuned amplifier is given in Fig. 8-23. The features of greatest practical interest are the amplification at the resonant or center frequency, the useful bandwidth, the shape of the amplification curve in the vicinity of resonance, and the discrimination against frequencies differing appreciably from resonance (the so-called "off-channel selectivity").

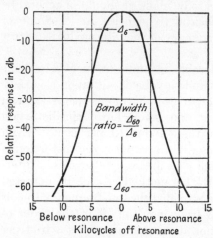

FIG. 8-23. Typical response characteristic of a multistage tuned amplifier, showing bandwidths corresponding to a reduction in response of 6 db and 60 db.

The gain of an amplifier can be measured by the use of a signal generator, following one of the procedures outlined in Sec. 8-2. In carrying out the measurement, it is necessary to be particularly careful that the measuring apparatus does not alter the impedance relations or the regeneration in such a way as to modify the amplification.

Shape of Response Curve by the Use of a Sweeping Oscillator. The shape of the response characteristic near resonance can be obtained by determining the gain at a number of frequencies. Alternatively, a sweeping oscillator, such as discussed on page 501, may be used in conjunction with a cathode-ray oscillograph to give a visual presentation of the shape of the response curve.

A typical test arrangement using a sweeping oscillator is shown schematically in Fig. 8-24a. The oscillator frequency is shown as being varied by a modulating voltage, which is preferably a saw-tooth wave. The modulating voltage is also applied to the horizontal-deflecting plates of the cathode-ray oscilloscope on which the amplifier characteristic is to be displayed. In this way the horizontal position of the spot on the cathode-ray screen is a function of the radio frequency applied to the amplifier under test, *i.e.*, the horizontal axis can be calibrated in terms of frequency.

The amplifier output may be applied directly to the vertical-deflecting electrode of the cathode-ray oscilloscope. This gives a pattern, such as illustrated in Fig. 8-24b, in which the envelope represents relative output as a function of frequency provided the amplitude of the radio-frequency voltage applied to the amplifier input is independent of the frequency. Alternatively, the amplifier output may be first applied to a detector, and the resulting rectified output used to produce vertical deflection of the cathode-ray oscilloscope. In this case the pattern observed is the envelope, as shown in Fig. 8-24c.

A calibration of the frequency scale can be obtained in several ways. Qualitative results may frequently be obtained from the characteristics of the sweeping generator. A more precise indication of frequency is obtained by employing markers to indicate points on the frequency scale that correspond exactly to frequencies that are accurately known.

One method of providing these markers is indicated schematically in Fig. 8-24, and consists in loosely coupling an absorption wavemeter to the

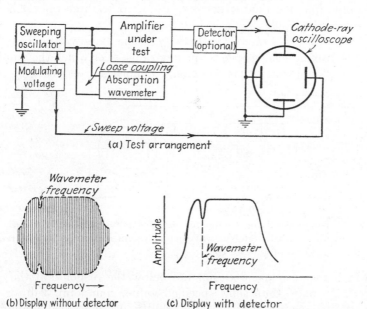

Fig. 8-24. Sweeping-oscillator arrangement for determining shape of response characteristic. The particular system shown involves an absorption wavemeter that is used to introduce a notch that gives a frequency marker.

sweeping oscillator. Each time the oscillator frequency sweeps through the frequency at which the wavemeter is resonant, the resulting absorption of energy causes the output of the sweeping generator to dip as shown. By tuning the wavemeter over the frequency range covered by the sweeping oscillator, a complete calibration of the sweep is possible. Wavemeters for this purpose are sometimes provided as an integral part of the sweeping oscillator, particularly in the case of sweeping oscillators designed for the higher frequencies.

Another method of providing a frequency marker is illustrated schematically in Fig. 8-25. Here a very small amount of energy derived from the amplifier output is combined in a mixer with the output of a heterodyne wavemeter (*i.e.*, oscillator with frequency calibration). The mixer output is then passed through a low-pass filter. Each time the frequency of the sweeping oscillator passes through the frequency of the heterodyne wavemeter, the filter output delivers a pulse having a length equal to the time it takes the frequency of the sweeping oscillator to traverse $2f_0$ cycles, where f_0 is the bandwidth of the low pass filter. This pulse thus marks the instant when the sweeping oscillator has a frequency coinciding with that of the heterodyne wavemeter. The pulse can be used as a frequency marker in any one of several ways; for example, one possible method of employing the marker is to use it to brighten the oscilloscope trace, giving the result shown in Fig. 8-25.

Bandwidth and Off-channel Selectivity. The bandwidth of a tuned amplifier represents the usable frequency range over which the amplification is fairly uniform. It is commonly defined as the frequency range

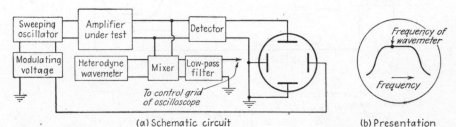

(a) Schematic circuit   (b) Presentation

FIG. 8-25. Sweeping-oscillator system for presenting response characteristic of an amplifier, together with heterodyne-wavemeter system for introducing a frequency marker consisting of a brightened spot.

over which the response does not fall below the response at the center frequency by more than some specified value, commonly 3 db or 6 db.

The off-channel selectivity is the ability of the tuned amplifier to discriminate against signals differing appreciably in frequency from the center frequency of the amplifier response characteristic. The commonest means of expressing off-channel selectivity is as the ratio of the bandwidth of the amplifier when the amplification is 60 db less than at resonance, to the bandwidth of the amplifier system when the amplification is 6 db less than at resonance, as illustrated in Fig. 8-23. This ratio is termed the *bandwidth ratio* or *selectivity ratio;* multistage amplifiers will typically have a value of bandwidth ratio of the order of 2.5 to 5.

In broadcast work, where channels are spaced 10 kc apart, there is particular interest in the discrimination against signals in the channel adjacent to the one for which the amplifier is tuned. This property is termed *adjacent-channel selectivity,* and can be defined as the ratio of the amplification at the resonant frequency of the amplifier, to the amplification at a frequency 10 kc different from this resonant frequency.

The off-channel, or the adjacent-channel, selectivity of a tuned amplifier is measured experimentally in the same manner as is the off-channel
selectivity of a radio receiver (see Sec. 9-3). That is, as the signal-
generator frequency departs from resonance, the signal-generator voltage
applied to the amplifier input is increased in such a manner as to maintain
constant output.

*Nonlinear Distortion in Tuned Amplifiers (Cross Modulation and Cross-
talk).* The most important consequence of nonlinear distortion in tuned
amplifiers is cross-talk (also called cross modula-
tion). Other effects possible are (1) an amplification that varies with amplitude of the signal,
thus causing a distortion of the envelope of
modulated waves; (2) intermodulation between
two strong signals lying outside of the response
range of the amplifier which produces a distortion component having a frequency lying within
the response range. Because of the narrow
response band of tuned amplifiers, harmonics
and sum and difference frequencies of signals
within the response band all lie outside of the
range of frequencies that are amplified, so are of
little importance.

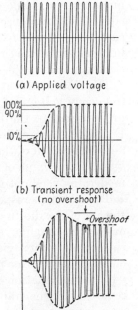

(a) Applied voltage

(b) Transient response
(no overshoot)

(c) Transient response
(with overshoot)

Fig. 8-26. Typical tran-
sient response of a tuned
amplifier, showing cases
with and without over-
shoot.

These various consequences of nonlinear distortion in tuned amplifiers are the same as the
corresponding effects discussed in Sec. 9-5, in
connection with radio receivers, where details as
to measurement are given.

**8-10. Transient Response of Tuned Ampli-
fiers.**[1] When a radio-frequency voltage is suddenly applied to a tuned amplifier, the response
of the output builds up to a final value in the
manner illustrated in Figs. 8-26 and 8-28. The
transient response of the amplifier is defined as
the envelope of this build-up curve.

When the frequency of the applied voltage closely approximates the
center frequency of the response band of the amplifier, as is the case in
Fig. 8-26, the transient response is similar in character to that observed

[1] Discussions of the transient behavior that can be expected from tuned amplifiers
under different conditions, with particular reference to the relationship between ampli-
fier design and transient behavior are given in "Vacuum Tube Amplifiers," *op. cit.*,
Chap. 7; Tucker, *loc. cit.*; Transient Response of Tuned Circuit Cascades, *Wireless
Eng.*, vol. 23, p. 250, September, 1946; C. C. Eaglesfield, Carrier-frequency Amplifiers,
Wireless Eng., vol. 22, p. 523, November, 1945, vol. 23, p. 67, March, 1946.

with an audio or video amplifier. In fact, there is a one-to-one cor-respondence between the transient behavior of an untuned amplifier, and the transient behavior of an amplifier having a transmission character-istic representing the low-pass analogue of the response characteristic of the tuned amplifier.[1] Thus the transient response of the tuned amplifier first rises rapidly, and then settles down to the steady-state value in a manner that is sometimes asymptotic, and sometimes characterized by overshoot. The exact behavior depends upon the bandwidth of the amplifier, the shape of the response band, the sharpness of cutoff at the edge of the response band, and the phase-shift characteristic. In any case, the principal features of the transient characteristic can be described in terms of the rise time and overshoot; these have the same definition and significance as in the case of audio and video amplifiers (see Sec. 8-7).

The rate at which the response of a tuned amplifier rises when a radio-frequency voltage of resonant frequency is suddenly applied is inversely proportional to the bandwidth, just as in the video amplifier. In fact Eq. (8-5) also applies to tuned amplifiers provided B is defined as the 3-db bandwidth of the gain characteristic of the amplifier. The quantity k then has a value of 0.7 if the overshoot is small or zero, and up to 0.9 if moderate overshoot is present.

The transient response of a tuned amplifier is ordinarily obtained with the aid of a radio-frequency voltage that is modulated by a square wave or by a rectangular pulse. The resulting amplifier output produced by this signal is then viewed on a cathode-ray oscilloscope employed as an envelope viewer (see page 263), in which the sweep voltage is synchronized with the modulation of the signal. Such an arrangement gives a periodic repetition of the transient, and permits continuous viewing. A suitable experimental arrangement is illustrated schematically in Fig. 8-27. The signal generator may be of any convenient type which can be modulated by a square wave or pulse. The modulation is essentially of the on-off type in which alternate half cycles of a square wave turn the oscillations on and off; in the case of pulse modulation, the wave is on only during the pulse. The modulation in all cases should be as nearly rectangular as possible. The amplifier output can be applied directly to the vertical-deflecting electrodes of the cathode-ray oscilloscope, or alternatively one may rectify the amplifier output and apply the rectified voltage to the vertical electrodes after amplification (see page 263).

When the frequency of the square-wave modulating voltage is adjust-able over a wide range, it is possible to determine rise time in terms of the frequency calibration of the square-wave generator, in analogy with Fig. 8-16. The idea is to increase the frequency until the peak amplitude is

[1] This assumes that the bandwidth is a small fraction of the center frequency, and that the tuned-amplifier gain characteristic is symmetrical about the center frequency.

first reduced to 90 per cent and then to 10 per cent of full amplitude of response obtained under steady-state conditions. The rise time is then determined from the time intervals represented by the half cycles of the square waves involved. Alternatively, one may obtain the same information by using a pulse-modulated wave in place of the square-wave modulation, and varying the pulse length instead of the repetition frequency.

Transient Response with Detuned Test Frequency. When making tests of the transient behavior of tuned amplifiers it is necessary to pay close attention to the relationship between the frequency of the test voltage and the center frequency of the amplifier response curve. When the test

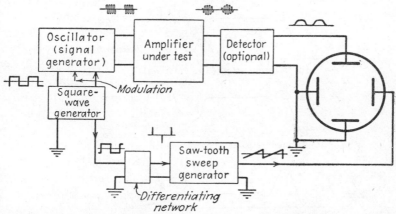

Fig. 8-27. Arrangement of apparatus for obtaining transient response of a tuned amplifier.

and center frequencies are approximately the same, the transient response has the character illustrated above in Fig. 8-26b and c, and also in Fig. 8-28b; this can be thought of as the normal situation. However, if there is a difference between the test and center frequencies that is of the same order of magnitude or greater than the reciprocal of the rise time of the amplifier, then the envelope of the transient response is greatly modified in shape, as shown in Fig. 8-28c and d. In particular, a damped radio-frequency oscillation is present which has a frequency corresponding to the center frequency of the circuit. This oscillation combines with the applied frequency, causing the envelope amplitude to pulsate at a frequency equal to the difference between the center frequency of the circuit and the test frequency. In the particular case where the test frequency has a value such that the steady-state response of the amplifier to this frequency is much less than the steady-state response to the center frequency, then there will initially be a large transient amplitude which ultimately settles down to a smaller steady-state amplitude as shown in Fig. 8-28d. This effect is particularly prominent in multistage tuned amplifiers.

Detuned operation also modifies the decay transient that occurs when the test voltage is suddenly removed. This decay transient is then no longer the mirror image of the building-up transient; in addition, its frequency is the center frequency of the amplification curve rather than the

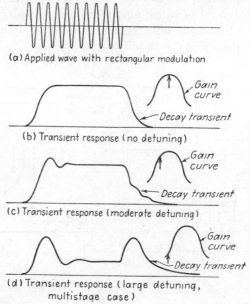

(a) Applied wave with rectangular modulation

(b) Transient response (no detuning)

(c) Transient response (moderate detuning)

(d) Transient response (large detuning, multistage case)

FIG. 8-28. Transient response of a tuned amplifier to a pulse-modulated wave, showing the effect of detuning the applied wave from the center frequency of the response curve. These response curves give the envelope of the actual wave.

frequency of the test voltage. Again, if the response to the test frequency is much less than the response to the center frequency, then the decay transient has a correspondingly larger amplitude than the steady-state response, as illustrated in Fig. 8-28d.

All of these considerations make it important that the difference between the test frequency and the center frequency of the tuned amplifier be less than one-fifth to one-tenth of the reciprocal of the rise time of the amplifier if the response obtained is to represent the true transient response of the circuit. Test frequencies detuned by greater amounts from the center frequency should be used only when investigating the effect of detuning upon the transient response.

Transient Response to a Sudden Change in Frequency. The transient response to a sudden change in frequency has an importance in frequency-modulation systems corresponding to the importance in amplitude-modulation systems of the transient response resulting from a sudden change in amplitude.[1]

The transient response to a sudden change in frequency can be measured in a manner analogous to the arrangement of Fig. 8-27. The only differences are (1) that the square-wave modulating voltage is applied to a reactance tube that shifts the frequency of the signal generator output back and forth between two values, and (2) that the amplified output of the system is applied to a frequency-modulation detector, the output of which is applied to the vertical-deflecting electrode of the cathode-ray oscilloscope. The transients observed in this way when the input wave is frequency-modulated are very similar in character to those observed when the input wave is amplitude-modulated.

Use of Impulses and Short Pulses. Impulse excitation of a tuned amplifier is obtained when the applied voltage is an impulse having a length short compared with a half cycle of the center frequency. Under such conditions the envelope of the response corresponds to the impulse response of a video amplifier, as discussed in connection with Fig. 8-18.

A typical example of such an impulse response, together with the equivalent envelope, is given in Fig. 8-29. It will be noted by comparing c and d of Fig. 8-29 that for each value of time t_1, t_2, etc., at which the envelope passes through zero amplitude, the equivalent sign of the

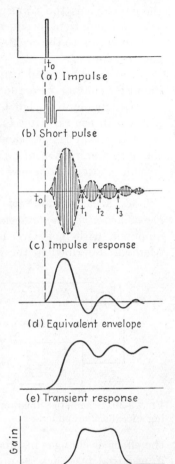

(a) Impulse

(b) Short pulse

(c) Impulse response

(d) Equivalent envelope

(e) Transient response

(f) Amplitude response to sine waves

FIG. 8-29. Response of a tuned amplifier to an impulse, and to a very short modulated pulse.

envelope is reversed. The shape of the envelope of the impulse response of a tuned amplifier is determined only by the characteristics of the amplifier, and is independent of the exact shape of the impulse. As in the corresponding video case, the peak amplitude of the envelope of the

[1] The theory of such transients is discussed by C. C. Eaglesfield, Carrier-frequency Amplifiers, *Wireless Eng.*, vol. 23, p. 96, April, 1946; H. Salinger, Transients in Frequency Modulation, *Proc. IRE*, vol. 30, p. 378, August, 1942.

impulse response is proportional to the maximum rate of rise of the transient response characteristic of the amplifier; likewise, the integral of the envelope is the transient response (see Fig. 8-29e).   The radio-frequency oscillations produced by the impulse response have a frequency corresponding to the center frequency of the response characteristic of the tuned amplifier.

An alternative, and usually more practical, means of obtaining the impulse behavior in a tuned amplifier, is to employ a pulse-modulated radio-frequency test signal, in which the length of the pulse is small compared with the rise time of the amplifier (see Fig. 8-29b).   If the carrier frequency that is thus modulated approximates the center frequency of the amplifier response band, then the envelope of the resulting radio-frequency oscillations has exactly the same shape as though an impulse had been used.

8-11. Measurement of Feedback Factor of Feedback Amplifiers. *Fundamental Concepts Regarding Feedback.*   Under normal conditions, an amplifier with negative feedback behaves like any other amplifier. Methods described in the preceding sections for measuring steady-state and transient behavior therefore apply equally well to amplifiers with negative feedback as to other amplifiers.[1]

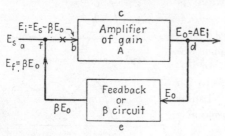

FIG. 8-30. Schematic diagram illustrating a feedback amplifier.

The presence of negative feedback does, however, influence the characteristics possessed by the amplifier.   Specifically, negative feedback reduces nonlinear distortion, modifies the response as a function of frequency, minimizes the effect of changes in tube characteristics, reduces the gain, etc.   Also, if negative feedback is not properly handled, it may be the cause of oscillation; alternatively, the possibility of oscillation may limit the amount of negative feedback that may be employed.

The nature of negative feedback can be explained with the aid of Fig. 8-30.   Here an amplifier of gain A delivers an amplified output voltage E_o when a signal E_s is applied as shown.   A fraction β of the output voltage E_o is superimposed upon E_s in such a manner as to be nominally in phase opposition to E_s.   The actual voltage E_i applied to the input terminals of the amplifier is accordingly the difference between the applied signal E_s and βE_o.   It is this difference voltage $E_i = E_s - \beta E_o$ that when amplified A times gives an amplified output voltage E_o.

---

[1] A summarizing discussion of amplifiers incorporating negative feedback, including the properties and the design of such systems, is given by Terman, *op. cit.*, pp. 311–326.

The effect that the presence of feedback produces in a system such as illustrated in Fig. 8-30 can be expressed in terms of the quantity $A\beta$. Thus, the voltage amplification from point a to point d is given by the relation

$$\text{Amplification with feedback} = \frac{\text{Amplification } A \text{ in the absence of feedback}}{1 - A\beta} \tag{8-9a}$$

Similarly the effect on nonlinear distortion is

$$\text{Distortion with feedback} = \frac{\text{Distortion in the absence of feedback}}{1 - A\beta} \tag{8-9b}$$

In each case it will be noted that the effect of the feedback that has been added to the amplifier is determined by the quantity $A\beta$. Measurement of $A\beta$ is accordingly of fundamental importance in determining the properties of a system involving feedback. The quantity $A\beta$ represents the transmission around the closed loop $bcdef$ in Fig. 8-30, i.e., if a voltage E_i is applied across the input to the amplifier at point b, then the feedback voltage βE_o superposed on this input voltage is $A\beta$ times as large as E_i.

The addition of negative feedback to an amplifier always introduces the possibility of oscillation. This arises from the fact that although the feedback may be negative in the normal frequency range of the amplifier, phase shifts exist at high and low frequencies, and under unfavorable conditions can transform what was negative feedback in the normal range of frequencies to positive feedback at other frequencies. If this positive feedback is sufficiently large in magnitude, the system will then oscillate.

To avoid all possibility of oscillation, it is necessary that the transmission $A\beta$ around the feedback loop be less than unity when the phase of $A\beta$ becomes 180° different from the phase corresponding to negative feedback. That is, no oscillations will occur if at any frequency where the negative feedback has changed to positive feedback, the transmission around the feedback loop $bcdef$ in Fig. 8-30 is less than unity. If the transmission is more than unity under these conditions, then a small voltage that starts circulating around and around the feedback loop will become progressively larger on each round trip, and oscillations will be established.

The behavior of the feedback factor $A\beta$ is often presented in the manner illustrated in Fig. 8-31a, which is known as a Nyquist diagram. Here values of $A\beta$ for frequencies from zero to infinity are plotted on the complex plane. If the resulting curve does not enclose the point 1,0, then oscillations will not be generated;[1] however, the closer the curve repre-

---

[1] This is true even when the curve representing $A\beta$ has the character illustrated in Fig. 8-31c, where 1, 0 is not enclosed even though $A\beta$ is greater than unity under

sented by $A\beta$ comes to the point 1,0, the nearer the system approaches an oscillating condition, *i.e.*, the lower the stability. Thus, in Fig. 8-32, curve 1 corresponds to a relatively stable system; however, if $A\beta$ is increased by increasing the amplification A to give conditions correspond-

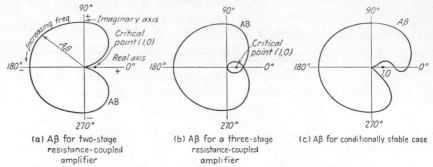

(a) $A\beta$ for two-stage resistance-coupled amplifier

(b) $A\beta$ for a three-stage resistance-coupled amplifier

(c) $A\beta$ for conditionally stable case

FIG. 8-31. Feedback characteristics for various conditions.

ing to curve 2, the system is then on the verge of oscillation. If the amplification is still further increased so that $A\beta$ is represented by curve 3, oscillation will be present. Further, when the point 1,0 is almost but not quite inclosed in the $A\beta$ diagram, then the amplification of the feedback

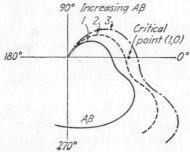

FIG. 8-32. Behavior of the feedback factor $A\beta$ as it is increased by increasing the amplification A.

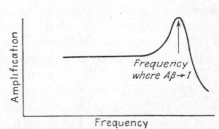

FIG. 8-33. Amplifier characteristic showing response peak existing at a frequency where the feedback factor $A\beta$ is positive and approaches unity.

system as given by Eq. (8-9a) will show a pronounced peak in response at frequencies corresponding to points on the $A\beta$ curve which are close to the critical point, 1,0. This is illustrated in Fig. 8-33, and results from the fact that then $|1 - A\beta|$ is appreciably less than unity.

---

conditions corresponding to positive feedback. This special case is known as "conditional stability"; when it exists, a reduction in the amplification of the system will cause oscillation to start up since a reduction in A will reduce $A\beta$, thereby causing 1, 0 to be enclosed.

Measurement of Feedback Factor Aβ.   The above discussion makes it apparent that the effects introduced by negative feedback can best be determined by making a measurement of the transmission $A\beta$ around the feedback loop *bcdef* in Fig. 8-30.   It is necessary that both the magnitude and phase of this transmission be determined, and that the measurement extend from very low to very high frequencies.

To measure the transmission $A\beta$, one reduces the signal voltage E_s in Fig. 8-30 to zero, opens the circuit at point x, applies a voltage E_i to the amplifier input at the right-hand side of x, and observes the magnitude of the voltage $E_f = \beta E_o$ that is thereby developed to the left of x.   Then

$$A\beta = \frac{E_f}{E_i} \qquad (8\text{-}10)$$

The actual procedure for carrying out the measurement of $A\beta$ is the same as would be followed in determining the magnitude and phase of voltage amplification, with E_i being considered as the input voltage, and $E_f = \beta E_o$ being regarded as the output voltage.

In measuring the feedback factor $A\beta$ in this way, it is necessary that opening the feedback loop at x should not alter the impedance conditions in the system.   That is, opening the loop should not affect either the amplification A of the amplifier, or the fraction β of the output voltage E_o that is fed back and superimposed upon the input when the loop is closed.

In cases where it is not possible to open the loop at the input to the main amplifier without disturbing the circuit characteristics excessively, it is permissible to open the loop at some other point.   An example of this is shown in Fig. 8-34, where the feedback is obtained by passing the load current through the cathode resistor R_1.   In this example it would be more convenient to open the loop at the point a shown in the figure.   The input voltage E_i would then be supplied by a signal generator, and the output voltage E_f would be indicated by voltmeter V as shown in Fig. 8-34. There is also added a small capacitance C' such that C' in combination with the voltmeter input capacitance and the plate-ground capacitance C_0 of T_1 equals the normal shunting capacitance C that is present at a in Fig. 8-34a.   Omission of this capacitance would result in test conditions at high frequencies that differ from those actually existing in the amplifier.

8-12. Noise in Amplifiers—Fundamental Concepts.   The weakest signal that can be usefully amplified is limited by randomly varying voltages and currents existing in the circuits and tubes of the amplifier. These voltages and currents are referred to as *noise;* their behavior and measurement are thus of fundamental importance in amplifiers which are to be used with weak signals.

Resistance Noise.   Every electrical conductor produces an irregularly varying voltage across its terminal as a result of the random motion of the free electrons in the conductor caused by thermal action.   This effect is referred to by such names as *thermal noise, resistance noise,* and *Johnson*

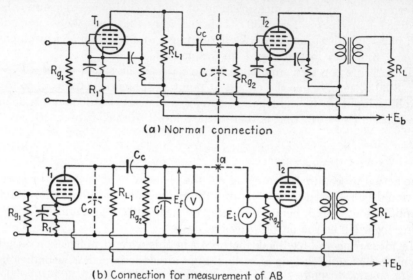

(a) Normal connection

(b) Connection for measurement of AB

FIG. 8-34. Feedback amplifier in which the feedback factor $A\beta$ can be most readily measured by opening the amplifier at point a.

noise.   The magnitude of this noise voltage associated with a resistance is[1]

$$\left.\begin{array}{l}\text{Square of rms value of voltage com-}\\ \text{ponents lying between frequencies } f_1 \text{ and}\\ f_2\end{array}\right\} = e_n{}^2 = 4kT \int_{f_1}^{f_2} R\,df \quad (8\text{-}11a)$$

where k = Boltzmann's constant = 1.374×10^{-23} joule per °K

T = absolute temperature, °K

R = resistance component of impedance across which the thermal agitation is produced (a function of frequency)

f = frequency

In the special case where the resistance component of the impedance is constant over the range of frequencies from f_1 to f_2, Eq. (8-11a) reduces to the much simpler form

$$e_n{}^2 = 4kTR(f_2 - f_1) = 4kTRB \qquad\qquad (8\text{-}11b)$$

Here $B = f_2 - f_1$ is the bandwidth of the noise.

The mean-square voltage $e_n{}^2$ is the *average* value of the square of the randomly varying noise voltage.   The length of time over which an

---

[1] Certain types of resistors will have a noise voltage in excess of that given by Eqs. (8-9) when a direct current is passed through them.   This phenomenon is discussed further in Sec. 14-5.

average must be taken to obtain a value substantially independent of time depends upon the width of the band B; it is greater the narrower this band, having a value in seconds that is a few times the reciprocal of the bandwidth in cycles.

It is important to note that Eq. (8-11a) shows that the mean-square noise voltage $e_n{}^2$ developed across a resistance is proportional to the bandwidth B, and is independent of the center frequency of the band. This means that the mean-square noise voltage developed across a given resistance in a frequency band from 1000 to 2000 cycles is exactly the same as the mean-square noise voltage developed in any other band of the same width, as for example from 1,001,000 to 1,002,000 cycles. The effective value of the noise voltage e_n observed across a resistance is proportional to the *square root* of the bandwidth of the noise being observed.

If the noise voltage e_n developed across a resistance is amplified by an ideal amplifier that introduces no noise itself and has a response independent of frequency, then the noise *energy* in the amplifier output will be proportional to the bandwidth B of the noise under investigation, and independent of the center frequency of this band. That is to say, the noise energy developed by a resistance is uniformly distributed over the frequency spectrum. Such noise is sometimes referred to as "white" noise, in analogy with the fact that white light represents a mixture of light of different frequencies.

Although a given value of resistance will generate noise that is uniformly distributed with respect to frequency, the uniform distribution may be modified by the circuits associated with the resistor. For example, shunting such a resistance by a capacitance will cause the noise voltage observed across the terminals of the resistance to decrease with increasing frequency. This is a result of the short-circuiting effect of the capacitance at the higher frequencies, and is taken into account in Eq. (8-11a) by the fact that the capacitance causes the resistance component of the impedance across the resistor terminals to decrease with increasing frequency. Thus, although a noise source will commonly generate noise that is uniformly distributed with frequency, the observed noise will vary with frequency in accordance with the transmission or amplification curve to which the noise originally generated is subjected before observation.

A resistance R and its associated noise voltage e_n may be represented by the equivalent circuit given in Fig. 8-35a. Here the noise voltage is represented by an equivalent generator e_n, and the resistance R is regarded as being noise-free.

It follows from the equivalent circuit of Fig. 8-35a and Eq. (8-11b), that if a resistance is short-circuited, the mean-square noise current $i_n{}^2$ that flows through the short circuit has the value

$$\left.\begin{array}{c}\text{Mean-square}\\\text{noise current}\end{array}\right\} = i_n{}^2 = \frac{e_n{}^2}{R^2} = \frac{4kTB}{R} \qquad (8\text{-}12)$$

This noise current behaves in exactly the same way as the noise voltage e_n in so far as distribution with frequency, and the effect of bandwidth, are concerned.

A concept termed *available noise power* is sometimes useful in dealing with sources of noise. The available noise power represents the noise power that would be delivered to the load resistance R_L in the equivalent

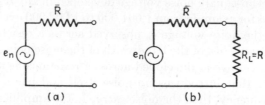

(a)   (b)

FIG. 8-35. Equivalent circuits used in dealing with thermal noise.

circuit of Fig. 8-35b, where $R_L = R$, and where the equivalent noise voltage e_n is the value given by Eq. (8-11b) for a resistance R. From this definition it follows that

$$\left.\begin{array}{c}\text{Available noise power}\\\text{from resistance } R\end{array}\right\} = \frac{e_n{}^2}{4R} = kTB \qquad (8\text{-}13)$$

It will be noted that the available noise power associated with a resistance is independent of the magnitude of the resistance generating the noise, and depends only upon the bandwidth and absolute temperature.

The concept of available noise power, although useful, is purely mathematical, since it assumes that the load resistance R_L does not have resistance noise associated with it. Thus the "available noise power" is not actually available to the load resistance R_L, since it can be physically realized only if the load resistance R_L is at a temperature of absolute zero. If the load resistance R_L is at the same temperature as the resistance R, then thermal effects exist in both resistances R and R_L, and the situation postulated in the definition of available noise power no longer exists.

Tube Noise. Noise similar in character to resistance noise is also generated in tubes. The principal causes of tube noise include (1) random variations in the rate of emission of electrons from the cathode, termed shot effect; (2) chance variations in the division of current between two or more positive electrodes, termed partition noise; (3) induced grid noise, a result of random variations in the number of electrons passing adjacent to a grid; (4) gas noise, caused by random variations, introduced by ionization, and by the resulting positive ions; and (5) random variations in the rate of production of secondary electrons.

Tube noise is in general like resistance noise in many respects. It is distributed continuously with frequency, and can be described in terms of the average square of a voltage or current, or the average energy in a given bandwidth. Most forms of tube noise are uniformly distributed with frequency, so that the associated energy is proportional to the band-width and independent of the center frequency of the band in which the noise is observed. An exception to this is the case of induced grid noise, in which the energy is proportional to the square of the frequency. However, over a limited frequency range, such that the bandwidth involved is a small fraction of the center frequency of the band, induced grid noise can be considered as uniformly distributed.

Signal-to-noise Ratio. The ratio of signal to noise describes the extent to which noise is associated with the signal. This ratio can be expressed either as a voltage or power ratio, or by the decibel equivalent of the power ratio.

The maximum possible signal-to-noise ratio that can be associated with a signal source having an internal resistance R occurs when the only noise present is that resulting from the resistance noise of R, and an open-circuit condition exists. In this case, the equivalent circuit of Fig. 8-36a applies, and one has, using Eq. (8-11b),

$$\left.\begin{array}{l}\text{Maximum possible}\\\text{signal-to-noise}\\\text{power ratio}\end{array}\right\} = \frac{E_s{}^2}{e_n{}^2} = \frac{E_s{}^2}{4kTRB} \qquad (8\text{-}14a)$$

By use of Eq. (8-13) this relation can also be written in the form

$$\left.\begin{array}{l}\text{Maximum possible}\\\text{signal-to-noise}\\\text{power ratio}\end{array}\right\} = \frac{\text{available signal power}}{\text{available noise power}} \qquad (8\text{-}14b)$$

Here the available signal power is the signal power $E_s{}^2/4R$ that would be delivered to a load resistance R_L that matched the source resistance R on a maximum-power-absorption basis, $i\ e.$, to a load such that $R_L = R$ [also see Eq. (8-3)].

It is important to note that the maximum possible signal-to-noise ratio as given by Eqs. (8-14) is obtained only when the load is an open circuit. If a load resistance R_L is connected across R as in Fig. 8-36b, then under practical conditions where the temperature of R_L is the same as the temperature of R, the signal-to-noise ratio is reduced. For example, if $R_L = R$, then the signal voltage across terminals aa is exactly half the open-circuit voltage. However, the noise voltage across these same terminals as given by Eq. (8-11b) is now $1/\sqrt{2}$ times the open-circuit noise voltage across R, since the equivalent resistance between terminals aa that produces the noise is R in parallel with R_L, or $R/2$. The signal-to-noise power ratio is hence $0.707^2 = 0.5$ times the open circuit signal-to-noise ratio. Thus the addition of the matched load resistance R_L has degraded the signal-to-noise ratio by 3 db.

If the voltage developed across terminals aa in Fig. 8-36a is amplified, both the signal and noise will be amplified equally. However, practical amplifiers always introduce some additional noise into the system as a result of tube noise. Accordingly, the signal-to-noise ratio observed at the output terminals of an actual amplifier will always be degraded below the maximum possible value that can exist at the input terminals as given

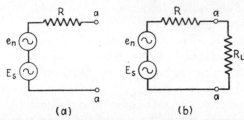

FIG. 8-36. Equivalent circuits showing a signal voltage associated with thermal noise.

by Eqs. (8-14). The extent of this reduction is expressed in terms of a quantity called the *noise figure* of the amplifier, which is defined and discussed in Sec. 8-13.

In interpreting the significance of signal-to-noise ratios, and in measuring them, it is necessary to take into account the bandwidths involved. The signal will typically be a modulated wave, and thus will have all of its energy confined to a limited band of frequencies; indeed, if the signal is a simple sine wave, all of its energy will be confined to a single frequency. On the other hand, the noise power developed across a resistance will be proportional to the bandwidth under consideration, and if this bandwidth extends from zero to infinity, the noise would, in fact, be infinite, and the signal-to-noise ratio would always be zero.

In practical circumstances one deals only with a limited frequency band, however, and it is the noise in this limited band that is of practical significance. In most cases the useful bandwidth is determined by the characteristics of the circuits involved; thus amplifiers always have a limited bandwidth and will therefore develop noise power at the output only in a frequency range determined by the amplifier response characteristic. In other cases, noise lying outside of some particular frequency range can be ignored; thus in audio-frequency amplifiers, noise at frequencies above audibility is of no significance.

Equivalent Noise Bandwidth of an Amplifier. The preceding discussion of signal-to-noise ratio assumes that the noise is uniformly distributed over the frequency range of interest, and is either zero or can be ignored at frequencies outside this band, corresponding to an idealized rectangular characteristic such as is illustrated in Fig. 8-37a. In actual practice, however, one is confronted with noise distributed in frequency in accordance with a response characteristic of the type illustrated in Fig. 8-37b, in which the noise drops off gradually at the edge of the band rather than abruptly. Such a characteristic is produced either by the response curve of the amplifier, or by the response curve of the measuring equipments used in observing the noise, whichever is the factor limiting the bandwidth.

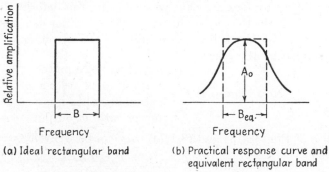

(a) Ideal rectangular band

(b) Practical response curve and equivalent rectangular band

FIG. 8-37. Ideal and actual response bands.

If the solid curve in Fig. 8-37b represents the noise voltage as a function of frequency, as would be the case if it were the curve of voltage gain of an amplifier as a function of frequency, [1] then the mean-square noise voltage that would be observed with this response characteristic would be

$$\left.\begin{array}{l}\text{Total mean-square}\\ \text{noise voltage}\end{array}\right\} = E_n{}^2 = M \int_0^\infty A^2\, df \qquad (8\text{-}15)$$

where M is a constant, and A is the relative voltage gain of the system (A^2 is relative power gain).

The rectangular response curve shown dotted in Fig. 8-37b, and having a response A_0 equal to the maximum response of the actual curve, will give the same noise output as the actual system, if the bandwidth B_{eq} of the rectangular characteristic is

$$B_{eq} = \frac{\int_0^\infty A^2\, df}{A_0{}^2} \qquad (8\text{-}16)$$

[1] This response curve can be obtained by the usual procedure for measuring voltage gain, using a sine-wave signal from a signal generator.

The equivalent bandwidth B_{eq} is a property of the response curve. It is particularly useful in interpreting and defining the effective bandwidth when specifying signal-to-noise ratios, and in connection with measurements of noise power.

The response curve that is effective in determining the equivalent bandwidth is the over-all response. If different parts of a multistage system have greatly different bandwidths, then the over-all response, and hence B_{eq}, is determined primarily by the part of the system having the narrowest band.

8-13. Noise Figure of Amplifiers.[1] The term noise figure as applied to an amplifier provides a means of specifying the deterioration in the signal-to-noise ratio that is produced by the amplifier as a result of the noise generated by the tubes and circuits of the amplifier.[2] The noise figure is defined by the relation

$$\text{Noise figure} = F = \frac{\text{signal-to-noise power ratio of ideal system}}{\text{actual signal-to-noise power ratio of output}} \tag{8-17a}$$

By the use of Eqs. (8-13) and (8-14b), this can be written as

$$\text{Noise figure} = F = \frac{P_s/kTB_{eq}}{\text{actual signal-to-noise power ratio of output}} \tag{8-17b}$$

where P_s is the available signal power in Eq. (8-14b). If P_o is the available signal power at the output, and N_o is the available output noise power, then

$$\text{Noise figure} = F = \frac{P_s/kTB_{eq}}{P_o/N_o} = \frac{N_o}{(P_o/P_s)kTB_{eq}} \tag{8-17c}$$

Here P_o/P_s is the available power gain as defined by Eq. (8-2), for the center frequency of the response curve.

In Eqs. (8-17a) to (8-17c) it is implied that the equivalent bandwidths B_{eq} of the noise that is involved, as defined by Eq. (8-16), are the same for the ideal and actual systems at both the input and output. These

---

[1] For further discussions of noise figure see H. Goldberg, Some Notes on Noise Figures, *Proc. IRE*, vol. 36, p. 1205, October, 1948; Shepard Roberts, Some Considerations Governing Noise Measurements on Crystal Mixers, *Proc. IRE*, vol. 35, p. 257, March, 1947; "Vacuum Tube Amplifiers," *op. cit.*, pp. 596–604, 621–635, 695–720; Peter G. Sulzer, Noise Generator for Receiver Measurements, *Electronics*, vol. 21, p. 96, July, 1948; D. O. North, Absolute Sensitivity of Radio Receivers, *RCA Rev.*, vol. 6, p. 332, January, 1942; H. T. Friis, Noise Figures of Receivers, *Proc. IRE*, vol. 32, p. 419, July, 1944.

[2] Although the discussion here is directed specifically toward amplifiers, the concept of noise figures can be applied to any four-terminal system irrespective of whether or not amplification is involved.

equations are valid only if the system is linear.   This means that the amplifier must not clip noise peaks, or compress the signal, etc.   It also means that rectification cannot be involved, since diode rectification of a mixture of signal and noise will commonly change the signal-to-noise ratio.   In this connection, frequency translation such as carried out in a superheterodyne receiver does not introduce a nonlinearity as far as noise considerations are concerned, provided a linear relation exists between the input and output voltages of the frequency converter.   Such a linear relationship is nearly always present under practical conditions.

Noise figure can be expressed either as a ratio of powers, or in decibels. Thus a noise figure of 13 db means that the signal-to-noise power ratio actually observed at the output is twenty times worse than would be the case in an ideal system.

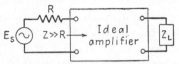

An ideal system is illustrated in Fig. 8-38.   It consists of a signal source generating an open-circuit voltage E_s and having an internal resistance R, and a perfect amplifier that introduces no noise, and which has an input impedance much larger than R.   The signal-to-noise ratio

FIG. 8-38. Schematic diagram showing a signal source E_s of internal impedance R exciting an ideal amplifier in which the output power is delivered to a load impedance Z_L.

in such an ideal system is given by Eqs. (8-14).   This is because the signal E_s, and the resistance noise voltage e_n of R, are both amplified equally, while no other source of noise is present.   Under these conditions amplification does not alter the signal-to-noise ratio provided the equivalent bandwidth B_{eq} of the noise that is relevant is the same before and after amplification.

It is important to note that the noise figure of a system involving an ideal amplifier will be unity only if the source impedance R associated with the signal E_s operates into an open-circuit load.   This fact was discussed above in connection with Fig. 8-36.   In particular, matching the source impedance on a maximum-power basis always causes the noise figure to be twice as great (that is, 3 db worse) than when the input impedance is infinite.

In practice, the noise figure of an amplifier is usually determined by the first tube and its input circuit.   This is because noise introduced by other tubes and circuits of the system will undergo less amplification, and so will be less important in the amplifier output.   The only exception is when the amplification of the first stage is low.

Noise Figure of Systems in Cascade.   In practical work involving noise-figure problems, it is often necessary to deal with two separate amplifier systems in cascade, as illustrated in Fig. 8-39.   To the extent that the individual amplifiers have identical rectangular response bands, then the over-all noise figure F_{12} of the combined system is related to the noise figures F_1 and F_2 of the individual amplifiers as follows,[1]

$$F_{12} = F_1 + \frac{F_2 - 1}{G_1} \qquad (8\text{-}18)$$

where G_1 is the *available power gain* of amplifier 1 in Fig. 8-39. This equation assumes that the noise figure F_2 of amplifier 2 is the value that is applicable when No. 2 is excited by a signal source having an interval resistance equal to the resistance that No. 2 sees when looking toward amplifier 1.

Although Eq. (8-18) is derived on the assumption that the two amplifiers have identical rectangular response characteristics, this equation can sometimes be used when the bandwidths are not the same. Thus if the noise bandwidth B_{eq} of amplifier 2 as defined by Eq. (8-16) is appreciably less than that of No. 1, then the equivalent noise bandwidth of the overall system is likewise B_{eq}. If one then determines F_{12} and F_2 experimentally and substitutes the values into Eq. (8-18), the resulting value F_1

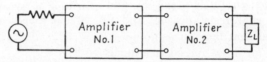

Fig. 8-39. System involving two amplifier networks in cascade.

of the noise figure of the first amplifier will be the value for this same equivalent noise bandwidth B_{eq}.

8-14. Measurement of Noise Figure of Amplifiers. The process of determining the noise figure of an amplifier consists in measuring the noise output that is actually present, and comparing this with the theoretical minimum possible noise that would be present in an ideal system. Thus consider Fig. 8-38, in which the source exciting the input to the amplifier has an internal impedance R as shown. In the ideal case, the only noise in the system would be that resulting from the thermal voltage across the resistance R as amplified by the amplifier. In actual practice, however, the amplifier will contribute additional noise of its own, so that the noise in the amplifier output will be greater than the amplified thermal noise of the resistance R.

Single-frequency and Integrated Noise Figures. In making a determination of the noise figure, one must pay particular attention to the bandwidth of the system under test relative to the bandwidth of the measuring equipment used to evaluate the noise. For example, assume that the bandwidth of the measuring equipment is very much greater than that of the noise being measured, and that the measuring equipment has a response independent of frequency over this much wider range. The

---

[1] The derivation of this relation is given by Friis, *op. cit.*

measuring equipment then determines the total noise in a frequency band corresponding to the equivalent band B_{eq} of the system being tested, as defined by Eq. (8-16). The noise observed under this case is called the *integrated noise*, and the noise figure derived from it is termed the *integrated noise figure*.

Alternatively, if the bandwidth of the equipment used to measure the noise is very small compared with the bandwidth of the noise being measured, then the experimental determination indicates the noise level produced by the amplifier in a narrow frequency band B_{eq} representing the equivalent bandwidth of the measuring equipment. Noise obtained in this way is called the *single-frequency* or *incremental* noise, and gives rise to a corresponding noise figure. The single-frequency noise figure thus equals the ratio of the noise energy actually present in a very narrow frequency range, to the noise energy that would be present in the same frequency range of an ideal system.

The single-frequency and integrated noise are related by the fact that if one observes the single-frequency noise at a succession of frequencies, it is possible to plot a curve of noise level as a function of frequency. The area under this curve then gives the total noise over the frequency band, and is the integrated noise; the curve itself is the response curve of the system.

Measurement of Amplifier Noise Figure—Brute-force Method. An obvious means of determining the noise figure of an amplifier is to make direct use of Eq. (8-17c). To do this one first obtains experimentally a curve of relative gain as a function of frequency, and then calculates the equivalent bandwidth B_{eq} using Eq. (8-16). Next, the absolute value of available gain at the center frequency of this response band is determined, as is the available output noise power N_o. These various numbers are then substituted into Eq. (8-17c).

Although this method of determining the noise figure is straightforward, it is somewhat laborious. Moreover, if the noise figure is small, it is difficult to determine the amplifier response characteristic, available gain, and available output noise power, with sufficient precision to give accurate results. The chief usefulness of the brute-force approach to the measurement of noise figure lies in the fact that it gives a clear picture of the physical significance of the noise figure; practical determinations of noise figure, however, are ordinarily made by other means.

Measurement of Noise Figure—Noise-generator Method.[1] A second method of measuring noise figure consists in comparing the noise actually

[1] For further discussion see H. Johnson, Coaxial Line Noise Diode, *RCA Rev.*, vol. 8, p. 169, March, 1947; J. Moffatt, A Diode Noise Generator, *J. IEE (Radiolocation Conv.)*, vol. 93, pt. IIIA, p. 1335, March-May, 1946; "Vacuum Tube Amplifiers," *op. cit.*, pp. 701–708.

present with the noise produced by a noise signal generator, *i.e.*, a calibrated and controllable source of noise power.   Consider the situation illustrated in Fig. 8-40a, where E_n is a generator producing a controllable noise voltage, and is calibrated in terms of available noise power P_n. This noise generator has an internal resistance R, which is also the source resistance with which the amplifier is intended to operate.   This resistance generates its normal thermal voltage e_n as given by Eqs. (8-9) in addition to the noise voltage E_n produced by the noise generator.   A number of types of relatively simple noise generators for use in a system

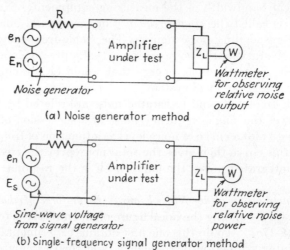

(a) Noise generator method

(b) Single-frequency signal generator method

Fig. 8-40.   Schematic diagram showing arrangement of apparatus for measuring the noise figure by the noise-generator and the single-frequency signal-generator methods.

of this type have been devised; several of the more common are described in Sec. 8-16.

The measurement of noise figure now proceeds as follows: With the noise signal generator producing no noise (*i.e.*, with $E_n = 0$), but with resistance R between the input terminals of the amplifier, the noise power in the amplifier output is observed; this corresponds to the noise-power output under normal conditions of operation, taking into account the thermal noise e_n of R and the imperfections of the system.   The noise generator is next turned on, and its available noise power P_n is adjusted until the observed noise output *power* of the amplifier is increased to a value n times the noise power corresponding to the noise power when the signal generator is inactive.   The noise figure, expressed as a power ratio, is then[1]

[1] This is derived as follows: An actual amplifier with a noise figure F gives the same output noise as would be obtained from an ideal noise-free amplifier having an input noise power of $FkTB_{eq}$.   Hence, if an added input noise power P_n per cycle increases

$$\text{Noise figure} = F = \frac{P_n B_{eq}}{kTB_{eq}(n-1)} = \frac{P_n}{kT(n-1)} \qquad (8\text{-}19a)$$

Here P_n is the available noise power per cycle of bandwidth from the noise generator, and is given by the calibration of this generator. The total noise power produced by the noise generator in an equivalent bandwidth B_{eq} is $P_n B_{eq}$. Maximum accuracy is ordinarily obtained when $n = 2$, that 's, when the noise generator is adjusted so that it exactly doubles the output power. Under these conditions Eq. (8-19a) becomes

$$F = \frac{P_n B_{eq}}{kTB_{eq}} = \frac{P_n}{kT} \qquad (8\text{-}19b)$$

The noise-generator method of determining the noise figure has the advantage that the accuracy depends only upon the accuracy with which the characteristics of the noise generator are known, and on the accuracy with which one can observe a doubling of the noise output power. Nothing whatsoever need be known about the magnitude of the amplification, or the shape of the response characteristic of the amplifier. This results from the fact that the amount of noise from the noise generator that arrives at the output of the amplifier under test is governed by the effective bandwidth of the amplifier in exactly the same manner as are the thermal and tube noise of the system. The result obtained is either the single-frequency or integrated noise figure, according to whether the bandwidth of the equipment measuring the output noise is narrow or wide compared with the bandwidth of the amplifier.

The noise signal-generator method is the most desirable method to use when a suitable noise signal generator is available. However, most available noise generators will not produce sufficient noise to determine with accuracy large values of noise figure, i.e., values above about 20 db. When the noise figure is much larger than this, the single-frequency signal-generator method will determine the noise figure with greater accuracy. These limitations of noise signal generators are discussed in greater detail in Sec. 8-16.

Measurement of Noise Figure—Single-frequency Signal-generator Method. In this method of determining noise figure, the noise generator E_n of Fig. 8-40a is replaced by a sine-wave signal generator of voltage E_s, and internal impedance R, as illustrated in Fig. 8-40b. The measuring procedure is then much as before. First, with $E_s = 0$, the noise-power output of the amplifier is observed. Then the frequency of the signal

---

the noise of the actual system n times, then

$$P_n B_{eq} + FkTB_{eq} = nFkTB_{eq}$$

Solving for F gives Eq. (8-19a).

generator is set to the center of the response band of the system, and the signal-generator voltage E_s is adjusted until the power indicated by the output-measuring equipment is exactly twice as great as before.   Under these conditions one has, in analogy with Eq. (8-19b),

$$\text{Noise figure} = F = \frac{P_s}{kTB_{eq}} \qquad (8\text{-}20)$$

where $P_s = E_s{}^2/4R$ is the available power from the signal-generator voltage E_s having an internal impedance R.

In interpreting Eq. (8-20) careful attention must be paid to the effective bandwidth B_{eq}, which must be known.   This is because the signal generator voltage E_s is a single-frequency signal, whereas the noise involved represents a continuous distribution of energy over a frequency band of equivalent width B_{eq}, and the bandwidth no longer cancels out as it did when using a noise signal generator.

When one desires to obtain the single-frequency noise figure, then the noise output of the amplifier is observed with measuring equipment having a relatively narrow bandwidth.   Care must also be taken to adjust the frequency of the signal generator so that it lies in the center of this band.

If the integrated noise figure is desired, the noise power of the amplifier output should be observed with measuring equipment having a much wider bandwith than the amplifier.   The equivalent over-all bandwidth of the system then has a value corresponding to B_{eq} of the amplifier as given by Eq. (8-16).   The frequency of the signal-generator voltage E_s should be set at the center frequency of the amplifier response characteristic.

The use of a single-frequency signal generator instead of a noise signal generator in the determination of noise figure has the disadvantage that one must know the equivalent bandwidth B_{eq} in Eq. (8-20).   The method has the advantage, however, in that single-frequency signal generators are more readily available than noise signal generators; moreover single-frequency signal generators are available for the higher microwave frequencies, whereas there are no satisfactory noise signal generators for these frequencies.

The single-frequency method of determining noise figure will have higher accuracy than the noise-generator method when the noise figure is large, as for example 30 db.   This is because the maximum noise that can be obtained from available noise generators will give a value of n in Eqs. (8-19) that differs only slightly from unity when the noise figure is large.   However, when the noise figure is small, and particularly when it is only a few decibels, it is generally found that the noise generator will give P_n in Eqs. (8-19) with greater accuracy than a single-frequency signal generator will give P_s in Eq. (8-20).   This is because the calibration of the usual noise generator is based on the direct generation of noise by some natural phenomenon that follows exact mathematical laws.   In contrast, the calibration of the single-frequency signal generator is obtained by starting from a relatively large reference voltage or power. When the noise figure is small, then P_s in Eq. (8-20) is so small that large values of attenuation are required, as for example 100 db.   Under these conditions an error of only 1 db in the attenuator introduces 1 db error in the noise figure   While this is not important if the correct noise figure is 20 db, it is very important if the true noise figure is only 2 or 3 db.

8-15. Special Considerations Involved in Measuring Noise Power.[1] All methods for determining the noise figure require a measurement of the noise output power of the system under test.   Except in the brute-force method, this determination need be only relative, the requirement merely being that the power-measuring equipment indicate with accuracy the ratio of power increase when the power is roughly doubled.

Several basic considerations are involved in the output-power determination.   *First*, since output power is proportional to the square of the rms voltage (or current) supplied to the measuring device, the power-measuring instrument must have a square-law characteristic if it is to be above question.   *Second*, the noise power to be determined is often quite small.   The power-measuring device must therefore be quite sensitive and amplification of the unknown noise before measurement is often required to bring the noise up to the minimum power level that can be determined by the more sensitive bolometer wattmeters (see page 42). *Third*, noise has a high ratio of peak to rms amplitude, so that to avoid errors from clipping of the peaks, the square-law characteristic must be maintained up to amplitudes at least three times the rms amplitude.[2] *Fourth*, the noise power fluctuates from moment to moment so that the device indicating the average noise power must smooth out these fluctuations, *i.e.*, must have a time constant that is not too small.   This time constant must be greater the narrower the bandwidth involved, and should be somewhat greater than the reciprocal of the bandwidth in cycles.   *Finally*, in the single-frequency signal generator method of measuring noise figure, it is necessary that the measuring system also accurately indicate the relative power of a wave consisting of noise plus a sine wave.

The most satisfactory means of observing the average value of the square of the rms amplitude is by the use of a thermocouple or bolometer

---

[1] Helpful information on this subject is given in "Vacuum Tube Amplifiers," *op. cit.*, pp. 709–715.

[2] See R. L. Bell, Linearity Range of Noise-measuring Amplifiers, *Wireless Eng.*, vol. 24, p. 119, April, 1947.

instrument. These devices give an indication exactly proportional to power, and their thermal inertia is such as to give the required averaging effect. A square-law vacuum-tube voltmeter, or square-law crystal, is also satisfactory provided the noise peaks do not extend into regions where a true square-law characteristic is not maintained. Half-wave square-law, and average-reading devices, will measure the *relative* power of pure noise without error, but introduce serious errors when one desires the power of a wave consisting of noise plus a sine wave. Peak-reading instruments are generally to be avoided.

Apparatus Arrangements. The actual details involved in determining relative noise power depend upon the power level of the noise being measured. When the system under test possesses considerable amplification,

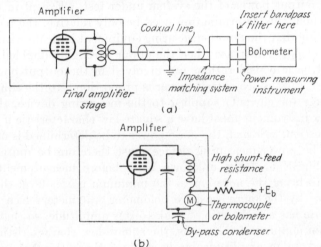

FIG. 8-41. Typical apparatus arrangements for measuring relative noise output power of an amplifier.

the output noise power commonly is large enough to be determined directly by a thermocouple or bolometer arrangement. Powers as small as 10^{-5} watt can be readily determined in this manner with a sensitive bolometer (see page 46). On the other hand, it is sometimes necessary to make noise measurements on systems having little or no amplification. In these cases the equipment for observing relative noise power must include sufficient amplification to bring the noise power under investigation up to a level where it can be accurately observed.

Typical circuit arrangements for the direct determination of relative noise power are illustrated in Fig. 8-41. At *a* the output power of the system under test is delivered to a coaxial transmission line. The power-measuring apparatus is then matched to the line in such a way as to provide a characteristic impedance termination. Under these conditions, all the available noise power is delivered to the measuring instrument, and what is observed is the integrated available noise power of the amplifier output.   An alternative arrangement for determining relative power is shown at *b*.   Here a bolometer or thermocouple is placed in series with the tuned output circuit of the final tuned stage of the amplifier.   This tuned circuit presents the tube with the appropriate plate load impedance, while the thermocouple or bolometer measures the average value of the square of the current flowing in the resonant circuit.   Under these conditions the indication obtained is proportional to the average square of the noise voltage developed across the tuned circuit, and is therefore proportional to the total noise power over the equivalent bandwidth of the amplifier.

The direct determination of noise power in a narrow frequency band, *i.e.*, the "single-frequency" noise, requires that the measuring equipment respond to noise only in a narrow frequency range.   This result can be achieved by associating the thermocouple, bolometer, or other indicating device with selective circuits in such a manner that only currents in a restricted frequency range reach the indicating device.   Thus in Fig. 8-41a, this result could be achieved by inserting a filter with a narrow passband in the circuits leading to the measuring equipment, as indicated. The bandwidth of the noise power observed will then be determined by the bandwidth of this frequency-selective system associated with the power-indicating device.

When the noise power is too small to be determined directly, the measuring equipment must provide means for amplifying[1] as well as indicating the noise; such an arrangement is illustrated schematically in Fig. 8-42. In many cases it is convenient to use an ordinary radio receiver as the amplifier;[2] when this is done, the second detector of the receiver is replaced by a suitable bolometer or thermocouple, and the automatic-volume-control system is disconnected and replaced by a manual control for adjusting the sensitivity to a value appropriate to the power level of the noise under investigation.

The bandwidth of the noise indicated in the system of Fig. 8-42 depends upon the bandwidth of the amplifier being tested relative to the bandwidth of amplifier of the measuring equipment.   As explained in connec-

[1] A measuring amplifier of this type is often called a postamplifier.

[2] The receiver may be and usually is of the superheterodyne type; the fact that there is a frequency conversion in such an arrangement does not alter the essential behavior, which is that the receiver acts as a frequency-selective system that delivers an output representing a restricted frequency range.   The fact that the noise power is actually measured at a frequency different from the frequency of the noise that is delivered to the input of the receiver is not significant; what counts is the over-all bandwidth of the system, including particularly that of the intermediate-frequency amplifier.

tion with Fig. 8-39, if the bandwidth of the amplifier being tested is much less than that of the measuring amplifier, then the measurement gives the integrated noise, whereas if the bandwidth of the measuring amplifier is much the narrower, then the measurement gives the incremental or single-frequency noise for the equivalent bandwidth of the measuring amplifier.

When the noise-power-measuring equipment includes an amplifier, it is necessary to take into account the noise figure of this amplifier; otherwise noise generated in the measuring amplifier as a result of its own imperfections would be incorrectly treated as though generated by the apparatus under test. This situation is handled by considering that the system in Fig. 8-42 consists of two systems in series (also see Fig. 8-39). Under these conditions Eq. (8-18) applies. The measuring procedure consists in determining the noise figure F_{12} of the complete system by one of the

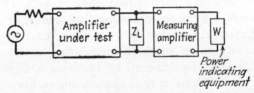

FIG. 8-42. System for measuring relative noise output of an amplifier when the noise output is too small to be measured directly; the measuring amplifier shown is often a radio receiver.

usual methods. The noise figure F_2 of the measuring amplifier and the gain G_1 of the test amplifier are next separately determined. The results are then introduced into Eq. (8-18) and the noise figure F_1 of the system under test is calculated. Since this calculation is essentially equivalent to that of taking a difference, the accuracy of the result will be less the greater the fraction of the total output noise power that is introduced by the measuring amplifier. When the noise to be measured is at very low power level, *i.e.*, when the amplification of the amplifier under test is small, so that the gain G_2 of the measuring amplifier must have a high value, then if accurate results are to be obtained the noise figure F_2 of the measuring equipment must be small. Otherwise F_1 cannot be accurately determined from Eq. (8-18).

A simple and frequently used expedient for determining with high accuracy when the output power has been doubled, is illustrated schematically in Fig. 8-43. Here the smaller value of output power is determined in the usual way, and the resulting indication of the measuring equipment very precisely noted. Switch S is then thrown to insert an attenuator which introduces exactly 3 db loss, after which the power from the noise or single-frequency signal generator is increased to a value that restores exactly the original indication of the power-measuring equipment.

The output power is now twice the original value, to a precision determined only by the accuracy of the attenuator. Since the power indicator in this arrangement always operates at the same level, linearity or stability of its calibration is unimportant.

In making measurements of noise power, consideration must be given to the input impedance of the measuring equipment. When an absolute determination of noise power is involved, the impedance relations must not be disturbed by the measuring equipment in a way that alters the noise-power output in the band of frequencies of importance in the measurement. This is accomplished either by making the input impedance of the measuring equipment so high that it can be neglected, or by using the impedance of the measuring equipment to supply part or all of the normal load impedance.

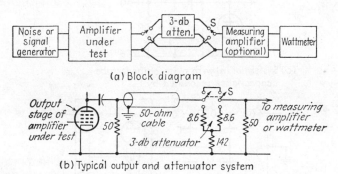

(a) Block diagram

(b) Typical output and attenuator system

Fig. 8-43. Means of using an attenuator to determine accurately when output power has been doubled.

In most noise-figure measurements, it is merely necessary to determine the *relative* increase in output power when the noise (or single-frequency) signal generator is turned on. In these cases the impedance of the measuring equipment will not ordinarily introduce an error provided it does not change the relative shape of the response characteristic of the system under test.

8-16. Noise Signal Generators. A noise signal generator, commonly referred to as simply a noise generator, is a device for producing a known and preferably controllable amount of noise for use as a standard of comparison in making noise-figure measurements. Noise generators make use of natural phenomena in which the noise is generated by exact physical laws so that the noise can be accurately calculated in terms of some easily measurable or known quantity. Successful noise generators meeting these requirements include those employing shot noise in a temperature-limited tube, those utilizing thermal noise at elevated temperatures, and those utilizing certain types of gas discharges.

Diode Noise Generators.   Most noise generators used in practice are based on the shot noise generated by a diode so operated that the plate current is limited by the cathode temperature.   If the tube involved has a pure metal filament,[1] and if the transit time of the electrons is negligibly small compared with the time represented by a cycle in the frequency range of interest, then there is a precise relationship between the noise

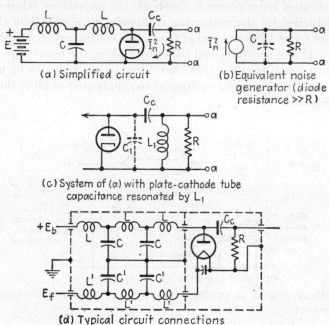

(a) Simplified circuit

(b) Equivalent noise
generator (diode
resistance >> R)

(c) System of (a) with plate-cathode tube
capacitance resonated by L₁

(d) Typical circuit connections

FIG. 8-44.   Circuit arrangements for diode noise generator.

current available from such a diode, and the d-c plate current.   The quantitative relation is

$$i_n{}^2 = 2eI_{dc}B_{eq} \qquad (8\text{-}21)$$

where $i_n{}^2$ = mean-square noise current in bandwidth B_{eq}

e = charge on the electron, coulombs

I_{dc} = direct current flowing between anode and cathode, amp

B_{eq} = equivalent bandwidth of noise involved

A typical circuit arrangement for a noise generator of this type is illustrated schematically in Fig. 8-44a, and in greater detail in Fig. 8-44d. The latter is a shunt-feed arrangement, in which the noise current as given by Eq. (8-21) flows through a resistor R, while the plate voltage and the

---

[1] Oxide-coated cathodes exhibit a phenomenon known as "flicker effect," as a result of which the total noise, particularly at the lower frequencies, is greater than shot noise alone.

filament current are supplied through the filter networks LC and $L'C'$ designed to be effective in the frequency range in which the amplifier is being tested. These filters, together with blocking condenser C_c, make it possible to separate the noise currents from the direct current in the system; they also prevent any high-frequency noise from being lost in the d-c supply system, and likewise eliminate the possibility of regeneration occurring in a high-gain amplifier through stray couplings involving the power-supply circuits of the noise generator. Simple shielding is likewise indicated in Fig. 8-44d to provide additional insurance against stray coupling.

The noise generator of Fig. 8-44a has the equivalent circuit of Fig. 8-44b in so far as noise at terminals aa is concerned.[1] The internal resistance R of the equivalent noise generator should be chosen to correspond to the source resistance with which the amplifier under test is normally used. The shot effect in the diode causes a noise voltage E_n to be developed across R that corresponds to the current i_n of Eq. (8-21) flowing through the resistance R, that is, $E_n = i_n R$; this noise is in addition to the thermal noise also generated in R. This "excess" noise due to the presence of the diode has all the properties of thermal or resistance noise except that it is determined by the d-c plate current of the diode tube. The mean-square value $E_n{}^2$ of the excess noise, and the available noise power P_n introduced by the presence of the noise generator, are then related by the equation

$$\text{Excess noise power} = P_n = \frac{E_n{}^2}{4R} = \frac{eI_{dc}RB_{eq}}{2} \tag{8-22}$$

The notation in Eq. (8-22) is the same as indicated above and as used in Eq. (8-21).

The noise figure can be determined with the aid of a diode noise generator by the procedure discussed in connection with Eqs. (8-19), using the value of P_n given by Eq. (8-22). In making such a noise-figure measurement, it is customary to adjust the filament current of the diode until the d-c plate current I_{dc} has a value that causes the output noise of the system under test to be exactly doubled when the diode is turned on. In this case, Eq. (8-19b) applies, and if the temperature of R is taken as 290°K, the expression for noise figure then assumes the very simple form

$$F = \frac{P_n}{kT} = 20I_{dc}R \tag{8-23}$$

where I_{dc} is in amperes.

---

[1] This equivalent circuit assumes that the radio-frequency choke system LC is fully effective, and that to noise currents it acts as an open circuit relative to R. The tube can be regarded as an open circuit since it is operated under temperature-limited conditions, where its effective plate resistance is extremely high.

Diode noise generators possess limitations at high frequencies as a result of tube capacitance, inductance and capacitance of leads, and transit-time effects. Careful examination of the circuit of Fig. 8-44a shows that resistance R is shunted by the plate-filament tube capacitance, and by the capacitance between leads aa. When the reactance of the shunting capacitance is comparable with the resistance R, then a significant part of the noise current as given by Eq. (8-21) is by-passed around R. The resulting error can be minimized by shunting R with an inductance L_1 that resonates with the shunt capacitance C_1 at the center of the frequency band of interest. Such an arrangement, illustrated in Fig. 8-44c, provides a very low-Q parallel resonance system because R normally has a low value. The bandwidth of the parallel resonant circuit will therefore usually be many times greater than the bandwidth of the amplifier under test.

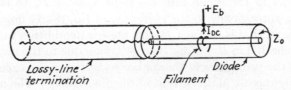

FIG. 8-45. Schematic diagram of transmission-line diode for noise generation at very high frequencies.

Leads from the diode tube to the output terminals aa, and from there to the actual input of the amplifier under test, not only add capacitance to the system, but also contribute inductance as well. The result is that at very high frequencies partial resonance effects may arise which cause the noise voltage that is actually applied to the amplifier input to differ from the value calculated by the aid of Eq. (8-21) and Fig. (8-44b). This difficulty can be overcome by employing physically small tubes and by arrangements that minimize lead length. Commercially available diodes with favorable characteristics can be used satisfactorily as noise generators up to several hundred megacycles.

The limitations introduced by tube capacitance and by lead inductance can be largely eliminated by the use of special diodes constructed to represent a short length of coaxial transmission line, as shown in Fig. 8-45.[1,2] The plate electrode of such a diode serves as the outer conductor

[1] See Johnson, loc. cit.; "Vacuum Tube Amplifiers," op. cit., p. 704; R. Kompfner, J. Hutton, E. E. Schneider, and L. A. G. Dresel, The Transmission-line Diode as Noise Source at Centimetre Wavelengths, J. IEE, (Radiolocation Conv.), vol. 93, pt. IIIA, p. 1436, March–May, 1946; R. W. Slinkman, Temperature-limited Noise Diode Design, Sylvania Tech., vol. 2, p. 6, October, 1949.
[2] An alternative method of overcoming tube and circuit limitations consists in generating the noise at intermediate frequency by a diode, and then shifting the fre-

of the line, while the filament consists of one or more turns of tungsten wire wrapped closely around the center conductor as shown. The filament is at the same radio-frequency potential as the center conductor, but has one end insulated therefrom to provide a circuit for the d-c heating current. One end of the diode is terminated in the characteristic impedance of the line, sometimes provided by a length of lossy coaxial line of the same characteristic impedance as that of the diode. The other end of the diode (or of a cable extension) serves as the output connection of the noise generator. In such an arrangement, the characteristic impedance of the line corresponds to the resistance R in Fig. 8-44a. It is possible to construct diode noise generators of the transmission-line type with negligible circuit error at frequencies as high as 3000 Mc.

The ultimate useful upper frequency limit of diode noise generators is set by transit-time effects, since when the transit time is not small compared with the time of a cycle, then Eq. (8-21) no longer applies.[1] Transit time can be minimized by the use of close-spaced diodes, and by taking advantage of the fact that large anode voltages can be employed. In this way it is readily possible to keep transit-time errors as low as 3 db at frequencies as great as 3000 Mc.

Diode noise generators are particularly useful in measuring noise figures of the order of 20 db or less. When the noise figure is much larger than this, the diode current required to double the output noise of the system under test becomes excessively large. For example, if the resistance R in Fig. 8-44a is 50 ohms, then the diode current for noise figures of 10, 20, and 30 db is, respectively, 10, 100, and 1000 ma. The latter value is obviously impractically large; at an anode potential of only 100 volts, it corresponds to a power dissipation of 100 watts at the plate of the diode.

Within its limitations, the diode noise generator is almost ideal. It is inexpensive, usually available, simple to use, and gives accurate results.

Noise Generators Employing Thermal Noise at Elevated Temperatures. Another means of adding an accurately known amount of noise to a system consists in heating the input resistance. Equation (8-9) shows that the mean-square noise voltage (*i.e.*, the available noise power) is exactly proportional to the absolute temperature of the resistance.

A suitable circuit arrangement for a noise generator of this type is

---

quency of the noise to a higher value by the use of a mixer and heterodyne oscillator. For details see Leslie A. Maxon, Measurement of Overall Noise Figure and Conversion Loss in Microwave Receivers, *Proc. IRE*, vol. 37, p. 1433, December, 1949.

[1] The error in Eq. (8-21) will, however, be less than 10 per cent if the transit time does not exceed about 80 electrical degrees; thus, see R. B. Fraser, Noise Spectrum of Temperature Limited Diode, *Wireless Eng.*, vol. 26, p. 129, April, 1949.

illustrated in Fig. 8-46.[1] Here resistance R is a tungsten filament in a vacuum that is heated by direct current transmitted through filter LC that isolates R from the d-c system. Noise voltage that is free of the d-c voltage across R is obtained with the aid of blocking condenser C_c. Resistor R' is an adjustable compensating resistance provided for the purpose of maintaining constant the resistance $R_0 = R + R'$ between terminals aa as R changes with temperature.

The procedure for measuring the noise figure with such an arrangement is analogous to the procedure involving the diode noise generator. First, with R at room temperature and R' adjusted to give the desired source resistance R_0, the noise output of the amplifier under test is observed. Then heating current is passed through R and adjusted so that the observed noise output is increased by a convenient amount, preferably

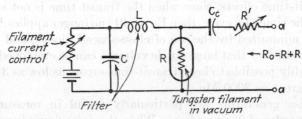

FIG. 8-46. Circuit arrangement for utilizing a resistance R at an elevated temperature as a standard noise generator.

doubled, while readjusting R' to maintain R_0 constant as R changes with temperature. The available noise power P_n introduced by the heating of R, that is, the "excess" noise, is then

$$P_n = kB_{eq}T_1\left(\frac{T_2R}{T_1R_0} + \frac{R'}{R_0} - 1\right) \tag{8-24}$$

where k = Boltzmann's constant, as in Eq. (8-9)
             B_{eq} = equivalent bandwidth
             T_2 = temperature of R when hot
             T_1 = room temperature
R, R', and R_0 = resistances shown in Fig. 8-46
The noise figure is obtained by substituting the value of P_n into Eq. (8-19a).

In carrying out the above determination, a calibration giving the relationship between filament current and temperature for any particular resistor can be obtained by the aid of an optical pyrometer, or by observing the variation of R as a function of filament current, and utilizing the known relationship between temperature and resistance of tungsten.

---

[1] Another possible way to use a heated resistance as a noise source is to stretch it across a waveguide in place of the fluorescent lamp in Fig. 8-47a.

The use of thermal noise at elevated temperatures to provide known values of noise suffers from two fundamental limitations. First, the method is awkward to apply experimentally; second, the method is only suitable for the accurate measurement of noise figures of the order of 10 db or less. Noise generators using thermal noise at elevated temperatures find their principal usefulness as a check against other methods.[1]

Noise Generators Employing a Gas Discharge.[2] If an electrical discharge takes place in a gas at low pressure, where the resultant light energy is principally monochromatic at a wavelength λ_m, noise is produced that is uniformly distributed over the radio-frequency spectrum. This noise acts like resistance noise corresponding to a temperature T that is related to the wavelength λ_m by Wien's displacement law, *viz.*,

$$\lambda_m T = 0.289 \text{ cm }°\text{K} \tag{8-25}$$

For mercury vapor, radiating at a wavelength of 2536.52×10^{-8} cm, the corresponding temperature is $11,394°$K.

The ordinary household fluorescent lamp contains mercury vapor, and therefore acts as a source of thermal noise having a temperature of $11,394°$K. This is true irrespective of the color of the light from the lamp, or the current passing through it, or the geometrical dimensions of the lamp, since this result depends only on the fact that all fluorescent lamps contain mercury vapor.

A fluorescent-lamp noise generator is a particularly convenient noise source for use with waveguides. The lamp can be inserted through the waveguide, using metal tubes at the openings of the guide that have a small diameter such that these tubes function as waveguides beyond cut-off (see Fig. 8-47a); in this way noise energy cannot leak either into or out of the waveguide. This arrangement also keeps the metal electrodes of the lamp away from the fields inside the waveguide, thereby insuring that noise produced at the electrodes does not enter the guide.

The lamp shunts an admittance across the waveguide that has both susceptance and conductance components. An impedance match to the waveguide can be achieved by means of a tuning stub and tuning screw, as illustrated in Fig. 8-47a, and by varying the direct current to control the conductance that the discharge shunts across the waveguide. The magnitude of the direct current, however, has relatively little effect upon the susceptance component. The adjustments required to obtain an impedance match at any desired frequency can be obtained by using the

[1] For example, see E. H. Ullrich and D. C. Rogers, An Absolute Method of Measurement of Receiver Noise Factor, *J. IEE (Radiolocation Conv.)*, vol. 93, pt. IIIA, p. 1347, March–May, 1946.

[2] W. W. Mumford, A Broad-band Microwave Noise Source, *Bell System Tech. J.*, vol. 28, p. 608, October, 1949.

noise generator and its associated waveguide as the load on a slotted section, and then adjusting for minimum standing-wave ratio. Once an impedance match has been achieved between the fluorescent lamp and the guide, any desired length of waveguide may be inserted between the noise generator and the amplifier under test, provided only that the length is short enough so that the waveguide can be assumed to have zero attenuation.

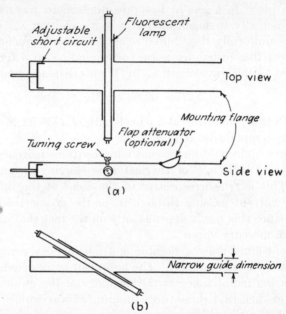

FIG. 8-47. Arrangements for utilizing a fluorescent lamp as a standard noise generator.

Because of the necessity of matching the gas-discharge tube to the waveguide, a noise generator of this type has a limited bandwidth. However, the shunting conductance is relatively low, so that the bandwidth of the equivalent noise-generator impedance is large, as for example 500 Mc at a center frequency of 4000 Mc, for a typical case.[1]

When the gas noise generator is matched to its waveguide, the available noise power associated with the open end of the guide will be kT_2B_{eq} where B_{eq} is the equivalent bandwidth involved, and T_2 is 11,394°K. When the fluorescent lamp is turned off, and the waveguide readjusted to give reflectionless termination, the available noise power is kT_1B_{eq} where

---

[1] The sensitivity of the susceptance adjustment to frequency can be minimized or eliminated by arranging the gas-discharge tube as illustrated in Fig. 8-47b. Here the gas tube serves as a form of tapered and distributed load, and the conductance necessary to match the waveguide impedance can then be realized by varying the direct current through the gas tube.

T_1 is room temperature.   The available "excess" noise power P_n introduced by the fluorescent lamp is hence

$$P_n = kB_{eq}(T_2 - T_1) \tag{8-26}$$

This is the value of P_n to be used in Eqs. (8-19).

The available "excess" noise power obtainable from a noise generator of the gas-discharge type can be controlled by inserting an adjustable attenuator in the waveguide that leads from the gas tube to the equipment under test, as illustrated in Fig. 8-47a.   This attenuator may be calibrated at relatively high power levels by the use of bolometer techniques. The value of P_n to be substituted in Eqs. (8-19) then becomes the value of P_n given by Eq. (8-26) as reduced by the attenuator.

Noise generators of the gas-discharge type find their principal usefulness at microwave frequencies, where diode noise generators cannot be used because of transit-time and circuit difficulties.   They permit the accurate determination of noise figures of microwave amplifiers and receivers up to 15 or 20 db.   When the noise figure is larger than this, the amount of "excess" noise that is introduced by the gas discharge represents such a small percentage increase over the noise normally present, as to prevent accurate determination of the noise figure.

Uncalibrated Noise Generators.   Noise generators are sometimes used in which the noise cannot be determined by calculation, but rather is obtained by calibration against another type of noise generator, or against a single-frequency signal generator.   An example of such a device is a crystal detector through which is passed a direct current.[1] This arrangement generates "white" noise having a magnitude that is in excess of the thermal noise associated with the crystal resistance, and can be controlled by varying the direct current.   Other examples of uncalibrated noise generators are high-gain photomultiplier tubes, and klystron tubes operated in a nonoscillating condition.[2]

[1] Further information is given by "Technique of Microwave Measurements" (vol. 11 of Radiation Laboratory Series), pp. 278–281, McGraw-Hill Book Company, Inc., New York, 1947.

[2] Thus see "Technique of Microwave Measurements," *op. cit.*, pp. 274–278.

CHAPTER 9

RECEIVER MEASUREMENTS

9-1. Basic Considerations. The radio receiver has several distinct functions to perform. Briefly, it must accept a very small signal voltage provided by the receiving antenna, and must amplify this signal to a sufficiently high level so that visual or aural reproduction is possible. Further, it should amplify only one desired signal, and reject all others. Moreover, a detector must be incorporated which extracts from the modulated waves, as originally transmitted, the desired information, so that it can be presented by some means, such as a loudspeaker or television picture tube. This final output of the receiver must represent the original modulation with as little frequency and nonlinear distortion as possible. In the sections to follow, various types of measurements are outlined, whereby the effectiveness of a given receiver in performing these functions can be evaluated.

Because of the large number of variables involved, standardization is required in receiver measurements so that results obtained in different laboratories can be compared on a common basis. Industry standards for entertainment receivers have been provided in the United States by the Institute of Radio Engineers since 1930, with appropriate revisions from time to time as technical advances have made it necessary. These IRE standards are so widely used that much of what is to be said in this chapter is conditioned by them.[1]

A typical laboratory arrangement for determining the characteristics of a radio receiver is depicted in Fig. 9-1. Here a standard signal generator is connected to the input terminal of the receiver in series with an imped-

---

[1] The standards of particular importance are the following: IRE Standards on Radio Receivers; "Methods of Testing Amplitude-modulation Broadcast Receivers," 1948; "Methods of Testing Frequency-modulation Receivers," 1947, and Supplement, *Proc. IRE*, vol. 37, p. 1376, December, 1949; "Methods of Testing Television Receivers," 1948; "Methods of Testing Television Signal Levels, Resolution, and Timing of Video Switching Systems," *Proc. IRE*, vol. 38, p. 551, May, 1950.

An excellent over-all discussion of methods for determining the performance of receivers covering the frequency range 30 to 30,000 kc is given by W. J. Bray and W. R. H. Lowry, The Testing of Communication-type Radio Receivers, *J. IEE (Radiocommunication Conv.)*, vol. 94, pt. IIIA, p. 313, March-April, 1947; vol. 95, pt. III, p. 271, July, 1948.

ance, termed a "dummy antenna," that in association with the internal impedance of the signal generator simulates the impedance of a typical antenna (see Sec. 9-10).   The standard signal generator is a well-shielded oscillator that is equipped with an attenuator for developing a variable and known output voltage, as discussed in Sec. 15-7.

The output power of a sound receiver is measured on an objective basis by replacing the loudspeaker with a resistance equal to the loudspeaker impedance at 400 cycles.   The output power is then measured by means of a voltmeter connected across this load.   In the picture section of a television receiver, the output is measured as the voltage at the control electrode of the cathode-ray picture tube.

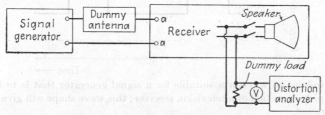

FIG. 9-1. Typical arrangement of equipment for laboratory measurement of the performance of a radio receiver that is intended to be used with a separate antenna.

9-2. Sensitivity.   As the term implies, the *sensitivity* of a radio receiver is a measure of the ability to receive weak signals.   In this regard, the receiver functions very much like an ordinary amplifier, except of course that the input signals are at radio frequencies, whereas the output comprises audio or video frequencies.

The sensitivity of a radio receiver (sometimes called *maximum sensitivity*) is defined quantitatively as the input carrier voltage with *standard modulation*[1] that must be supplied by the signal generator in Fig. 9-1 in order to develop a standard value of test output with all volume or gain controls set at maximum.[2]   For a receiver capable of developing an output of at least 1 watt of undistorted power, the standard test output is 0.5 watt, and is thus a figure well below the value where nonlinear distortion limits the output.   For a receiver in the 0.1- to 1-watt bracket, the

---

[1] For amplitude-modulation broadcast receivers the standard is 30 per cent modulation at 400 cycles; for frequency-modulation broadcast receivers it is 22.5 kc deviation (30 per cent of 75 kc maximum) at 400 cycles.   For the sound section (frequency modulation) of 6-Mc black-and-white television receivers 7.5 kc deviation (30 per cent of 25 kc maximum) at 400 cycles is considered standard, while for the picture section, modulation having the waveform of Fig. 9-2 is used (corresponding to a medium-gray uniform field), or alternatively, 30 per cent amplitude modulation with a 400-cycle sine wave is permissible.

[2] For the picture section of the television receiver, the contrast control is set to a maximum.

standard test output is 0.05 watt; for automobile receivers the normal test output is considerably higher, namely, 1.0 watt. For the television picture channel, 20 volts peak to peak at the picture-tube control electrode is the standard.

The sensitivity can be expressed in microvolts, or in the equivalent decibels below 1 volt (*i.e.*, a sensitivity of 2 μv corresponds to 114 db

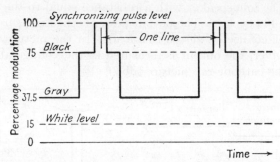

Fig. 9-2. Modulation waveform suitable for a signal generator that is to be used in testing the picture section of a television receiver; this wave shape will give a uniform gray background.

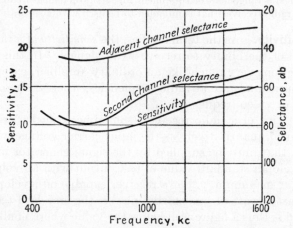

Fig. 9-3. Typical sensitivity and selectance curves of a standard broadcast receiver.

below 1 volt).[1] Alternatively, the sensitivity can be expressed in terms of the available power at terminals *aa* in Fig. 9-1, usually in decibels below 1 mw (dbm). A typical sensitivity curve is shown in Fig. 9-3.

At the higher radio frequencies, where noise generated *within* the receiver determines the weakest signal that is usable, the practical per-

---

[1] Receivers with loop antennas are an exception. As explained in Sec. 9-10, the sensitivity of such receivers is taken as the field strength required to develop the standard output.

formance of the receiver is affected by both the sensitivity as defined above, and the noise figure (see Sec. 9-11). Thus, if the receiver gain is sufficient to make the noise in the output objectionably large in comparison with the standard test output, then a further increase in the receiver sensitivity does not increase its usefulness in receiving weak signals.[1]

9-3. Selectivity. *Amplitude-modulation Receivers.* A radio receiver, if it is to be useful, must "select" the signal to which it is tuned, and reject signals of other frequencies. *Selectivity* is expressed in the form of a curve that gives the carrier signal strength with standard modulation that is required to produce the standard test output, plotted as a function of cycles off resonance of the test signal. Very commonly the carrier signal strength at the resonant frequency of the receiver is used as a reference, as illustrated in Fig. 9-4. The reciprocal of such a selectivity curve represents the response as a function of frequency.

The usual experimental procedure for obtaining a selectivity curve is as follows: With the apparatus arranged as in Fig. 9-1, the receiver is tuned to the desired frequency, and the manual volume control is set for maximum volume.[2] The signal-generator frequency is then set at the resonant frequency of the receiver, standard modulation is applied, and the carrier output of the signal generator varied until the standard test output is obtained. Without changing the tuning of the receiver, the signal generator is then set at a succession of frequencies, above and below the frequency to which the

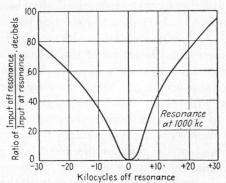

FIG. 9-4. Typical selectivity curve of a broadcast receiver.

receiver is tuned. At each new frequency, the signal-generator voltage applied to the receiver input is adjusted to give the standard test output from the receiver. The resulting data are then plotted as shown in Fig. 9-4.

The discrimination that a receiver possesses against signals differing from the frequency to which the receiver is tuned by amounts correspond-

---

[1] Further discussion of this point, and a suggested "combined sensitivity figure," is given by Joseph M. Pettit, Specification and Measurement of Receiver Sensitivity at the Higher Frequencies, *Proc. IRE*, vol. 35, p. 302, March, 1947.

[2] If the automatic-volume-control system has a selectivity that differs from the selectivity at the input to the second detector, then the AVC voltage should be held constant at the value obtained when the signal-generator frequency is at the "on-tune" value.

ing to one and two channels, is termed the *adjacent-channel attenuation*, and the *second-channel attenuation*, respectively. In the case of signals in the standard 540- to 1600-Mc broadcast band, this represents carrier frequencies differing from the resonant frequency of the receiver by 10 and 20 kc, respectively; in the case of frequency-modulation receivers where the channels are spaced 200 kc, it means frequencies differing from the resonant frequency by 200 and 400 kc, respectively.

In specifying the adjacent-channel attenuation, and the second-channel attenuation, it is customary to take the geometric mean values of attenuation for the corresponding channels on the higher and lower frequency sides of the selectivity curve. The resulting value can then be presented as shown in Fig. 9-3, as a function of the frequency to which the receiver is tuned.

The discrimination against signals an integral number of channels off tune is sometimes called *selectance*. Thus in broadcast receivers for the standard band, the attenuation suffered by a signal having a carrier differing by 20 kc from the desired carrier, *i.e.*, the second-channel attenuation, is also called the second-channel selectance.

Frequency-modulation Receivers. In frequency-modulation receivers, the normal behavior of the limiters, together with the characteristics of frequency modulation, makes it rather pointless to measure a selectivity characteristic of a receiver unless there is present at all times a signal of the frequency to which the receiver is tuned. Selectivity curves of frequency-modulation receivers are accordingly always obtained by simultaneously applying voltages from two signal generators to the receiver input in the manner discussed in connection with Fig. 9-19. The first signal generator, which is unmodulated, represents the desired signal; it is adjusted to the frequency to which the receiver is tuned, and is set to some arbitrary carrier level. The second signal generator is subjected to the standard test modulation, and represents an interfering signal. It is set at progressively increasing frequencies off resonance, and at each frequency its amplitude is adjusted until the standard test output is obtained. The resulting curve of carrier amplitude required from the second generator, as a function of cycles off resonance, can then be plotted to give a selectivity curve similar to that of Fig. 9-4.

The shape of the selectivity curve obtained by the above procedure will depend somewhat upon the amplitude of the unmodulated carrier applied to the system by the signal generator adjusted to the resonant frequency of the receiver and representing the "desired" carrier. A further complicating factor, ordinarily not present when determining selectivity of amplitude-modulation receivers, is that the shape of the selectivity curve of a frequency-modulation receiver also depends upon the amplitude selected for the standard test output. Thus a complete picture of the selectivity characteristics of a frequency-modulation receiver requires that many curves be obtained.

Because of this situation, combined with the fact that the "capture effect" usually makes unimportant any signals that differ from the resonant frequency of the receiver by more than two channel spacings, it is common practice to present the selectivity of frequency-modulation receivers in terms of adjacent-channel and second-channel attenuation or selectance curves. Typical results of this type are shown in Fig. 9-5. The failure of the interfering signal output in these curves to be proportional to the strength of the input value of the interfering signal results from the action of the limiter and automatic-volume-control systems.

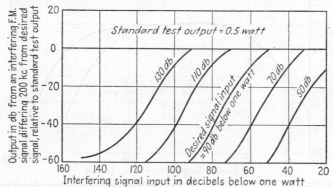

Fig. 9-5. Typical adjacent-channel selectance curves of a frequency-modulation broadcast receiver.

9-4. Fidelity. The term *fidelity* is used to denote the manner in which the output of a radio receiver depends on the modulation frequency.[1] The electric fidelity denotes the fidelity of the receiver up to the loudspeaker, but does not take into account the effectiveness with which the electric output of the receiver is transformed into sound output. The acoustic fidelity shows the manner in which the acoustic or sound output of a radio receiver depends upon the modulation frequency, and differs from the electric fidelity by taking into account the characteristics of the loud speaker.

The electric fidelity of amplitude-modulation and frequency-modulation receivers, and of the sound section of television receivers, is determined with the aid of apparatus arranged as in Fig. 9-1. The loudspeaker is ordinarily replaced by a resistance corresponding to the voice-coil

---

[1] In a broader sense, fidelity can be regarded as representing the faithfulness with which the receiver reproduces the intelligence modulated upon the radio wave that is being received. In this case it would include nonlinear or amplitude distortion as well as frequency distortion. However, in terms of the formally recognized standards, fidelity denotes the variation of response with modulation frequency.

impedance at 400 cycles; alternatively one may consider the electric output to be the voltage developed across the voice coil of the loudspeaker. The carrier frequency of the signal generator is adjusted to resonance with the receiver, standard 400-cycle modulation is applied, the signal-generator carrier level is set at a convenient arbitrary level, and the manual volume control of the receiver is adjusted to give the standard test output. The modulation frequency is then varied over the audio range, while keeping the degree of modulation constant. The fidelity is then presented as the output relative to the 400-cycle output, plotted as a function of frequency, as shown in Fig. 9-6.

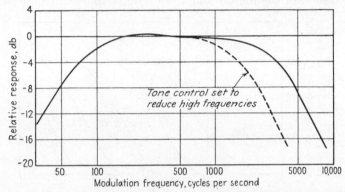

FIG. 9-6. Electric fidelity of a typical amplitude-modulated broadcast receiver.

Acoustic fidelity is obtained in the same way as electric fidelity, except that the determination of the receiver output is a problem in acoustic measurements. The acoustic fidelity includes all the characteristics of the receiver, including the loudspeaker itself. Accordingly, it may at first be thought to be the only test of significance; yet it suffers from the difficulty of standardization. Ideally, the receiver should be located in an acoustic environment identical with that where it will ultimately be used by the listener. This involves many factors such as size of room, location of the receiver in the room, location of the listener, and the acoustic characteristics of all the furnishings. Clearly, it is more difficult to standardize on such surroundings, although an attempt has been made.[1]

The electric fidelity of the picture channel of a television receiver is determined in the same way as the electric fidelity of an amplitude-modu-

[1] "Standards on Electroacoustics: Definitions of Terms, Letter and Graphical Symbols, Method of Testing Loud Speakers, 1938," Institute of Radio Engineers, New York; for additional information also see Harold A. Wheeler and Vernon E. Whitman, Acoustic Testing of High Fidelity Receivers, *Proc. IRE*, vol. 23, p. 610, June, 1935; Stuart Ballantine, High Quality Radio Broadcast Transmission and Reception, *Proc. IRE*, vol. 23, p. 618, June, 1935.

lated receiver. The only differences are the wider range of modulation frequencies involved, and the fact that the reference test output is standardized as 10 volts peak at 100 kc. Thus to measure electric fidelity, the signal generator is modulated 30 per cent with a sine wave, and then the variation of voltage at the picture tube is observed as a function of the modulating frequency as this frequency is varied from 30 cycles to 5,000,000 cycles. This measurement is commonly carried out in the absence of synchronizing and blanking signals.

The phase shift of the output wave as a function of the modulating frequency can be measured by connecting the signal-generator modulating voltage to the vertical-deflection terminals of a wide-band cathode-ray oscilloscope, and connecting the sine-wave output voltage developed at the control grid of the picture tube to the horizontal-deflection terminals. If the vertical and horizontal oscilloscope amplifiers then have identical phase characteristics, the resulting Lissajous figures give the phase shift, as discussed in connection with Fig. 6-24.

The characteristic of a television receiver that is most directly related to the electric fidelity of the picture channel is the transient response. In contrast, the amplitude and phase fidelity represent an indirect means of determining the extent to which the receiving system will satisfactorily reproduce the transients that compose the video modulation possessed by the signal. The transient response of a receiver is determined by employing a standard signal generator with square-wave or pulse modulation, and then observing the output of the receiver on a wide-band oscilloscope in which the sweep circuit is synchronized with the modulating voltage of the signal generator, as discussed in Sec. 8-10. It is to be noted that the transient response will be affected by the nonlinear distortion of the system, as well as by the amplitude and phase characteristics of the receiver.

Visual fidelity tests in a television receiver correspond to acoustic fidelity tests of a sound receiver, only there are many more things to measure. These include resolution, i.e., the ability to distinguish between closely spaced black-and-white segments; contrast range between white and black portions of the picture; geometric distortion of the picture; focus; and the imperfections of synchronizing and interlace. Most of these characteristics can be observed by applying to the input of the receiver a signal modulated by the standard resolution chart, and observing on the face of the picture tube the extent to which the receiver reproduces the detailed features of the chart.[1]

---

[1] This measurement requires a complicated pattern generator. A rough test can be made by using an auxiliary television receiver of high video fidelity which is tuned to a local television station during those hours when a test pattern is being broadcast. The video output of this receiver, including synchronizing and blanking signals, is then used to modulate the standard signal generator.

9-5. Nonlinear Distortion in Radio Receivers. Nonlinear or harmonic distortion occurs in a radio receiver when the receiver output contains frequency components not present in the modulation envelope of the input signal. The most important cause of such distortion is usually overloading of the audio or video amplifier of the receiver. In amplitude-modulation receivers, the diode second detector also ordinarily introduces distortion as a result of "clipping" when the degree of modulation approaches 100 per cent; this can be quite serious if the detector is not properly designed.[1]

The radio-frequency portions of the receiver will also introduce non-linear distortion if the amplification depends upon signal amplitude; in this case the peaks of a modulated wave will not be amplified the same amount as the troughs, with resulting distortion of the modulation envelope. However, nonlinear distortion from this cause is seldom encountered in significant amount in practical receivers.

Nonlinear or harmonic distortion is determined by applying to the receiver input a signal from a signal generator which possesses sine-wave modulation, and then observing the resulting distortion present in the audio- or video-frequency output of the receiver by the means discussed in Secs. 6-4 and 6-6. In the case of broadcast receivers, 400-cycle modulation is very commonly used; it is possible to employ other modulation frequencies, however, and in fact two modulation frequencies may simultaneously be applied to the carrier of the input signal to provide a test of intermodulation distortion. Distortion tests should be repeated with different degrees of modulation of the test signal, including particularly 100 per cent modulation, since certain types of distortion, notably detector clipping, depend upon the degree of modulation. The results of a harmonic-distortion test will also depend upon the output power. They may likewise be affected by the setting of the manual volume control, by the carrier amplitude of the input signal, and by the modulation frequency. Thus it is necessary carefully to record all test conditions if the results are to have significance, and also to determine distortion under a variety of conditions.

It is customary to consider that the rated value of maximum output power which a radio receiver can deliver is the power for which the total harmonic distortion, as defined by Eq. (8-6), is 10 per cent. If the degree of modulation is not so high as to cause detector clipping, this distortion will normally arise almost entirely in the final power stage of the output amplifier of the receiver.

9-6. Tests for Spurious Responses, Including Cross Modulation. Receivers very commonly will respond in undesired ways to very strong

---

[1] For further discussion of diode detector clipping see F. E. Terman, "Radio Engineering," 3d ed., pp. 502–513, McGraw-Hill Book Company, Inc., New York, 1947.

signals.   Some types of such spurious responses arise with only one strong signal present, while other types require the simultaneous presence of two or more strong signals.

Spurious Responses Arising from a Single Signal.   The most important spurious response of this type is the response to the image frequency in a superheterodyne receiver.   This is measured by adjusting the signal generator to the image frequency,[1] and with standard modulation applied, increasing the signal-generator output until one obtains either the standard test output from the receiver, or the largest output that is possible. Without changing the receiver adjustment, the signal generator is then set at the frequency to which the receiver is tuned, and the signal-generator voltage adjusted to develop the same receiver output as before.   The ratio of the signal-generator voltages for these two situations is then referred to as the *image ratio*.   In a good receiver the image ratio will be 60 db or more.

Another important spurious-response frequency in a superheterodyne receiver arises from the possibility that signals of intermediate frequency may be able to produce output in the receiver.   The magnitude of this spurious response can be determined with the aid of a signal generator adjusted first to the intermediate frequency, and then to the frequency to which the receiver is tuned, and comparing the two input signals required to produce the same output.

Still other spurious-response frequencies are possible.   Their existence may be searched for by setting the receiver successively to a number of frequencies over the band, and for each setting tuning the signal generator through a wide frequency range while maintaining the signal-generator output at a high value, such as 1 volt.   When a spurious response is noted, its relative magnitude may be defined in the same way as the image response.

In superheterodyne receivers receiving only a single unmodulated carrier frequency, a whistle whose pitch varies rapidly with tuning will sometimes be observed.   This is the result of interaction between various parts of the receiver, and most frequently occurs when the receiver carrier frequency approximates a harmonic of the intermediate frequency.   The existence of such "whistle modulation" can be investigated in the same manner as one would search for other spurious responses, except that an unmodulated carrier is used.   The whistle modulation can be expressed quantitatively by adjusting the pitch of the whistle to 400 cycles, and measuring the amplitude of the resulting 400-cycle output voltage produced in the receiver.   The whistle modulation is then the percentage

---

[1] The image frequency will differ by twice the intermediate frequency from the frequency to which the receiver is tuned.   The image frequency will be higher than the receiver frequency in the usual case where the local oscillator frequency is higher than the receiver frequency.

modulation at 400 cycles that applied to the unmodulated test voltage would produce the same receiver output as is caused by the whistle.

Cross-talk and Other Forms of Two-signal Spurious Responses. Various forms of spurious responses can arise when two signals of different frequencies are simultaneously applied to a receiver. The most important of these is termed *cross-talk*, and is heard under the following circumstances: The receiver is tuned to a "desired" signal which is so strong as to cause the automatic-volume-control system to reduce the gain of the receiver to a low value. At the same time, a strong "unwanted" signal operating on a frequency not greatly different from that of the desired frequency is simultaneously present. During the intervals when the carrier wave of the desired station is unmodulated, then the modulation of the unwanted signal is heard, but if the desired signal is turned off the interference from the unwanted signal disappears. Such cross-talk is caused by the unwanted signal modulating the carrier wave of the desired signal; it is introduced by third-order curvature in the first one or two tubes of the receiver.[1]

The magnitude of such cross-talk can be determined quantitatively by simultaneously applying output from two signal generators to the receiver input.[2] The first, or desired, signal is tuned to resonance with the receiver, and its carrier amplitude is set at an appropriate level. The manual volume control of the receiver is adjusted to give standard test output when the signal is modulated 30 per cent at 400 cycles, after which the modulation is switched off. An unwanted, or interfering, signal from the second generator is then turned on, and is applied to the receiver input in addition to the desired signal carrier, which remains unchanged. This interfering carrier is modulated 30 per cent at 400 cycles, and is tuned through a wide frequency range while readjusting its carrier amplitude as required to give an arbitrarily chosen value of interference output, commonly 30 db less than the standard test output for the desired signal. The results are then plotted in curves giving the unwanted carrier strength as a function of the difference in frequency between the interfering and the desired signals. Typical results are given in Fig. 9-7.

The results of a cross-talk test can also be expressed in terms of the cross-talk factor, which is defined as[3]

$$\text{Cross-talk factor} = \frac{\text{degree of unwanted modulation produced on "desired" carrier}}{\text{degree of modulation of unwanted carrier}} \qquad (9\text{-}1)$$

[1] The quantitative relations involved in this form of cross-talk are given by Terman, *op. cit.*, pp. 277–284, 354.

[2] Techniques whereby the outputs of two signal generators may be simultaneously impressed on the input of a single receiver are described in connection with Fig. 9-19.

[3] For further discussion see Terman, *op. cit.*, p. 355.

The cross-talk factor can be readily determined from the two-signal-generator test described above. First, with the desired signal unmodulated, the output at the modulation frequency of the unwanted signal is observed for a known degree of modulation of the unwanted signal. Then the modulation on the latter signal is turned off, the desired signal is modulated at the same frequency as was the unwanted signal, and this degree of modulation is adjusted to give the same modulation-frequency output amplitude as before. This last degree of modulation is the numerator of Eq. (9-1), and its ratio to the known degree of modulation of the unwanted signal is then the cross-talk factor.

Two signals can also interact in other ways to produce spurious responses. Thus if the difference between the frequencies of two signals

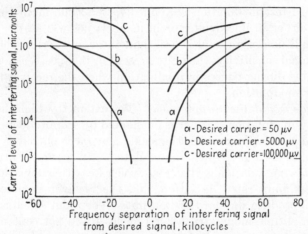

Fig. 9-7. Typical result of a cross-talk interference test of an amplitude-modulated broadcast receiver.

lies in the tuning range of the receiver, a spurious response at the difference frequency can result. For example, if signals having frequencies of 1400 and 600 kc are simultaneously applied to a receiver tuned to 800 kc, then if these signals are strong enough to overload the first tube of the receiver, a difference frequency of 800 kc is produced to which the receiver responds. Again the combination of a desired and an unwanted signal simultaneously applied to a receiver can in some cases result in a whistle that will disappear if the unwanted signal is turned off. Such spurious responses can be sought, and also measured, by obvious applications of the two-signal-generator techniques described above.

9-7. Miscellaneous Tests on Frequency-modulation Receivers. *Deviation Sensitivity.* The deviation sensitivity is a measure of the adequacy of the audio gain of the frequency-modulation receiver. A voltage from a signal generator is applied to the receiver input in series with a 300-ohm resistance representing the standard dummy antenna, and the carrier level of this input signal is adjusted to a standard value, typically 1100 μv. With the manual volume control set at maximum, the frequency deviation is then adjusted so that the receiver delivers the standard test output. The resulting frequency deviation expressed either in kilocycles, or as a percentage of maximum rated deviation, is termed the *deviation sensitivity*. Clearly, if the audio gain is low a larger deviation will be required to give the standard test output; hence the lower the deviation sensitivity the better the receiver.

Quieting-signal Sensitivity. The quieting-signal sensitivity is the smallest unmodulated carrier voltage which when applied to the receiver through the standard 300-ohm dummy antenna reduces the noise output of the receiver to a value of 30 db below the receiver output obtained when the standard test modulation is applied to the same input signal. It is expressed either in microvolts, or in decibels below 1 watt. When the carrier amplitude of a signal is less than the value corresponding to the quieting-signal sensitivity, the noise present in the receiver output will be objectionable during pauses in modulation when the receiver noise is not masked by modulation.

Amplitude-modulation Suppression. The extent to which the output of a frequency-modulation receiver is unaffected by amplitude modulation is determined by a test in which the signal-generator output is simultaneously amplitude- and frequency-modulated. In a typical arrangement, the frequency modulation is at a 1000-cycle rate with a deviation of 30 per cent of maximum rated deviation, and the receiver volume control is adjusted to produce standard test output. The input signal is then additionally amplitude-modulated at 400 cycles to 30 per cent modulation. The intensity of the output at 400 cycles is a measure of the response to amplitude modulation, and the amplitude suppression can be defined as the ratio of the 400-cycle output to the standard 1000-cycle output. Since the amplitude suppression will depend upon the amplitude of the input carrier voltage, this test should be carried out with several values of input signals.

If a signal generator capable of being simultaneously amplitude- and frequency-modulated is not available, two signal generators may be used, one amplitude-modulated and one frequency-modulated. The signals from these two generators are then simultaneously impressed on the receiver, and precautions are taken so that the beat note between the two carriers does not contribute to the observed output at either 400 or 1000 cycles.

In tests of amplitude-modulation suppression, it is particularly important that any signal generator that is amplitude-modulated be free from incidental frequency modulation.

Co-channel Interference. In a frequency-modulation system, an interfering signal having the same carrier frequency as the desired signal will tend to be suppressed when the desired signal is stronger, and will in turn suppress the desired signal if the undesired carrier is the stronger. This action results from the inherent effects of the detector, limiter, and automatic-volume-control system.

The co-channel interference that remains can be determined by the use of two signal generators that are simultaneously applied to the receiver. First, the desired signal generator is subjected to standard modulation, and is set at an arbitrarily chosen amplitude. The audio-frequency output of the receiver is then adjusted to the standard test value by means of the volume control, after which the modulation on the desired signal

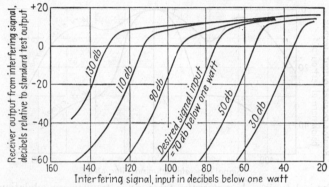

Fig. 9-8. Typical results of a co-channel interference test of a frequency-modulation broadcast receiver.

is removed. The interfering signal is next turned on and frequency-modulated with the standard test modulation. The co-channel interference is then the resulting receiver output caused by the presence of the modulated interfering signal. The test should be repeated at each of several levels for the desired signal.

The results of the co-channel-interference test may be plotted as illustrated in Fig. 9-8. The co-channel interference may also be expressed as the interfering signal input in decibels below the desired signal input, which produces an undesired output that is 30 db below the output that results when the desired signal has standard test modulation.

The extent to which the interfering signal will suppress the desired signal is termed the masking interference. It is obtained by rearranging the test conditions so that the desired signal possesses standard modulation, while the interfering signal is left unmodulated. The output of the receiver is then observed as the level of the interfering signal is increased. The results are plotted in the same way as the co-channel interference, except that the ordinates now give the desired output.

Tuning Characteristic. The tuning characteristic denotes the variation in audio output as the receiver is tuned through a signal.

In practice, this characteristic is more easily determined by varying the signal-generator frequency, than by varying the receiver tuning, since the signal generator usually has a better frequency calibration than does the receiver.   The tuning characteristic is hence obtained by tuning the signal generator to resonance with the receiver, setting the amplitude of the input signal at some appropriate reference value, and adjusting the volume control of the receiver to give standard test output when the standard signal generator has standard modulation.   The receiver output is then observed as the frequency of the signal generator is detuned to each side of the receiver frequency, while keeping the signal-generator

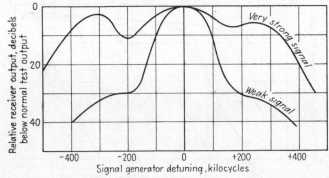

Fig. 9-9. Typical tuning characteristics taken on a frequency-modulation receiver designed for 75 kc deviation.

output constant.   The results are presented in curves such as shown in Fig. 9-9.   The test must be repeated for different values of input signal, since as shown in Fig. 9-9, the tuning characteristic will depend considerably upon signal level.

The tuning characteristic is of particular importance in frequency-modulation receivers, since such receivers sometimes have spurious output responses adjacent to the correct tuning point.   This effect arises from the nature of the frequency-modulation detector, and tends to be more pronounced when the input signal is large.

9-8. Miscellaneous Receiver Tests. *Automatic Volume Control.* Most radio receivers are provided with some form of automatic volume control (also called automatic gain control) to reduce the extreme ranges of receiver audio output that would result if the output were directly proportional to the signal strength at the antenna.

The standard procedure for evaluating the effectiveness of the automatic-volume-control system is to apply to the antenna terminals a signal with standard modulation, that is, 30 per cent at 400 cycles, and a carrier amplitude corresponding to a typical signal level, such as 5000 μv for an amplitude-modulation broadcast receiver, or 1100 μv for a frequency-modulation or television receiver.   The manual volume control of the receiver is then adjusted to provide the standard test output.   With this manual setting left fixed, the carrier level at the receiver input is varied over a large range, usually from 1 μv to 1 volt.   The relative receiver output power is then observed, and plotted as a curve giving receiver output in decibels as a function of carrier input level, also in decibels.   In some cases it is desirable to repeat the test with several degrees of modulation.   Typical results are shown in Fig. 9-10; the flatter the curve the better the automatic-volume-control system.

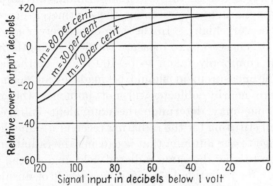

FIG. 9-10. Characteristics of a typical automatic-volume-control system used in an amplitude-modulation broadcast receiver.

Radiation from Receivers.[1]   A radio receiver, and especially a television receiver, can radiate radio-frequency power which may cause interference in similar nearby receivers, or even receivers operating in an entirely different frequency range.   In many circumstances it is necessary that such radiated power be an absolute minimum, or at least within an acceptable standard limit.

A radio receiver ordinarily contains a number of sources of radio-frequency power.   The most obvious is the local oscillator in a super-heterodyne receiver; in addition, harmonics of the local oscillator are present in the output of the converter.   Also the power level of the inter-mediate-frequency energy at the second detector is often appreciable, and the output circuits of the second detector contain harmonics of the

[1] For additional information see G. J. McDonald and D. A. Thorn, Radiation from Receivers, *J. IEE* (*Radiocomm. Conv.*), vol. 94, pt. IIIA, p. 437, March–April, 1947; C. G. Seright, Open-field Test Facilities for Measurement of Incidental Receiver Radiation, *RCA Review*, vol. 12, p. 45, March, 1951; Standards on Radio Receivers: Open Field Method of Measurement of Spurious Radiation from Frequency Modulation and Television Broadcast Receivers, 1951, *Proc. IRE*, vol. 39, p. 803, July, 1951.

intermediate frequency that have appreciable amplitude. Finally, television receivers contain additional sources of energy; thus harmonics of the saw-tooth wave used to produce the horizontal deflection are distributed through the radio-frequency spectrum, the video signal itself contains frequencies up to 4.5 Mc, and in some television receivers a radio-frequency oscillator is used to generate the high anode voltage for the picture tube.

There are three principal mechanisms by which a receiver may radiate energy. The most obvious and probably the most harmful is radiation by the receiving antenna. When appreciable, this action can be easily evaluated by connecting a sensitive radio-frequency vacuum-tube voltmeter or a receiver across the antenna terminals in parallel with the standard dummy antenna (assuming the voltmeter or receiver input impedance to be very high). In the case of a receiver having a built-in loop antenna, it is necessary to measure the field strength produced some distance away, commonly taken to be 100 ft, by methods described in Chap. 11. The measurement should be made in an open field or on a flat roof, where nearby objects will not influence the measurement. Alternatively, one may determine the equivalent voltage causing the radiation by substituting for the radiating receiver a signal generator that applies a voltage to the antenna that is causing the radiation, and adjusting this voltage to give the same radiated field as does the receiver.[1]

A second way for radiation to occur is as a result of unshielded electrostatic or electromagnetic fields associated with the receiver chassis or receiver components. While this effect is normally not very great in magnitude, it can cause trouble in nearby equipment. The amount of such radiation can be evaluated by disconnecting the antenna and replacing it by a noninductive resistor of appropriate magnitude. The receiver is then placed at some standard height above the ground, and operated from a self-contained power supply (or from a power line that is isolated by proper shielding and filtering). The resulting radiation is measured using field-strength measuring equipment.

The third way in which power can be radiated from a receiver is through radio-frequency current flowing in the power-supply cord, and in particular, current resulting from voltages generated between this cord and ground. These voltages can be measured with a vacuum-tube voltmeter, or a receiver, using appropriate coupling means to filter out the

[1] In the case of high-frequency receivers in which the input terminals are balanced with respect to ground, it is necessary to investigate the way or ways in which antenna radiation is being produced. This is because the radiation can result from either (1) a voltage existing between the two wires of the antenna transmission line, or (2) a voltage existing between ground and the transmission line, considering the two wires of the latter as being in parallel to form one side of the circuit.

60-cycle voltage.   Alternatively, one may replace the receiver by a signal generator, and specify the power-line radiation in terms of the signal-generator voltage that must be applied to the power line to produce the same radiation as does the receiver that is involved.

The maximum radiation that can be permitted from a receiver depends upon circumstances.   In the case of naval vessels, where radiation must be kept low in order to minimize interference between the many receivers used on the same ship, and also for security reasons, a typical standard is a radiated field not to exceed 0.1 μv per m at 1 mile, or a radiated power not to exceed 400×10^{-12} watt.

Hum Measurement.   Hum is a tone having a 60-cycle fundamental that is produced as a result of the action of alternating power-frequency currents.   Hum may be introduced directly into the audio-frequency system of a receiver as a result of inadequate filtering of the plate-supply system, by stray coupling, or by alternating currents used in filaments and heaters of tubes.   Alternatively, hum can appear in a receiver output as a result of modulation by hum voltages or fields of a radio-frequency signal present in the intermediate-frequency, converter, and radio-frequency stages of the receiver.

The hum voltages present in the receiver output can be observed by employing either a harmonic analyzer or an rms (square-law) measuring instrument.   The results obtained will usually depend upon the setting of the manual volume control, and may be affected by the presence or absence of a radio-frequency signal.

Amplification of Individual Stages and Sections of Radio Receivers. The sensitivity of a receiver, defined in terms of the input power required to give a standard test output, is determined by the over-all amplification of the receiver.   It is therefore sometimes desirable to measure the amplification of individual sections of the receiver in order to determine how each contributes to the total gain.

This can be done by the same method used to obtain the gain of individual stages of a multistage amplifier, as discussed in connection with Fig. 8-9.   That is, a signal-generator voltage of suitable frequency is applied at successive points a, b, c, d, etc., in Fig. 9-11, with the amplitude in each case adjusted so that the same audio-frequency output is obtained at all times.[1]   The ratio of the voltage associated with any two particular points then gives the voltage amplification of the portion of the receiver lying between these two test points.   Thus, the ratio of the intermediate-frequency carrier voltage with standard modulation that is applied to the control grid of the first intermediate-frequency amplifier stage, to the

[1] Note that the signal-generator frequency changes from signal to intermediate frequency on the two sides of the converter, and from intermediate to audio (modulation) frequency at the second detector.

radio-frequency carrier voltage with standard modulation that must be applied to the signal grid of the converter to give the same receiver output, is the conversion gain of the converter.   As in the corresponding multi-stage-amplifier case (see page 321), measurements made in this way give results that are very close to the actual gain existing in the receiver, including regenerative effects.   Results showing the voltage gain of different parts of a typical receiver are given in Fig. 9-11 for a representative case when receiving a moderately weak signal.

An alternative method of investigating the gain of individual parts of a receiver consists in applying a modulated test signal to the receiver, and observing the relative voltage at successive points in the receiver by

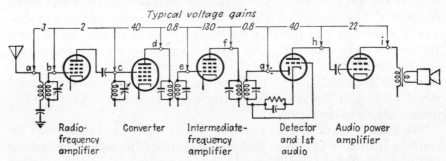

Fig. 9-11. Schematic diagram of a receiver, showing points at which a signal generator would be connected to determine the amplification of individual sections of the receiver.   Typical values of voltage gain are shown for various sections of the receiver, for conditions corresponding to a moderately weak signal.

the use of a vacuum-tube voltmeter having such a high input impedance as not to alter the amplification appreciably.[1]   In the audio-frequency section of the receiver, a conventional type of vacuum-tube voltmeter can be used, measuring voltages with respect to ground.   The voltmeter is moved from point to point, starting from the loudspeaker and working backward toward the detector output.   The voltages in the radio-frequency portion of the receiver can be observed with the aid of an amplifier-detector type of vacuum-tube voltmeter, typically employing one stage of tuned radio-frequency amplification.   In order that such a measuring system will not alter the characteristics of the receiver, it is connected to the point in the receiver at which the relative voltage is to be observed by the use of an extremely small series capacitance.   As the point of connection is moved, the signal-generator input to the receiver is read-

---

[1] It is also possible to use an untuned-crystal-detector and high-gain audio-amplifier combination in place of the tuned amplifier.   Such an arrangement is capable of observing signal levels of less than 1 mv, and has the advantage of being untuned.

justed to maintain a constant indication in the vacuum-tube voltmeter. The gain between any two points in the receiver is then taken as the ratio of the signal-generator voltages required to maintain the constant reading of the vacuum-tube voltmeter. Where the frequency of the signal changes, as when one is determining the gain from a point in the radio-frequency section to a point in the intermediate-frequency section of a receiver, it is necessary to retune, and also perhaps change tuning coils in the vacuum-tube voltmeter. In this case, the relative sensitivity of the vacuum-tube voltmeter at the two frequencies involved can be determined by means of the signal generator, and allowed for in the resulting calculations. This method of investigating the characteristics of a radio receiver is widely used in servicing equipment. It gives a good general idea of the receiver behavior, although it does not accurately take into account regeneration that may be present in the intermediate-frequency and radio-frequency sections.

In determining the gain of individual parts of a receiver, it is necessary to disconnect the automatic-volume-control lead from the second detector circuit, and connect it to a source of fixed voltage so chosen as to correspond to the AVC voltage that would be appropriate for the condition under which the receiver gain is being investigated. Thus with weak signals, a small negative AVC voltage would be employed, while strong signals would correspond to a large negative voltage.

9-9. Requirements for Signal Generators. A detailed discussion of signal generators will be found in Chap. 15. However, it is desirable here to emphasize those features which are particularly important in the testing of radio receivers.

The principal objective of the signal generator is to develop at its output terminals an adjustable and accurately known voltage, ranging from approximately 1 volt to between 1 and 10 μv. It is important that the signal generator be sufficiently well shielded so that stray voltages introduced into the receiver by leakage from the signal generator are small compared with the voltage developed at the output terminals of the signal generator.

In general, it is desirable that the output impedance of the signal generator be low. This is because the impedance must commonly be modified by the addition of a dummy antenna in the output circuit (see Sec. 9-10), and this is somewhat more easily done if the signal generator has a low output impedance.

The type of modulation must, of course, be appropriate to the receiver being tested, e.g., amplitude modulation for a conventional broadcast receiver, and frequency modulation for the sound section of television receivers. The modulation capability of a signal generator for testing the picture section of a television receiver depends upon whether the measurement requirements are simple or complex.

The picture section of television receivers utilizes amplitude modulation, and a sine-wave modulated signal at 400 cycles and 30 per cent modulation can be used for a sensitivity test. A more realistic signal involves a modulation waveform of the type shown in Fig. 9-2, simulating a medium-gray uniform field, together with blanking and synchronizing pulses. For a complete test of visual fidelity, with sufficient detail and accuracy to meet the requirements of a television-receiver manufacturer, a signal generator is used which provides an actual picture of the so-called resolution chart. This chart consists of a pattern of white, gray, and black bars and wedges well dispersed over the pattern so that many aspects of the receiver performance can be tested, such as resolution, range of shade, contrast, etc. Such a pattern generator is costly and complex; it is too specialized to be described here.

9-10. Signal-generator Connections Involving Dummy Antennas and Loop Antennas. An important aspect of receiver measurement concerns

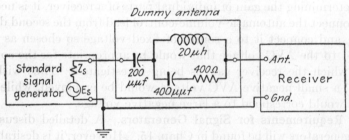

Fig. 9-12 "Dummy" antenna that has been standardized for broadcast receivers.

the manner in which the standard signal is introduced into the receiver. Two types of receivers need to be considered, those having built-in loop antennas, and those having a terminal (or terminals) to which an external antenna is connected.

Receivers Using External Antennas—Dummy Antennas. In testing a receiver intended to be used with an external antenna, the signal generator is connected to the receiver through a series impedance or dummy antenna as illustrated in Fig. 9-1. This series impedance is chosen so that when supplemented by the internal impedance of the signal generator, the total impedance that is connected between the receiver input terminals represents the impedance of a typical antenna.

In some cases the dummy antenna has been standardized. Thus the standard antenna used in testing amplitude-modulation broadcast receivers in the frequency range 540 to 23,000 kc is shown in Fig. 9-12. The impedance characteristic of this antenna is shown in Fig. 9-13. In the standard broadcast frequency range 540 to 1600 kc, such an antenna simulates a single-wire antenna having an effective height of 4 m; at very high frequencies it approximates a 400-ohm transmission line.[1]   The use of a dummy antenna in the manner shown in Fig. 9-12 results in an open-circuit voltage at the receiver input terminals equal to the signal-generator open-circuit voltage, and an equivalent source impedance equal to the sum of the impedance of the dummy antenna plus the internal impedance of the signal generator. Most signal generators designed for testing of broadcast receivers have an output impedance of 10 ohms or less, and thus the over-all impedance of the system is essentially that of the dummy antenna. The dummy antenna ensures that the measurements take into account the effectiveness with which the receiver would utilize energy available from a typical antenna.

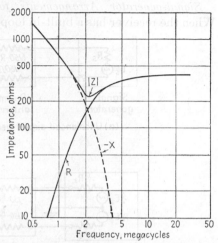

Fig. 9-13. Impedance characteristic of the dummy antenna of Fig. 9-12.

At frequencies higher than the 500- to 1600-kc broadcast band, the antenna is usually connected to the receiver by means of a transmission line.   The antenna is then almost always designed so that its impedance matches approximately the characteristic impedance of the transmission line.   As a result, the energy source exciting the receiver then consists of a voltage in series with a resistance equal to the characteristic imped-ance (usually resistive) of the transmission line.   The antenna-to-receiver line is usually standardized for the various classes of service; for instance, for television and frequency-modulation broadcast receiver systems, a parallel-wire balanced transmission line of 300 ohms characteristic impedance is used.   In this case the signal generator can be connected to the receiver input as shown in Fig. 9-14.[2]   At still higher frequencies it is customary to use a coaxial transmission line, typically having a character-istic impedance of 50 ohms resistance.   The outer terminal of the coaxial

[1] The design of a dummy antenna simulating a half-wave dipole can be readily car-ried out by the use of curves given by Hans Salinger, A Dummy Dipole Network, *Proc. IRE*, vol. 32, p. 115, February, 1944.

[2] When the signal-generator output is unbalanced as at *a*, then the system is no longer perfectly balanced to ground.   However, the impedance of the ground return circuit is so high as to introduce negligible error provided the distance involved is not such as to give half-wave resonance.   For further discussion on the problem of how to use a signal generator with unbalanced output to test a receiver with balanced input see John A. Rankin, Receiver Input Connections for U-H-F Measurements, *RCA Rev.*, vol. 6, p. 473, April, 1942.

line is grounded, and the resulting signal-generator connections are as shown in Fig. 9-15.

Signal-generator Arrangements for Receivers with Loop Antennas.[1] When the receiver has a built-in loop antenna, it is not feasible to connect

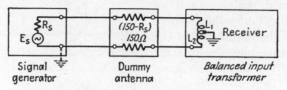

(a) Unbalanced signal generator output

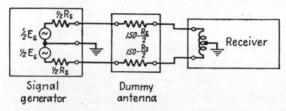

(b) Balanced signal generator output

FIG. 9-14. Methods of connecting a signal generator to a receiver in which the input is balanced with respect to ground.

the signal generator directly to the receiver. The loop usually supplies the inductance of the tuned circuit of the input stage, and hence cannot be disconnected; nor can it be shunted by the signal generator. Instead, the signal generator is inductively coupled to the loop, and the

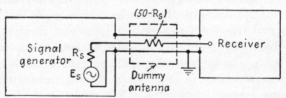

FIG. 9-15. Signal-generator connections for a receiving system designed to employ a 50-ohm coaxial-line input.

input to the receiver is expressed in terms of the average strength of the induction field at the receiver loop antenna.

There are two convenient ways of generating an induction field of known strength. One of these is to use the signal generator to excite a loop, as shown in Fig. 9-16. The signal-generator and receiver loops

[1] For further details see IRE Standards on Radio Receivers: "Methods of Testing Amplitude-modulation Broadcast Receivers," 1948; W. O. Swinyard, Measurement of Loop Antenna Receivers, *Proc. IRE,* vol. 29, p. 382, July, 1941.

should be of about the same size; their separation should be at least twice the diameter of either loop, yet small compared with a wavelength. The distance to surrounding objects (with the exception of the receiver chassis, which is normally left in place) should be several times the separation of the two loops. If the self-resonant frequency of the signal-generator loop is very high compared with the operating frequency, so that

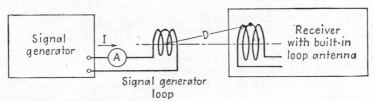

FIG. 9-16. Arrangement involving a signal generator and a loop, for generating an induction field of known strength.

capacitive currents are negligible, then the field strength produced by the signal-generator loop is

$$E = \frac{47.15Nd^2I}{D^3} \tag{9-2}$$

where E = equivalent electric field strength, volts per m at center of receiver loop

N = number of turns in signal-generator loop

d = diameter of signal-generator loop, m

I = current in signal-generator loop, amp

D = distance from center of signal-generator loop to periphery of receiver loop.

The current I corresponding to large values of field strength can be measured directly by means of a thermocouple. This gives a relation between I and the voltage setting of the signal generator which can then be used to obtain I when the value is too small to measure directly. Alternatively, one can measure or calculate the inductance (or reactance) of the signal-generator loop, and then obtain the loop current I as the signal-generator voltage divided by the loop reactance. Still another possibility of determining I that finds extensive practical use is illustrated in Fig. 9-17a. Here a low-impedance loop is connected to the signal generator through a relatively high series resistance R_1, as for example 400 ohms. To a fair approximation the loop current I is then the signal-generator voltage divided by $R_1 + R_s$; still higher accuracy can be obtained by calculating the inductance of the loop and allowing for it in computing I^*. The loop in Fig. 9-17a can be connected to the

* By properly selecting the dimensions of the loop and the series resistance in such an arrangement, it is possible to achieve a simple relationship between volts per meter

signal generator through a coaxial line as shown in Fig. 9-17b.   Here resistance R_0 is so chosen that R_0 and R in parallel equal the characteristic impedance of the line.   Under these conditions the current I in the loop can be calculated by assuming that the voltage developed by the standard

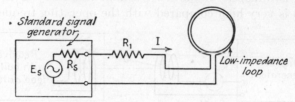

(a) Low-impedance loop fed through a series resistance

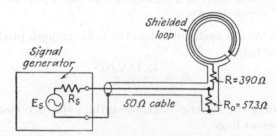

(b) Low-impedance shielded loop fed from a coaxial line and series resistance

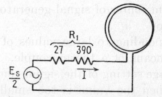

(c) Equivalent circuit of (b), assuming $R_s=50$ and that loop impedance is small

FIG. 9-17. Arrangements commonly employed for utilizing a signal generator to produce a known current in a loop; in these arrangements, the loop inductance is small, and the resistance R_1 is considerably larger than the loop reactance.

signal generator across a load impedance equal to the characteristic impedance of the line is applied to the loop in series with the resistance R_1, as shown in Fig. 9-17c, where R_1 equals R plus the resistance formed by R_0 in parallel with the characteristic impedance of the line.

at some convenient test distance (as 24 in.), and the open-circuit voltage developed by the signal generator.   For details see IRE Standards on Radio Receivers, "Methods of Testing Amplitude-modulation Broadcast Receivers," 1948, p. 20.

An alternative arrangement for generating a standard field, that is particularly appropriate where the measurement is to be made in a shielded room, is illustrated in Fig. 9-18. Here a wire traverses the shielded room near the ceiling, midway between the two walls, as shown, and acts as the inner conductor of a coaxial transmission line. The outer conductor of this line consists of the walls, floor, and ceiling of the shielded room. The signal generator is connected in series with one end of the transmission line as indicated, and the opposite end is terminated in the

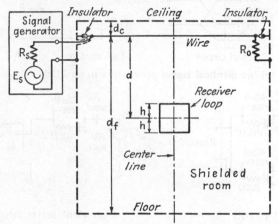

FIG. 9-18. Method of generating an induction field of known strength in a shielded room.

characteristic impedance of the line. The terminating impedance can be computed,[1] or alternatively it can be adjusted by standing-wave observations. The signal generator can conveniently be located outside the shielded room, thus minimizing the difficulties from leakage fields that tend to be troublesome when testing loop-antenna receivers.

The average field strength at the center of a square loop antenna situated directly below the wire as shown in Fig. 9-18, is given approximately by the following relations (where the wire is relatively close to the ceiling):

$$E = \frac{69E_s}{h(R_s + R_0)}$$
$$\log_{10} \frac{(d + h)(2d_c + d - h)(2d_f - d + h)(2d_f + 2d_c - d - h)}{(d - h)(2d_c + d + h)(2d_f - d - h)(2d_f + 2d_c - d + h)} \quad (9\text{-}4)$$

[1] The formula is

$$\text{Characteristic impedance} = 138 \log_{10} \frac{4d_c}{a} \quad (9\text{-}3)$$

where d_c is the distance to the ceiling, and a is the diameter of the wire.

where E is the average field strength around the loop perimeter in volts per meter, and the remaining notation is as shown in Fig. 9-18, with distances being expressed in meters. The receiver loop should be placed midway between the sides of the room. In this way the discontinuities introduced by the two ends of the line because the line is not infinite in extent, will exactly cancel out.

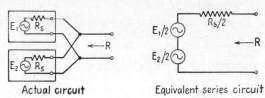

Actual circuit   Equivalent series circuit

(a) Two identical signal generators in parallel

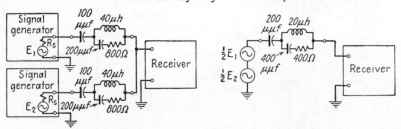

Actual circuit   Equivalent series circuit

(b) Parallel connection of signal generators involving dummy antennas

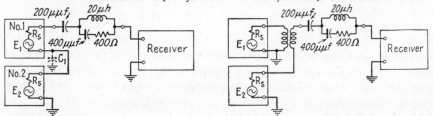

(c) Series connection of two signal generators   (d) Transformer connection of two signal generators

FIG. 9-19. Methods of simultaneously applying outputs from two signal generators to a radio receiver utilizing an external antenna.

Two-generator Tests. In some tests made on receivers it is necessary to connect two signal generators to the receiver input to represent, respectively, the desired signal and an interfering signal. This must be done so that the equivalent circuit as viewed from the receiver terminals consists of signal-generator voltages that act in series with each other, and are in series with an equivalent output impedance corresponding to the standard dummy antenna.

There are three principal ways of accomplishing this result. These are illustrated in Fig. 9-19 for the case of a receiver using an external antenna, and one example is shown in Fig. 9-20 for a loop-antenna situation. At a and b in Fig. 9-19 the two signal generators are in parallel, so each can have one terminal grounded. However, to the receiver input terminals, the system behaves as shown by the equivalent circuit, in which the effective impedance seen by the receiver input terminals is half the impedance of the individual dummy antenna,[1] and the equivalent signal-generator voltages that are effectively in series with this impedance are one-half of the voltages actually developed by the individual signal generators on open circuit. The arrangement of Fig. 9-19c has the advantage

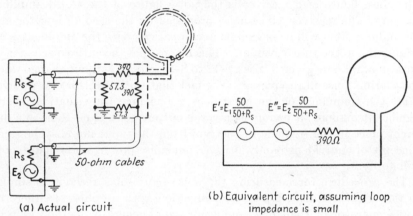

$$E' = E_1 \frac{50}{50+R_s} \qquad E'' = E_2 \frac{50}{50+R_s}$$

(a) Actual circuit

(b) Equivalent circuit, assuming loop impedance is small

FIG. 9-20. Method of simultaneously applying the output of two signal generators to a low-impedance loop for producing an induction field of known strength for testing receivers with built-in loop antennas.

that the normal standard dummy antenna can be used, but care must be taken to ensure that the stray capacitance C_1 between the chassis of signal generator No. 1 and ground represents a very high reactance compared with the output impedance R_s of generator No. 2 at the frequency of operation. If this condition is not met, the equivalent open-circuit voltage of generator No. 2 will be in error by the amount of the voltage-divider action of the internal impedance of No. 2 and the capacitance C_1. The transformer connection of Fig. 9-19d is useful when the frequency range involved is sufficiently limited so that it can be handled by a single transformer; otherwise the arrangement becomes cumbersome.

The two-generator connection for testing of loop receivers shown in Fig. 9-20 is the analogue of Fig. 9-19a as applied to the single-loop circuit of Fig. 9-17b.

---

[1] Each circuit element in the individual dummy antenna must therefore have twice the impedance of the corresponding circuit element in the standard dummy antenna desired in the equivalent circuit.

9-11. Noise in Receivers. The output of a sensitive radio receiver always contains a certain amount of noise. Some of this noise may be randomly varying electromagnetic waves, or "static" received by the antenna. The remaining noise arises in the tubes and circuits of the receiver;[1] it can be evaluated either in terms of the receiver noise figure, or the equivalent noise side-band input (ENSI).

Receiver Noise Figure. The noise figure of a receiver indicates the closeness with which the noise actually present approaches the noise that would be present in an ideal system of the same equivalent bandwidth. The noise figure of a receiver is the noise figure of the tuned amplifier system of the receiver, since noise produced by the second detector and the audio system will be negligible in comparison with the amplified noise originating in the tuned system. This means that the entire discussion of noise in amplifiers given in Secs. 8-12 to 8-15 applies without change when considering noise in receivers.[2] The fact that the converter of a receiver shifts the frequency of the noise does not change the situation in any significant manner; it merely causes the output noise band to lie in a different place in the frequency spectrum from the input noise. The same concepts of equivalent bandwidth, output noise power, noise figure, etc., still apply.

The procedure for measuring the noise figure of a receiver is similar to that outlined in Sec. 8-14 in connection with amplifiers; either the noise-generator or the single-frequency signal-generator method may be used. The source impedance that should be associated with the receiver input terminals is supplied by a dummy antenna. The noise output of the receiver is measured at the final stage of intermediate-frequency amplification either by entering this stage in the manner illustrated in Fig. 8-41, or alternatively by connecting a square-law vacuum-tube voltmeter across

---

[1] An extensive discussion of the sources of noise that exist within a radio receiver is given by E. W. Herold, An Analysis of the Signal-to-noise Ratio of Ultra-high-frequency Receivers, *RCA Rev.*, vol. 6, p. 302, January, 1942.

[2] The only exception is when the receiver has no image rejection. In this case the noise figure of the receiver is 3 db worse than it would be for a receiver with complete image rejection, but otherwise the same. The reason is that without image rejection the noise power in the image band appears in the receiver output along with the noise power in the signal band, thereby doubling the output noise over the value for image suppression. The single-frequency signal-generator method of measuring noise figure will give the correct value irrespective of the degree of image suppression, or lack thereof. In contrast, the noise figure obtained by use of the noise-generator method is the value that would apply if the image suppression were complete, and this result is still obtained even if there is no image suppression. The reason is that unlike the single-frequency signal generator, the noise signal generator delivers power to the receiver at the image frequency as well as at the signal frequency. *Thus if no image suppression is present, the true noise figure is 3 db worse than the experimental value obtained by the use of a noise signal generator.*

the final tuned circuit to indicate the relative noise power at this point.[1] The automatic volume control must be disconnected from the second detector and held at a fixed potential corresponding to the conditions for which the noise figure is desired; thus to obtain the noise figure under conditions of maximum sensitivity, the AVC bus would be returned to a potential that is only slightly negative.

In practice, the value of the noise figure possessed by a receiver is ordinarily determined by the noise generated in the input circuits and the first tube of the receiver, because this noise is amplified more than is the noise contributed by subsequent circuits and tubes. Only in cases where the first tube introduces very little amplification will the second tube and its input circuit have significant effect on the noise figure.

The receiver noise figure is of considerable practical importance in the case of receivers operating at frequencies of the order of 30 Mc and higher. At lower frequencies, the practical factor that determines the weakest signal that can be received is ordinarily static noise rather than receiver noise. In contrast, in microwave receivers, and to a lesser extent in the ultra-high-frequency band, the weakest signal that is usable is determined in practice by receiver noise, and any improvement in the noise figure of the receiver will give a corresponding improvement in useful sensitivity.

Receiver Noisiness—Equivalent Noise Side-band Input (ENSI). The noise figure represents the merit of the actual receiver as compared with an ideal receiving system having the minimum possible noise. However, it does not give the signal-to-noise ratio of the receiver output after detection and audio (or video) amplification. This information is obtained from a test that determines the equivalent noise side-band input, often referred to by the letters ENSI.

The ENSI test is made by first applying to the receiver an unmodulated carrier obtained from a signal generator, and observing the noise output P_n that is present in the audio (or video) system, using a square-law indicating device, preferably a thermocouple instrument. Modulation at 400 cycles is then applied to the carrier, and the degree of modulation m increased until the 400-cycle output of the receiver has a value P_s that approximates the noise power P_n previously observed.[2] The equivalent

---

[1] When the noise figure is determined with the aid of a standard noise generator, satisfactory results can be obtained by using the second detector of the receiver as a vacuum-tube voltmeter for observing the relative output noise power. This is permissible because although such a detector is a peak device, it will still give a fairly dependable comparison of the *relative* magnitudes of noise power. However, the second detector should never be used for this purpose when the noise figure is determined by the single-frequency signal-generator method, as then large and uncertain errors will almost certainly be present.

[2] Instead of measuring the 400-cycle output directly, one can use a square-law device to observe $P_s + P_n$, and then obtain P_s by subtracting P_n from $P_s + P_n$.

noise side-band input voltage E_n is then given by the relation

$$E_n = mE_s \sqrt{\frac{P_n}{P_s}} \tag{9-5}$$

where E_s is the amplitude of the carrier wave supplied by the signal generator and m is the degree of modulation of this wave. In making this measurement, it is necessary that the unmodulated carrier amplitude E_s be at least three and preferably ten times the equivalent noise side-band input voltage as given by Eq. (9-5). When this is the case, the ENSI value obtained is determined only by the product mE_s, and is relatively independent of the actual carrier voltage E_s, or the percentage modulation m used in the test.[1] However, the value of ENSI that is observed may depend upon the voltage of the AVC bus, which should accordingly be disconnected from the second detector, and held at a fixed negative value appropriate for the occasion.

The signal-to-noise voltage ratio at the receiver output can be expressed in terms of E_n, according to the relation

$$\text{Signal-to-noise voltage ratio} = \frac{m_0 E_0}{E_n} \tag{9-6}$$

Here E_0 and m_0 are the carrier amplitude and degree of modulation, respectively, of the signal supplied to the receiver input for which the signal-to-noise ratio is desired.

---

[1] In making the ENSI test, care must be taken to ensure that power-frequency (hum) components present are eliminated from the output by use of a suitable high-pass filter.

CHAPTER 10

ANTENNAS

10-1. Antenna Measurements. *General Considerations.*[1] Measurements are made on antennas for the purpose of obtaining design data, and in order to determine the performance of completed antenna systems. The principal types of measurements made for these purposes are (1) the determination of the impedance of the antenna, (2) the field pattern of the antenna, and (3) the power gain of the antenna. In some cases it is also helpful to investigate the current distribution on the radiating elements of the antenna. With microwave antennas used to illuminate reflectors and lenses, the contours of constant phase of the radiated field in the vicinity of an antenna are also important.

The detailed procedures used in measuring the characteristics of an antenna are determined very greatly by the frequency involved. Thus, at microwave frequencies the loss resistance associated with the antenna is commonly so small as to be negligible compared with the radiation resistance, the field pattern is commonly highly directional, the antenna is physically small, ground effects are often quite negligible, etc. In contrast, at lower radio frequencies the loss resistance of the antenna is often comparable with or even larger than the radiation resistance, the field pattern is only slightly to moderately directional, the antennas are generally physically large and fixed in position, and the ground is usually an essential part of the radiating system.

Reciprocal Relations between Transmitting and Receiving Properties of Antennas. The properties of an antenna when used to abstract energy from a passing radio wave are closely related to the corresponding properties of the same antenna when acting as a radiator. For example, when a receiving antenna is subjected to the action of a plane radio wave it abstracts energy from this wave and will deliver power to a load impedance. In so far as the load impedance is concerned, such a receiving antenna acts as an equivalent generator having an internal voltage E

---

[1] Much useful information relating to antenna measurements, with particular reference to microwave antennas, is to be found in "Microwave Antenna Theory and Design" (Vol. 12, Radiation Laboratory Series), Chaps. 15, 16, McGraw-Hill Book Company, Inc., New York, 1949; "Technique of Microwave Measurements" (Vol. 11, Radiation Laboratory Series), Chap. 15, McGraw-Hill Book Company, Inc., New York, 1947.

determined by the characteristics of the antenna and the strength of the radio wave, and possessing an internal impedance Z_a, as illustrated in Fig. 10-1b. This equivalent impedance of the receiving antenna is exactly the same impedance that the antenna presents when acting as a transmitting antenna excited from the same terminals aa, as in Fig. 10-1c. Similarly, the field pattern that an antenna possesses when radiating energy corresponds exactly to the pattern giving the relative sensitivity of the antenna to similarly polarized plane radio waves arriving from different directions.

These reciprocal relations between the transmitting and receiving properties of antennas are extremely useful. They make it possible to deduce the characteristics of an antenna from either receiving or transmitting tests, whichever are most convenient.

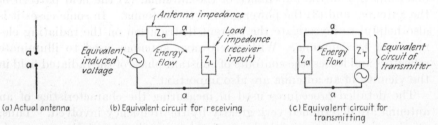

(a) Actual antenna   (b) Equivalent circuit for receiving   (c) Equivalent circuit for transmitting

Fig. 10-1. The equivalent circuit of an antenna when transmitting and when receiving.

The reciprocal relations between the transmitting and receiving properties of an antenna are incorporated in several theorems, the most important of which was first formulated by Rayleigh, and extended to include radio communication by John R. Carson.[1] It is to the effect that *if an electromotive force E inserted in antenna 1 causes a current I to flow at a certain point in a second antenna 2, then the voltage E applied at this point in the second antenna will produce the same current I (both in magnitude and phase) at the point in antenna 1 where the voltage E was originally applied.* The Rayleigh-Carson theorem fails to be true only when the radio wave is appreciably affected by an ionized medium in the presence of a magnetic field, and so holds for all conditions except short-wave transmission over long distance.

10-2. Antenna Impedance. One of the most important properties of an antenna is the impedance that it offers to an applied voltage. The resistance component of this impedance is equal to the sum of the radiation resistance and the loss resistance. In many cases the loss resistance is negligible, as for example in practically all microwave antenna systems,

[1] John R. Carson, Reciprocal Theorems in Radio Communication, *Proc. IRE*, vol. 17, p. 952, June, 1929.

in short-wave directional arrays, broadcast-tower antennas, etc. Under these conditions the resistance component of the antenna impedance can be considered as being the radiation resistance, and the power that is dissipated in this resistance by a current in the antenna is the radiated power. The reactive component of the antenna impedance indicates the nature of the resonance existing in the antenna; thus if the reactive component is zero the antenna is in resonance, while inductive and capacitive reactive components indicate that the frequency is on one or the other side of resonance.

A knowledge of the resistive and reactive components of the impedance of an antenna provides the data required to design a network to match the antenna impedance to a generator. For example, if an antenna with an impedance $R_a + jX_a$ is to be matched to a coaxial cable having a characteristic impedance R_0, then the matching network must transform the impedance $R_a + jX_a$ to a value R_0. The variation of the resistive and reactive components of the antenna impedance with frequency defines the problem involved in matching the antenna impedance to a generator over a band of frequencies. When such data are available over a frequency range, it then becomes possible to determine by calculation the frequency range over which a given compensating and impedance-matching system will match the antenna impedance to the generator to any desired degree of tolerance.

The impedance of an antenna system is determined in the same way as is any other impedance. At ultra-high frequencies and with microwaves, standing-wave arrangements (see Sec. 4-7) are normally used. At lower frequencies one can employ a radio-frequency bridge, a Q meter, or the substitution method (see Chap. 3).[1] No special precautions need be taken because the impedance being determined is an antenna, other than the fact that since the antenna radiates power, it is often necessary to take somewhat more than average care in shielding the measuring equipment.

The impedance of an antenna will depend upon the point in the antenna system at which the impedance is measured. The impedance will also be affected by the presence of neighboring objects, such as other antennas, guy wires, buildings, obstacles, etc. The effect of such objects is particularly important in the case of directional antennas which are rotated, since they can cause the impedance to depend upon the orientation.

Impedance is always measured in practice by exciting the antenna, *i.e.*, by using it as a transmitting device. While it would be possible to measure impedance with the antenna operating as a receiving antenna, this is

---

[1] Impedance measurements of broadcast antennas are discussed by W. A. Fitch and W. S. Duttera, Measurement of Broadcast Coverage and Antenna Performance, *RCA Rev.*, vol. 3, p. 340, January, 1939; D. B. Sinclair, Impedance of Broadcast Antennas, *Communications* (*N.Y.*), vol. 19, p. 5, June–July, 1939.

experimentally much more difficult, and by the reciprocity theorem gives the same results as for the transmitting case.

Mutual Impedance between Antennas. Two antennas placed close to each other act as coupled circuits. Thus if only one of the antennas is excited, a current is induced in the second antenna. Also, the induced current in this second antenna induces a back voltage in the first antenna, thus modifying the equivalent impedance of the first antenna. The quantitative relation that exists under these circumstances can be represented by the simultaneous equations

$$E_1 = I_1 Z_{11} + I_2 Z_{12} \qquad (10\text{-}1a)$$
$$0 = I_1 Z_{12} + I_2 Z_{22} \qquad (10\text{-}1b)$$

where E_1 = voltage applied to antenna 1
  I_1 = current flowing in antenna 1
  I_2 = current flowing in antenna 2
  Z_{11} = self-impedance of antenna 1 (*i.e.*, impedance with antenna 2 removed)
  Z_{22} = self-impedance of antenna 2
  Z_{12} = mutual impedance between antennas 1 and 2

The actual impedance Z of antenna 1 in the presence of antenna 2 is $Z = E_1/I_1$, and by simultaneous solution of Eqs. (10-1) is

$$Z = \frac{E_1}{I_1} = Z_{11} - \frac{Z_{12}{}^2}{Z_{22}} \qquad (10\text{-}2)$$

The mutual impedance Z_{12} can be determined experimentally by the following procedure: First the impedance of antenna 1 is measured with antenna 2 present under the conditions for which the mutual impedance is desired; this is the impedance Z represented by Eq. (10-2). Next the self-impedance Z_{11} of antenna 1 is measured by open-circuiting antenna 2 or otherwise arranging matters so that antenna 2 carries negligible current. Finally, the self-impedance Z_{22} of antenna 2 is measured in like manner by open-circuiting or otherwise disabling antenna 1. Substituting these values of Z, Z_{11}, and Z_{22} in Eq. (10-2) makes it possible to calculate the mutual impedance Z_{12}.

Equation (10-2) is completely analogous to the corresponding equation for an ordinary inductively coupled circuit. Such an arrangement, with primary and secondary circuit impedances Z_p and Z_s, respectively, and mutual inductance M offers an impedance at the primary terminals that is

$$\text{Input impedance} = Z_p - \frac{(j\omega M)^2}{Z_s} \qquad (10\text{-}3)$$

Thus the antenna mutual impedance Z_{12} corresponds to $j\omega M$, while the "coupled impedance" in the antenna case is $-Z_{12}{}^2/Z_{22}$. It is to be noted, however, that in the case of coupled antennas, the mutual impedance Z_{12} will commonly have both resistive and reactive components.

10-3. Field Pattern of Antennas. The field pattern of an antenna, also often referred to as the directional characteristic, can be defined for a transmitting antenna as the relative radiation that the antenna produces in different directions. In the case of a receiving antenna, the field pattern represents the relative response of the antenna to radio waves arriving from different directions. In accordance with the reciprocity theorem, the field pattern of a given antenna is the same when receiving as when transmitting, provided the waves transmitted and received have the same polarization.

The field pattern may be expressed in terms of relative voltage, relative power, or decibels referred to some convenient reference level. When it is

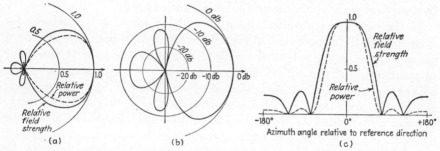

Fig. 10-2. Different methods of representing the same directional pattern.

desired to portray the details of the pattern in directions where the radiation is low, decibels are advantageous. In contrast, plotting the pattern in terms of relative power suppresses the details of side lobes. The common method of using relative field strength (voltage) is intermediate between these extremes. Directional patterns are most frequently plotted on polar paper; however, rectangular coordinates are preferable when it is desired to show the details of the minor lobes. Examples of a directional pattern represented in various ways are shown in Fig. 10-2.

A typical procedure for obtaining the field pattern is to radiate power from the antenna under test, and then to observe the relative strength of the field (or power) produced in different directions, using simple field-strength measuring equipment (see Sec. 11-6) that can be moved about relative to the transmitting antenna under test. A variation sometimes possible consists in mounting the field-strength measuring equipment at a fixed location, and rotating the transmitting antenna under test to change its relative orientation. An alternative procedure is to employ the antenna under test as a receiving antenna, which is then excited by waves generated by a small transmitting system.   Relative direction may be changed either by moving the transmitting system about the receiving antenna, or by rotating the receiving antenna.   According to the reciprocity theorem, it makes no difference whether the antenna under test acts as a receiving or radiating device; the field patterns obtained from the two methods will be identical provided one is concerned with waves having the same polarization in both cases.

The experimental determination of a complete pattern giving the relative radiation for all directions in space, requires the recording of an enormous number of experimental points.   There is, moreover, no really satisfactory graphical method of presenting a complete directional pattern except by the use of three-dimensional solid figures.[1]   The usual procedure consists in showing the radiation as a function of azimuth angle Φ for different values of the vertical angle θ, or conversely showing the radiation in a vertical plane for a succession of azimuth angles.

In the case of highly directional antenna systems, it is sufficient for most practical purposes to obtain directional patterns only (1) for a plane containing the axis of the main lobe and also parallel to the plane of polarization of the electric field, and (2) for the plane containing the axis of the main lobe but at right angles to the electric field.   From these patterns, termed the E and H patterns, respectively, one obtains directly the information that is ordinarily of most practical importance.   In some cases, it may be desirable in addition to obtain the corresponding pattern for the two mutually perpendicular planes oriented 45° with respect to the E and H planes, and intersecting at the axis of the main lobe.   In the case of highly directional beams, the most important characteristics are the shape and width of the main lobe, and the magnitude and direction of the principal side lobes.

In dealing with field patterns it is necessary to take into account the polarization of the radiation from the antenna.   Ordinarily there is a well-defined plane of polarization, and unless otherwise stated it is implied that the pattern is for components polarized in this way.   However, in some cases the plane of polarization of the radiated field varies significantly with direction.   An example is provided by a rhombic antenna having its plane parallel to the ground.   Here the dominant radiation is horizontally polarized; however, in certain directions there is also an appreciable component that is vertically polarized, and the field pattern of this vertically polarized component differs appreciably from the pattern for the horizontally polarized component of radiation.   Again, in the case of a parabola, the radiation commonly contains a component polarized

[1] The only exception to this is where circular symmetry exists, as for example in the case of a single vertical radiator.   It can then be assumed that the radiation at any particular vertical angle is the same in all azimuth directions.

at right angles to the polarization of the principal component of radiation. This "cross-polarized" component is particularly prominent in side lobes located in planes differing by $\pm 45°$ from the principal plane of polarization. A complete directional pattern accordingly should indicate not only the magnitude of the fields radiated in all directions in space, but also the polarization of these fields.

When an antenna is used for reception, the relationship between the polarization of the wave being received, and the polarization of the wave which the antenna would radiate in the particular direction, is especially important. This is because the antenna responds only to that component of the radio wave that is polarized in the direction of the antenna polarization defined on the basis of the transmitted wave. Thus if the wave being received is vertically polarized, the field pattern that is effective in the reception of this wave is the pattern of the transmitting antenna for the vertically polarized component of the radiation. However, if at the same time this antenna is subjected to another wave that is horizontally polarized, its directional pattern for this second wave will be the field pattern for the horizontally polarized component of the radiation.

10-4. Spacing Required When Making Measurements of Antenna Field Patterns.[1] When making measurements of field patterns of an antenna, the spacing between the transmitting and receiving antennas involved must not be too small. Otherwise effects are introduced that prevent the experimental results from being representative of the actual performance of the antenna system at large distances.

The minimum permissible spacing between the two antennas involved in a measurement must be such that the induction field at the separation distance is negligible as compared with the radiation field. Separations of two to three wavelengths are adequate to achieve this result when the antennas are small, and this is the minimum separation that is permissible under any conditions. At the lower radio frequencies, this represents a considerable distance. Thus measurements of the field radiated by a broadcast antenna operating at a wavelength of 500 m should be made not much closer than 1 mile to the transmitting antenna. Correspondingly, at a wavelength of 5000 m the minimum distance for making field-pattern measurements approaches 10 miles.

When at least one of the antennas involved in the measurement is not physically small compared with a wavelength then additional effects are present that require even greater spacing. Under these conditions

---

[1] For further information, and in particular for supporting theoretical analyses, see "Technique of Microwave Measurements," *op. cit.*, pp. 900–905; "Microwave Antenna Theory and Design," *op. cit.*, pp. 574–576, 587–592; C. C. Cutler, A. P. King, and W. E. Kock, Microwave Antenna Measurements, *Proc. IRE*, vol. 35, p. 1462, December, 1947.

the principal errors that result from inadequate spacing are (1) phase errors, (2) amplitude errors, and (3) errors from interaction.

The phase error that results when one of the antennas is physically large and the spacing is too small, can be understood with the aid of Fig. 10-3. In this illustration one of the antennas involved, normally the one being tested, has an aperture[1] D that is relatively large, whereas the other antenna is considered as being physically small. If the distance between the two antennas is very great, waves originating from the small antenna will have a plane wavefront by the time they reach the large antenna, and the phase of the radiation will be everywhere the same over the aperture D. However, if the distance between the two antennas is made small, as in Fig. 10-3, then there is an appreciable difference in the distance R from the small antenna to the center of the large antenna, and the distance R' to the edge of this antenna. As a result, the phase of the radiation is not uniform over the surface of the large antenna, being increasingly lagging as one moves from the center to the edge of aperture D, in proportion to the increasing distance from the

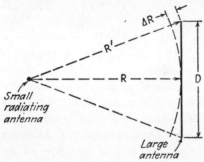

FIG. 10-3. Geometry involved in a system consisting of a small radiating antenna and a receiving antenna with large aperture.

small radiator as one approaches the edge. The resulting error in received power arising from inadequate range will be negligible *for the case of one small antenna*, only if the distance R satisfies the relation

$$R \geq \frac{2D^2}{\lambda} \tag{10-4}$$

where λ is the wavelength, and D is the maximum aperture dimension of the large antenna. All lengths must be expressed in the same units. If the spacing is less than called for by Eq. (10-4), the relative field strength observed in different directions will in general differ from the field pattern observed at greater distances.

An indication of the significance of the criterion represented by Eq. (10-4) is given by the fact that the power received by an antenna with a circular aperture of diameter D will be 5 per cent (0.21 db) in error when the distance is half that given by Eq. (10-4). The condition repre-

---

[1] The term "aperture" is commonly used in connection with directional antennas, such as horns, parabolas, mattresses, etc., to denote an over-all dimension. Thus an aperture of 5 wavelengths denotes an antenna that is 5 wavelengths across.

sented by Eq. (10-4) corresponds to a maximum permissible difference $\Delta R = R' - R$ in distance of $\lambda/16$ (see Fig. 10-3).

Amplitude error can occur when both of the antennas involved in the test setup have directional characteristics.   Thus consider the case illustrated in Fig. 10-4, where the transmitting antenna has a directional pattern as shown.   The intensity of radiation from the transmitting antenna is seen to be appreciably less toward the edge of the large receiving antenna than it is toward the center of this antenna.   The result is that the received power is less than if the field intensity did not drop off at the edges of the receiving antenna.   The smaller the spacing between the antennas, the greater will be this effect, as a smaller spacing causes a

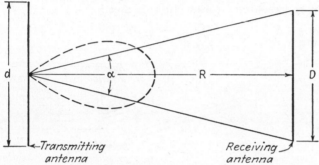

FIG. 10-4. Closely spaced transmitting and receiving antennas having large apertures, showing how with inadequate spacing the directivity of the transmitting antenna can be sufficiently great to cause the amplitude of power radiated toward the receiving antenna to vary from the center to the edge of the receiving antenna.

given receiving antenna to subtend a larger angle α, and the variation in field intensity over the aperture becomes greater.   On the basis of reasonable but rather rough assumptions, it can be demonstrated that if the error in received power is to be not greater than 0.25 db (6 per cent), then the spacing R between antennas must satisfy the relation

$$R \geq \frac{(D + d)^2}{\lambda} \tag{10-5}$$

where D and d are the apertures of the two antennas involved in the measurement (see Fig. 10-4).   When the smaller aperture d is larger than $0.414D$, then the minimum spacing called for by Eq. (10-5) is greater than specified by Eq. (10-4); under these conditions the minimum permissible spacing is determined by amplitude rather than phase variation over the aperture, and Eq. (10-5) must be used.   With values of d smaller than $0.414D$, the phase variation determines the minimum spacing, and Eq. (10-4) applies.

Interaction occurs between transmitting and receiving antennas when both have large apertures and the spacing between them is small. Thus in Fig. 10-4 an appreciable amount of the power radiated from the transmitting antenna is intercepted by the aperture of the receiving antenna. A portion of this received power is scattered (*i.e.*, reradiated) by the receiving antenna. Some of the scattered power is intercepted by the transmitting antenna, and a portion of this is in turn reradiated toward the receiving system, and so on. Since this interaction is not present when the spacing is large, it introduces an erroneous element in the performance when the spacing is inadequate. A rough analysis shows that if the minimum spacing satisfies Eq. (10-5) the interaction effect is negligible and that it will ordinarily be small even when the less severe requirement represented by Eq. (10-4) is met.[1]

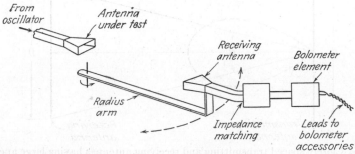

Fig. 10-5. Experimental arrangement for measuring the field pattern of a microwave antenna of low directivity.

10-5. Field-pattern Measurement at Microwave Frequencies.[2] In measuring the field pattern of microwave antennas a distinction must be made between large antennas that are highly directional, and antennas that possess only a nominal amount of directivity. Examples of the latter are a dipole with small reflector, a short horn having an aperture of one wavelength or less, etc. Such antennas are used to illuminate parabolic reflectors and lenses, and are therefore of very considerable importance. The most important feature of the directional pattern of antennas of this class is the character of the main lobe; the finer details of the side-lobe structure are usually of relatively little practical importance.

Antennas with Moderate Directivity. A typical experimental setup for measuring the field pattern of a microwave antenna of nominal directivity is illustrated in Fig. 10-5. Here the antenna under test, shown as a

[1] See "Technique of Microwave Measurements," *op. cit.*, p. 909; or "Microwave Antenna Theory and Design," *op. cit.*, pp. 587–592.

[2] For further general discussion of this subject see "Very High Frequency Techniques," Vol. 1, pp. 46–52, McGraw-Hill Book Company, Inc., New York, 1947; "Microwave Antenna Theory and Design," *op. cit.*, pp. 557–580, 593–613.

small horn, serves as a transmitting antenna excited from a reflex klystron that is square-wave-modulated in order to provide amplitude modulation without frequency modulation. Radiation from this transmitting antenna is picked up by a small receiving antenna, shown in Fig. 10-5 as a horn, which can be rotated about the transmitting antenna at a fixed distance of 10 or more wavelengths by means of a radius arm centered at the position of the transmitting antenna, as illustrated. The energy absorbed by the receiving antenna is delivered to a detector consisting of a current-biased bolometer of the type discussed in connection with Fig. 2-8. The modulation-frequency output of the bolometer is amplified, and then measured by a vacuum-tube voltmeter. A bolometer operated in this way acts as a square-law device, giving an output voltage that is proportional to the power dissipated in the bolometer element.[1]

The polarization of the radiated field can be determined in Fig. 10-5, by arranging so that the pickup horn can be rotated about its axis. The adjustment corresponding to maximum response of the bolometer then corresponds to the angle of polarization. While the apparatus shown in Fig. 10-5 measures the pattern only in a single plane, which with the transmitting-horn orientation shown in Fig. 10-5 is the H, or magnetic, plane, the field pattern in other planes can be obtained merely by rotating the two horn antennas appropriately about their axes. Thus the pattern in the electric plane would be obtained by rotating both transmitting and receiving antennas through 90° from their orientation shown in Fig. 10-5 before carrying out the measurement.

In setting up the apparatus of Fig. 10-5 care must be taken to prevent reflected waves of appreciable amplitude from reaching the receiving horn. Thus the measurements should be made in an open space, free of walls or neighboring objects that might reflect appreciable amounts of energy. In addition, it is also often desirable to cover the supporting structure of the receiving antenna with material that absorbs rather than reflects radio waves. It is also helpful if the receiving antenna has a moderate amount of directivity, such as possessed by the small horn in Fig. 10-5, since this helps discriminate against reflections coming from side directions.

Highly Directional Systems. Consider next the case of a microwave antenna having a large aperture and resulting high directivity, such as a parabolic reflector or a lens-antenna arrangement. The large aperture in such a case makes the minimum permissible distance between antennas relatively large. For example, if the antenna under test has an aperture of 10 ft and is operated at a wavelength of 3 cm, the minimum permissible spacing on the basis of Eq. (10-5) is approximately 4000 ft if the second

---

[1] A crystal detector could be used, but has the disadvantage that it follows a square law with less certainty than does a bolometer.

antenna used in making the test likewise has an aperture of 10 ft.   Also, with highly directional antenna systems of this type, one not only is interested in the general character of the main lobe, but also commonly desires to know details of the side-lobe characteristics such as the maximum amplitude and location of each of the more important minor lobes.

In view of these considerations, a typical arrangement for obtaining the field pattern of a high-gain microwave antenna takes the form illustrated in Fig. 10-6.   Here the antenna under test, and an auxiliary antenna, are located on towers spaced an appropriate distance apart over flat unobstructed terrain.   The auxiliary antenna is preferably highly directional, and its main lobe is pointed directly toward the antenna under test.   A directional pattern is obtained by transmitting from one of these antennas to the other, rotating the test antenna, and observing the received power as a function of azimuth angle.   By tilting the antenna

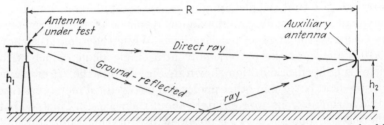

FIG. 10-6. Experimental arrangement for determining the field pattern of a highly directional antenna having a wide aperture.

under test so that it is pointed upward at an angle instead of horizontally, one can determine the azimuth distribution of field strength at any desired vertical angle.   When making these measurements, it is essential that the site be free of reflecting objects, particularly buildings.   Such objects can readily cause the side-lobe structure that is observed to be quite different from the true characteristic.   The use of a highly directional auxiliary antenna is of considerable assistance in minimizing the undesirable consequences of spurious reflections.

In an arrangement such as is illustrated in Fig. 10-6, errors may also result from ground reflections unless particular care is taken.   In the presence of the ground, energy may travel not only directly between the two antennas, it may also travel along a path involving a ground reflection, as illustrated.   The magnitude of the resultant field at the receiving antenna is the vector sum of these two component waves.   The phase with which the direct and ground-reflected waves combine depends upon the difference in lengths of the two paths, with the result that for a ground-reflection coefficient that has an absolute value of unity, one has[1]

---

[1] Proof for this relation can be found in many places; thus see F. E. Terman,

$$\left.\begin{array}{l}\text{Field strength at}\\\text{receiving point}\end{array}\right\} = \frac{2E_0}{d}\sin\frac{2\pi h_s h_r}{\lambda d} \qquad (10\text{-}6)$$

where E_0 = strength of direct wave at unit distance

$\dfrac{E_0}{d}$ = field strength of direct wave at the receiving point in the absence of a ground-reflected wave

h_s = height of transmitting antenna

h_r = height of receiving point

d = distance

λ = wavelength

The variation of field strength with the height h_r of the receiving point is shown in Fig. 10-7 for two values of transmitter height h_s, for a typical

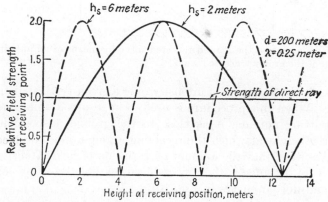

FIG. 10-7. Typical curves showing variation of field strength as a function of height above ground, for the case of unity reflection coefficient at the ground.

case calculated by Eq. (10-6). It is apparent that if the receiver antenna has an appreciable aperture width in the vertical direction, the ground-reflected wave will cause the field intensity to vary over the aperture, with resulting errors being introduced.

This effect can be minimized in several ways. One method is to relate the height of the auxiliary antenna above ground with the directional characteristic of this auxiliary antenna, so that for the spacing used in the test, the auxiliary antenna has a null in its field pattern in the direction of

---

"Radio Engineering," 3d ed., p. 615, McGraw-Hill Book Company, Inc., New York, 1947.

In the special case where the distance is so great in relation to heights and distance that $2\pi h_s h_r/\lambda d$ is less than about 0.3, then one can assume that the sine of the angle can be replaced by the angle, and Eq. (10-6) becomes

$$\left.\begin{array}{l}\text{Field strength at}\\\text{receiving point}\end{array}\right\} = E_0\,\frac{4\pi h_s h_r}{\lambda d^2} \qquad (10\text{-}7)$$

the ground-reflected wave, as illustrated in Fig. 10-8. In this way no transmission of energy can take place between the two antennas by way of the ground.

A second method of attacking the problem is to adjust the heights of the two antennas so that the auxiliary (receiving) antenna is in the region where the direct and ground-reflected waves add in phase to produce a maximum.   Figure 10-7 shows that in the region of such a maximum (as

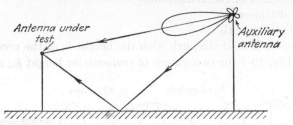

FIG. 10-8. Elimination of the ground-reflected wave by means of an antenna null in . the direction of the ground-reflected wave.

for $h_r = 6$ m), the variation of intensity over a given vertical distance is a minimum.   When this procedure is used, best results are obtained when the transmitting antenna is as close to the ground as possible.   This increases the height at which the receiving antenna must be placed, but has the advantage that the amount of variation of field intensity over a given aperture distance is thereby reduced, as illustrated by comparing the solid and dotted curves in Fig. 10-7.

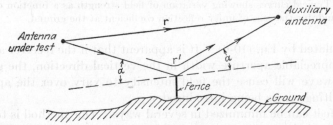

FIG. 10-9. The elimination of ground reflection by means of a fence.

Finally one may eliminate the ground-reflected wave entirely by using a straight diffraction edge placed perpendicular to the transmission path between the antennas, and made high enough to shield the antennas from ground-reflected waves.   This is illustrated in Fig. 10-9, where the diffraction edge may consist of a wire fence of fine mesh.   In such a system, diffraction effects from the top of the fence will be negligible if the antenna heights are now made such that the difference in lengths of the paths r and r' in Fig. 10-9 is many wavelengths; the system then behaves as though there were no ground and no fence present.[1] When the surface of the ground is rough and not level, it may be desirable to employ several fences.

The oscillator power used to excite the transmitting antenna, and the sensitivity of the detector used with the receiving antenna, must be properly coordinated to obtain satisfactory results when testing antennas of high directivity. With the minimum permissible spacing, and an auxiliary antenna having an aperture equal to that of the antenna under test, the power absorbed by the receiving antenna is typically about 20 db less than the total power radiated from the transmitting antenna. This represents the maximum possible power that is available at the receiving antenna; if the spacing is greater than the minimum permissible value, or if the auxiliary antenna has a smaller aperture than the antenna under test, then the maximum power available to the receiver is correspondingly less. The field-pattern measuring system must hence be designed on the assumption that the maximum power available at the receiving point will range between 20 and 40 db less than the oscillator power supplied to the transmitting antenna. In addition, the receiving equipment must have a dynamic range of about 30 db if the side-lobe structure is to be obtained with a reasonable amount of detail. Thus the receiving equipment should be able to record a minimum power of the order of 70 db less than the oscillator power.

If a bolometer is used for the receiving detector, an average transmitting power of the order of 10 watts or more is commonly desirable. This can be conveniently obtained at frequencies of 3000 Mc and higher by means of a magnetron, a power klystron, or a power traveling-wave tube. At frequencies below about 2500 Mc, close-spaced triodes may be employed. When the transmitted power is obtained from a reflex klystron, or when the space attenuation is large, then a superheterodyne receiver with radio-frequency or intermediate-frequency attenuator and output-indicating meter must be used. The receiving equipment under these conditions is the same as that employed in measuring field strength, and is discussed in Chap. 11.

When many directional patterns are to be taken it is desirable to employ equipment that will automatically record the intensity of the received signal in the test setup on a piece of paper which is moved in synchronism with the rotation of the antenna. Such equipment is relatively complicated and its construction involves considerable effort; however, when once built and in working order the labor required to obtain an antenna pattern becomes only a small fraction of the effort required when

---

[1] As the difference $r' - r$ in path lengths increases, the diffraction field may be obtained from diffraction theory, and follows Cornu's spiral; see Cutler, King, and Kock, *op. cit.*

manual recording is employed. The actual details of the automatic recording equipment may take a wide variety of forms, and typical examples are discussed in the literature.[1]

10-6. Phase Front and the Center of Phase in Microwave Antennas.[2] In a radio wave, a surface so chosen that the wave has the same phase everywhere in this surface is termed the *phase front*. In microwave

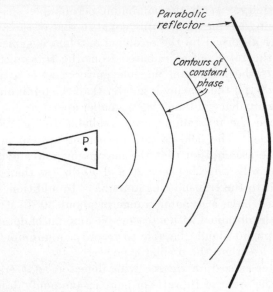

Fig. 10-10. A small horn antenna illuminating a parabolic reflector, showing spherical contours of constant phase.

antenna systems the phase front has an important role in design. Consider for example the situation illustrated in Fig. 10-10, which shows a parabolic reflector illuminated by radiation from a small horn antenna. In the ideal case the phase front of the radiation produced by the horn will consist of concentric spherical surfaces. The center P of these surfaces is termed the *center of phase*, and for proper operation, the focus of the parabolic reflector in Fig. 10-10 should coincide with P. In practical circumstances it is quite possible, however, that the phase front will

[1] For example see "Microwave Antenna Theory and Design," *op. cit.*, pp. 609–613; H. LeCaine and M. Katchky, Microwave Antenna Beam Evaluator, *Electronics*, vol. 20, p. 116, August, 1947; O. H. Schmitt and W. P. Peyser, Aircraft Antenna Pattern Plotter, *Electronics*, vol. 20, p. 88, 1947; J. Dyson and B. A. C. Tucker, An Automatic Contour Plotter for the Investigation of Radiation Patterns of Directive Antennae, *J. IEE (Radiolocation Conv.)*, vol. 93, pt. IIIA, p. 1403, March–May, 1946.

[2] For further discussion see "Technique of Microwave Measurements," *op. cit.*, pp. 915–922; "Microwave Antenna Theory and Design," *op. cit.*, pp. 564–572; Cutler, King, and Kock, *loc. cit.*

not be a spherical surface; in this case the center of phase is different for different parts of the phase front, as shown in Fig. 10-11.   The parabola or lens will then not be properly illuminated by the antenna.   Thus a knowledge of the phase front makes it possible to determine whether or

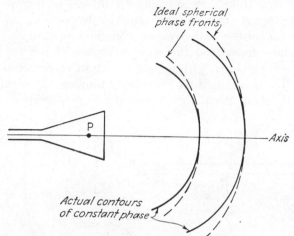

FIG. 10-11. Small antenna with nonspherical contours of constant phase.

not a distinct center of phase is present, and exactly where the center of phase is located in case one does exist.   Moreover, if the phase front has an unsatisfactory characteristic, a knowledge of its configuration will aid the designer in determining how the radiating antenna should be modified.

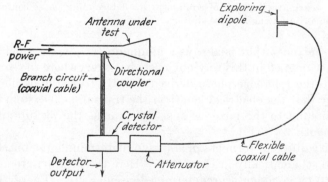

FIG. 10-12. Schematic diagram of apparatus for determining contours of constant phase.

Typical apparatus for determining the surfaces of constant phase of a microwave antenna of small aperture is shown in Fig. 10-12.   Here power from a square-wave-modulated reflex klystron oscillator is radiated from the antenna under test, which is shown as a horn.   A reference sample of the energy supplied to the radiating antenna is tapped off by a directional coupler as illustrated, and delivered to a crystal detector. The radio-frequency energy picked up by an exploring antenna, shown as a dipole in Fig. 10-12, is also delivered to the same detector through a flexible transmission system of constant length, such as a coaxial cable. The amplitudes of the two signals thus combined in the mixer are preferably approximately equal; this can be achieved by placing an adjustable attenuator in one of the radio-frequency circuits as shown. The crystal output will then depend on the relative phases of the two sources of energy that are combined, with minimum output corresponding to phase opposition. The manipulation consists in moving the pickup antenna back and forth about the radiating antenna to determine a surface over

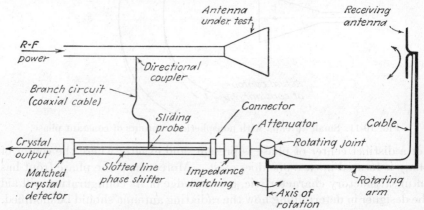

FIG. 10-13. Schematic diagram of equipment for determining phase contours, using an arrangement involving a phase shifter.

which the mixer output is always a minimum (or always a maximum).[1] The surface defined in this way obviously has everywhere the same phase relative to the reference phase derived directly from the oscillator, provided only that the electrical length of the transmission system from the pickup antenna to the mixer is kept constant as the pickup antenna is moved about.

A slightly different form of apparatus for determining the phase front is illustrated schematically in Fig. 10-13. Here the pickup antenna is constrained to move along a predetermined circular arc. Energy from the pickup antenna is combined in a crystal detector with a reference signal derived from the oscillator exciting the radiating antenna, as before. However, some form of adjustable phase shifter is introduced in one of

[1] Equipment for carrying out this procedure automatically and plotting the results on a piece of paper is described by H. Iams, Phase-front Plotter for Centimeter Waves, *RCA Rev.*, vol. 8, p. 270, June, 1947.

the radio-frequency circuits to control the relative phase with which the two voltages combine at the detector. Any form of phase shifter can be used, although a common arrangement makes use of a slotted line with sliding probe to control the point at which the two sources of radio-frequency energy come together, as shown in Fig. 10-13. To determine a surface of constant phase, the pickup antenna is moved about along its circular arc while keeping the phase shifter adjusted to give minimum (or maximum) output of the crystal detector. In this way one determines the variation in phase of the radiation field that exists along the circular arc. From this variation, the surface of constant phase can be readily determined from the fact that a phase shift of α degrees corresponds to a distance in space of $\lambda(\alpha/360°)$, where λ is the wavelength.

It will be noted that the process of determining a phase front is essentially that of comparing the phase of the energy derived from the pickup antenna against a reference phase derived directly from the oscillator that excites the antenna. Thus the determination of the phase front is essentially a phase determination, such as discussed in Sec. 6-9, but modified in accordance with the special circumstances involved.

The accuracy obtainable in phase-front measurements is quite good provided the apparatus is properly designed and operated. In particular, movement of the pickup antenna (and of the probe in Fig. 10-13) must not introduce changes in the electrical length of the associated transmission system. Also, if the attenuator is of a type that introduces a phase shift that varies with the attenuation, then the attenuator setting must be left unchanged as a surface of constant phase is traced out.

The determination of a complete surface of constant phase requires a great many individual measurements, just as does the determination of a complete directional pattern. However, for nearly all practical purposes it is sufficient to determine the lines of constant phase in two mutually perpendicular planes, which are normally chosen as the electric, or E, plane, and the magnetic, or H, plane. To the extent that these particular contours both have the same center of curvature, then it is usually safe to assume that the entire surface of constant phase has a single definite center of phase.

The usefulness of the phase-front concept is not limited to exploration of the fields about a small antenna used to illuminate a parabola or lens. Thus helpful information about the functioning of a large horn, a parabola, or a lens, can be obtained by determining the surfaces of constant phase in the vicinity of the aperture. It is possible in this way to detect defects in the functioning of the system such as could arise from failure of the reflecting surface to have the required parabolic contour, improper design of a lens, incorrect positioning of the antenna that illuminates the lens or parabola, etc.

10-7. Field Patterns at Lower Radio Frequencies. At frequencies well below the microwave range, the antennas ordinarily used are fixed structures, and are often of considerable physical size. The problem of determining the field pattern is then much different from that at very high frequencies. In particular, these antennas have much simpler and less directive patterns than do many microwave systems, so that less experimental information is needed to define the character of the pattern.

A typical experimental procedure for pattern determination at the lower frequencies is to excite the antenna under test so that it radiates power. The resulting radiation field about the antenna is then explored with the aid of portable field-strength measuring equipment, such as described in Chap. 11. This equipment consists of a small portable antenna, a receiver provided with an output indicator, and suitable calibrating means. The receiver sensitivity that is required depends upon the transmitter power, distance, power gain of antenna, etc. Depending upon the circumstances, the receiver may range from a simple system such as described in Sec. 11-6, to a highly sensitive superheterodyne receiver. The antenna is commonly a short dipole or half-wave doublet in the case of the higher frequencies, and a loop antenna at broadcast and lower frequencies. An alternative measuring procedure consists in employing a portable standard field generator, such as discussed in Sec. 11-4, to illuminate the antenna under test, which is then used as a receiving antenna. The voltage, current, or power induced in this antenna is then observed as the orientation of the field generator with respect to the antenna is changed.

The field pattern in the horizontal plane is obtained by moving the portable equipment about the antenna under test. The distance is preferably kept constant, but when practical problems arising from roads, etc., make this impossible, a correction can be made for varying distance. In the case of free-space propagation, or ground-wave propagation where the "numerical distance" is not large,[1] the field strength can be considered to be inversely proportional to distance. At very high frequencies, where one must consider a direct wave and a ground-reflected wave, as in Fig. 10-6, then the situation can be quite complicated, as indicated by Eq. (10-6). However, when the distance is great enough so that Eq. (10-7) applies, the field strength is then inversely proportional to the square of the distance provided the distance is small enough so that the curvature of the earth may be neglected.

Determination of the directional pattern in a vertical plane, of antennas

---

[1] In the theory of ground-wave propagation the natural unit of distance is the "numerical distance," which is determined by the ground constants, the frequency, and the actual distance in wavelengths, as given in Fig. 11-17. For further discussion see Terman, *op. cit.*, p. 611.

operating at frequencies lower than the microwave range is a difficult problem. The vertical pattern under conditions of actual use is commonly very greatly affected by the presence of the ground, and so cannot be determined by tilting the antenna being tested, even in cases where this would be physically possible. It then becomes necessary to mount portable equipment in an airplane if the field pattern is to be explored at appreciable angles of elevation. This introduces such problems as the determination of the exact position of the airplane with respect to the test antenna when a measurement is being made, etc. As a result, field patterns in the vertical plane are commonly inferred on the basis of theoretical calculation rather than being obtained by actual measurement, when dealing with antennas in this frequency range.

At the radio frequencies lower than the microwave range, the effects arising from the ground commonly must be understood and properly allowed for in interpreting the experimental results. Thus at broadcast and lower frequencies, the field adjacent to the earth can be considered as vertically polarized,[1] since any horizontally polarized component that might be present in free space is almost completely canceled near the surface of the earth because the earth is conducting, and because any reasonable height above earth is only a small fraction of a wavelength. In addition, the antenna structures used at these frequencies are normally inherently vertically polarized, so that little or no horizontally polarized component is radiated by them anyway.

Under these conditions, one has a vertically polarized ground wave adjacent to the ground, the behavior of which is extensively described in the literature.[2] At moderate distances, such that the numerical distance does not exceed 1 or 2, the field at the surface of the earth is inversely proportional to distance, while at large numerical distances, of the order of 10 or greater, the field strength is inversely proportional to the square of the distance. Also, the strength of this vertically polarized ground wave is independent of height above ground provided the height does not exceed a small fraction of a wavelength. This is important, since it means that the experimental results obtained at broadcast and lower frequencies will be independent of whether the measuring equipment is, for example, 2 ft or 4 ft above the earth. At heights of the order of a few wavelengths this independence of field strength with respect to height can no longer be depended upon, and at still greater heights corresponding to a reasonable angle above the horizon, the field strength varies with height in accordance with the vertical field pattern of the transmitting antenna,

[1] This does not consider the tilt component (see Sec. 11-7), which arises from ground losses and can be considered as a horizontally polarized component traveling directly downward, with the electric vector parallel to the direction to the transmitter.

[2] See Terman, *op. cit.*, p. 611; also see Fig. 11-17.

as modified close to the earth by ground-wave propagation losses in the earth.

In contrast, at frequencies above about 30 Mc, such as are used in frequency-modulation broadcasting, television, etc., the ground wave attenuates to a negligible value in a very short distance. One must accordingly then deal with a direct wave and a ground-reflected wave, as illustrated in Fig. 10-6. In making field-strength measurements in the horizontal plane under these conditions, it is accordingly necessary to take care that the antenna of the portable measuring equipment is kept at constant height above the ground. Because of the complicated nature of the correction with distance, it is also desirable that the distance be kept substantially constant throughout a measurement.

A further complicating factor in making measurements at these frequencies is introduced by the possibility that the reflection coefficient at the surface of the ground may affect the experimental results. Under conditions of glancing incidence at the surface of the ground, where Eq. (10-7) applies, then if the ground surface is reasonably flat and clear it is normally safe to assume that the coefficient of reflection approximates unity, independently of the exact ground constants. However, if the combination of distance and antenna heights is such that the angle of incidence of the ground-reflected wave at the surface of the earth is not glancing, then the observed field strength (and hence pattern) will be modified by an amount that is determined by the reflection coefficient. If the reflection coefficient is different in different azimuth directions from the antenna under test, then errors will be introduced if the field pattern is obtained by exploring the field produced in various directions, even though the portable antenna is kept at a fixed height and the spacing is constant. To eliminate this error, the distance between antennas can be increased until the reflection coefficient approximates unity irrespective of ground constants. Alternatively, both antennas can be located at fixed positions, with provision being made to rotate the antenna under test; in this way an azimuth pattern can be obtained without changing the point of reflection, and hence without changing the reflection coefficient.

At frequencies between about 30 Mc and 2000 kc, an intermediate situation exists with respect to determination of antenna patterns. Here, with vertically polarized antennas it is found that at distances corresponding to the minimum distance at which it is permissible to make measurements of field patterns, a ground wave of considerable strength is present. Under these conditions a field pattern in the horizontal plane may be obtained by using portable equipment to measure the strength of the ground wave as a function of azimuth direction; the results so obtained are not critical with respect to small variations in height of the portable antenna above ground. However, when horizontally polarized waves are involved, as is the case with most directional antenna systems designed for operation at these frequencies, the ground wave dies out so quickly with distance as to be of negligible consequence. The situation is then the same as at higher frequencies, except that the height above ground in relationship to wavelength is so small, that in the immediate vicinity of the ground one can assume that Eq. (10-7) applies. The field strength is then proportional to the height of the portable antenna above ground, which must be kept constant.

10-8. Power Gain of Antennas. The term *gain* as applied to an antenna system is a measure of the directivity of the field pattern of the actual antenna as compared with the field pattern of an isotropic radiator.[1] Quantitatively, *the gain is the ratio of the power that must be radiated by the isotropic antenna to deliver a particular field strength in the desired direction, to the power that must be radiated by the actual antenna to obtain the same field strength in the same direction.*[2]

Determination of Power Gain from Field Pattern. When a complete field pattern is available, it is possible to determine gain by calculation. The idea is to imagine that the antenna is at the center of a large sphere (or hemisphere in the case where the earth is present). The radiated power passing through each unit area of the spherical surface is then[3]

$$\text{Power in watts per unit area} = \frac{\mathcal{E}^2}{120\pi} \tag{10-8}$$

where $\mathcal{E}$ is the field strength in volts per unit length. The total radiated power represented by this field configuration is obtained by integration over the entire spherical surface. The power gain is obtained by comparison with the power associated with an isotropic radiator, and is[4,5]

---

[1] An isotropic radiator is an antenna that radiates uniformly in all directions. Although it can be theoretically shown that such a radiator cannot exist, this fact need not introduce any confusion since such a radiator can be readily imagined.

[2] This definition of gain is on the basis of power actually radiated. Alternatively, one can define gain as the ratio of power that must be supplied to an ideal lossless isotropic radiator to develop a particular field strength in a given direction, to the power that must be supplied to the actual antenna to develop the same field strength in this direction. Since the power *radiated* by the actual antenna is less than the power *supplied* to it, by the amount of the power dissipated in the antenna loss resistance, this definition in terms of power supplied leads to a lower value of gain unless the loss resistance is negligible compared with the radiation resistance. This approximation is realized in all ordinary microwave antenna systems, for most practical transmitting antennas for broadcast and higher frequencies, and for properly matched receiving antennas involving half-wave dipoles, or more elaborate arrangements.

[3] For derivation, see Terman, *op. cit.*, p. 693.

[4] In the case where the earth is present, the integration with respect to θ in Eq. (10-9) is carried out between the limits $\theta = 0$ and $\theta = -\pi/2$. The quantity used in the denominator of Eq. (10-9) is then twice the value of the integral obtained for these limits.

[5] This relation is derived as follows: If the sphere has a radius r, then the isotropic

$$\text{Power gain} = \frac{P_1}{P_2} = G = \frac{4\pi \mathcal{E}_0{}^2}{\displaystyle\int_{-\pi}^{0}\int_{0}^{2\pi} \mathcal{E}^2 \sin\,\theta\,d\theta\,d\phi} \qquad (10\text{-}9)$$

where $\mathcal{E}_0$ is the value of $\mathcal{E}$ in the desired direction, and the space coordinates are as shown in Fig. 10-14.

The usefulness of Eq. (10-9) is limited by the fact that except for the very simplest types of antennas, the double integral must be evaluated by

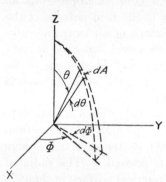

graphical methods. This is true even when the field pattern can be expressed by an equation, since except for the two or three of the simplest cases that can be imaged, the mathematical manipulations called for become extremely difficult at best, and in many instances there is no known method of carrying out the indicated integration mathematically.

The graphical integration of the antenna field pattern indicated in Eq. (10-9) can be systematically carried out by the following procedure: *First*, the average effective field strength at the spherical surface is determined as a function of angle of elevation. This average effective field

Fig. 10-14. Coordinate-system notation.

strength for any given angle of elevation is defined as the strength of the field that, if constant as one rotates about the vertical axis, would represent the same total energy as does the actual field distribution for that vertical angle. In the usual case where the radiated field varies with the azimuth angle ϕ, the average effective field strength at a given vertical angle θ is obtained by plotting the actual distribution of field strength at

---

radiator has a surface area $4\pi r^2$ and since it radiates $\mathcal{E}_0{}^2/120\pi$ watts through each unit area of the surface, the power P_1 radiated by the isotropic antenna is

$$P_1 = 4\pi r^2 \times (\mathcal{E}_0{}^2/120\pi) \text{ watts.}$$

The power dP_2 radiated by the actual antenna through an elementary surface area dA is $(\mathcal{E}^2/120\pi)dA$. However, in terms of the coordinate system of Fig. 10-14,

$$dA = (r\,d\theta)(r\,d\phi\,\sin\,\theta) = r^2 \sin\,\theta\,d\theta\,d\phi,$$

so that

$$dP_2 = \frac{\mathcal{E}^2}{120\pi}\,r^2 \sin\,\theta\,d\theta\,d\phi$$

or

$$P_2 = \frac{1}{120\pi}\,r^2 \int_{-\pi}^{0}\int_{0}^{2\pi} \varepsilon^2 \sin\,\theta\,d\theta\,d\phi$$

Equation (10-9) follows by noting that by definition $G = P_1/P_2$.

this vertical angle on polar paper as a function of azimuth, as in Fig. 10-15. The radius of the circle (shown dotted in Fig. 10-15) that encloses the same area as does this actual pattern, is then the average effective field strength of the pattern for the particular vertical angle involved. *Second,* this average effective field strength is plotted on polar paper as a function of elevation angle θ, from $\theta = 0$ to $\theta = 90°$ and the resulting curve is multiplied by $\sqrt{\sin \theta}$ (see dotted and solid curves in Fig. 10-16). This multiplication takes into account the fact that on approaching the vertical ($\theta = 0$) the length of the strip of angular width $d\theta$ that is swept through in traveling about the axis Z through a 360° variation in the azimuth angle ϕ is proportional to $\sin \theta$ (see Fig. 10-14).

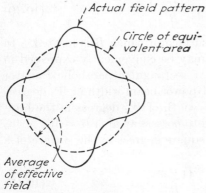

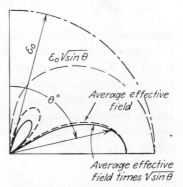

FIG. 10-15. Determination of average effective field strength from a curve of actual field strength plotted on polar paper.

FIG. 10-16. Comparison of total power radiated from the actual antenna, with the corresponding power that would be radiated by an isotropic radiator producing the same field in the desired direction.

The square-root sign is necessary because the area under a curve plotted in polar form is proportional to the square of the radius vector; in this way the area under the curve of field strength as a function of θ is weighted by the factor $\sin \theta$. *Finally,* the area under this curve, which is proportional to the total radiated power, is compared with the corresponding area for an isotropic radiator. This isotropic case corresponds to the dashed curve in Fig. 10-16 in which the radius vector has the value $\mathcal{E}_0 \sqrt{\sin \theta}$, where $\mathcal{E}_0$ is the field strength of the actual pattern in the desired direction, expressed in the same units as the average effective field strength referred to above. It is to be noted that in general $\mathcal{E}_0$ will be larger than the maximum value of the average effective field; this is apparent from Fig. 10-15, which shows that for any particular elevation angle, the maximum field can in general be expected to exceed the average effective value. The ratio of the area under the dashed curve in Fig. 10-16 to the area under the solid curve is the power gain.

With pencillike beams, such as are produced by parabolic and lens antennas, a fairly accurate estimate of gain can be made by the following simple procedure.[1] Let B be the area of the beam, defined as the area over which the power density in the beam is at least half of the power density on the beam axis. It is now arbitrarily assumed that all of the power radiated from the directional antenna is concentrated within this area. The resulting power gain for this hypothetical situation is the quotient of the surface represented by the complete sphere, divided by the beam area B; that is,

$$\text{Power gain} = \frac{4\pi r^2}{B} \tag{10-10}$$

where r is the radius of the spherical surface in which B is located. In the case of narrow beams, the area B may be conveniently expressed in terms of "square degrees." Thus if a rectangular parabolic radiator that is uniformly illuminated has a half-power beam width of W_1 degrees in the vertical plane, and a half-power width of W_2 degrees in the horizontal, then the beam can be considered to possess an area $B = W_1 \times W_2$ square degrees. The total number of square degrees in the surface of a sphere is $4\pi \times 57.3^2 = 41,253$, so that

$$\text{Power gain} = \frac{41,253}{B} \tag{10-11}$$

In the case of a circular beam having a half-power width of W degrees, the area in square degrees is $B = \pi W^2/4$. Elliptical beams would similarly have a cross-sectional area moderately less than that of the circumscribed rectangle. The results of gain calculations made with the aid of Eq. (10-11) are not exact, because they fail to take into account the precise shape of the beam and the details of the minor lobes. However, the method is useful in making estimates of gain unless the beam has an unusual shape. In the case of beams having one well-defined major lobe, with small minor lobes, it will usually give results accurate within ± 3 db.

Relation between Gain and Capture Area of Antennas. At the higher radio frequencies, particularly microwave frequencies, it is possible to

---

[1] In the special case where over the main beam the field pattern in the vertical plane is substantially independent of azimuth, while the directivity as a function of azimuth at a given vertical angle is independent of this vertical angle, it is possible to obtain fairly good results by still another simplification. This case corresponds to a rectangular reflector illuminated by a line antenna, or to a sectoral horn. For further details see J. D. Lawson, Some Methods for Determining the Power Gain of Microwave Aerials, *J. IEE (Radio & Comm.)*, vol. 95, pt. III, no. 36, p. 205, July, 1948; also "Technique of Microwave Measurements," *op. cit.*, p. 914.

measure accurately the power gain of an antenna by simple experimental methods. This is in part because at these frequencies the physical size of antennas is small even when they possess considerable gain. It is also due in part to the fact that at the higher frequencies, the loss resistance in the antenna system can normally be considered so small that any power supplied to the antenna can be assumed to be radiated, and that all power abstracted by the antenna from a passing radio wave can be assumed to be delivered to the connected load.

When measuring antenna gain under these conditions, advantage is normally taken of the relationship that exists between the gain of the antenna when acting as a radiator of waves, and the maximum power that this antenna can absorb from a passing radio wave. By means of the reciprocity theorem it can be shown that[1]

$$\begin{matrix} \text{Maximum possible} \\ \text{received power} \end{matrix} \Big\} = \frac{G\mathcal{E}^2\lambda^2}{480\pi^2} \qquad (10\text{-}12)$$

Here G is the power gain of the antenna relative to an isotropic radiator, λ is the wavelength, and $\mathcal{E}$ is the field strength at the receiving antenna in volts per unit length expressed in the same units of length as λ. This maximum possible received power can be considered as the power contained in a section of the wavefront having an area A, which by combining Eqs. (10-8) and (10-12) is found to have the value

$$A = \frac{G}{4\pi}\lambda^2 \qquad (10\text{-}13)$$

The area A is variously termed the capture area, intercept area, and absorption cross section, of the receiving antenna. This area, expressed in square wavelengths, is seen to depend only upon the power gain of the antenna. In the case of lens, parabolic, horn, and mattress antennas, with apertures that are large when measured in wavelengths, A is ordinarily moderately less than the aperture area, typically 60 to 80 per cent as great.

The power that a receiving antenna delivers to a load is maximum when the load impedance has a reactive component equal in magnitude but opposite in sign to the reactive component of the antenna impedance, and when simultaneously the resistive component of the load impedance equals the resistance component of the antenna impedance. To the extent that the loss resistance of the antenna can be neglected in comparison with the radiation resistance, the power delivered by the antenna to a load adjusted for maximum load power will have the value given by Eq. (10-12).

[1] For a derivation of this relation see Terman, *op. cit.*, pp. 726–729.

10-9. Gain of Microwave Antennas.[1] *Comparison Methods.* The simplest method of measuring the power gain of a microwave antenna is to take advantage of the fact that Eq. (10-12) shows that for a given field strength at a given frequency, the maximum possible power that can be absorbed is proportional to the antenna gain. One therefore can determine gain by experimentally comparing the ability of the antenna under test to absorb power from a given radio wave, against the ability of a standard antenna of known gain to absorb power from the same passing radio wave.

A suitable arrangement of apparatus is illustrated in Fig. 10-17. Here a transmitter of any convenient type is located an appropriate distance

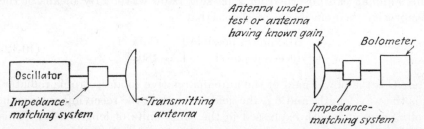

Fig. 10-17. Schematic diagram indicating experimental arrangement for measuring power gain of an antenna by comparison with an antenna of known power gain.

away, and used to generate a radio wave. A bolometer is normally used to measure the receiver power, and is provided with a matching system that is adjusted in each case so that the bolometer absorbs the maximum possible power that the antenna system is capable of delivering to it. On the assumption that all of the received power is delivered to the bolometer and none is otherwise dissipated, then by Eq. (10-12) the gains of the standard and unknown antennas will be in proportion to the power absorbed by each from the wave.

An alternative procedure consists in modifying Fig. 10-17 by radiating a known power from a transmitting antenna of known gain, and measuring the maximum power that can be absorbed by the other antenna acting as a receiving antenna. One then has[2]

[1] For general discussions of the measurement of gain of microwave antennas the following references are suggested: Lawson, *loc. cit.;* Cutler, King, and Kock, *loc. cit.;* "Microwave Antenna Theory and Design," *op. cit.,* pp. 580–587, 594–609; "Technique of Microwave Measurements," *op. cit.,* pp. 907–914.

[2] This relation can be derived as follows: The transmitter power per unit area at distance r from the transmitter is $P_T G_T / 4\pi r^2$. Since the capture area of the receiving antenna by Eq. (10-13) is $G_R \lambda^2 / 4\pi$, then

$$P_R = \frac{P_T G_T}{4\pi r^2} \frac{G_R \lambda^2}{4\pi}$$

Solving for $G_T G_R$ gives Eq. (10-14).

$$G_T G_R = \frac{P_R}{P_T} \left(\frac{4\pi r}{\lambda}\right)^2 \qquad (10\text{-}14)$$

where G_T = gain of transmitting antenna relative to an isotropic radiator
$\quad\;\; G_R$ = gain of receiving antenna relative to an isotropic radiator
$\quad\;\; P_T$ = radiated power
$\quad\;\; P_R$ = maximum possible received power
$\quad\;\; \lambda$ = wavelength
$\quad\;\; r$ = distance between antennas

The transmitted power can be conveniently measured by first adjusting the impedance-matching system associated with the transmitting system so that the antenna draws the maximum possible power from the oscillator, as indicated by maximum received signal. The antenna is then replaced by a bolometer or other power-measuring unit, and the impedance match is readjusted to cause the oscillator to deliver maximum possible power to the bolometer. The measured power will then be the same as was delivered to the transmitting antenna. Alternatively, a directional coupler of known coupling can be used to monitor the power delivered to the transmitting antenna.

In both of the above methods of measuring power gain, it is necessary to have available an antenna of known gain. An absolute determination of the gain of this reference antenna can be obtained in several ways as described below. If the standard antenna is a horn, its gain can ordinarily be determined by calculation with an error that normally does not exceed 5 per cent.[1] In the case where it is permissible for the standard antenna to have a low gain, it is possible to employ a half-wave dipole as the standard antenna. The gain of such an antenna is 1.64.

Absolute Measurement of Gain of Microwave Antennas.[2] The absolute gain of an antenna can be determined experimentally by employing the arrangement of Fig. 10-17, but using identical transmitting and receiving antennas. Under these conditions Eq. (10-14) reduces to

$$\text{Gain} = \frac{4\pi r}{\lambda} \sqrt{\frac{P_R}{P_T}} \qquad (10\text{-}15)$$

If it is not convenient to employ two identical antennas, an absolute determination of gain can still be made by employing three dissimilar antennas. Measurements of transmitted and received power are then carried out exactly as in the two-antenna method of Fig. 10-17, for each of the three pairs of antennas that may be formed. Following Eq. (10-14), one can write

[1] For the necessary formulas, see "Microwave Antenna Theory and Design," *op. cit.*, p. 587.
[2] For further information see the references cited on p. 438.

$$G_1 G_2 = \left(\frac{4\pi r}{\lambda}\right)^2 \frac{P_{R_{12}}}{P_{T_{12}}}$$

$$G_2 G_3 = \left(\frac{4\pi r}{\lambda}\right)^2 \frac{P_{R_{23}}}{P_{T_{23}}} \qquad (10\text{-}16)$$

$$G_1 G_3 = \left(\frac{4\pi r}{\lambda}\right)^2 \frac{P_{R_{13}}}{P_{T_{13}}}$$

The notation is as in Eq. (10-14), with the addition that subscripts 1, 2, and 3 denote the three antennas. Double subscripts indicate antennas involved in the particular transmitting-receiving combination involved; thus G_2 is the gain of antenna 2, and $P_{R_{12}}$ is the received power when the two antennas involved are antennas 1 and 2 and the transmitted power

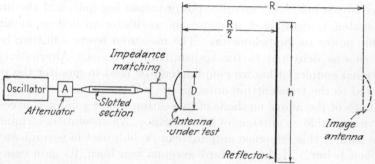

FIG. 10-18. Schematic arrangement of apparatus for determining antenna gain by the reflection method.

is $P_{T_{12}}$. By simultaneous solution of these three equations, one can obtain the gain of any one of the antennas. Thus

$$G_1 = \frac{4\pi r}{\lambda} \sqrt{\left(\frac{P_{R_{12}}}{P_{T_{12}}}\right)\left(\frac{P_{R_{13}}}{P_{T_{13}}}\right)\left(\frac{P_{T_{23}}}{P_{R_{23}}}\right)} \qquad (10\text{-}17)$$

Another method of measuring the absolute power gain is illustrated in Fig. 10-18.[1] This can be called the reflection method. Here the antenna under test is first carefully matched to its feed line, which includes a slotted section, so that in the absence of the reflector no standing waves are present on the slotted line. A reflector consisting of a conducting surface, flat to better than $\lambda/16$, is then placed at right angles to the axis of the antenna as shown. This surface reflects the radiation that strikes it, producing a reflected wave directed backward in the general direction of the antenna. Part of the reflected wave is intercepted by the antenna, and enters the feed line of this antenna to produce a backward-traveling wave. The energy represented by this backward-traveling wave is the

[1] This method was originated by C. H. Purcell.

same as the energy that would be absorbed in the absence of the reflector by an antenna identical with the transmitting antenna and representing its image with respect to the reflector, as shown dotted in Fig. 10-18. The magnitude of this reflected power that enters the transmitting antenna can be determined from the standing-wave ratio that is produced by the presence of the reflector, as measured by the slotted section. To prevent the oscillator from being affected by the backward wave, an attenuator A is introduced between the oscillator and antenna. The antenna side of this attenuator must also present a good impedance match to the slotted line, so that a backward-traveling wave from the slotted line into A will be absorbed without reflection.

The quantitative relations that exist in Fig. 10-18 are[1]

$$G = \frac{4\pi R}{\lambda} \frac{S - 1}{S + 1} \tag{10-18}$$

where G = gain of antenna compared with an isotropic radiator

R = spacing between antenna and its image (see Fig. 10-18)

S = voltage standing-wave ratio

λ = wavelength

The distance R in Fig. 10-18 should be no greater than necessary, since the greater the distance the more nearly will the standing-wave ratio that is to be measured approach unity, with resulting loss in the accuracy of the determination. At the same time, the distance S between the radiating antenna and its image should be not less than about $2D^2/\lambda$, where D is the aperture of the antenna under test. Otherwise the errors from inadequate spacing will exceed the improved accuracy resulting from having a larger standing-wave ratio to measure.

It is also necessary that the reflector be large enough to intercept most of the main beam. Since the total width of this beam is of the order of $2\lambda/D$ radians, then for a square mirror the height h must be not less than $R\lambda/D$. For $R = 2D^2/\lambda$, the required height is hence $2D$.

In carrying out gain determinations with the arrangement of Fig. 10-18, complications arise if the capture area of the antenna is less than the actual cross section of the aperture, as is nearly always the case. Under these conditions, some of the reflected energy that strikes the aperture of the antenna is reradiated toward the reflector by the antenna, to produce a second reflected wave that can enter the transmitting antenna and

---

[1] This equation follows from Eq. (10-15) when it is noted that the antenna and its image represent two identical antennas spaced a distance R, and that $(S - 1)/(S + 1)$ is the ratio of the voltage amplitudes of two waves, one of which is the wave that produces radiated power, while the other represents the resulting power that would be induced in the image receiving antenna.

complicate the standing-wave pattern.[1] Error from this source can be eliminated by making standing-wave determinations with the reflector in two positions corresponding to values of $R/2$ that differ by a quarter of a wavelength. Such a quarter-wavelength displacement of the reflector reverses the phase of the spurious second-order signal. Hence by taking the arithmetic mean of the gains as computed for the standing-wave ratios observed for the two positions, the error is canceled. This procedure also simultaneously removes most of the error caused by any small residual mismatch that may have originally existed between the antenna and its transmission line before the reflector was put in place.

The chief merit of the method of measuring power gain illustrated in Fig. 10-18 is the fact that it uses no apparatus that is not ordinarily available. The accuracy obtainable in practice is, however, less than obtained with other methods of measuring the absolute gain that are described here. The method is best suited to antennas in which the aperture is small or moderate.

10.10. Determination of Antenna Gain at the Lower Radio Frequencies. Most of the methods used to determine gain at microwave frequencies become increasingly difficult to apply as the frequency becomes progressively lower. This is because as the frequency is reduced the antennas become physically larger, loss resistances are less likely to be negligible, and reflections from the ground introduce increasing complications.

Graphical methods find increased use at the lower frequencies, particularly at broadcast and lower frequencies. Here the directional patterns are sufficiently simple so that they can be known relatively accurately from a limited quantity of data, or can be calculated with satisfactory accuracy from a knowledge of the antenna geometry and the relative magnitudes and phases of the currents in the individual antenna elements.

When the frequency is relatively high, gain can be satisfactorily determined by the comparison method, commonly using a half-wave doublet as the antenna of known gain.[2] Such an antenna when in free space has a power gain of 1.64 as compared with an isotropic radiator. When the ground must be taken into account this can be satisfactorily done by

---

[1] This is the interaction effect discussed on p. 414, and which is more serious in the reflector method of gain determination than in other experimental methods of measuring gain. For further discussion of the interaction problem in the reflector method of measuring gain see A. B. Pippard, O. H. Burrell, and F. F. Crome, The Influence of Re-radiation on Measurements of the Power Gain of an Aerial, *J. IEE* (*Radiolocation Conv.*), vol. 93, pt. IIIA, p. 720, 1946; also "Microwave Antenna Theory and Design," *op. cit.*, p. 586, and "Technique of Microwave Measurements," *op. cit.*, p. 912.

[2] The determination of gain in this manner in the frequency range 44 to 216 Mc is discussed by E. G. Hills, Impedance Measurements at VHF, *Electronics*, vol. 20, p. 124, July, 1947.

calculation, using the mutual impedance between the antenna and its image, and assuming the ground is a perfect conductor.[1]

A very common method of determining gain at these lower radio frequencies consists in delivering to the transmitting antenna a known power, and observing the field strength $\mathcal{E}_0$ produced in the direction of maximum radiation. This field strength can be obtained as explained in Chap. 11. The power gain for free-space conditions is then[2]

$$\text{Power gain} = \frac{\mathcal{E}_0{}^2 r^2}{30 P_T} \tag{10-19a}$$

where $\mathcal{E}_0$ = field strength in desired direction, volts per unit length
      r = distance to measuring point
      P_T = power delivered to transmitting antenna, watts
When the ground causes the power that is radiated to be confined to a hemisphere, as is usually the case, then

$$\text{Power gain} = \frac{\mathcal{E}_0{}^2 r^2}{60 P_T} \tag{10-19b}$$

This method requires only a measurement of the power delivered to the transmitting antenna, and the availability of a simple field-strength measuring equipment. The accuracy of the method, however, is limited by the fact that the portion of the power delivered to the transmitting antenna that is dissipated in the loss resistance of the antenna, instead of being radiated, causes the observed gain to be less than that which would be obtained from an integration of the field pattern, as discussed in the footnote on page 433.

10-11. Miscellaneous Antenna Measurements. *Use of Models in Antenna Measurements.* Antennas which have the same geometrical proportions and differ only in physical size, will have the same field pattern, gain, and impedance, provided the wavelength is exactly proportional to the size.[3] This fact makes it possible to obtain the characteristics of an antenna system by the use of a model that has a more con-

---

[1] Such calculations are discussed in Terman, *op. cit.*, pp. 695–698. Data on mutual impedance values between pairs of dipoles are to be found in F. E. Terman, "Radio Engineers' Handbook," pp. 776–782, McGraw-Hill Book Company, Inc., New York, 1943.

[2] This relation is derived as follows: A field strength $\mathcal{E}_0$ produced by an isotropic radiator over a spherical surface of radius r (and hence area $4\pi r^2$) is seen from Eq. (10-8) to represent a total radiated power of $4\pi r^2 \times (\mathcal{E}_0{}^2/120\pi) = \mathcal{E}_0{}^2 r^2/30$ watts. Dividing this by the power P_T actually supplied to the antenna to produce the field $\mathcal{E}_0$ gives the power gain.

[3] An exception to this is the loss resistance, which is not necessarily the same, although the reactance components of the antenna impedance and the radiation resistance will be unchanged.

venient size than does the actual antenna. Thus the characteristics of low-frequency antennas may be conveniently determined by the use of small-scale models, which are inexpensive to construct and can be readily modified to determine the effect of design changes.[1]

Models are particularly useful in determining the characteristics of air-plane and ship antennas. The geometry of the airplane is so very complex, that the field pattern cannot be calculated with accuracy. The pattern is furthermore affected very greatly by changes in location of the antenna with respect to the wings, fuselage, and tail structure. Flight tests for determining the field pattern and gain of antennas actually

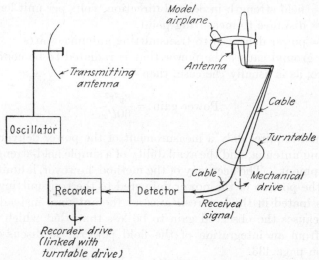

Fig. 10-19. Schematic diagram of apparatus for measuring aircraft-antenna field patterns on a model basis.

installed on an airplane are both slow and prohibitively expensive. The most satisfactory means of obtaining design and performance information applying to aircraft antennas at frequencies below 1000 Mc accordingly consists in constructing a small-scale copper-plated wooden model of the airplane upon which is installed an antenna similar to that under consideration, and appropriately scaled in size. This model plane with its model antenna is then mounted on a tower that can be rotated, and is investigated in the manner illustrated schematically in Fig. 10-19, using an appropriate frequency. Thus if the model is one-fiftieth of full size, and if the frequency for which the characteristics are desired is 115 Mc, a test frequency of 5750 Mc is required. The model method of studying

[1] Thus the effect of taper in the broadcast tower radiator has been studied by means of models; see H. E. Gihring and G. H. Brown, General Consideration of Tower Antennas for Broadcast Use, *Proc. IRE*, vol. 23, p. 311, April, 1935.

airplane and ship antennas is very satisfactory, and has found wide practical use.[1]

Current Distribution in Transmitting Antennas.   In short-wave directional antenna arrays, it is possible to determine whether the system is
operating properly by observing the distribution of current over the wires
of the antenna system.   Thus in a system using resonant elements, if the
loops and nodes of the current distribution are at the expected locations,
then it can be safely assumed that the antenna is behaving as desired.
Similarly, in the case of nonresonant antennas, a knowledge of the current
distribution will determine whether or not the nonresonant condition is
being realized in fact.

The current distribution along the wires of an antenna system can be
determined by operating it as a transmitting antenna, and then coupling

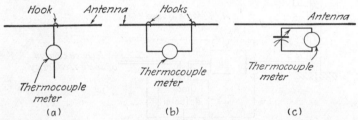

Fig. 10-20. Methods for measuring the current distribution in a radio antenna. The
same arrangements may be used for measuring the current distribution along two-wire
transmission lines.

a sensitive thermocouple instrument to the system.   Various arrangements suitable for this purpose are illustrated in Fig. 10-20.   In the
device shown at *a*, the stray capacitance between the antenna and the
free wire hanging from the thermocouple instrument supplies the return
path for the current, and the amount of coupling to the antenna depends
upon the length of the hanging wire.   The indication of the thermocouple
will be proportional to the intensity of the electric field adjacent to the
wire, *i.e.*, to the voltage distribution along the wire; the meter will therefore read maximum where the antenna current is a minimum, and vice
versa.   The arrangement at Fig. 10-20*b* can be considered as operating
either by shunting a portion of the antenna current through the meter,
or by considering that the meter is excited by the magnetic flux that
threads the small loop formed by the antenna wire and meter leads.   The
loop at *c* couples to the magnetic field produced by the antenna current,
and has the advantage of avoiding the necessity of contact with the

[1] Equipment and detailed techniques suitable for model measurements of airplane
antennas are discussed by Schmitt and Peyser, *loc. cit.*; G. Sinclair, E. C. Jordan, and
E. W. Vaughan, Measurement of Aircraft-antenna Patterns Using Models, *Proc. IRE*,
vol. 35, p. 1451, December, 1947.

antenna. The loop may be tuned or untuned, according to the pickup sensitivity desired.

In broadcast antenna arrays, one often desires to compare the amplitudes and phases of the currents in different antennas of the same array.[1] The usual method of doing this is illustrated schematically in Fig. 10-21. Here a large one-turn shielded loop is mounted on one corner of each tower antenna at or near a current maximum, and the resulting induced energy is transmitted to an observing point, commonly the transmitter

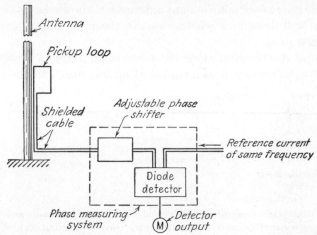

Fig. 10-21. Schematic diagram of system for determining relative amplitude and phase of current in a broadcast tower antenna.

house, by means of a shielded coaxial cable terminated in its characteristic impedance. The magnitude of the voltage across this terminating impedance is proportional to the magnitude of the current in the antenna at the point where the pickup loop is mounted. The phase of this output voltage is determined by the phase of the antenna current, and the length of the shielded cable. The latter contribution to the phase can be determined by measurement or calculation, and then allowed for. Using the methods that are discussed in Sec. 6-9, the phase of the voltage developed across the terminating resistance can be compared with the phase of any desired reference voltage, such as a voltage similarly derived from another tower radiator simultaneously excited by the same transmitter.[2] Arrangements of this type find extensive use in the adjustment

[1] See John F. Morrison, Simple Methods for Observing Current Amplitude and Phase Relations in Antenna Arrays, *Proc. IRE*, vol. 25, p. 1310, October, 1937; Simplifying the Adjustment of Antenna Array, *Bell Labs. Record*, vol. 17, p. 390, August, 1939.

[2] A typical example of equipment of this type is described in detail by B. C. O'Brien and F. L. Sherwood, Phase Monitor for Broadcast Arrays, *Electronics*, vol. 20, p. 109, December, 1947.

of the currents of the individual antennas of a broadcast antenna system composed of two or more radiating towers, and also in the monitoring of these currents once the proper condition has been established.

Measurements of Effective Height.[1]   The effective height of a receiving antenna is a hypothetical length h such that the product $\mathcal{E}h$ is equal to the equivalent induced voltage E in the equivalent antenna circuit of Fig. 10-1, where $\mathcal{E}$ is the field strength of the radio wave.[2]

The value of the effective height for a given antenna can be measured by subjecting the antenna to a radio wave produced either by a convenient radio station, or by a suitable test oscillator equipped with a radiating antenna.   One then measures the open-circuit voltage E induced in the antenna under test, and the associated field strength $\mathcal{E}$. By definition, the effective height of the antenna is then $E/\mathcal{E}$.

[1] Effective-height measurements are discussed by Dudley E. Foster and G. Mountjoy, Measurement of Effective Height of Automobile Antennas, *RCA Rev.*, vol. 3, p. 369, January, 1939.

[2] The concept of effective height is also sometimes applied to low-frequency grounded transmitting antennas.   In this case, the effective height is the length of vertical grounded wire which carrying a constant current I_0 of uniform phase will radiate the same field in the desired direction as does the actual grounded antenna when the base current is I_0.   The effective height defined in this way for transmitting is numerically the same as the effective height of the same antenna when used as a receiving antenna.

CHAPTER 11

RADIO WAVES

11-1. Methods of Measuring the Strength of Radio Waves.[1] Two general methods are available for the determination of the strength of a radio wave. In the first, sometimes called the standard antenna method, use is made of an antenna in which the relationship between the field strength of the radio wave, and the equivalent lumped voltage that the wave induces in the antenna (see Fig. 10-1), is known, either as a result of calculation or previous measurement. The field strength is then determined by measuring this equivalent induced voltage, and making use of the known relationship between it and the field strength to determine the latter. The second method of measuring field strength is known as the standard field-generator method, and consists in comparing the strength of the radio wave with a field of known strength produced by a standard field generator.

Standard Antennas. The most widely used form of standard antenna is the loop. When the largest dimension of the loop is small compared with a wavelength (not over about $\lambda/12$), and when the loop is used at a frequency that is not more than one-third of the self-resonant frequency obtained by considering the loop as a coil with distributed capacitance, the relationship between the field strength and the voltage induced in the loop is accurately given by the equation[2]

$$\text{Induced voltage} = E = 2\pi \mathcal{E} N \frac{A}{\lambda} \qquad (11\text{-}1)$$

where $\mathcal{E}$ = field strength of radio wave, volts per unit length
N = number of turns in loop
A = area of loop cross section in same units of length as $\mathcal{E}$ and λ
λ = wavelength

[1] Good summary papers on this subject include "Standards on Radio Wave Propagation-measuring Methods," Supplement to *Proc. IRE*, vol. 30, July, 1942; R. L. Smith-Rose, Radio Field-strength Measurement, *Proc. IEE (Radio & Comm.)*, vol. 96, pt. III, p. 31, January, 1949; C. R. Englund and H. T. Friis, Methods for the Measurement of Radio Field-strength, *Trans. AIEE*, vol. 46, p. 492, 1927.

[2] This relation is derived in many places; for example see F. E. Terman, "Radio Engineering," 3d ed., p. 818, McGraw-Hill Book Company, Inc., New York, 1947.

448

The ratio $E/\mathcal{E} = 2\pi NA/\lambda$ is termed the effective height of the loop antenna. Equation (11-1) assumes that the radio wave is plane-polarized in the plane of the loop, and that the loop is oriented for maximum reception.

Loops find wide use in field-strength measurements at frequencies below about 40 Mc. They have the advantage that with proper precautions the properties of the loop can be accurately predicted by calculation. Furthermore, loops are portable, do not depend on ground constants, and can be designed to operate even at very low radio frequencies where most alternative types of antennas would have prohibitive physical size. Loops are not particularly satisfactory at frequencies higher than about 40 Mc, however, because of various consequences of the fact that the physical size of the loop must be decreased with increasing frequency.

The principal alternatives to the loop antenna are the doublet antenna, the half-wave dipole, and the vertical grounded antenna. A half-wave dipole is commonly used at frequencies too high for satisfactory loop operation. With such an antenna[1]

$$\text{Induced voltage} = E = \frac{\lambda\mathcal{E}}{\pi} \qquad (11\text{-}2)$$

where λ is the wavelength, and $\mathcal{E}$ the field strength. The effective height of such a half-wave antenna is $2/\pi$ times the actual length, or λ/π. This is considerably greater than can be obtained from a loop operating at the same frequency.

The doublet antenna finds use in the borderline range of frequencies where the half-wave dipole is physically too large, and where a loop is still not entirely satisfactory for one reason or another. If the doublet is operated at a frequency that does not exceed one-third of the actual resonant frequency, then to a good approximation

$$\text{Induced voltage} = E = \frac{\mathcal{E}L}{2} \qquad (11\text{-}3)$$

where L is the length of the doublet, and $\mathcal{E}$ is the field strength. The corresponding effective height is $L/2$.

Short vertical grounded antennas are sometimes found desirable in fixed installations. The equivalent lumped voltage induced in a grounded vertical antenna that is short compared with a quarter wavelength is given by Eq. (11-3), provided the quantity L is now interpreted to mean

[1] This is for an ideal very thin antenna. Practical antennas commonly have appreciable thickness, and also usually possess some form of gap at the center. These departures from the ideal case modify the antenna properties to some extent. A discussion of this matter, and a description of means for achieving a standard antenna of high theoretical merit are given by D. D. King, Two Standard Field-strength Meters for Very-high Frequencies, *Proc. IRE*, vol. 38, p. 1048, September, 1950.

the length of the grounded antenna. In case the vertical grounded antenna is exactly a quarter wavelength long, the induced voltage is half the value given by Eq. (11-2).

If there are circumstances that raise an uncertainty as to the accuracy of the calculated behavior of the vertical grounded antenna (or of the dipole, doublet, or loop, for that matter) the relation between field strength and induced voltage can always be determined experimentally. The idea is to measure the equivalent lumped voltage that is induced by a field of known strength produced by a standard field generator, or by a field whose strength is measured with the aid of an antenna about which there is no question.

In the case of microwave systems, the standard antenna commonly consists of a horn or a parabola having a known power gain that has been previously determined either by experiment as described in Sec. 10-9, or by calculation.[1] When such an antenna is matched to a load impedance so that the load absorbs the maximum possible power from the antenna, the relation between field strength ε and load power P_r is given by Eq. (10-12), which rewritten becomes

$$\varepsilon = \sqrt{\frac{480\pi^2 P_r}{\lambda^2 G}} \qquad (11\text{-}4)$$

where G is the antenna power gain relative to an isotropic radiator.[2] Equation (11-4) implies that the antenna loss resistance is negligibly small compared with the radiation resistance. This is a permissible assumption when dealing with half-wave antennas, or antennas with appreciable power gain, such as arrays, horns, parabolas, etc.

11-2. Determination of Induced Voltage by Receiver with Calibrated Intermediate-frequency Attenuator. A common method of measuring the field strength with a standard antenna is illustrated in Fig. 11-1.[3] Here, a loop is shown, although other antenna arrangements could be employed. The voltage developed at the output terminals of the antenna system by the radio wave is applied to a superheterodyne receiver provided with a microammeter M that measures the rectified output current developed by the second detector. The receiver is provided with an adjustable attenuator located between the mixer and the first intermediate-frequency amplifier tube. This attenuator operates at the intermediate-frequency, and makes it possible to change the receiver

---

[1] While half-wave dipoles could be used at microwave frequencies and sometimes are, in general their gain (and hence effective height) is so low that such antennas are suitable only when the signals involved are relatively strong.

[2] The power gain of a doublet antenna is 1.5, of a half-wave dipole 1.64.

[3] This arrangement was first described by H. T. Friis and E. Bruce, A Radio Field-strength Measuring System for Frequencies Up to Forty Megacycles, *Proc. IRE*, vol. 14, p. 507, 1926.

amplification by accurately known amounts. Additional equipment required includes a vacuum-tube voltmeter capable of reading about 1 volt, and a signal-frequency oscillator that is moderately well shielded and is provided with an adjustable output control (uncalibrated).

A typical procedure for measuring the field strength with such an arrangement is as follows: With the switch in position a, the signal is tuned in and the loop orientation adjusted for maximum response. The

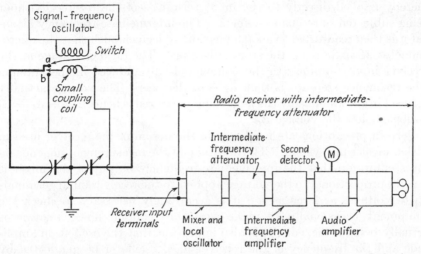

Fig. 11-1. Schematic diagram of field-strength measuring equipment of the inter-mediate-frequency-attenuator type.

intermediate-frequency attenuator is then adjusted to a value α_1 such that a convenient deflection on the microammeter M is obtained. Next, the signal-frequency oscillator is turned on, thus inducing a voltage in series with the antenna, and is set at the frequency of the incoming signal. The output of the signal-frequency oscillator is adjusted until a voltage E_0 (commonly 1 volt) appears at the input terminals of the receiver as determined by the vacuum-tube voltmeter.[1,2] The intermediate-frequency attenuator is now readjusted to an attenuation of α_2 decibels such that the microammeter M gives the same reading as before. The voltage produced at the receiver input terminals by the field being meas-

[1] In some cases, it may be desirable to turn off the local oscillator of the receiver during this adjustment, although if a pentagrid mixer or pentagrid converter tube is used and is of a type in which negligible local oscillator current is developed in the signal circuit, this is unnecessary.

Also, if the voltage produced at the input terminals of the receiver by the field being measured is not very small compared with E_0, then the loop should be rotated 90° while the signal-frequency oscillator is applied to the system.

[2] This vacuum-tube voltmeter is sometimes obtained by reconnecting the mixer tube to function as a plate-rectifier type of voltmeter (see Sec. 1-8).

ured is then $\alpha_2 - \alpha_1$ decibels less than E_0. This voltage differs from the potential actually induced in the antenna by the radio wave as a result of resonance effects in the antenna. The ratio of the voltage produced at the receiver input terminals to the voltage actually induced in the loop can be determined by reconnecting the signal-frequency oscillator by throwing the antenna switch to position b in Fig. 11-1. The voltage induced in series with the antenna by the signal-frequency oscillator is thereby applied directly to the input terminals of the receiver without being subjected to resonance effects. The intermediate-frequency attenuator is then readjusted to an attenuation α_3 decibels such that the micro-ammeter M again reads the standard value. The ratio of voltage at the receiver input terminals to the voltage actually induced in the antenna (the resonance step-up) is then $\alpha_2 - \alpha_3$ decibels. The voltage actually induced in the antenna by the field being measured is hence $2\alpha_2 - \alpha_1 - \alpha_3$ decibels below the voltage E_0.

Certain precautions are necessary in the design of the receiver used in such a measuring system. The accuracy of the measurement depends on the assumption that the intermediate-frequency output of the mixer is exactly proportional to the voltage applied to the receiver input terminals up to voltages as large as E_0; it is accordingly necessary to check the equipment occasionally to make sure the required linear relation is actually being achieved. It is also important that the oscillation amplitude and the frequency of the receiver local oscillator be unaffected by the tuning of the input circuit of the receiver. Otherwise, the mixer gain may change when the output from the signal-frequency oscillator is connected directly to the input terminals of the receiver in place of the tuned antenna system. It is important that the intermediate-frequency attenuator be located immediately following the mixer rather than between two intermediate-frequency amplifier tubes; otherwise it is difficult to prevent overloading of the first intermediate-frequency amplifier stage under some conditions. Such overloading will cause the gain of the receiver to depend upon the amplitude of the input to the receiver, and so will introduce errors.

It will be observed that this method of measuring field strength is essentially a comparison method in which the voltage induced in the antenna by the unknown signal is compared with a voltage E_0 of the same frequency produced by the signal-frequency oscillator, and having a magnitude large enough to be readily measured by a vacuum-tube voltmeter.[1] The ratio between these two voltages is obtained through the

[1] A modified procedure, in which a measured loop current is used in place of the measured voltage E_0, is described by F. M. Colebrook and A. C. Gordon-Smith, A Method of Calibrating a Field Strength Measuring Set, *J. IEE (Wireless Sec.)*, vol. 88, pt. III, p. 15, March, 1941.

attenuator settings required to maintain constant output from the radio receiver, which otherwise remains unchanged. Thus, the characteristics of the receiver do not enter into the measurement provided only that the first detector of the receiver is linear, and that there is no interaction between the local oscillator of the receiver and the impedance connected across the input terminals of the receiver.

The intermediate-frequency-attenuator method of measuring voltage induced in an antenna has the advantage that its accuracy depends only on the intermediate-frequency attenuator. The accuracy is high and independent of signal frequency because this attenuator operates at a constant and not particularly high frequency and so can easily be designed to give excellent performance. Also, there are no serious shielding problems, since when the signal-frequency oscillator is turned on, it is merely necessary that the leakage from this oscillator be small compared with the voltage E_0, which is commonly of the order of 1 volt.

11-3. Determination of Induced Voltage by Substitution.[1] In this method, illustrated schematically in Fig. 11-2, a sensitive radio receiver is connected to the standard antenna (shown as a loop) and tuned to the signal with the loop oriented for maximum reception. The receiver gain is adjusted to give a convenient indication on a d-c microammeter M in the output circuit of the second detector of the receiver. The loop is then rotated 90° so that little or no signal is received. Next, a known voltage of the same frequency as the signal, obtained from a standard signal generator, is introduced in series with the loop through the resistance R, which is typically 1 or 2 ohms. This known voltage is adjusted in amplitude until the radio receiver indicates the same output as produced by the actual signal. The known voltage is then obviously equal to the voltage induced in the standard antenna by the passing wave. Variations of this arrangement consist in introducing the signal into the loop by a coil having mutual inductance to the loop, and in using other types of antennas.

This method of measuring field strength is very convenient when a well-shielded signal generator is available. In addition to the standard signal generator, it requires only a standard antenna and an ordinary radio receiver in which a microammeter has been connected in the output

---

[1] This method was first proposed by Carl Englund in *Proc. IRE*, vol. 5, p. 248, August, 1917. Detailed discussion of procedures for carrying out the measurement, and of typical apparatus, is given by Ralph Bown, Carl R. Englund, and H. T. Friis, Radio Transmission Measurements, *Proc. IRE*, vol. 11, p. 115, April, 1923; H. H. Beverage and H. O. Peterson, Radio Transmission on Long Wavelengths, *Proc. IRE*, vol. 11, p. 661, December, 1923; Greenleaf W. Pickard, The Direction and Intensity of Waves from European Stations, *Proc. IRE*, vol. 10, p. 161, June, 1922; Axel F. Jensen, Portable Receiving Sets for Measuring Field Strengths at Broadcasting Frequencies, *Proc. IRE*, vol. 14, p. 333, June, 1926.

circuit of the second detector.   In contrast, the intermediate-frequency-attenuator method does not require that a standard signal generator of the appropriate frequency be available, but does call for a special radio receiver.   The accuracies that can be realized by the two methods are of the same order of magnitude.

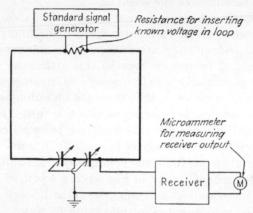

Fig. 11-2. Measurement of field strength by the substitution method, using a standard signal generator and an ordinary receiver.

11-4. Measurement of Field Strength with the Aid of a Standard Field Generator.[1]   A standard field generator consists of a compact portable oscillator associated with an antenna of such character that when the antenna is supplied with a known current or power, the field that is produced can be calculated from the antenna dimensions.   Suitable antenna arrangements are shown in Fig. 11-3, and include a balanced loop carrying a known current, a short vertical antenna with high capacitance top, and a half-wave dipole supplied by a known current or power.   A directional antenna of known gain, such as a horn, supplied with a known power can

[1] This method of measuring field strength was first proposed by J. C. Schelleng, C. R. Burrows, and E. B. Ferrell, Ultra-short-wave Propagation, *Proc. IRE*, vol. 21, p. 427, March, 1933.   Further discussions of systems involving a standard field generator are given by J. S. McPetrie and B. G. Pressey, A Method of Using Horizontally Polarized Waves for the Calibration of Short-wave Field-strength Measuring Sets by Radiation, *IEE* (*Wireless Sec.*), vol. 13, p. 267, September, 1938 (also *J. IEE*, vol. 83, p. 210, 1938); F. M. Colebrook and A. C. Gordon-Smith, The Design and Construction of a Short-wave Field-strength Measuring Set, *IEE* (*Wireless Sec.*), vol. 14, p. 146, June, 1939 (also *J. IEE*, vol. 84, p. 388, 1939); J. S. McPetrie and J. A. Saxton, Theory and Experimental Confirmation of Calibration of Field-strength Measuring Sets by Radiation, *J. IEE* (*Wireless Sec.*), vol. 88, pt. III, p. 11, March, 1941; F. M. Colebrook and A. C. Gordon-Smith, The Design of Ultra-short-wave Field-strength Measuring Equipment, *J. IEE* (*Wireless Sec.*), vol. 90, pt. III, p. 28; March, 1943.

also be used provided the loss resistance is small compared with the radiation resistance. The fields produced in these cases are as follows:

Loop (see Fig. 11-3a):

$$\mathcal{E}_0 = \frac{120\pi^2}{d} N \frac{A}{\lambda^2} I_a \tag{11-5}$$

Short vertical antenna carrying uniform current (Fig. 11-3b):

$$\mathcal{E}_0 = \frac{60\pi}{d} \frac{h}{\lambda} I_a \tag{11-6}$$

Half-wave dipole (Fig. 11-3c):

$$\mathcal{E}_0 = \frac{60 I_a}{d} = \frac{7.02}{d} \sqrt{P_a} \tag{11-7}$$

Directional antenna:

$$\mathcal{E}_0 = \frac{5.48}{d} \sqrt{P_a G} \tag{11-8}$$

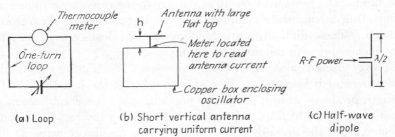

(a) Loop   (b) Short vertical antenna carrying uniform current   (c) Half-wave dipole

Fig. 11-3. Typical antenna arrangements used in standard field generators.

In these equations,

$\mathcal{E}_0$ = field strength, volts per m, at distance d

d = distance, m

λ = wavelength, m

h = height of antenna (see Fig. 11-3b), assumed less than $\lambda/10$

N = number of turns in loop

A = area of loop, sq m

P_a = power radiated by antenna, watts

I_a = current flowing in antenna, amp

The values of field-strength given by Eqs. (11-5) to (11-8) are the *free-space values in the direction of maximum radiated field.*

The combination of a standard field generator with a radio receiver having an intermediate-frequency attenuator, represents a field-strength measuring system. To measure field strength with such equipment, the signal that is to have its strength determined is tuned in on the radio receiver using any convenient receiving antenna. The intermediate-frequency attenuator is then adjusted to a value such that the microammeter in the output of the second detector gives a convenient indication. The standard field generator is then turned on and adjusted to the frequency of the radio wave being measured. The receiver attenuator is next adjusted to a value such that the microammeter indication is the same as before. If the values of attenuation for these two cases are α_1 and α_2 decibels, respectively, then the strength of the unknown field is $\alpha_2 - \alpha_1$ decibels less than the strength of the field produced by the standard field generator *at the antenna* used with the radio receiver.

The standard-field-generator method of measuring field strength is widely used at frequencies above about 30 Mc. The accuracy that can be obtained is determined only by the accuracy with which the known field can be generated, and the accuracy of the intermediate-frequency attenuator of the receiver. Other characteristics of the receiving system, including the receiving antenna, have no effect whatsoever on the result.[1] In particular, the method avoids the technical difficulties associated with determining the resonant step-up of voltage in the receiving antenna, and in injecting an accurately known voltage in series with the receiving antenna. These difficulties are very great when dealing with very high frequencies and with microwave systems.

Effect of Ground on Standard Field Generator. When using the standard field generator it is necessary to take into account the fact that the field strength produced at any particular point in space is a combination of a direct wave given by Eqs. (11-5) to (11-8), and an indirect wave that is reflected from the ground, and combines with the direct wave as illustrated in Fig. 10-6. When the reflection coefficient at the ground is approximately unity, as can be assumed to be the case for smooth ground with horizontally polarized waves for all vertical angles, and for vertical polarization with grazing incidence, the field strength at the receiver antenna can be accurately calculated from Eq. (10-6).

Variation of field strength with height of the standard-field-generator antenna above ground as calculated from Eq. (10-6) is given in Fig. 11-4 for a typical case. It will be noted that the field strength oscillates between zero and twice the free-space field. When the reflection coefficient cannot be assumed unity, as is the case with vertical polarization except at very glancing incidence corresponding to $d \gg (h_s + h_r)$, the behavior is as illustrated by the dotted curve in Fig. 11-4. The minima are no longer zero, and the maxima are less than twice the free-space field, but the average of the maxima and minima of the oscillations is still the free-space field given by Eqs. (11-5) to (11-8).

A typical procedure for using a standard field generator in the usual case where the reflection from the earth must be taken into account is as follows: The distance d is first so chosen that the maximum height h_{sm} at

[1] Provided the direction of arrival is the same for both the test and the standard waves.

which it is practical to place the standard field generator satisfies the
relation

$$h_{sm} > \frac{d\lambda}{2h_r} \qquad (11\text{-}9)$$

where h_r is the height of the receiving antenna.   The height h_s of the
standard-field-generating system above ground is then raised from
ground level up to a value that is at least slightly greater than $d\lambda/2h_r$, and
a curve of relative field strength at the receiving antenna as a function of
height h_s is obtained from the attenuator settings of the receiver required

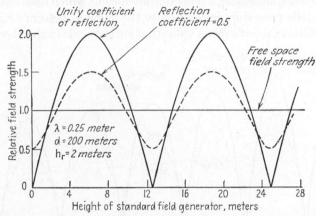

Fig. 11-4. Variation of field strength at a given point in space as the height of the
standard field generator above ground is varied.

to maintain constant receiver output during this process.   If the curve
of field strength that results shows a deep minimum at which the field
strength is only a very small fraction of the maximum value, the reflection
coefficient at the ground approximates unity, and Eq. (10-6) applies.
The maximum value of field observed as the height of the standard field
generator is increased then has a value twice the theoretical free-space
value calculated by Eqs. (11-5) to (11-8).

However, if the curve of field strength as a function of standard-field-
generator height does not show deep minima, as will be the case if the
reflection coefficient does not approximate unity, then the mean amplitude of the maxima and minima of the curve obtained corresponds to the
theoretical free-space value calculated for the standard-field equipment.
The field strength at the maxima can then be determined from the calculated free space and the experimentally observed ratio E_{min}/E_{max} of
minimum to maximum amplitude, according to the relation[1]

$$\frac{\text{Maximum of field strength}}{\text{Free-space field strength}} = \frac{2}{1 + (E_{min}/E_{max})} \qquad (11\text{-}10)$$

[1] This is derived by noting that the free-space field is $(E_{min} + E_{max})/2$.

An alternative procedure for taking into account the effect of the ground reflection, consists in maintaining the heights of the field generating and receiving antennas constant, and varying the distance. Under these conditions the relative field strength observed at the receiving point will vary as illustrated in Fig. 11-5. In the case of a reflection coefficient approximating unity, the minima will be very deep compared with the maxima, and the latter can be considered as having an amplitude that is twice the theoretical free-space value as calculated by Eqs. (11-5) to (11-8). When the minima are not very small compared with the maximum amplitudes, indicating a reflection coefficient which does not approximate unity, the procedure is essentially the same as before; *i.e.*, the field strength oscillates about a mean value that corresponds to the theoretically

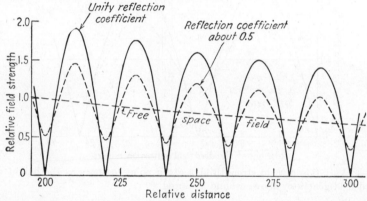

Fig. 11-5. Variation of field strength with increasing distance for a typical case with constant transmitting and receiving antenna heights.

calculated free-space value. In making use of this alternative method it is desirable that the antenna height be such that the increase in distance required to change a maximum to a minimum, or vice versa, is a relatively small percentage. Otherwise an excessive change in intensity due to varying distance will be superimposed upon the oscillatory effects resulting from ground reflection.

Both of these procedures assume that the only field produced at the receiving antenna by the standard field generator is due to a direct wave and a ground-reflected wave, and that the ground wave is negligible. When horizontally polarized waves are involved, this situation is true under all conditions of interest. However, with vertically polarized waves, it is possible for the ground wave component to have significant amplitude at frequencies of the order of 40 Mc and less, particularly if the spacing between transmitting and receiving antenna is not too great. This possibility can be checked by calculating the strength of the ground wave in the usual manner; if the resulting amplitude is not negligible compared with the theoretical free-space field strength then trouble from the ground-wave effects can be expected.

The distance between transmitting and receiving antennas in Fig. 11-4 must be small enough to satisfy Eq. (11-9).   At the same time this distance must be great enough to satisfy the criteria given in Sec. 10-4.

11-5. Special Considerations Relating to the Measurement of Field Strength at Ultra-high and Microwave Frequencies.   At frequencies above about 300 Mc it is more practical to deal with power than with voltage and current.   Also, loop antennas are not satisfactory at these frequencies, and it is customary to employ either a half-wave dipole, or a

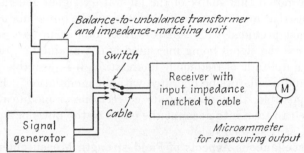

FIG. 11-6.   The substitution method of Fig. 11-2 as modified for use at very high frequencies, where it is much easier to measure power than voltage or current.

directional antenna such as a simple array, a horn, or a parabola.   At very high frequencies such antennas can be assumed to have negligible loss resistance, so that substantially all the power delivered to them is radiated, and virtually all of the power that they absorb from a passing radio wave is delivered to the load impedance associated with the antenna.

These considerations cause field-strength measuring equipment intended for use at very high frequencies to be modified in some respects, as compared with the corresponding equipment intended for use at short-wave and lower frequencies.[1]   Thus, in applying the standard-field-generator method, the standard field would be determined from the radiated power and the antenna gain, using Eq. (11-8).[2]   A similar modification of the substitution method of measuring field strength is shown in Fig. 11-6.[3]

---

[1] A description of a complete field-strength measuring system for microwave frequencies is given by H. Archer-Thomson and E. M. Hickin, Radio Technique and Apparatus for the Study of Centimetre-wave Propagation, *J. IEE* (*Radiolocation Conv.*), vol. 93, pt. IIIA, no. 1, p. 215, March–May, 1946.

[2] An example of such an arrangement is described by A. C. Grace, A Radio Field Strength Measuring Set for Use in the Frequency Range 400 to 4,000 Mc/s, *J. IEE* (*Radiolocation Conv.*), vol. 93, pt. IIIA, p. 1325, March–May, 1948.

[3] See R. J. Clayton, J. E. Houldin, H. R. L. Lamont, and W. E. Willshaw, Radio

Here the input to the coaxial line can be switched from the receiving antenna to a signal generator which is then adjusted to deliver the same power to the coaxial line as does the actual radio wave of unknown field strength. The relationship between the power which the signal generator delivers to the line, and the field strength of the radio wave is then given by Eq. (11-4) in terms of the gain of the receiving antenna. It will be noted that this arrangement requires that the signal generator be calibrated in terms of the power that it delivers to a terminated coaxial line, instead of in terms of the voltage that it develops across a resistance, as is the case in Fig. 11-2. It is also necessary that the power gain of the receiving antenna be known.

It is to be noted that many of the laboratory signal generators, oscillators, etc., used at microwave frequencies are of the pulse-modulated type, or are at least provided with square-wave modulation (see Sec. 12-11). In cases where the signal being measured is not modulated, or possesses only simple amplitude or frequency modulation, it is desirable that signal generators and oscillators be operated without modulation. However, if this is not possible, then appropriate corrections or modifications must be introduced to take into account the effect of the pulse or square-wave modulation, as described below.

11-6. Miscellaneous Aspects of Field-strength Measurements. *Simplifications When Very Strong Fields Are Being Measured.* When the fields being measured have a large amplitude, the apparatus required in making the field-strength measurements can be greatly simplified. For example, if the field is very strong, a vacuum-tube voltmeter can be used to indicate directly the induced voltage in an untuned antenna. Much greater sensitivity can be obtained, however, by tuning the antenna system to resonance, and using the vacuum-tube voltmeter to determine the voltage that is developed across the tuning condenser.[1] This voltage is Q times the induced voltage, and the value of Q applicable to the antenna system can be readily measured by the reactance-variation method (Sec. 3-8), using the field being measured to excite the antenna system.

In the case of microwave fields of moderate or high strength, the received power can be directly measured by a bolometer matched to an antenna of known gain in such a manner as to abstract the maximum pos-

Measurements in the Decimetre and Centimetre Wavebands, *J. IEE*, vol. 93, pt. III, p. 97, March, 1946; R. W. George, Field Strength Measuring Equipment at 500 Megacycles, *RCA Rev.*, vol. 5, p. 69, July, 1940; Field Strength Measuring Equipment for Wide-band UHF Transmission, *RCA Rev.*, vol. 3, p. 431, April, 1939.

[1] Paul B. Taylor, A Compact Radio Field Strength Meter, *Proc. IRE*, vol. 22, p. 191, February, 1934. Alternatively, one may use an antenna and thermocouple; see D. D. King, *loc. cit.*

sible power.[1]   The relation between this power, the antenna gain, and the field strength, is given by Eq. (11-4).

Accuracy of Field-strength Measurements.[2]   If careful attention is paid to details, it is generally possible to determine the field strength with an error which does not exceed 10 to 25 per cent (that is, 1 to 2 db).   The inherent accuracy obtainable by the different methods of measuring field strength is about the same.   The accuracy is also not significantly dependent upon frequency, at least up to 10,000 Mc.

A detailed study[3] of the accuracy of field-strength measuring equipment designed for use at standard broadcast frequencies (500 to 1600 kc), shows that the typical error is about 20 per cent.   However, when care is taken to minimize all sources of error, it is possible to hope for an accuracy of 5 per cent or better.   The principal error in such equipment arises from the distributed capacitance of the loop.   This capacitance causes the voltage produced at the output terminals of the loop by a given comparison voltage inserted in series with the loop, to depend upon the point of insertion. Thus, in the substitution method in Fig. 11-2, the error introduced in the field-strength determination is greatest when the standard voltage is introduced into the loop midway between the output terminals.   In this case the voltage that must be inserted at the center of the loop to give the same voltage at the terminals of the loop as does the actual field, is smaller than the value given by Eq. (11-1).   The relationship that applies is approximately[4]

$$\left.\begin{array}{l}\text{True voltage induced in loop} \\ \text{as given by Eq. (11-1)}\end{array}\right\} = \left[1 + 0.27\left(\frac{f}{f_0}\right)^2\right]\left(\begin{array}{l}\text{voltage inserted at} \\ \text{mid-point of loop}\end{array}\right) \quad (11\text{-}11)$$

where f/f_0 is the ratio of the actual frequency to the frequency at which the loop is resonant when tuned only by its distributed capacitance.

In investigating the field strength produced by standard broadcast stations, it is common practice to mount the loop antenna of the field-strength measuring equipment on the top of a car.   The radio wave then induces currents in the metal parts of the car.   These currents in turn produce secondary or distortion fields that induce voltages in the loop, and

[1] J. A. Saxton and A. C. Grace, A Field Strength Meter and Standard Radiator for Centimetre Wavelengths, *J. IEE (Radiolocation Conv.)*, vol. 93, pt. IIIA, p. 1426, March–May, 1946.

[2] See Smith-Rose, *loc. cit.*

[3] H. Diamond, K. A. Norton, and E. G. Lapham, On the Accuracy of Radio Field Intensity Measurement at Broadcast Frequencies, *J. Research Natl. Bur. Standards.*, vol. 21, p. 795, December, 1938.

[4] *Ibid.*

so introduce errors. Experience indicates that errors from this cause can be of the order of 25 per cent (2 db), that they depend upon the orientation of the car with respect to the direction of wave travel, and that within the standard broadcast frequency band they are independent of frequency.[1]

Measurement of Field Strength of Pulsed Signals. When the field being measured is produced by a pulse-modulated transmitter, certain modifications in the measuring procedure are required. In particular, the receiver output indicator used in the field-strength measuring equipment must be able to indicate peak amplitude independently of duty cycle. The usual method of doing this is to amplify the output of the second detector by a video amplifier, and then observe the amplified pulse on a cathode-ray oscilloscope in which the sweep circuit is synchronized with the pulse repetition frequency.[2] Alternatively, it is possible to substitute for the cathode-ray tube, a vacuum-tube voltmeter designed to read peak amplitudes (see Sec. 1-6).

When dealing with pulsed signals it is necessary that the signal generator, signal-frequency oscillator, or standard field generator, also be pulsed. If cathode-ray presentation is used, the pulse repetition frequency should be similar to that of the signal. However, the pulse lengths for the various signals may be quite different; in particular it is permissible to use on-off modulation, corresponding to 50 per cent duty cycle. In contrast, where bolometers are involved, it is necessary that the several duty cycles involved be accurately known.

Adjustment of Field-strength Measuring Equipment to Standard Sensitivity by Means of Noise.[3] In systems involving an intermediate-frequency attenuator it is possible to simplify the measuring procedure by initially adjusting the receiver to a standard gain. This is most conveniently done by using the noise generated in the input circuit to supply a standard signal, and providing the receiver with an uncalibrated gain control in addition to the calibrated intermediate-frequency attenuator. The procedure is then to set the calibrated intermediate-frequency attenuator to zero attenuation, and adjust the manual gain control

---

[1] J. H. Dewitt, Jr., and A. C. Omberg, The Relation of the Carrying Car to the Accuracy of Portable Field-intensity-measuring Equipment, *Proc. IRE*, vol. 27, p. 1, January, 1939.

[2] For example, see B. G. Pressey and G. E. Ashwell, A Pulse Field Strength Set for Very High Frequencies, *J. IEE (Radiolocation Conv.)*, vol. 93, pt. IIIA, p. 1359, March–May, 1946.

[3] This method was originated by the British Post Office; see A. H. Mumford and P. L. Barker, A Field-strength Measuring Set Using Thermal Agitation Noise as the Calibrating Source, *Post Office Elec. Eng. J.*, vol. 28, p. 40, 1935. Also see Pressey and Ashwell, *loc. cit.*; F. M. Colebrook and A. C. Gordon-Smith, The Design and Construction of a Short-wave Field-strength Measuring Set, *IEE (Wireless Sec.)*, vol. 14, p. 146, June, 1939.

until the noise generated in the system gives a convenient indication in the receiver output meter. This establishes a standard receiver sensitivity that is accurately reproducible. For any other adjustment of the intermediate-frequency attenuator, the sensitivity of the system is then less than the standard sensitivity by the setting of the intermediate-frequency attenuator. A calibration of the system when the sensitivity has the standard value can be made with a standard field generator, or by use of a signal-frequency oscillator as in Fig. 11-1. When receiver noise is used in this manner to adjust the receiver to a standard sensitivity, it is highly desirable that the preponderant source of noise be the input circuits of the receiver.

The use of noise to provide a standard calibrating signal in field-strength measuring equipment allows the equipment to be periodically calibrated by the signal-frequency-oscillator or standard-field-generator method under carefully controlled laboratory conditions. The standard field generator or signal-frequency oscillator then does not need to be a part of the field-measuring equipment, and may in fact be left in the laboratory when the equipment is taken into the field for use.

Automatic Recording of Field Strength. It is often desired to record the field strength continuously on a chart over a period of time in order to determine fading characteristics, diurnal variations in field intensity, etc. A common method of doing this consists in employing an ordinary receiver provided with automatic volume control. The d-c voltage developed by the automatic-volume-control system is amplified and used to operate the recorder.[1,2] The resulting deflection of the recorder pen is then approximately proportional to the logarithm of the applied signal voltage (*i.e.*, the deflection follows a linear decibel scale). An alternative arrangement uses an ordinary receiver with automatic volume control, with the recorder operated by direct current obtained by rectifying the output of the intermediate-frequency amplifier system.[3] This likewise leads to a response that is approximately logarithmic. The receiver employed in automatic recording must be stable in its characteristics, and have the voltage of its power supply closely regulated.

[1] Details of a rather elaborate field-strength recorder of this type are described by W. B. Smith, Recording Sky-wave Signals from Broadcast Stations, *Electronics*, vol. 20, p. 112, November, 1947.

[2] Auxiliary equipment that will automatically record the amount of time that the strength of a received signal that is fading exceeds different arbitrarily chosen levels is described by Ralph W. George, Signal Strength Analyzer, *Electronics*, vol. 24, p. 75, January, 1951.

[3] Still another type of recording arrangement is described by W. W. Mutch, A Note on an Automatic Field Strength and Static Recorder, *Proc. IRE*, vol. 20, p. 1914, December, 1932. Also see H. T. Friis, A Static Recorder, *Bell System Tech. J.*, vol. 5, p. 282, April, 1926.

The calibration of an automatic recording system can be checked at regular intervals by introducing a known voltage in the antenna from a signal generator.

Measurements of Noise Fields. The strength of fields representing noise (or static) is determined by the same general methods that are employed to determine the strength of fields resulting from radiation of signals by an antenna. However, additional problems arise as a result of the random character of noise, and because noise from some sources is characterized by infrequent peaks of high intensity, while noise from other types of sources is of a more continuous character.

The character of the noise that reaches the output-indicating system of a field-strength measuring equipment depends upon the bandwidth of the receiving system.[1] The noise power is always directly proportional to the bandwidth, with the result that the equivalent rms noise voltage is directly proportional to the square root of the bandwidth for all cases. However, the peak amplitude of the noise is directly proportional to the bandwidth if the noise consists of sharp, widely separated pulses, and is proportional to the square root of bandwidth when the noise consists of a large number of overlapping pulses. The average amplitude of the noise behaves still differently, being independent of bandwidth for the case of very sharp widely separated pulses, and proportional to the square root of bandwidth with overlapping pulses.

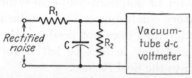

FIG. 11-7. Circuit for indicating rectified noise. The system shown will indicate peak or average noise according to the circuit constants used.

The particular aspect of the noise that is indicated by a noise-measuring system depends upon the time constants of the equipment, as well as upon the bandwidth. For example, consider the case where the rectified output of the intermediate-frequency amplifier is applied to the resistance-capacitance combination shown in Fig. 11-7, with the output being indicated by a vacuum-tube d-c voltmeter connected across the condenser C. Assuming that $R_1 \gg R_2$, and that capacitance C is quite large, then the voltmeter indicates the *average* noise amplifier averaged for a period of time approximating the time constant R_2C. On the other hand, if the circuit is proportioned so that $R_1 \ll R_2$, the condenser C will charge up to the peak amplitude of the noise provided the noise peaks have a duration appreciably in excess of the time represented by the time constant R_1C, expressed in seconds. The output meter then gives an indication deter-

---

[1] See Karl G. Jansky, An Experimental Investigation of the Characteristics of Certain Types of Noise, *Proc. IRE*, vol. 27, p. 763, December, 1939.

mined by the peak noise occurring during a period of the order of magnitude of R_2C seconds.[1]

In practical measurements of noise fields it is accordingly necessary to determine what type of indication will be most significant for the purpose at hand, and then to arrange the output system accordingly.[2] In this connection it is to be noted that the mechanical inertia of the output meter, or of a recording pen, produces an additional averaging effect that must be taken into account if the time constant of the electrical system is not appreciably greater than the time constant of the mechanical indicating device.

When it is necessary to obtain information about the peak amplitude of noise, a cathode-ray oscillograph may be used in much the same manner as when dealing with pulsed signals. However, in interpreting such results it is necessary to keep in mind the fact that the peak amplitude is determined not only by the characteristics of the noise, but also by the bandwidth of the receiver, or of the circuits through which the noise has passed.

11-7. Determination of Wave Structure. In order to describe a wave completely, one must know not only the strength, but also the direction of travel in azimuth and in vertical angle, the polarization, and the tilt.

Direction-finder Systems. The direction of arrival of a radio wave in azimuth can be determined by the direction-finder techniques commonly used for radio navigation. This is a subject far too extensive to be summarized here, and is, moreover, adequately presented in the literature.[3] For the moment it is sufficient to note that at short-wave and lower fre-

---

[1] If the noise peaks are appreciably shorter than R_1C seconds, then the vacuum-tube voltmeter indicates the average noise amplitude over a period of $[R_1R_2/(R_1 + R_2)]C$ seconds.

[2] Discussions of noise measurements from the point of view of the interference that the noise produces on the reception of broadcast and similar signals are given by C. V. Aggers, D. E. Foster, and C. S. Young, Instruments and Methods of Measuring Radio Noise, *Trans. AIEE*, vol. 59, p. 178, March, 1940; Charles M. Burrill, Progress in the Development of Instruments for Measuring Radio Noise, *Proc. IRE*, vol. 29, p. 433, August, 1941; An Evaluation of Radio-noise-meter Performance in Terms of Listening Experience, *Proc. IRE*, vol. 30, p. 473, October, 1942; Harold E. Dinger and Harold G. Paine, Factors Affecting the Accuracy of Radio Noise Meters, *Proc. IRE*, vol. 35, p. 75, January, 1947; L. H. Daniel and G. Mole, The Measurement of Interference at Ultra-high Frequencies, *J. IEE*, pt. III, vol. 88, p. 41, March, 1941; H. A. Thomas, A Subjective Method of Measuring Radio Noise, *Proc. IEE*, vol. 97, p. 329, September, 1950.

[3] For example see R. Keen, "Wireless Direction Finding," 4th ed., Iliffe and Sons, Ltd., London, 1947; also a group of 19 papers in *J. IEE (Radiocomm. Conv.)*, vol. 94, pt. IIIA, no. 15, pp. 673–870, March-April, 1947; a convenient summary of loop and similar direction-finding systems is given F. E. Terman, "Radio Engineers' Handbook," pp. 872–891, McGraw-Hill Book Company, Inc., New York, 1943.

quencies, direction finding is ordinarily based on the loop antenna or its Adcock equivalent, while at microwave frequencies, directional antennas such as horns or parabolas are commonly used. Lobe switching is customarily used at microwave frequencies, and is also sometimes employed at lower frequencies. The accuracy of loop and similar types of direction finding arrangements is of the order of 1° under favorable conditions, while greater accuracy can be obtained by employing lobe switching, particularly if highly directional microwave beams are involved.

Direction-finding techniques are also sometimes applied to determine the vertical angle of arrival. Thus, lobe-switching arrangements find extensive use for this purpose at microwave frequencies; however, at short-wave and lower frequencies the

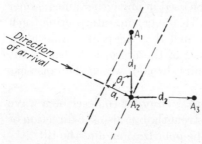

FIG. 11-8. Spaced antennas for determining the direction of arrival of a radio wave by means of phase difference.

vertical angle of arrival is more easily obtained by phase-difference methods.

Direction of Angle of Arrival by Phase Difference. In research studies on radio waves, the direction of arrival is commonly determined by observing the differences in phase of the voltages induced by the wave in two or more spaced antennas.[1] For example, consider two antennas A_1

and A_2 arranged as in Fig. 11-8 at the same height above earth. If the phase difference of the voltages induced in these antennas is α_1, then the radio wave must arrive somewhere along the conical surface making an angle θ_1 with the axis A_1A_2, where[2]

$$\cos \theta_1 = \frac{\alpha_1}{2\pi d_1/\lambda} \tag{11-12}$$

Here α_1 is in radians, and d_1/λ is the spacing of the two antennas in wavelengths. If other circumstances make it known that the vertical com-

[1] Thus see H. T. Friis, C. B. Feldman, and W. M. Sharpless, The Determination of the Direction of Arrival of Short Radio Waves, *Proc. IRE*, vol. 22, p. 47, January, 1934; H. T. Friis, Oscillographic Observations on the Direction of Propagation and Fading of Short Waves, *Proc. IRE*, vol. 16, p. 658, May, 1928; A. F. Wilkins, Measurement of the Angle of Incidence at the Ground of Downcoming Short Waves from the Ionosphere, *J. IEE*, vol. 74, p. 582, 1934 (also *Wireless Sec.*, vol. 9, p. 154, June, 1934); Frederick E. Brooks, A Receiver for Measuring Angle-of-arrival in a Complex Wave, *Proc. IRE*, vol. 39, p. 407, April, 1951.

[2] From the geometry of Fig. 11-8, the voltage induced in antenna A_2 lags behind the voltage induced in antenna A_1 by the time it takes the wave to travel the distance $a_1 = d_1 \cos \theta_1$. But this distance corresponds to a_1/λ cycles, so $\alpha_1 = 2\pi a_1/\lambda$. Equation (11-12) then follows by combining these two relations to eliminate a_1.

ponent of the angle of arrival is relatively small (such as 15° or less), then Eq. (11-12) gives the azimuth direction of arrival with considerable precision.

An absolute determination of the direction of arrival can be obtained by observing the phase difference of the voltages induced in a second pair of antennas A_2 and A_3 arranged in the horizontal plane, at right angles to the first pair, as illustrated in Fig. 11-8, where antenna A_2 is a member of both the first and second pairs. The phase difference α_2 between the voltages induced in the antenna pair A_2A_3, corresponds to a wave arriving somewhere along the conical surface that makes an angle θ_2 with the axis, A_2A_3, where

$$\cos \theta_2 = \frac{\alpha_2}{2\pi d_2/\lambda} \tag{11-13}$$

As before α_2 is in radians, and d_2/λ is the spacing of antennas A_2 and A_3 in wavelengths. When the axis A_2A_3 is known to coincide with the azimuth direction of arrival, then the angle θ_2 given by Eq. (11-13) is the vertical angle of arrival. However, in the more general case, the absolute direction of arrival, including both azimuth and elevation, is given by the intersection of the two conical surfaces defined with the aid of Eqs. (11-12) and (11-13), and the axes A_1A_2 and A_2A_3.

The phase difference between the voltages induced in two antennas may be determined in a number of ways. One procedure is to bring the two voltages to a common point through transmission lines of the same length, and measure phase by balancing the two voltages against each other with the aid of a phase shifter and attenuator, in the manner illustrated in Fig. 6-27. An alternative procedure consists in amplifying the induced voltages and applying the two outputs to the vertical and horizontal electrodes, respectively, of a cathode-ray tube to produce a Lissajous figure as in Fig. 6-24. A modification of this latter arrangement involves using superheterodyne receivers employing a common local oscillator; by arranging so that the local oscillator voltages applied to the two receivers have identical phase, then as explained in Sec. 6-9 the intermediate-frequency voltages in the two receivers will have the same phase difference as existed in the radio-frequency voltages induced in the antennas.

Polarization of Radio Waves. The plane perpendicular to the direction of travel of a radio wave is termed the *wavefront*. The component of the electric vector that lies in the wavefront and is parallel with the earth is termed the horizontally polarized component of the wave. Similarly, the component of the electric vector that is in the direction perpendicular to the horizontal component and lies in the plane of the wavefront, is termed the vertically polarized component. When the vertical and horizontal components have the same phase, the wave is plane-polarized, while when the two components have a different phase, the wave is said to be elliptically polarized.

Elliptical polarization is characterized by the fact that the resultant electrostatic (and magnetic) field never at any instant has zero amplitude; rather, the resultant field rotates in the plane of the wavefront about an axis perpendicular to the wavefront at a rate corresponding to the frequency of the wave, while at the same time pulsating in amplitude. The resultant field produced by elliptical polarization can therefore be represented by a rotating vector of varying length as illustrated in Fig. 11-9. The field can never be zero because the vertical and horizontal components do not become zero at the same instant.

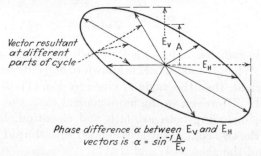

Vector resultant
at different
parts of cycle

E_V A

E_H

Phase difference α between E_V and E_H
vectors is $\alpha = sin^{-1} \dfrac{A}{E_V}$

Fig. 11-9. Diagram illustrating electric field components of an elliptically polarized wave, when the wavefront is in the plane of the paper.

The strength of the horizontally polarized component of a wave may be measured by utilizing a standard antenna that is horizontal, and oriented in a direction at right angles to the direction in which the wave is traveling. The vertical component can be similarly measured by using an antenna that is perpendicular to the horizontal component and tilted so that it lies in the wavefront. When the vertical angle of arrival of the wave does not exceed about 20°, it is permissible to neglect the vertical angle of arrival and measure the vertically polarized component on a vertical antenna. The phase difference between the voltages induced in the vertically and horizontally polarized antennas, measured in any convenient way, is the angle α in Fig. 11-9. If this phase difference is zero, the wave is plane-polarized; otherwise, the polarization is elliptical. The sense of the polarization, *i.e.*, the direction in which the fields appear to rotate in the wavefront, can be obtained by determining whether the voltage induced in the horizontal antenna leads or lags the voltage induced in the vertical antenna.[1]

[1] A different method of obtaining information about elliptically polarized waves is described by A. L. Green, The Polarization of Sky Waves in the Southern Hemisphere, *Proc. IRE*, vol. 22, p. 324, March, 1934.

Wave Tilt of Ground Wave.   In a ground wave moving over the surface of the earth, the electric vector is vertical only if the ground is a perfect conductor.   With a practical ground, there is always a small horizontal component of electric force in the direction of propagation.   This phenomenon is referred to as *wave tilt*, since the horizontal vector in a vertical plane perpendicular to the wavefront, combined with the much larger vertically polarized component of the wave, causes the resultant electric vector to be tilted forward.   In addition, the horizontal component of the ground wave is generally slightly out of phase with respect to the vertically polarized component, so that the resultant electric vector is elliptically polarized in a plane parallel to the direction of travel along

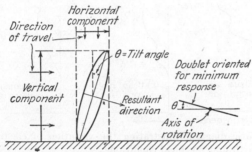

Fig. 11-10. Diagram illustrating the tilt of a ground wave.

the horizontal, as illustrated in Fig. 11-10.   The angle θ of the major axis of this ellipse with respect to the vertical is termed the wave tilt. The magnitude of the wave tilt, and also the phase difference between the vertically and horizontally polarized components, is determined by the conductivity and dielectric constant of the earth, and the frequency.[1]

Values of tilt typically encountered range from a maximum of 10 to 20° at high frequencies where the earth's impedance is primarily capacitive, to quite small values when the frequency is low and the earth is resistive. When the earth is primarily resistive, then the tilt angle is less the lower the frequency, and for a given frequency the tilt becomes greater the lower the ground conductivity.

The phase angle between the vertically and horizontally polarized components of the ground wave can never exceed 45°.   This phase difference is largest at the lower frequencies and with high conductivity.

The tilt angle θ of a ground wave can be measured by the aid of a doublet antenna so mounted that it can be rotated about a horizontal

[1] For details see K. A. Norton, The Propagation of Radio Waves over the Surface of the Earth and in the Upper Atmosphere, *Proc. IRE*, vol. 25, p. 1203, September, 1937.

axis that is perpendicular to the horizontal direction of wave travel.[1] The measurement is made by swinging the doublet about this horizontal axis until the signal strength is minimum. This occurs when the doublet antenna is tilted slightly from the horizontal, as illustrated in Fig. 11-10, with the angle θ corresponding to the tilt angle. The phase angle between the horizontally and vertically polarized components of the wave may be obtained by observing the phase difference between the voltages induced in two antennas, one of which is vertical while the other is horizontal and aligned so that it points in the direction in which the wave is traveling.

11-8. Measurements on the Ionosphere. The long-distance propagation of radio waves is controlled by the properties of the ionosphere.[2]

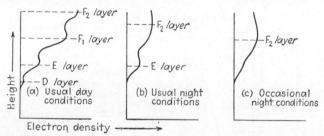

FIG. 11-11. Schematic diagram illustrating the variation of electron density with height above the earth under typical conditions.

This ionized region begins at a height of above 80 km about the earth's surface, and is characterized by an electron distribution of the character illustrated schematically in Fig. 11-11. The maxima in this distribution are termed layers. There are three such layers commonly associated with the ionosphere; in order of ascending height these are designated by the letters E, F_1, and F_2, as illustrated in Fig. 11-11. The important characteristics of a layer are its height above the earth, and the maximum electron density associated with it.

Pulse Technique for Investigating Ionosphere Characteristics. The characteristics of the ionosphere are normally determined by the pulse method originated by Breit and Tuve.[3] In this method, short wave trains lasting for perhaps 10^{-4} sec are transmitted toward the ionosphere. A receiver

---

[1] Discussions of tilt measurements are given by E. W. B. Gill, A Simple Method of Measuring Electrical Earth-constants, *Proc. IEE (Radio & Comm.)*, vol. 96, pt. II, p. 141, March, 1949; R. H. Barfield, Some Measurements of the Electrical Constants of the Ground at Short Wavelengths by the Wave-tilt Method, *J. IEE*, vol. 75, p. 214, 1934 (also *Wireless Sec.*, vol. 9, p. 286, September, 1934).

[2] For further information on the role of the ionosphere in radio propagation see F. E. Terman, "Radio Engineers' Handbook," pp. 709–733, McGraw-Hill Book Company, Inc., New York, 1943.

[3] G. Breit and M. Tuve, A Test of the Existence of the Conducting Layer, *Phys. Rev.*, vol. 28, p. 554, September, 1926.

located in the immediate vicinity of the transmitter (commonly only a few feet away) is then used to pick up the transmitted wave trains, and also any wave trains returned from the ionosphere. The output of the receiver is presented in some manner by a cathode-ray oscillograph.

When the receiver output is applied to the vertically deflecting plates of the cathode-ray tube, while a timing wave synchronized with the transmitted pulses is used to give horizontal deflection, the result is as shown in Fig. 11-12. The first pulse is the outgoing transmitted signal, while the remaining pulses represent reflections from the various layers, or in some cases pulses that have made more than one round trip between the earth and a particular layer in the ionosphere. The time delay of the pulses returned from the ionosphere can be interpreted in terms of an

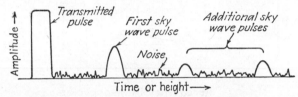

Fig. 11-12. Examples of the oscillograms received when a transmitter is within ground-wave range, and the transmitted signal consists of a pulse formed by a short wave train.

equivalent or virtual height, on the basis that the wave travels with the velocity of light. For example, a time delay of 1 msec corresponds to a distance of 300 km for a wave traveling with the velocity of light. Since the wave travels from earth to ionosphere and back to earth, such a time delay represents a virtual height of 150 km. The actual height reached by the pulse will, however, be somewhat less than the virtual height, since the velocity with which the wave travels when in the ionized region is less than the velocity in free space. The difference between the actual and the virtual height is not great, however, unless the frequency of the wave is close to a critical frequency.

When the frequency of the transmitted pulses is varied, the virtual height of the layer will depend upon frequency in the general manner illustrated in Fig. 11-13. As the frequency is increased, the curve of virtual height is characterized by discontinuities represented either by a sudden jump, or by crinkles such as occur at each end of the segment representing the F_1 layer in Fig. 11-13. Such a discontinuity or crinkle corresponds to a frequency at which the wave is just barely able to penetrate the layer. The corresponding frequency is termed a *critical frequency*, and is related to the maximum electron density of the layer according to the equation[1]

[1] Actually each layer has two possible critical frequencies as a result of the fact that a wave propagating in an ionized region in the presence of a magnetic field (from the

$$\left.\begin{array}{l}\text{Maximum electron density of}\\\text{layer in electrons per cc}\end{array}\right\} = \frac{f_c^2}{81} \qquad (11\text{-}14)$$

where f_c is the critical frequency in kilocycles.

When information such as given by Fig. 11-13 is available from vertical-incidence pulse tests, it is possible to deduce the behavior of the iono-sphere for oblique incidence.[1] These same data also makes it possible

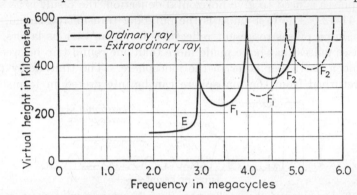

FIG. 11-13. Reproduction of experimentally observed curves of virtual height as a function of frequency, showing ordinary and extraordinary rays, E, F_1, and F_2 layers, and large time retardations in the vicinity of each critical frequency.

to estimate the true height of the layer, and the distribution of electron density within the ionosphere.[2]

Apparatus for Making Pulse Studies of the Ionosphere.[3] Ionosphere tests are made with the aid of an ordinary transmitter that is pulse-modulated, and has a peak power in the range 1 to 10 kw. The pulse length is usually about 100 μsec, and the repetition frequency is typically 60 cycles.

earth) is split into two components. These components, which are designated as the *ordinary* and *extraordinary* rays, travel along different paths with different velocities through the ionized medium, and hence have different virtual heights. Also the extraordinary ray has a higher critical frequency than the ordinary ray, the difference being about 730 kc for the higher frequencies. This is shown in Fig. 11-13.

[1] See Newbern Smith, The Relation of Radio Sky-wave Transmission to Ionosphere Measurements, *Proc. IRE*, vol. 27, p. 332, May, 1939.

[2] Thus see H. G. Booker and A. L. Seaton, Relation between Actual and Virtual Ionosphere Height, *Phys. Rev.*, vol. 57, p. 87, Jan. 15, 1940; Laurance A. Manning, The Determination of Ionosphere Electron Distribution, *Proc. IRE*, vol. 35, p. 1203, November, 1947; The Reliability of Ionospheric Height Determinations, *Proc. IRE*, vol. 37, p. 599, June, 1949.

[3] For further discussion and additional details see T. R. Gilliland, Note on a Multi-frequency Automatic Recorder of Ionosphere Heights, *Proc. IRE*, vol. 22, p. 236, February, 1934; Ionospheric Investigation, *Nature* (London), vol. 134, p. 379, September, 1934; T. R. Gilliland and A. S. Taylor, Field Equipment for Ionosphere Measurements, *J. Research Natl. Bur. Standards*, vol. 26, p. 377, May, 1941.

The associated receiver is ordinarily of the superheterodyne type, with a manual rather than automatic volume control, and with a bandwidth which may range from 10 to 40 kc. The receiver can be placed in the same room with the transmitter, and often uses the same antenna. As the receiver is then subjected to very high overloads by the transmitted pulse, it must be so designed that these overloads do not cause damage. It is also necessary that in the interval between the end of the transmitted pulse and the time the first ionosphere reflection returns, the receiver should be able to recuperate from any overloading, and be restored to normal sensitivity. The principal requirement for achieving this result is so to proportion all resistance-capacitance combinations in the receiver that they have a very small time constant RC. Abnormal charges received by the receiver condensers as a result of the action of the transmitted pulse can then be discharged very quickly.

Multifrequency records of the type illustrated in Fig. 11-13 are obtained by simultaneously varying the frequency of the transmitter and receiver. Presentation is ordinarily by means of a cathode-ray tube, in which the horizontal deflection is produced by a voltage that is varied by the tuning control of the transmitter oscillator, and so indicates frequency. Vertical deflection is obtained by a saw-tooth deflecting voltage that is synchronized with the transmitted pulse; vertical deflection is accordingly proportional to time (or distance). The output of the receiver is applied to the control electrode of the cathode-ray tube, superimposed upon a bias such that in the absence of an incoming signal the cathode-ray spot is turned off. In this way, spots appear whenever a pulse is received, with the position of the spot along the vertical axis being determined by the time delay of the pulse, and hence by the virtual height.

In making multifrequency records of the type illustrated in Fig. 11-13, it is necessary that the receiver be accurately tuned to the transmitter frequency as the latter is varied. Two methods have been used to achieve this result. The first of these is shown schematically in Fig. 11-14. Here a fixed-frequency oscillator operating at the intermediate-frequency f_1 of the receiver (typically about 475 kc) is pulsed in some convenient manner. These radio-frequency pulses are then applied to a mixer tube, to which there is also applied voltage from a continuously operating oscillator that generates a variable frequency f_0. The difference frequency $f_0 - f_1$ produced by the mixer is selected by a tuned circuit in the output of the mixer, and applied to a power amplifier that delivers power to the transmitting antenna. At the same time, output from the continuously operating oscillator is used as the local oscillator for the mixer of the receiver. The mixer hence always generates the desired intermediate frequency irrespective of the transmitted frequency, provided only that the intermediate-frequency oscillator maintains its assigned frequency to within a few kilocycles. It will be noted that no oscillator in the system operates at the frequency that is to be received, and furthermore, the intermediate-frequency oscillator operates only when pulses are being transmitted. In this way there is no interference with the reception of the relatively weak pulses returned from the ionosphere. In this system it is necessary that the tuned circuit of the power amplifier, and also that the radio-frequency circuits (if any) of the mixer, be mechanically ganged with the tuning control of the variable-frequency

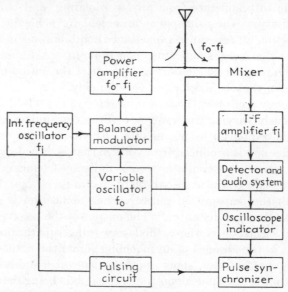

Fig. 11-14. Interlocking system for producing and receiving pulses for ionosphere investigations.

oscillator. However, these circuits can be broadly tuned, and since they do not control any frequency in the system, failure to track exactly merely reduces the amplitude of the pulses slightly.

In a modified form of this equipment[1,2] the intermediate frequency is chosen as 30 Mc, while the oscillator f_0 is varied from 31 to 55 Mc, thus producing a difference frequency ranging from 1 to 25 Mc. Wide-band techniques are used in the mixer, power-amplifier, and radio-frequency circuits of the receiver such that the entire frequency range of 1 to 25 Mc is passed without tuning. This greatly simplifies the equipment by

[1] See Peter G. Sulzer, Sweep Frequency Ionosphere Equipment, *J. Applied Phys.*, vol. 20, p. 187, February, 1949.

[2] Still another variation involving a double frequency conversion in both transmitter and receiver, is described by T. L. Wadley, A Single-band 0–20 Mc/s Ionosphere Recorder Embodying Some New Techniques, *Proc. IEE (Radio & Comm)*, vol. 96, pt. III, p. 483, November, 1949.

covering the entire frequency range in a single band, and by making mechanical ganging unnecessary; also the use of an intermediate frequency higher than the highest frequency to be transmitted eliminates most of the complications that might otherwise arise from harmonics of the intermediate frequency.

The second type of multifrequency ionosphere equipment uses a different manner to solve the problem of tracking the transmitter and receiver.[1] Here the transmitter employs a continuous-wave (not pulsed) oscillator which is swept through the full frequency range about 25 times per second. The Class C amplifier which is excited by this oscillator and develops the power that is to be radiated, is mechanically ganged with the receiver. The combination of Class C amplifier and receiver is then slowly tuned in such a manner as to cover the full frequency range in approximately 1 min. Each time the frequency of the oscillator passes through the passband of the Class C amplifier, a pulse is produced. At any particular time this pulse has a frequency corresponding to the frequency to which the Class C amplifier and receiver are tuned at the moment. This arrangement has the advantage that by designing the Class C circuits to be broadly tuned, close ganging of the transmitter frequency and receiver tuning is unnecessary. The effective pulse length in this arrangement is the time it takes the transmitter sweeping oscillator to pass through the response band of the receiver. Thus if the oscillator frequency varies at the rate of 200 Mc per sec, and the receiver bandwidth is 20 kc, then the equivalent pulse length is about $20/200,000 = 10^{-4}$ sec.

It is also possible to employ servo techniques to maintain tracking between transmitter and receiver.[2] Thus a voltage proportional to the tuning error between transmitter and receiver can be derived from a discriminator system, that after amplification is used to drive a servo motor that tunes the receiver in such a manner as to reduce the tuning error. The frequency of the transmitter is then varied by an independent motor drive, and the receiver tuning automatically follows the transmitter frequency with very little error.

Multifrequency recording equipment is commonly operated with a fixed receiver gain that is manually adjusted to a suitable value. There is, however, some advantage in using an instantaneously acting automatic volume control that will reduce the receiver gain for the stronger pulses, thereby making it possible to obtain a more uniform and cleaner presentation.[3] Interference from continuous-wave signals can be largely

[1] See H. A. Thomas and R. G. Chalmers, An Improved Ionospheric Height Recorder, *J. IEE* (*Radio Sec.*), vol. 95, pt. III, p. 7, January, 1948.

[2] For details, see R. Naismith and R. Bailey, An Automatic Ionospheric Recorder for the Frequency Range 0.55 to 17 Mc/s, *Proc. IEE*, vol. 98, p. 11, January, 1951.

[3] See Sulzer, *loc. cit.*

eliminated by introducing a differentiating circuit in the output of the receiver so arranged that the pulse actually applied to the control electrode of the cathode-ray tube is the differentiated incoming signal. In this way, pulses will produce a large indication because of their rapid rise, whereas continuous-wave signals with voice modulation, or telegraph signals, are greatly discriminated against.

The antenna system used with a multifrequency arrangement must have a broad-band characteristic. It must also be designed to radiate as much power as possible directly upward, since it is only this part of the power which produces a useful result. A common arrangement is a horizontal half-wave antenna placed at a height above ground that does not approach too closely a half wavelength at the highest frequency to be radiated; if the height is exactly a half wavelength then the ground reflection cancels the upward radiation. A wide-band characteristic can be obtained by constructing the dipole in the form of a cage of wires of relatively large diameter. In this way, the reactance component of the antenna impedance is greatly reduced, thereby making it possible to obtain a fairly satisfactory impedance match to a transmission line over a wide range of frequencies. It is also possible to use a directional antenna in which the main beam is directed upward; vertical rhombic antennas are particularly attractive for this purpose because of their inherently wide-band characteristic.[1]

Special problems are involved when an attempt is made to extend the pulse technique to very low frequencies, such as 100 kc. Single-frequency pulse-measuring equipment which has been found satisfactory for pulse studies at the lower radio frequencies is described by Helliwell.[2]

Miscellaneous Methods of Investigating the Ionosphere. While the pulse method of Breit and Tuve is the most widely used means of studying the ionosphere, other techniques have been employed and have their uses.

In one of these, the frequency of an unmodulated carrier is very slowly varied, and the changes in signal strength noted at a fixed receiving point where the strength of the ground and sky waves are of the same order of intensity. These variations are characterized by regular maxima and minima, as illustrated in Fig. 11-15, provided there is only one sky-wave reflection present. From a knowledge of the frequency increment Δf required to go from one maximum to the next, together with a knowledge of the distance between transmitter and receiver, one can determine the length of the path followed by the sky wave on the assumption that the sky wave travels with the velocity of light, and so can obtain the virtual height. This method was used to obtain the first experimental proof of

[1] See Thomas and Chalmers, *loc. cit.*

[2] R. A. Helliwell, Ionosphere Virtual Height Measurements at 100 Kilocycles, *Proc. IRE*, vol. 37, p. 887, August, 1949.

the existence of an ionosphere.[1] The method has the very serious practical limitation, however, that if there is more than one sky-wave reflection present, the interference pattern introduced at the receiving point with change in frequency becomes so complicated that it is difficult to interpret. The method is accordingly not generally suitable for high-frequency investigations, but is very satisfactory for studying the ionosphere at low radio frequencies.[2]

Another method of determining the virtual height of the ionosphere consists in observing the variations in field intensity as the distance

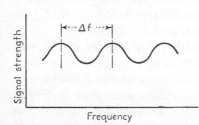

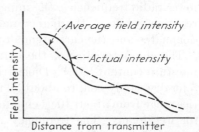

FIG. 11-15. Interference fringes produced at receiving point when the transmitted frequency is varied, under conditions where there is only one sky wave of somewhat smaller intensity than the ground wave.

FIG. 11-16. Schematic diagram illustrating the way in which the field intensity can be expected to vary with distance at moderate distances from a long-wave transmitter.

between transmitter and receiver is varied.[3] As this distance increases the average field intensity will diminish, but superimposed upon this major trend will be oscillations as illustrated in Fig. 11-16. The field-strength maxima obtained in this way correspond to points at which the ground and sky waves are in the same phase, while the minima correspond to points where they are of opposite phase. From this pattern one can readily deduce the virtual height of the ionosphere, and likewise the reflection coefficient of the wave at the ionosphere. This method is suitable only at the lower radio frequencies, where the wave paths are stable (i.e., no fading).

Still another method of determining the virtual height is to select a receiving point of the order of 200 to 400 km from the transmitter, and measure the angle of arrival of the downcoming wave refracted from the

[1] E. V. Appleton and M. A. S. Barrett, *Nature (London)*, vol. 115, p. 333, 1925.

[2] C. H. Smith, Indirect Ray Measurements on the Droitwich Transmitter, *Wireless Eng.*, vol. 14, p. 537, October, 1937.

[3] See J. Hollingworth, Propagation of Radio Waves, *J. IEE*, vol. 64, p. 579, May, 1926; J. E. Best, J. A. Ratcliffe, and M. V. Wilkes, Experimental Investigations of Very Long Waves Reflected from the Ionosphere, *Proc. Roy. Soc. (London)*, vol. 156, p. 614, September, 1936.

ionosphere. From this angle, and a knowledge of the distance to the transmitter, one can calculate a virtual height provided that only a single downcoming ray is present.

Theoretical studies show that the virtual heights obtained in these three ways are exactly the same as the virtual height obtained by the pulse method.

11-9. Measurement of Ground Constants. At radio frequencies the earth behaves like a condenser having a very conductive dielectric. It is thus characterized by a dielectric constant and a conductance. At the lower radio frequencies, the impedance offered by the earth is essentially resistive, while at the higher radio frequencies the dielectric effect predominates and the earth tends to act as a capacitive impedance.

The characteristics of the earth vary with the character of the soil, moisture content, etc.[1] Dielectric constants of soil typically range from 5 for dry sandy soil, to about 30 for wet loam; corresponding conductivities range from about 10^{-14} emu for dry sandy soil, to more than 10^{-13} emu for wet loam. The frequency at which the transition from resistive impedance to capacitive impedance occurs depends upon the constants of the soil, but in general it can be said that at standard broadcast and at lower frequencies the earth is primarily resistive except when the conductivity is unusually low, while at appreciably higher frequencies the earth is primarily capacitive.[2]

The constants of the ground can be determined in a number of ways. Thus one can take samples of the earth and measure their characteristics just as one would measure the characteristics of any other dielectric.[3]

---

[1] The frequency is also important unless the earth is homogeneous to a considerable depth. This is because the effective depth to which currents in the earth penetrate increases with decreasing frequency. Thus measurements made at high frequencies sample only that part of the earth near the surface, while at increasingly low frequencies an experimental determination averages the earth characteristics to progressively greater depth. Information on earth penetration is given in F. E. Terman, "Radio Engineers' Handbook," p. 697, McGraw-Hill Book Company, Inc., New York, 1943.

[2] The power-factor angle β of the earth is given by the equation

$$\tan \beta = \frac{\epsilon}{6\sigma\lambda \times 10^{12}} \tag{11-15}$$

where σ = earth conductivity, emu
    ϵ = dielectric constant of earth
    λ = wavelength

If this angle is of the order of 25 deg or less, the earth can be considered as primarily resistive, while if it is 60 deg or more, the earth can be regarded as primarily capacitive.

[3] For further discussion and details, see C. B. Feldman, The Optical Behavior of the Ground for Short Radio Waves, *Proc. IRE*, vol. 21, p. 764, June, 1933; R. L. Smith-Rose, Electrical Measurements on Soil with Alternating Currents, *J. IEE*, vol. 75, p. 221, 1934 (also *Wireless Sec.*, vol. 9, p. 293, September, 1934).

This method has the disadvantage, however, that the earth may not be homogeneous, so that there is always an uncertainty as to how representative any particular sample is.

At broadcast and lower frequencies, where the ground is primarily resistive, the conductivity of the ground is commonly obtained by measuring the ground wave at progressively increasing distance from the transmitter. If the earth were a perfect conductor the field strength would be inversely proportional to distance. However, the field actually observed decreases more rapidly than this as a result of the finite ground conductivity. The ratio A of the actual field strength to the field

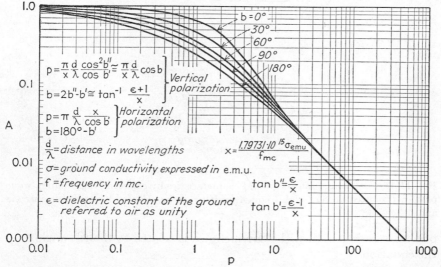

Fig. 11-17. Factor A which takes into account the effect of ground losses and capacitance on the amplitude of the ground wave (earth curvature neglected).

strength for an ideal ground of infinite conductivity is related to the ground constants according to the theoretical curves of Fig. 11-17.[1] To determine the conductivity one makes a reasonable but rough guess for the dielectric constant of the earth, and then determines the value of conductivity that will give the best agreement between the observed and theoretical values of A. The result obtained at broadcast frequencies is only slightly dependent upon the dielectric constant used; so the method gives a reliable determination of the average conductivity. This method is not particularly satisfactory at the very low radio frequencies, however, as then the reduction of ground-wave intensity introduced by the ground conductivity is too small to be determined accurately unless the distance is so large that the curvature of the earth cannot be neglected.

[1] For further discussion see F. E. Terman, "Radio Engineers' Handbook," p. 676, McGraw-Hill Book Company, Inc., New York, 1943.

Another method of determining the ground constants is from the tilt that the ground wave possesses.[1] In particular, if the frequency is high enough to make the earth primarily capacitive, then

$$\tan \theta = \frac{1}{\sqrt{\epsilon}} \tag{11-16}$$

where θ is the tilt angle (see Fig. 11-10), and ϵ is the dielectric constant of the ground. Similarly, if the frequency is low enough for the earth to be

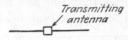

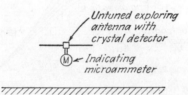

Fig. 11-18. Determination of ground characteristics by exploring the standing-wave pattern produced at very high frequencies between an elevated transmitting antenna and the earth.

primarily resistive, then the conductance is related to the tilt angle θ by the equation

$$\tan \theta = \frac{1}{\sqrt{12\sigma\lambda \times 10^{12}}} \tag{11-17}$$

where λ is the wavelength in meters, and σ is the conductivity in emu.

At wavelengths of a few meters, the dielectric constant of the ground may be conveniently measured by the arrangement illustrated in Fig. 11-18.[2] Here, a horizontal transmitting antenna is placed at a moderate height above earth, such as 40 ft. The field that exists in the space directly below the radiating antenna is then explored by an untuned probe antenna provided with a crystal detector and indicating meter. The combination of the reflected wave from the ground, and the incident

---

[1] See Barfield, *loc. cit.;* Gill, *loc. cit.,* Feldman, *loc. cit.;* Norton, *loc. cit.*

[2] See J. S. McPetrie and J. A. Saxton, The Electrical Properties of Soil at Wavelengths of 5 Metres and 2 Metres, *J. IEE (Radio Sec.),* vol. 92, pt. III, p. 256, December, 1945; The Determination of the Electrical Properties of Soil at a Wavelength of 5 Metres (Frequency 60 Mc/s), *J. IEE (Wireless Sec.),* vol. 90, pt. III, p. 33, March, 1943.

wave from the transmitting antenna, causes the resultant field in the space to vary with the height of the exploring antenna, with maxima and minima being present exactly as in the case of the voltage distribution on a transmission line possessing a reflected wave.   The dielectric constant ϵ is then given by the relation[1]

$$\epsilon = \left(\frac{S_{max}}{S_{min}}\right)^2 \tag{11-18}$$

where (S_{max}/S_{min}) is the standing-wave ratio of the field distribution in the space between the antenna and ground, as observed near the ground.   It is theoretically possible also to obtain the conductivity of the ground if one in addition knows the position of the minima of the standing-wave pattern with respect to the reflecting ground surface.   However, the precision required to obtain only a reasonably satisfactory value of conductivity is much greater than it is practical to achieve experimentally, particularly when one takes note of the uncertainty that exists as to the exact position of the effective reflecting plane at the surface of the ground.

[1] This follows from the fact that the reflection coefficient corresponding to a standing-wave ratio S_{max}/S_{min} is $[(S_{max}/S_{min}) - 1]/[(S_{max}/S_{min}) + 1]$, while the reflection coefficient for a wave striking a capacitive earth with vertical incidence is $(\sqrt{\epsilon} - 1/)(\sqrt{\epsilon} + 1)$.   The earth can be considered as capacitive because the wavelength is only a few meters.

CHAPTER 12

LABORATORY OSCILLATORS

12-1. Special Considerations Involved in Laboratory Oscillators.
Test or "bench" oscillators for laboratory use must meet requirements
that differ greatly from those associated with power oscillators. Only a
nominal amount of power is required, typically 0.1 to 10 watts, so that
efficiency is not important. Instead, the design is controlled by such
considerations as ease of tuning over a wide frequency range, ease of
modulating, frequency stability, freedom from harmonics, constancy of
output over a wide frequency range, etc.

Laboratory oscillators for audio and the lower radio frequencies are
used for testing audio and video amplifiers and circuits, for modulating
radio-frequency test oscillators, etc. They are often continuously tunable over wide frequency ranges, typically of the order of 1000 to 1 or even
more. A good wave shape that is also independent of the load impedance is essential. The frequency must likewise be independent of the
load impedance, reasonably stable, and free of short-time drifts. The
output power is customarily obtained from an untuned Class A amplifier
excited by the oscillator. In this way the oscillator is isolated from the
load so that the frequency, amplitude, and wave shape of the generated
oscillations are unaffected by load impedance. Distortion in the Class
A amplifier is minimized by the use of a generous amount of negative
feedback, combined with conservative operation so that the Class A
amplifier is only moderately loaded even when developing the full rated
output of the system.

Laboratory test oscillators very commonly include some means for controlling the amplitude of the generated oscillations. It is possible in this
way to obtain an amplitude that is substantially constant over a wide
frequency range. Amplitude control can also be used to ensure excellent
waveform by limiting the oscillations to the linear part of the oscillator
tube characteristic; this also generally results in improved frequency
stability.

12-2. Resistance-capacitance-tuned Oscillators.[1] The most common
type of tunable laboratory oscillator used for frequencies up to about

[1] F. E. Terman, R. R. Buss, W. R. Hewlett, and F. C. Cahill, Some Applications of
Negative Feedback with Particular Reference ot Laboratory Equipment, *Proc. IRE,*

200 kc is the resistance-capacitance-tuned type illustrated schematically in Fig. 12-1a. In such oscillators, the frequency is determined by the resistance-capacitance network $R_1R_2C_1C_2$ that provides regenerative coupling between the output and input of the two-stage amplifier, as shown. By proportioning the network so that $R_1C_1 = R_2C_2$ under all conditions, the ratio of voltage developed across the input (point b) of the amplifier, to the voltage existing across the amplifier output (point a), varies with frequency as shown in Fig. 12-1b. Oscillations tend to take place at the frequency at which this curve is a maximum.

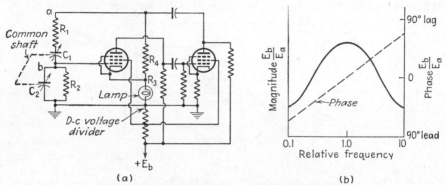

FIG. 12-1. Resistance-capacitance-tuned oscillator.

The amplitude of the oscillations is limited by using an incandescent lamp to supply the resistance R_3 in the resistance voltage divider R_3R_4 that provides negative feedback in the amplifier. The resistance R_3 increases with the temperature of the lamp filament, and so becomes greater as the current through the lamp increases. In the absence of oscillations the lamp resistance is accordingly a minimum, causing the negative feedback to be small. The amplification of the system is then large and oscillations begin building up. However, the oscillations cause a corresponding alternating current to flow through R_3. This increases the lamp resistance, which reduces the amplifier gain by making the negative feedback greater, and thus decreases the tendency to oscillate. Through this mechanism, the oscillations will stabilize at an amplitude that is substantially constant under widely varying conditions, and

vol. 27, p. 649, October, 1939; C. A. Cady, A Wide-range Oscillator for Audio and Supersonic Frequencies, *Gen. Rad. Expt.*, vol. 22, p. 1, November, 1947; H. H. Scott, A New Type of Selective Circuit and Some Applications, *Proc. IRE*, vol. 26, p. 226, February, 1938; A. R. A. Randall and F. A. Peachey, Variable A. F. Portable Oscillator, *Wireless Eng.*, vol. 25, p. 37, February, 1948.

An excellent discussion of the practical considerations involved in the resistance-capacitance oscillator is given by Brunton Bauer, Design Notes on the Resistance-capacitance Oscillator, *Hewlett-Packard J.*, vol. 1, November, December, 1949.

which by proper design can be a value that represents operation over a portion of the tube characteristics that is substantially linear.[1]

In analyzing the resistance-capacitance-tuned oscillator one can consider that the network $R_1R_2R_3R_4C_1C_2$ forms a Wien bridge, as illustrated schematically in Fig. 12-2. The amplified output is applied across one pair of diagonally opposite corners of this bridge, while the amplifier input is obtained from the other diagonally opposite corners. The regenerative coupling between the amplifier output and its input terminals is accordingly determined by the extent of unbalance of the bridge. When the oscillations are just starting to build up, the resistance R_3 is

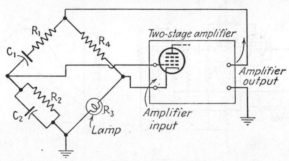

Fig. 12-2. Resistance-capacitance oscillator of Fig. 12-1 redrawn to show that it is equivalent to an amplifier in which the output is coupled to the input through a Wien bridge.

smaller than the value required to balance the bridge, so that very considerable transmission takes place from amplifier output to input. However, as the amplitude of the oscillations builds up, the resistance R_3 increases as explained above. This brings the bridge closer to balance, reducing the coupling between amplifier output and input, and thereby reducing the tendency to oscillate. The result is ultimately a stabilization of the oscillations at an amplitude such that the bridge is almost but not quite balanced.[2]

In practical resistance-capacitance-tuned amplifiers it is customary to make $R_1 = R_2 = R$ and $C_1 = C_2 = C$. Under these conditions the frequency of oscillation is given by the equation

$$\text{Frequency} = \frac{1}{2\pi RC} \qquad (12\text{-}1)$$

[1] A theoretical analysis of the behavior of the lamp, taking into account its thermal time constant, is given by W. H. B. Cooper and R. A. Seymour, Temperature-dependent Resistors, *Wireless Eng.*, vol. 24, p. 298, October, 1947.

[2] A general theoretical consideration of oscillators of this type is presented by W. G. Shepherd and R. O. Wise, Variable-frequency Bridge-type Frequency-stabilized Oscillators, *Proc. IRE*, vol. 31, p. 256, June, 1943; also see W. A. Edson, Intermittent Behavior in Oscillators, *Bell System Tech. J.*, vol. 24, p. 1, January, 1945.

Condensers C_1 and C_2 can conveniently be supplied by gang-tuning condensers such as used in standard broadcast receivers. Typical maximum capacitances used are 500 to 2000 $\mu\mu$f, depending upon the size of the individual gangs, and whether or not two gangs are connected in parallel. Since the ratio of maximum to minimum capacitance of variable condensers of this type is greater than 10, a frequency range of 10 to 1, as for example from 200 to 2000 cycles, can be covered by a half turn of the shaft on which the condenser rotors are mounted. This results from the fact, as shown by Eq. (12-1), that the operating frequency with resistance-capacitance tuning is inversely proportional to the tuning capacitance, whereas in ordinary inductance-capacitance tuning it is inversely proportional to the square root of the tuning capacitance.

Different frequency ranges may be covered while using the same variable capacitance by switching the resistances R_1 and R_2 to new values. In particular, changing these resistances by a factor such as 0.1 or 0.01 will multiply the frequency by 10 or 100, respectively, as is apparent from Eq. (12-1). However, if the different frequency ranges covered in this way are to track, $i.e.$, if changing R_1 and R_2 by a factor such as 0.1 is to change the frequency at every point on the scale by exactly 10, then it is necessary for the amplifier to have negligible phase shift over both frequency ranges involved. At low frequencies this can be obtained (1) by using very large screen and cathode by-pass condensers, or (2) by omitting cathode by-pass condensers and by obtaining the screen voltages from a resistance divider as in Fig. 12-1a, or (3) by compensating for the phase shift introduced by the by-pass condensers. At high frequencies, phase shifts can be minimized by designing the amplifier to have a very good high-frequency response, such that the top frequency for relatively uniform amplification is considerably higher than the highest frequency at which the oscillator is to operate.

It is also possible to control the frequency of a resistance-capacitance-tuned oscillator by simultaneously varying the resistances R_1 and R_2, while leaving the capacitances C_1 and C_2 fixed. Such an arrangement is satisfactory when several fixed frequencies are to be available, since then the resistances can be changed by contacts operated from a switch or by push buttons. When a continuous variation of frequency is required, tuning by a variable capacitance is preferred to using a variable resistance, however, as in this way an absolutely continuous variation of frequency is obtained without contact trouble.[1]

---

[1] An ingenious means for setting up any desired frequency with high accuracy by the use of decade resistance switches, in which one switch controls the first digit of the desired frequency, while the second switch controls the second digit, etc., is described by Charles M. Edwards, A Precision Decade Oscillator for 20 Cycles to 200 Cycles, $Proc.\ IRE$, vol. 39, p. 277, March, 1951.

The practical lower frequency limit of a continuously tuned resistance-capacitance oscillator is limited by the largest practical value of variable air capacitance C, which is about 0.004 μf, and the fact that the highest practical value of resistance R is of the order of 50 megohms.   This leads to a minimum continuously variable frequency of slightly less than 1 cycle per sec.[1]   For frequencies below a few cycles, the thermal time constant of the lamp resistance R_3 in Fig. 12-1a is such that the resistance of the lamp tends to follow the current variations of each cycle.   This severely distorts the wave shape.   If very low frequencies are to be generated it is hence necessary to use some other form of stabilizing resistance that possesses a larger thermal time constant than a lamp filament. This requirement can be met by including a thermistor as part of the resistance R_4, and making R_3 a fixed resistance.

The highest frequency at which a resistance-capacitance oscillator will operate satisfactorily is limited by the low impedance at high frequencies of the network $R_1R_2C_1C_2$ that shunts the plate circuit of the second tube of the amplifier, and by the phase shift introduced in the amplification by this circuit when its impedance is low.   Although oscillations may be obtained up to several megacycles by using video amplifier techniques, an upper limit of about 200 kc is typical for oscillators of this type when commercial requirements are to be met.   When appreciably higher frequencies are desired, the phase-shift oscillator circuit of Fig. 12-3 is preferable.[2]

The resistance-capacitance-tuned oscillator has very desirable characteristics for laboratory oscillator applications.   It is inexpensive, simple, dependable, and compact.   It can be built to operate at frequencies as low as a fraction of a cycle per second, and as high as 200 kc with continuous coverage between these limits.   When properly designed the harmonic content of the oscillator output is only a fraction of a per cent, and a substantially constant output is obtained irrespective of the frequency being generated by the oscillator.   Finally, the frequency stability is adequate for all ordinary applications, and in particular there is

---

[1] By deliberately designing the two-stage amplifier so that the amplification is given a lagging phase shift at low frequencies, it is possible to reduce this lower limit still further.   Thus when this phase shift is 45°, the frequency is about one-third of its value in the absence of such a phase shift.

Still lower frequencies can be reached by using for C_1 and C_2 fixed condensers of 0.01 μf or larger (or step variable condensers) that have extremely low leakage resistance.

[2] A form of resistance-tuned oscillator in which the Wien bridge is replaced by a bridged-T network is also more suitable for use at high frequencies than the circuit of Fig. 12-1; see Peter G. Sulzer, Wide-range R-C Oscillator, *Electronics*, vol. 23, p. 88, September, 1950.

no significant drift of the frequency at low-frequency settings, such as characterizes the beat-frequency oscillator.

12-3. Phase-shift Oscillators.[1] A typical phase-shift oscillator consists of a single amplifier tube in which the plate circuit is connected to the control-grid circuit through a resistance-capacitance network that produces a phase-shift of 180°. In this way the amplified output is fed back to the control electrode in exactly the phase that is required to produce sustained oscillations.

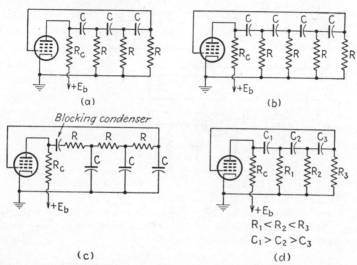

FIG. 12-3. Schematic circuits of various forms of phase-shift oscillators.

A common circuit arrangement for a phase-shift oscillator is shown schematically in Fig. 12-3a. In this particular instance, the phase-shift network is composed of three identical resistances R, and three identical condensers C. In such an arrangement, and assuming $R \gg R_c$, the required 180° phase shift is obtained when the frequency has the value

$$\text{Frequency} = \frac{1}{2\pi \sqrt{6}\, RC} \tag{12-2}$$

For this condition the attenuation of the resistance-capacitance network is 29; accordingly if the amplification introduced by the tube equals or exceeds 29, the system will oscillate at the frequency given by Eq. (12-2).

---

[1] E. L. Ginzton and L. M. Hollingsworth, Phase-shift Oscillators, *Proc. IRE*, vol. 29, p. 43, February, 1941; also discussion by A. Blanchard, *Proc. IRE*, vol. 32, p. 641, October, 1944.

The actual circuit details of a phase-shift oscillator may take a great variety of forms. Thus the number of resistances and capacitances in the phase-shift network may be more than three, as in Fig. 12-3b; more sections mean greater circuit complexity but less network attenuation for 180° phase shift, and hence less amplifier gain. It is also possible to interchange the resistances and the capacitances, as shown in Fig. 12-3c.

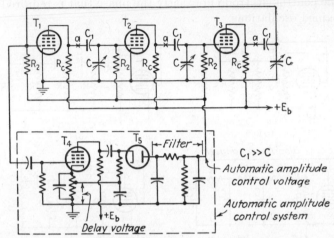

FIG. 12-4. Form of phase-shift oscillator particularly suitable for operation at high frequencies. This arrangement also can be used to generate three-phase oscillations. Automatic amplitude control is shown.

Again, one may taper the resistance-capacitance network as indicated in Fig. 12-3d. Tapering in this way has the advantage of giving the required phase shift with less total attenuation in the network, but has the disadvantage that tuning becomes more complicated because the circuit elements of one kind are no longer all identical.[1,2]

Another form of phase-shift oscillator is shown in Fig. 12-4, where each resistance-capacitance combination is separated by an amplifier tube.[3] Each stage in this particular arrangement is designed as an ordinary

[1] Phase-shift oscillators with tapered networks are discussed by P. G. Sulzer, The Tapered Phase-shift Oscillator, *Proc. IRE*, vol. 36, p. 1302, October, 1948; Rodney W. Johnson, Extending the Frequency Range of the Phase-shift Oscillator, *Proc. IRE*, vol. 33, p. 597, September, 1945.

[2] Phase-shift oscillators in which the frequency of operation is controlled by varying one, but only one, of the circuit elements of the phase-shift network, are discussed by W. C. Vaughan, Phase-shift Oscillator, *Wireless Eng.*, vol. 26, p. 391, December, 1949.

[3] A variation of this arrangement involves using cathode-coupled amplifier stages. If in addition, vacuum tubes are used to control the plate currents, and hence the transconductance of the cathode-coupled stages, the frequency obtained can be varied over a wide range simply by varying the grid bias of the control tubes. See Millard E. Ames, Wide-range Deviable Oscillator, *Electronics*, vol. 22, p. 96, May, 1949.

resistance-coupled amplifier with a mid-frequency gain of 2.0. The oscillations then occur at a frequency such that the reactance of the tuning capacitance C (including tube capacitances) is 0.5774 times the equivalent coupling resistance formed by R_c shunted by the grid-leak resistance R_2 and the plate resistance of the tube; at this frequency the gain per stage is $1.0\underline{/60°}$. It is possible in this way to generate very high frequencies. Thus if the tube transconductance is 5000 μmhos, and the minimum tuning capacitance (including tube capacitances) is 50 $\mu\mu$f, the top oscillator frequency is 14.4 Mc. For a given setting of the tuning condenser, the frequency can be reduced by any desired factor, such as 0.1 or 0.01 for example, by inserting a suitable resistance at points a, that proportionately increases the equivalent resistance in shunt with the condenser.

The amplitude of the oscillations generated by a phase-shift oscillator must be controlled in such a manner as to prevent serious waveform distortion. In many cases, it is sufficient to adjust the transconductance of the amplifier tube by varying the control-grid or screen voltages until oscillations are just barely able to start. The oscillations then build up until a small amount of nonlinearity introduced by the tube causes the amplitude to stabilize. Some waveform distortion is introduced in this way, but if the initial adjustment is such that oscillations are barely able to start, the distortion will be very small.

When extremely pure waveform is required, then some form of automatic amplitude control is essential. An example of such a control is given in Fig. 12-4, where the oscillations are amplified by tube T_4 and then rectified by diode T_5 to provide an automatic-volume-control system with delay, that controls the bias of the amplifier tubes T_1, T_2, and T_3. In this way oscillations can be stabilized at an amplitude corresponding to operation on a linear portion of the tube characteristics. It is also possible to employ an incandescent lamp or a thermistor arrangement for limiting the amplitude.[1]

The phase-shift oscillator is an alternative to the resistance-capacitance-tuned oscillator, and the two have many points of similarity.[2] In practice, however, resistance-capacitance-tuned arrangements are normally used for variable-frequency oscillators up to about 200 kc, while phase-shift oscillators find use in this frequency range primarily as fixed-

[1] The problem of avoiding self-oscillation in such a control system is analyzed by Edson, *loc. cit.*

[2] For instance, since the frequency of both types is proportional to $1/RC$, as can be seen from Eqs. (12-1) and (12-2), it has proved feasible to build an oscillator with one multisection variable capacitor and one dial which tunes in decades from 10 cycles to 100 Kc in a resistance-capacitance circuit, and from 100 Kc to 10 Mc in a phase-shift circuit.

frequency oscillators.   However, above about 200 kc, phase-shift oscillators of the type of Fig. 12-4 are preferable to resistance-capacitance-tuned arrangements for generating a continuously variable frequency.

12-4. Beat-frequency Oscillators.   In the beat-frequency oscillator, voltages obtained from two radio-frequency oscillators operating at slightly different frequencies are combined and applied to a mixer tube, as shown schematically in Fig. 12-5.   The difference-frequency current that is thus produced represents the desired oscillations.   The practical value of the beat-frequency oscillator arises from the fact that a small or moderate percentage variation in the frequency of one of the individual oscillators, such as can be obtained by rotation through half a turn of the shaft controlling a variable tuning condenser, will vary the beat- or difference-frequency output continuously from a few cycles per second

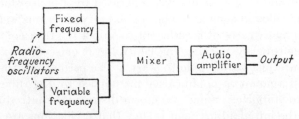

Fig. 12-5. Block diagram of beat-frequency oscillator.

throughout the entire audio range, or through the entire video-frequency range.   At the same time, amplitude of the difference-frequency output is substantially constant as the frequency is varied.

The principal factors involved in the performance of the beat-frequency oscillator are the frequency stability of the individual oscillators, the tendency of the oscillators to synchronize at very low difference frequencies, the wave shape of the difference-frequency output, and the tendency for spurious beat notes to be produced.   Frequency stability of the individual oscillators is important because any *slight change* in the *relative* frequency of the two oscillators will cause a relatively *large change* in the difference frequency.   To minimize drift of the difference frequency with time, the individual oscillators should accordingly have high inherent frequency stability with respect to changes in temperature and to supply-voltage variations, and then should be as nearly alike electrically, mechanically, and thermally, as is possible.   In this way, frequency changes will be small, and moreover, the frequency changes that do take place will tend to be the same in each of the individual oscillators, and so will have little effect on the *difference* in their frequencies.   It is particularly important in this connection that differential heating of the two oscillator circuits be avoided.   Heat-producing components such as rectifier tubes, etc., should be so located as to produce minimum temperature change in the resonant circuits of the two oscillators, and what temperature effects are produced should be the same in both oscillators.

The two radio-frequency oscillators must be completely isolated from each other. If coupling of any type exists between the two oscillators, they will synchronize when the difference frequency is small. This makes it impossible to obtain very low values of difference frequency, and in addition causes an interaction between the oscillators that results in low difference frequencies having a highly distorted wave shape. The necessary isolation at the mixer can be obtained by the use of buffer amplifiers, or by employing a very carefully designed pentagrid mixer, or both. Direct coupling between the oscillators can be prevented by proper shielding of coils, condensers, and tubes, and by placing filtering in leads.

The wave shape of the difference-frequency voltage developed by the mixer output is determined largely by mixer distortion, provided that there is no tendency for synchronization to be present. To ensure low distortion, one of the voltages applied to the mixer, preferably the one derived from the fixed-frequency oscillator, should be considerably smaller than the voltage derived from the other oscillator, and is preferably entirely free of harmonics.

Beat-frequency oscillators are commonly troubled with spurious beat notes, sometimes termed "whistles" or "birdies." These effects are usually the result of cross modulation in the audio-frequency amplifier between high-order radio-frequency harmonics generated by the mixer. These spurious whistles often appear when the output frequency is high. At audio frequencies the behavior is such that, as the desired component of output frequency is varied through only a few hundred cycles, the output also contains a component (i.e., whistle) that begins at the upper limit of audibility, decreases in pitch through zero, and then rises in pitch, finally reaching the upper limit of audibility again. This action results from some particular combination of harmonics of the radio frequencies, such as the tenth harmonic of the fixed frequency producing a beat note by cross modulation in the audio amplifier with the eleventh harmonic of the variable-frequency oscillator. These spurious whistles can be eliminated by operating the mixer so as to minimize the production of radio-frequency harmonics, and by using filters and shielding to prevent the harmonics that are generated in the mixer from reaching the amplifier tubes that follow the mixer. In this connection, it is helpful if the oscillator voltages applied to the mixer tube are relatively small. It is also desirable that the amplifier following the mixer be operated conservatively in order to minimize nonlinear effects that would contribute to cross modulation.

A schematic diagram of a typical beat-frequency oscillator circuit is shown in Fig. 12-6.[1]   In this particular arrangement, Hartley oscillator circuits are employed, with cathode-coupled buffer amplifiers.   A pentagrid mixer is used, with the bias voltages on the two signal grids carefully adjusted in relation to the amplitude of the signal voltages applied to these grids to minimize both wave-shape distortion of the beat frequency, and the production of spurious whistles.   The combination of isolating amplifiers and pentagrid mixer ensures complete freedom from coupling between the two oscillators, provided each individual oscillator is appropriately shielded, and provided filters are placed in the power leads entering the shielded compartments.   The mixer is followed by a low-pass filter to prevent radio-frequency oscillator harmonics generated by the mixer from being transmitted to the audio amplifier.   For this filter

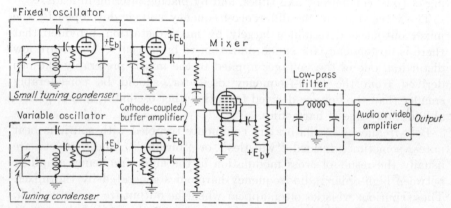

FIG. 12-6. Schematic circuit diagram of a typical beat-frequency oscillator.

to be fully effective, it is necessary that the circuits associated with the mixer electrodes be effectively isolated from the amplifier portions of the system by appropriate shielding and by filtering of the power leads.

The frequency at which the radio-frequency oscillators operate in a beat-frequency system is typically of the order of five to ten times the maximum difference frequency to be generated.   Higher values accentuate troubles from drift in the frequencies of the oscillators, and are therefore ordinarily avoided.   Lower frequencies mean that the variable oscillator must be tuned over an undesirably large percentage frequency variation.

In order that the calibration curve giving difference or output frequency as a function of variable condenser setting may be as accurate as possible, arrangements are always provided in a beat-frequency oscillator for

[1] For additional information see D. B. Sinclair, Making a Good Instrument Better, *Gen. Rad. Expt.*, vol. 23, June, 1948.

adjusting the frequency of the fixed oscillator to make some selected point on the calibration correct. When the radio-frequency oscillators are so well isolated from each other that they do not synchronize even when the difference frequency is only a fraction of a cycle per second, the necessary adjustment can be carried out by turning the dial setting to zero frequency, and adjusting the beat frequency so that a meter in the mixer plate circuit shows beats approaching zero frequency. Alternatively, one may set the dial to 60 cycles, inject 60-cycle voltage from the power supply into the system, and adjust the "fixed" oscillator until the beat frequency obtained approximates 60 cycles, as indicated by the slow waxing and waning of a neon lamp that is simultaneously subjected to both beat-frequency and power-frequency voltages. Immediately after such an adjustment is made, the frequency calibration of the beat-frequency oscillator is very accurate. With time, however, the frequencies of the two oscillators in the system may drift by unequal amounts, so that the calibration gradually becomes in error, particularly at low frequencies. It is therefore necessary periodically to check the adjustment, particularly when the oscillators are just warming up. This drift is one of the disadvantages of the beat-frequency oscillator.

Beat-frequency oscillators once found wide use in audio- and video-frequency test work requiring a variable frequency. However, the less expensive, drift-free, simpler, and physically more compact resistance-tuned oscillator is now preferred for most laboratory applications in the audio-frequency and lower radio-frequency range. Also, phase-shift oscillators of the type shown in Fig. 12-4 have similar advantages at the higher video frequencies. However, the beat-frequency principle continues to have fields of usefulness. For example, in automatic recording of a frequency characteristic, where it is necessary to cover a frequency range of more than 10 to 1 by a continuous rotation, rather than by a succession of rotations combined with operation of a decade range switch, the beat-frequency oscillator has no competitor. It is also useful when a relatively high radio frequency is to be swept through a very great frequency range; thus two reflex klystron oscillators operating at approximately 25,000 Mc can be used to produce a difference frequency that covers the range 2000 to 4000 Mc.

12-5. Audio Oscillators with Inductance-Capacitance Tuning. Systems employing inductance-capacitance tuning find only limited use as laboratory oscillators for audio and the lower radio frequencies. This is because it is cumbersome to tune such circuits over the enormous frequency ranges commonly required in such test oscillators. However, inductance-capacitance tuning finds occasional use, particularly where the frequency stability of the resistance-capacitance, phase-shift, and beat-frequency oscillator systems is not adequate.

A number of circuit arrangements have been successfully used for audio-frequency laboratory oscillators of the inductance-capacitance-tuned type. One satisfactory arrangement consists of a Hartley, Colpitts, or similar oscillator operated as a Class A device with automatic amplitude control, as discussed in connection with Fig. 12-10. A second system is the bridge-stabilized oscillator of Fig. 12-12. Still another possibility is the two-terminal oscillator (see page 504), preferably with automatic amplitude control. However, the simplest type of tuned-circuit audio-frequency test oscillators having a high standard of performance is the resistance-stabilized oscillator, discussed below.

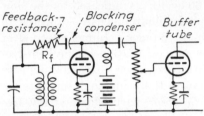

FIG. 12-7. Typical circuit diagram of resistance-stabilized oscillator.

Resistance-stabilized Oscillators.[1] The resistance-stabilized oscillator is a conventional oscillator, usually of either the tuned-plate or Hartley type, with the addition of a resistance R_f between the plate and the tuned circuit, as shown in Fig. 12-7. When properly designed, such an oscillator is characterized by excellent wave shape, a frequency that is substantially independent of the tube voltages and tube replacements, and an output that is substantially constant over wide frequency ranges.

The tube of a resistance-stabilized oscillator is arranged to operate as a Class A amplifier with fixed bias (usually self-bias). The feedback resistance R_f is then given a value so high that oscillations are barely able to start. When the plate voltage is turned on, oscillations build up until the grid goes slightly positive at the peak of each cycle. The added losses introduced by the resulting grid current then prevent further increase in amplitude. The proper value of feedback resistance can be obtained experimentally as the largest value for which oscillations occur. Alternatively one may place a microammeter in the control-grid circuit, and adjust the feedback resistance until this meter indicates some predetermined small grid current, such as 5 μa.

For good wave shape, the tube when considered as an amplifier must be adjusted so that it will amplify without distortion, an alternating voltage on the control grid having a crest value several volts greater than the grid bias. This corresponds to a bias slightly less than would be used at the same plate voltage for normal Class A amplifier operation without grid current. The actual value of feedback resistance required under these conditions will depend upon the parallel resonant impedance of the

[1] For further information, with particular reference to design considerations, see F. E. Terman, Resistance-stabilized Oscillators, *Electronics*, vol. 6, p. 190, July, 1933.

tuned circuit, the amplification factor of the oscillator tube, and the turn ratio between the primary and secondary windings of the tuned circuit. When the design is such that the feedback resistance R_f is considerably larger than the plate resistance of the tube, the frequency generated will be substantially independent of the voltages applied to the tube, and will change very little with tube replacement.

At one time the resistance-stabilized oscillator found extensive use in laboratory test equipment, as a beating oscillator in carrier systems, etc. It has now been largely displaced by newer types of oscillators, but still represents the best one-tube tuned-circuit arrangement for laboratory applications at audio and the lower radio frequencies.

Resonant Circuits for Audio Oscillators.   Tuned circuits at audio frequencies typically employ a paper or mica condenser, and a coil with a magnetic core.   When the circuit is to be tuned over a considerable frequency range, it is customary to use a decade-type condenser with a 0.0011-$\mu\mu$f variable air-dielectric condenser to bridge between the 0.001-μf fixed steps of the smallest decade.

The magnetic core may be one of several types, according to circumstances.   The best characteristics are obtained by using high permeability alloys such as permalloy, supermalloy, perminvar, etc.   When used in the form of dust rings, Q's of the order of 50 to 200 may be obtained from very low audio frequencies to over 100 kc, and the inductance is very nearly independent of the exact amplitude of the alternating magnetization provided this magnetization is small.   For many applications it is possible, however, to use ordinary audio-grade silicon-steel laminations.   In this way, values of Q of the order of 10 to 15 can be obtained throughout the audio-frequency range provided the core is not too small.   The chief disadvantage of silicon-steel cores is that the inductance depends to a significant extent upon the flux density even at low flux densities, so that the exact frequency will depend slightly upon the amplitude of the oscillations.

With any type of magnetic core, it is essential that d-c magnetization be avoided.   Thus shunt feed should be employed in all oscillators using a coil with a magnetic core.

12-6. Laboratory Oscillators for Radio Frequencies Using Ordinary Resonant Circuits.   Oscillators for frequencies below about 200 Mc, commonly use a standard circuit such as the Hartley, Colpitts, or tuned-plate grid-tickler arrangements of the type often employed in local oscillators of radio receivers.   Class C operation is customary.   The principal considerations in such oscillators are ease of tuning, frequency stability, isolation from load, and shielding.   The continuous tuning range obtainable with such arrangements at broadcast and lower frequencies is of the order of 3 to 1, while at very much higher frequencies it is commonly less.

The frequency range can be extended by changing tuning coils, using a coil-switching arrangement such as is typical of multiband receivers.

Radio-frequency test oscillators for laboratory use are ordinarily shielded at least moderately well. In this way it is possible to ensure that substantially all of the energy that reaches the circuits under test will leave the oscillator through the output terminals. The shielding may usually be fairly simple, since signal-generator shielding effectiveness is not normally expected.

Considerations Relating to Frequency Stability.[1] A high degree of frequency stability is required in radio-frequency laboratory oscillators in order to prevent excessive frequency drift during use, and to ensure the accuracy of the calibration. There are four principal factors that contribute to frequency stability. These are (1) a low temperature coefficient of resonant frequency of the oscillator tuned circuit, (2) circuit arrangements that make the frequency obtained depend primarily upon the coil and condenser of the resonant circuit, and only secondarily upon factors involving the tube, (3) isolation of the oscillator from the load, and (4) the use of a regulated power supply that maintains the voltages applied to the oscillator tube substantially constant.

A low temperature coefficient of the oscillator resonant circuit can be obtained by proper design of the coil and condenser, combined with the use of a temperature-compensated capacitance to correct for any residual temperature coefficient of the resonant frequency.[2] In this connection, a difficult problem is presented by the tube capacitances. These contribute to the capacitance that tunes the resonant circuit; at the same time the tube capacitances are subject to temperature effects as a result of heating of the tube electrodes during operation. . It is therefore desirable that the oscillator tube be operated conservatively with reference to power dissipated at the electrodes. Also, the use of a "high C" or equivalent resonant system results in the tube capacitances supplying a smaller proportion of the total tuning capacitance.

A high degree of frequency stability requires not only that the resonant circuit have a low temperature coefficient of resonant frequency; at the same time it is also necessary that the frequency of oscillations be deter-

[1] For additional information, particularly with reference to the temperature coefficient of the resonant frequency, see S. W. Seeley and E. I. Anderson, U-H-F Oscillator Frequency-stability Considerations, *RCA Rev.*, vol. 5, p. 77, July, 1940; John B. Moore, Design of Stable Heterodyne Oscillators, *Electronics*, vol. 18, p. 116, October, 1945; R. A. Heising, Stability in High-frequency Oscillators, *Proc. IRE*, vol. 31, p. 595, November, 1943; Chester I. Soucy, Temperature Coefficients in Electronic Circuits, *Electronics*, vol. 21, p. 117, January, 1948; Norman Lea, Notes on the Stability of *LC* Oscillators, *J. IEE*, vol. 92, pt. III, p. 261, December, 1945.

[2] See T. R. W. Bushby, Thermal-temperature-drift Compensation, *Proc. IRE*, vol. 30, p. 546, December, 1942 (also vol. 31, p. 232, May, 1943).

mined as far as possible only by the resonant circuit, and that it be influenced as little as possible by the grid and plate resistances and capacitances of the oscillator tube.   The most important means of achieving this result is to make the *effective Q* of the resonant circuit as high as possible.   This can be done by using a low ratio of inductance to capacitance in the resonant circuit (*i.e.*, a high-C circuit); alternatively one may use a large inductance and connect the tube across only a part of the resonant circuit, as illustrated in Fig. 12-8.[1]   In either case, the result is to minimize the effect on the frequency produced by the electrode capacitances and resistances of the oscillator tube, particularly if a high-*Q* coil and condenser system is employed.

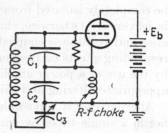

FIG.   12-8. A   conventional Hartley oscillator circuit arranged to minimize the effects of the tube on the generated frequency.

    In laboratory oscillators such as are here being discussed, it is customary to obtain the grid bias by means of a grid leak–condenser combination.   The highest frequency stability is obtained when the grid-leak resistance is as high as possible without causing intermittent oscillations, since this minimizes grid current and hence reduces the loading effect introduced by the tube.

    Experience also shows that the frequency stability of an oscillator can be improved by minimizing harmonic currents flowing in the plate and grid circuits, and by using circuit proportions, such as a high *effective Q*, that cause the harmonic voltages developed across the circuit impedances to be as small as possible.

    It has been found that a reactance inserted in series with the control-grid electrode (or the plate electrode), of the proper magnitude and sign, will sometimes improve the frequency stability with respect to plate-voltage changes in the tube.[2]   Thus it is often found in high-frequency oscillators that there is a particular value of grid-condenser capacitance

---

[1] In this circuit the capacitances C_1 and C_2 are very much larger than tuning capacitance C_3; in this way the tube has very little loading effect on the resonant circuit. The effective tank circuit Q then approaches very closely the actual Q of the resonant circuit; also the tube capacitances have little effect on the generated frequency since they are small compared with C_1 and C_2, which are in turn large compared with C_3. For further information on arrangements of this type see G. F. Lampkin, An Improvement in Constant Frequency Oscillators, *Proc. IRE*, vol. 27, p. 199, March, 1939; J. K. Clapp, An Inductance-capacitance Oscillator of Unusual Frequency Stability, *Proc. IRE*, vol. 36, p. 356, March, 1948; also discussion by W. A. Roberts, *Proc. IRE*, vol. 36, p. 1261, October, 1948.

[2] F. B. Llewellyn, Constant Frequency Oscillators, *Proc. IRE*, vol. 19, p. 2063, December, 1931.

for which the frequency stability is a maximum.   The practical difficulty in employing a compensating reactance of this sort, however, is that a readjustment of the reactance is ordinarily required when the frequency is changed.   Compensating reactances for improving frequency stability are of most value at very high frequencies.

When frequency stability is important, it is essential that the oscillator be completely isolated from the load to which the radio-frequency power is delivered.   Otherwise, changes in the load will alter the effective reactance and resistance coupled into the oscillator tuned circuit, with corresponding effects on frequency.   The required isolation can be obtained by the use of a power amplifier excited by the oscillator, combined with appropriate filtering and shielding.

Alternatively it is possible to combine the oscillator and power amplifier in a single tube, by employing a screen-grid or pentode tube in an *electron-coupled* arrangement, such as illustrated in Fig. 12-9.   Here the cathode, control grid, and screen grid function to form a triode oscillator, with the screen serving as the ordinary anode in a grounded plate circuit. Only a fraction of the electrons are intercepted by the screen, but these are enough to maintain the oscillations.   The remaining electrons, which

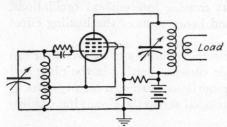

represent most of the space current, go on through the screen grid to the plate, and there produce the power output by flowing through the load impedance that is connected in series with the plate electrode.   The plate current is thus controlled by the oscillator portion of the tube. However, since the plate current of a pentode is independent of the plate potential, and hence of the

FIG. 12-9. Typical electron-coupled oscillator; the particular circuit shown is a Hartley circuit of the grounded-anode type.

load impedance in the plate circuit, there is little or no reaction between the load and the oscillator section of the tube provided only that no virtual cathode is present in the tube.   This arrangement is called an *electron-coupled circuit* because the oscillator and the output parts of the system are coupled only by the electron stream.

Conventional Oscillators Operated as Class A Devices with Automatic Amplitude Control.[1]   Advantages are to be gained by operating a test oscillator using a conventional circuit such as the Hartley or Colpitts

[1] See L. B. Arguimbau, An Oscillator Having a Linear Operating Characteristic, *Proc. IRE*, vol. 21, p. 14, January, 1933; Janusz Groszkowski, Oscillators with Automatic Control of the Threshold of Regeneration, *Proc. IRE*, vol. 22, p. 145, February, 1934.

arrangement, as a Class A amplifier instead of adjusting for Class C operation, as is customary, and providing for automatic control of the amplitude of the oscillations. A typical arrangement for doing this is illustrated in Fig. 12-10. Here a Hartley oscillator circuit is shown operated with a fixed bias voltage E_c, such that for a small amplitude of oscillations the tube behaves as a Class A amplifier. A diode tube T_1 with delay bias E_1 less than E_c is also provided. When the peak amplitude of the generated oscillations is such that the radio-frequency voltage applied to the diode exceeds the delay voltage E_1, rectified current passes

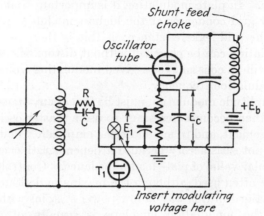

FIG. 12-10. Hartley oscillator circuit provided with a simple form of automatic amplitude control.

through the diode. This produces a d-c voltage across the condenser-leak combination RC that represents an additional negative-bias voltage applied to the control grid of the tube. This additional negative bias reduces the transconductance of the oscillator tube, thereby reducing the tendency for the oscillations to increase in amplitude. By proper design of the system, it is possible in this way to cause the oscillations to stabilize at an equilibrium amplitude that is quite small, and which represents Class A operation on a linear portion of the tube characteristics, and without grid current.[1,2]

Class A operation of conventional oscillators, with amplitude limitation, is characterized by a frequency that is unusually independent of

[1] The effectiveness of the amplitude control system can be increased by amplifying the radio-frequency oscillations before they are applied to the diode. This also has the advantage that the rectified current that passes through the diode is supplied by this auxiliary amplifier, rather than by the oscillator tuned circuit.

[2] Oscillators having control systems of this type are sometimes troubled by self-modulation of the generated oscillations. This is a form of self-oscillation in a negative-feedback system, and is discussed by Edson, *loc. cit.*

tube characteristics and electrode voltages.   This is because of the fact that the tube operates as a linear device with consequent freedom from harmonics, and also operates with the particular value of plate resistance that is the highest for which oscillations can exist.

Amplitude and Frequency Modulation of Radio-frequency Oscillators.   In a conventional Class C type of laboratory oscillator in which a small degree of frequency modulation can be tolerated, amplitude modulation is most satisfactorily achieved by plate modulation of the oscillator. In the case of an electron-coupled arrangement, one would modulate the screen electrode.   In plate modulation it is important that the reactance of the oscillator grid condenser at the highest modulating frequency be not less than the grid-leak resistance; if this is the case, substantially complete modulation can be obtained without distortion, and the degree of modulation will be constant for a given modulating voltage independently of the modulation frequency.

When the amplitude modulation must be free of any trace of frequency modulation, it then becomes necessary to use a master-oscillator–power-amplifier arrangement, and to modulate the amplifier.   Plate modulation is then usually not satisfactory because it depends rather critically upon having a particular value of plate load impedance.   Control-grid modulation is therefore often used, although the maximum depth of modulation that can be obtained in this way in low-power systems without excessive distortion of the modulation envelope is usually of the order of 80 per cent.

Amplitude modulation of an oscillator of the type shown in Fig. 12-10 can be readily accomplished by applying a modulating voltage in series with the delay voltage E_1 as indicated.   The amplitude at which the radio-frequency oscillations then stabilize varies with the changes in effective delay voltage produced by the modulating voltage.   It is possible in this way to obtain complete modulation with high fidelity, particularly, if the amplitude-limiting system includes amplification. The incidental frequency modulation associated with amplitude modulation of Class A oscillators of this type is quite small, in view of the excellent frequency stability of the oscillator.

Frequency modulation of laboratory oscillators is normally obtained with the aid of a reactance tube that varies the resonant frequency of the oscillator tuned circuit.   Standard practices may be followed, there being nothing unique in connection with the frequency modulation of an oscillator intended for laboratory test purposes.

The reactance-tube method of obtaining frequency modulation may be applied to all types of radio-frequency oscillators having tuned circuits, including Hartley, Colpitts, etc., arrangements, and irrespective of whether the operation is Class A or Class C.   This results from the fact that the frequency of the oscillations is determined by the resonant frequency of the tuned circuit, and the action of the reactance tube is to vary the resonant frequency of the circuit in accordance with the modulation voltage applied to the reactance tube.

Sweeping Oscillators. Radio-frequency oscillators for laboratory test use are frequently provided with means for sweeping the frequency back and forth over a band. Such a sweeping oscillator is useful in checking response curves, aligning intermediate-frequency and radio-frequency amplifiers, etc., and is an essential component in nearly all spectrum analyzers.

The sweeping oscillator is a special form of frequency-modulated oscillator in which the modulating frequency is relatively low, and the frequency deviation relatively large. Thus for testing of broadcast receivers, the generated frequency might be swept through a ± 10-kc frequency range at a rate of 60 times or less per second. In such an arrangement, the energy at any instant can for all practical purposes be considered as being concentrated in a sine-wave oscillation having a frequency equal to the instantaneous, or "quasi-steady-state frequency," of that moment. It is desirable that the amplitude of oscillations be substantially constant as the frequency is varied; if necessary, an automatic-amplitude-control system can be used to ensure that this is the case.

Most sweeping-oscillator systems make use of a reactance tube to vary the generated frequency.[1,2] The action of the reactance tube can be controlled by a suitable sinusoidal, saw-tooth, or triangular voltage as desired. The peak amplitude of this voltage determines the frequency range of the sweep, and the frequency of the sweep voltage determines the repetition rate of the sweep. Provision is commonly made whereby this control voltage is also available to serve as the horizontal deflecting voltage of a cathode-ray tube, or to synchronize the horizontal sweep frequency. When a 60-cycle control is used, a simple phase shifter is often

[1] Alternative arrangements include a trimmer capacitance that is mechanically varied either by a moving coil drive, or by a motor. For a summary of various practical means that can be used to sweep the frequency of an oscillator see C. B. Clark and Fred J. Kamphoefner, Panoramic Sweep Circuits, *Electronics*, vol. 22, p. 11, November, 1949.

[2] A completely different approach to the sweeping-oscillator problem, in which a phase-shift oscillator is used, is described by Millard E. Ames, *loc. cit.;* F. R. Dennis and E. P. Felch, Reactance-tube Modulation of Phase-shift Oscillators, *Bell System Tech. J.*, vol. 28, p. 601, October, 1949. Also see O. E. DeLange, A Variable Phase-shift Frequency-modulated Oscillator, *Proc. IRE*, vol. 37, p. 1328, November, 1949. Sweeping oscillators have also been devised that use a ferrite-cored tuning inductance and vary the frequency by saturating the magnetic core with current carried by an auxiliary winding. An example of such a system is described by A. I. Pressman and J. P. Blewett, A 300- to 4000-kilocycle Electrically Tuned Oscillator, *Proc. IRE*, vol. 39, p. 74, January, 1951.

included in this deflecting or synchronizing voltage to make it possible to superimpose the forward and return traces of the oscilloscope pattern.

The frequency deviation in cycles that a given control voltage causes in a frequency-modulation system will usually vary with the carrier frequency generated by the oscillator. This difficulty can be overcome by using a beat-frequency system to produce the desired frequency, and then sweeping the frequency of the "fixed" oscillator. Such an arrangement is shown schematically in Fig. 12-11, and is widely used in general purpose laboratory equipment. Here, if the "fixed" frequency is frequency-modulated through a range such as ±10 kc, at a rate of 60 cycles per sec, then the difference-frequency output, whatever value of frequency it

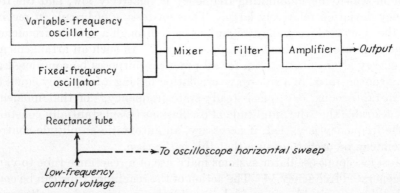

FIG. 12-11. Block diagram showing sweeping oscillator consisting of a beat-frequency oscillator in which the "fixed" oscillator is frequency-modulated.

may be, will likewise be swept through a frequency range of ±10 kc, 60 times per second. When the center frequency to be generated in such an arrangement corresponds to a broadcast or short-wave frequency, the individual oscillators may be of a conventional type. However, when the center frequency desired is quite high, as 50 Mc or greater, or if the range through which the frequency is to be swept is large, such as 10 to 50 Mc, one then employs reflex klystron oscillators in the beat-frequency system, and sweeps the frequency of the fixed oscillator by means of a suitable modulating voltage applied to the repeller.[1]

12-7. Miscellaneous Types of Oscillators. *Bridge-stabilized Oscillators Employing Resonant Circuits.*[2] A typical bridge-stabilized oscillator circuit in which a resonant circuit is the frequency-determining element, is shown schematically in Fig. 12-12. This arrangement is exactly

---

[1] An example of equipment of this type is given in the paper Wide-range Sweeping Oscillator, *Electronics*, vol. 30, p. 112, August, 1947.

[2] See L. A. Meacham, The Bridge-stabilized Oscillator, *Proc. IRE*, vol. 26, p. 1278, October, 1938; Shepherd and Wise, *loc. cit.*

analogous to the resistance-capacitance bridge-stabilized oscillator circuit of Fig. 12-2, except that the bridge now consists of three resistances, one of which R_4 is supplied by an incandescent lamp, while the fourth arm is the series impedance of resonant circuit $R_1L_1C_1$. The resistances R_1, R_2, and R_4 are so proportioned that at the resonant frequency of $R_1L_1C_1$, where the series impedance is the resistance R_1, the bridge would be balanced if R_4 were slightly higher. Oscillations then build up and stabilize at an amplitude such that the current through the lamp heats the filament enough to make R_4 assume a value that makes the bridge almost but not quite balanced.

If the amplifier has high gain and introduces negligible phase shift, the oscillations will have a frequency that is very precisely the series resonant

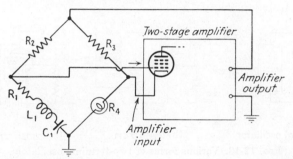

Fig. 12-12. Bridge-stabilized oscillator using a series resonant circuit for the frequency-determining element.

frequency of the tuned circuit. The frequency, and also the amplitude of oscillations, then becomes quite independent of the details of the amplifier, such as exact value of gain as affected by electrode voltages, aging of tubes, etc., and the behavior is as though there had been a very great magnification of the circuit Q.

Under certain conditions the oscillations generated by the bridge-stabilized arrangements will become self-modulated. This results from unfavorable time constants in the system that introduce a phase shift in the modulation envelope. The effect is a form of "hunting," and is analogous to oscillations in a feedback system with improper circuit proportions. The remedy is to modify the circuit details in such a manner as to prevent the spurious positive-feedback action.[1]

Bridge-stabilized circuits find their most extensive use in crystal oscillator systems, in which the resonant circuit is supplied by a quartz crystal. The arrangement can be used with inductance-capacitance resonant circuits, however, and has the merit that the frequency is determined almost solely by the resonant circuit. Also, the waveform is

[1] This situation is discussed in detail by Edson, *loc. cit.*

extremely good as a result of the fact that the amplitude-limiting action permits Class A operation of the amplifier system.

The bridge-stabilized arrangement can be used at either audio or radio frequencies; it is merely necessary that an amplifier (either tuned or untuned) of considerable gain and preferably of low phase shift be available. The bridge-stabilized oscillator with resonant circuit is most suitable for operation at a fixed frequency, or over a narrow range of frequencies. When a very wide frequency range is to be covered, the series resistance of the resonant circuit will normally change substantially. It then becomes necessary to vary one of the bridge resistors such as R_2 or R_3 with the tuning of the circuit in order to maintain at all times a suitable initial operating condition such that the bridge is moderately, but not excessively, unbalanced.

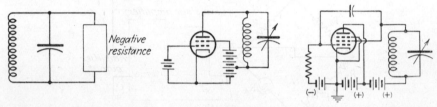

(a) Two-terminal oscillator   (b) Dynatron   (c) Transitron oscillator

FIG. 12-13. Various forms of two-terminal oscillators.

Two-terminal Oscillators. When a parallel resonant circuit is shunted by a negative resistance that has an absolute magnitude less than the parallel impedance of the circuit at resonance, oscillations start and increase in amplitude until limited by curvature of the tube characteristic, or by some form of automatic amplitude control. Such an arrangement, illustrated schematically in Fig. 12-13a, is termed a two-terminal oscillator because only two connections are required to the coil and condenser system of the oscillator.

A variety of negative resistive devices are available for use with two-terminal oscillators.[1] A common arrangement is the dynatron, illustrated in Fig. 12-13b, in which the negative resistance exists between the plate and cathode of a suitably operated screen-grid tube; such a negative resistance is the result of secondary emission at the plate when the screen voltage is greater than the plate voltage.[2] A second negative-resistance oscillator circuit is shown in Fig. 12-13c, where the negative resistance is

[1] In particular, see E. W. Herold, Negative Resistance and Devices for Obtaining It, *Proc. IRE*, vol. 23, p. 1201, October, 1935; also J. R. Tillman, A Note on Electronic Negative Resistors, *Wireless Eng.*, vol. 22, p. 17, January, 1945.

[2] A good discussion of such a negative resistance, with particular reference to the behavior at high frequencies, is given by G. A. Hay, Negative Resistance Circuit Element, *Wireless Eng.*, vol. 23, p. 299, November, 1946.

obtained by the retarding-field, or transitron, connection of a multigrid tube.[1] In both the dynatron and the transitron, the magnitude of the negative resistance can be controlled by varying the control-grid bias of the tube.

A negative resistance may also be realized by means of a two-stage feedback amplifier. Thus in Fig. 12-14a, a negative resistance exists across terminals xx as a result of back coupling introduced by resistance R_1. The magnitude of this negative resistance is directly proportional to R_1 and inversely proportional to the amplification of the two-stage

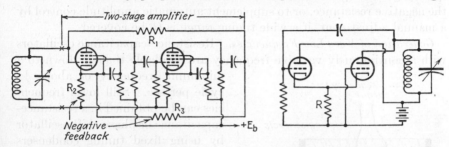

(a) Two-stage plate-coupled system   (b) Two-stage cathode-coupled system

Fig. 12-14. Two-terminal oscillators involving two-stage amplifiers.

amplifier. The negative resistance can thus be controlled by varying R_1, while for any given value of R_1, the magnitude can be made substantially independent of amplifier characteristics by negative feedback introduced with the aid of resistances R_2 and R_3, that stabilize the amplifier gain.[2] An alternative[3,4] method for achieving negative resistance with a two-stage amplifier is shown in Fig. 12-14b. Here, cathode coupling is used, and the magnitude of the negative resistance is determined by the coupling resistance R.

In all the two-terminal arrangements of Figs. 12-13 and 12-14, the frequency stability is highest and the wave shape best when the system is adjusted so that oscillations can barely exist, and so that they have a small amplitude. This desirable condition can be obtained by the use of

[1] For further discussion, see Cledo Brunetti, The Transitron Oscillator, *Proc. IRE*, vol. 27, p. 88, February, 1939.

[2] See Terman, Buss, Hewlett, and Cahill, *loc. cit.;* Cledo Brunetti and Leighton Greenough, Some Characteristics of a Stable Negative Resistance, *Proc. IRE*, vol. 30, p. 542, December, 1942.

[3] F. Butler, Cathode-coupled Oscillators, *Wireless Eng.*, vol. 21, p. 521, November, 1944; Murray G. Crosby, Two-terminal Oscillator, *Electronics*, vol. 19, p. 136, May, 1946; P. G. Sulzer, Cathode-coupled Negative Resistance Circuit, *Proc. IRE*, vol. 36, p. 1034, August, 1948.

[4] Still a third arrangement is described by Herbert J. Reich, A Low Distortion Audio-frequency Oscillator, *Proc. IRE*, vol. 25, p. 1387, November, 1937.

automatic amplitude control, by some form of limiting device, or by manual adjustment of the negative resistance to a value that is just barely able to cause oscillations to exist.

Two-terminal oscillators have the advantage that there are only two leads to be connected to the resonant circuit, and one of these can be at ground potential. However, they have the disadvantage that the properties of the usual resonant circuit are such that the value of negative resistance required for proper operation varies considerably with the frequency generated. As a result, it is necessary to use manual control of the negative resistance, or to supplement automatic amplitude control by a manual adjustment, if a wide tuning range is to be covered.

Generation of Very Low Frequencies. Resistance-capacitance oscillators with a continuously variable frequency are available that go down to a minimum frequency of about ¼ cycle per sec. Still lower frequencies can be obtained in a resistance-capacitance or phase-shift oscillator by using fixed tuning condensers possessing very low dielectric leakage, such as mica or polystyrene condensers.

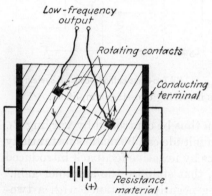

Fig. 12-15. A simple method of generating an alternating voltage of very low frequency.

It is also possible to obtain very low frequencies by a beat-frequency oscillator arrangement in which oscillations from two separate audio-frequency oscillators are combined in a mixer to give a difference frequency that is a small fraction of a cycle per second. In such an arrangement care must be taken to prevent synchronization of the two audio oscillations. Also, the mixer must be so operated as to minimize wave-form distortion; a square-law mixer in which one of the applied voltages is large, while the other is quite small, gives best results in such a situation.

A quite different method for generating a low frequency is illustrated schematically in Fig. 12-15. Here, a block of resistance material (or a wire-wound resistance card) has a d-c voltage applied across its ends. Two contacts bear on this material and are rotated about an axis as shown. The voltage difference between these rotating contacts is a sine-wave function of time, and the frequency of the voltage is equal to the rate of rotation in revolutions per second. The frequency is therefore varied by a speed control on the driving motor, and has a minimum value that can be as low as desired. The maximum frequency that can be obtained in this way is limited to about 20 cycles per sec by practical considerations having to do with moving contacts.[1]

Very low-frequency oscillations, in the range 0.02 to 0.1 cycles per sec, can be generated by using the thermal time lag of a thermistor to provide the equival of an inductive reactance.[2] Sine waves at frequencies in this range of values can also be generated by starting with a square wave that is integrated to form a triangular wave of the desired frequency. This triangular wave is in turn converted to a sine wave either by a filter or a nonlinear wave-shaping circuit.[3]

Frequency Modulation of Audio Oscillators. Frequency-modulated audio oscillations can be obtained in several ways. One procedure is to generate the audio frequency by means of a beat-frequency oscillator, and then frequency-modulate the fixed-frequency oscillator of the system by the use of a reactance tube (see Fig. 12-11). A frequency deviation, of say ±500 cycles, produced in the radio-frequency oscillator in this way then results in a similar ±500-cycle deviation of the audio-frequency oscillations. This arrangement has the advantage that a given modulating voltage always produces the same frequency deviation in the audio oscillation, irrespective of the value of the audio frequency.[4]

An alternative procedure for obtaining a frequency-modulated audio oscillation is to start with a phase-shift oscillator of the type illustrated in Fig. 12-3*a*. One or more of the resistances R are then supplied by the plate resistance of a triode tube (or tubes). Frequency modulation is obtained by applying the modulating voltage to the control grid of this tube (or tubes), thereby varying the plate resistance and hence the generated frequency.[5,6] A variation of the arrangement is to use the resistance-tuned oscillator of Fig. 12-1*a*, and place a reactance tube in

[1] Such a low-frequency generator is discussed by T. H. Clark and V. H. Clifford, Variable-frequency Two-phase Sine-wave Generator, *Elec. Commun.*, vol. 24, p. 382, September, 1947.

[2] Jay Edlin Stone, An Ultra-low-frequency Oscillator, *Electronics*, vol. 23, p. 94, January, 1950.

[3] See R. H. Brunner, A New Generator for Frequencies Down to 0.01 CPS, *Hewlett-Packard J.*, vol. 2, June, 1951; W. G. Shepard, Low Frequency Generator, *Electronics*, vol. 23, p. 116, October, 1950.

[4] An example of such an oscillator is given by J. L. Flanagan, Warbler for Beat-frequency Oscillator, *Electronics*, vol. 22, p. 93, December, 1949.

[5] Maurice Artzt, Frequency Modulation of Resistance-capacitance Oscillators, *Proc. IRE*, vol. 32, p. 409, July, 1944; also see Ames, *loc. cit.*, and Dennis and Felch, *loc. cit.*

[6] Corresponding arrangements can be used to frequency-modulate resistance-capacitance-tuned oscillators: thus see C. K. Chang, A Frequency-modulated Resistance-capacitance Oscillator, *Proc. IRE*, vol. 31, p. 22, January, 1943; Henry S. McGaughan and Chas. B. Leslie, A Resistance-tuned Frequency-modulated Oscillator for Audio-frequency Applications, *Proc. IRE*, vol. 35, p. 974, September, 1947.

shunt with the condenser C_2; the effect of the reactance tube is to vary this capacitance according to the modulating voltage, with the result that the generated frequency varies correspondingly.

In a tuned circuit type of audio-frequency oscillator, frequency modulation can be obtained by using a reactance tube to vary the tuning capacitance in accordance with the modulating voltage.

Polyphase Oscillators. A number of oscillator circuits have been devised which directly generate a polyphase voltage. Thus in Fig. 12-4, the voltages across the three condensers C represent the voltages of a three-phase system, provided the three individual stages are identical. If four identical stages are used instead of three, the voltages developed

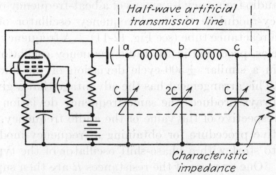

Fig. 12-16. Two-phase oscillator consisting of an amplifier tube in which the output and input circuits are coupled by a half-wave artificial transmission line provided by two quarter-wave sections in cascade.

by the four tubes correspond to the four voltages of a four-phase system; the voltages developed by alternate tubes then represent the two voltages of a two-phase system.[1]

Another form of two-phase generator is shown in Fig. 12-16. Here the plate of a tube is connected to the control grid of the same tube by an artificial transmission line terminated in its characteristic impedance, and consisting of two sections each a quarter wavelength long. Since the total line is a half wavelength long this arrangement gives the phase reversal necessary to produce oscillations. However, since each section is a quarter wave long, the voltage at b is exactly 90° out of phase with the voltage at either a or c. Thus a two-phase voltage can be obtained from the system.[2] The frequency is controlled by simultaneously varying the three condensers of the artificial line.

[1] Polyphase oscillators of this type are discussed by R. M. Barrett, "N"-phase Resistance-capacitance Oscillators, *Proc. IRE*, vol. 33, p. 541, August, 1945.

[2] F. Butler, New Valve-oscillator Circuit, *Wireless Eng.*, vol. 21, p. 317, July, 1944. An equivalent but quite different arrangement using a resistance-capacitance network is described by Oswald G. Villard, Jr., Tunable A-f Amplifier, *Electronics*, vol. 22, p. 77, July, 1949.

A two-phase voltage may be derived from a single-phase voltage by a suitable network. The simplest arrangement of this type is the resistance-capacitance phase splitter shown in Fig. 12-17a. Here a single-phase voltage is applied to a resistance R in series with a capacitance C, thus developing two output voltages E_r and E_c that differ in phase by 90°. If R and C are so chosen that at the frequency involved, the reactance of the capacitance C equals the resistance R, then the two voltages E_c and E_r are also equal in magnitude, and represent the phase voltages of a balanced two-phase system. This arrangement provides a satisfactory means of obtaining a two-phase voltage at a fixed frequency. However,

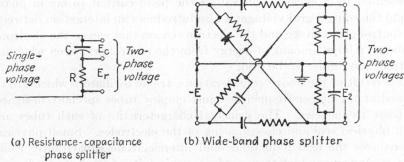

(a) Resistance-capacitance   (b) Wide-band phase splitter
phase splitter

FIG. 12-17.   Phase-splitting networks.

if the frequency is changed, it is necessary to readjust the circuit constants of the phase splitter in order to keep the phases balanced.

By the use of more complicated networks, it is possible to obtain satisfactory phase-splitting action over a substantial band of frequencies. For example, a resistance-capacitance network of the type shown in Fig. 12-17b, can be designed to develop two output voltages of equal magnitude, which have a phase difference that is within 5° of 90° over the range 200 to 3000 cycles. Still more complicated networks will give an even better performance.[1]

When one has obtained a polyphase voltage with a particular number of phases, it is possible to convert to any other number of phases by a suitable transformer arrangement. Thus, a two-phase system may be trans-

[1] See R. B. Dome, Wide-band Phase-shift Networks, *Electronics*, vol. 19, p. 112, December, 1946; D. G. C. Luck, Properties of Some Wide-band Phase Splitting Networks, *Proc. IRE*, vol. 37, p. 147, February, 1949; Sidney Darlington, Realization of a Constant Phase Difference, *Bell System Tech. J.*, vol. 29, p. 94, January, 1950; H. J. Orchard, Synthesis of Wide-band Two-phase Networks, *Wireless Eng.*, vol. 27, p. 72, March, 1950; W. Saraga, The Design of Wide-band Phase Splitting Networks, *Proc. IRE*, vol. 38, p. 754, July, 1950.

formed to a three-phase arrangement by means of the Scott transformer connection commonly used in 60-cycle power work.[1]

12-8. Triode Oscillators for the Higher Frequencies.[2]   When triode tubes are operated as oscillators at very high frequencies, the inductances of the leads inside the tube envelope, and the capacitances between the electrodes, become very important circuit elements.   They limit the highest frequency that can be obtained by associating resonant circuits with the oscillator,[3] and also modify the voltage and impedance relations in the oscillator circuit to an important extent.

At very high frequencies, the time that it takes an electron to travel from cathode to anode is no longer negligible in comparison with the time represented by a cycle.   This causes the plate current to lag in phase behind the control-grid voltage; it also introduces an interaction between the control-grid voltage and the electron stream that causes the electrons to absorb a large amount of energy from the control grid even when no electrons are drawn to the grid.

As a result of the above considerations, triode oscillators which are to be used at the higher frequencies must employ tubes specially designed for these frequencies.   The principal characteristics of such tubes are small physical size and close spacing of the electrodes.   Small physical size reduces the lead inductance and interelectrode capacitance, while close spacing gives a high transconductance in spite of small electrode size, and also minimizes transit-tune effects.   Additional features characteristic of many tubes designed for high-frequency service include leads of large diameter (hence of small inductance), physical arrangements that make very short leads possible, leads that merge with external circuits, and in some cases double leads to certain electrodes.   Examples of tubes specially designed for very high-frequency service include the "miniature" series such as the 6J6 and the 9002, the acorn series, including the 955 and the 6F4, and close-spaced triodes with parallel-plane construction such as the 2C40 and the 5767.

Oscillator Circuits for Use in Ultra-high-frequency Triode Oscillators.
The circuits commonly employed for ultra-high-frequency triode oscil-

[1] Thus see F. M. Bailey and H. P. Thomas, Phasitron F-M Transmitter, *Electronics*, vol. 19, p. 108, October, 1946.

[2] The principles involved in operating triode oscillators at very high frequencies are well covered by J. Bell, M. R. Gavin, E. G. James, and G. W. Warren, Triodes for Very Short Waves—Oscillators, *J. IEE (Radiolocation Conv.)*, vol. 93, pt. IIIA, p. 833, 1946; also see F. J. Kamphoefner, Feedback in Very-high-frequency and Ultra-high-frequency Oscillators, *Proc. IRE*, vol. 38, p. 630, June, 1950.

[3] However, frequencies higher than the resonant frequency resulting from the lead inductance and the associated tube capacitance can be achieved by the use of a series tuning condenser; see J. M. Pettit, Ultra-high-frequency Triode Oscillator Using a Series-tuned Circuit, *Proc. IRE*, vol. 38, p. 633, June, 1950.

lators are the same as those used at the lower frequencies.   However, at
the higher frequencies it becomes necessary to take into account the
inductive reactance of leads and the capacitive reactance of the interelectrode capacitances; in fact, such reactances very frequently represent
the most important reactances in the circuit.   As a result, design details,
and the physical construction of the oscillator, are commonly different at
very high frequencies than at lower frequencies.   For example, in low-
power oscillators for ultra-high frequencies, either the plate or the control
grid is sometimes grounded, instead of the cathode as is customary at low
frequencies (see Fig. 12-18).   Alternatively, in some cases no electrode is
grounded.   The potentials of the various electrodes with respect to
ground are then determined by the interelectrode capacitances of the
tube, and the capacitances to ground of the several electrodes and of
different parts of the circuit.   An example of such a circuit is given in
Fig. 12-19c.

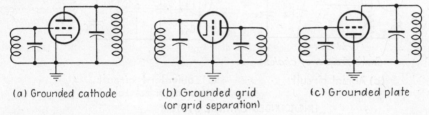

(a) Grounded cathode   (b) Grounded grid   (c) Grounded plate
                              (or grid separation)

Fig. 12-18.   Tuned-grid–tuned-plate arrangements with different electrodes grounded.

The circuit most widely used for ultra-high-frequency tunable laboratory oscillators of low power is shown in Fig. 12-19a.   When stray capacitances to ground, and interelectrode tube capacitances, are taken into
account this reduces to the equivalent of Fig. 12-19b.   This is a Colpitts
circuit in which the ratio of plate-cathode to grid-cathode alternating
voltages is determined by the stray capacitances C_1 and C_2, and the tube
capacitances C_{pk} and C_{gk}.   The principal advantage of this circuit is that
only one tuning adjustment is required, and that there are only two leads
from the tube to the associated resonant circuit.   The arrangement also
permits the use of a split stator type of tuning condenser C with resulting
avoidance of all moving contacts.

The circuit of Fig. 12-19a is frequently modified by insertion of a radio-
frequency choke between the cathode and ground as in Fig. 12-19c.   The
equivalent circuit of this arrangement is illustrated in Fig. 12-19d; the
ratio of plate-cathode to grid-cathode voltage is now determined primarily by the ratio C_{gk}/C_{pk} of interelectrode capacitances of the tube, and
is relatively independent of the stray capacitances C_1 and C_2 to ground.
Thus the feedback action in this case is determined by the tube and not
by the proximity to ground of the tube and various parts of the circuit.

Experience indicates that when other things are equal, best results are obtained with tubes in which the grid-plate and grid-cathode capacitances are approximately equal.

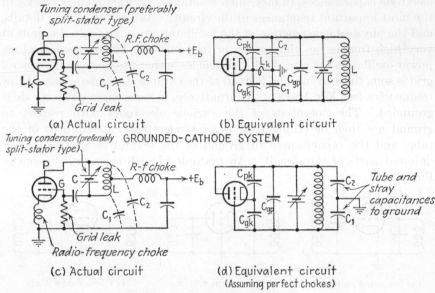

(a) Actual circuit   (b) Equivalent circuit

GROUNDED-CATHODE SYSTEM

(c) Actual circuit   (d) Equivalent circuit
(Assuming perfect chokes)

UNGROUNDED-CATHODE SYSTEM

FIG. 12-19. Widely used forms of ultra-high-frequency oscillators, showing actual and equivalent circuits.

An advantage gained by the use of an ungrounded cathode is that since no current flows from cathode to ground, the inductance of the lead from cathode to ground cannot adversely affect the operation of the oscillator.

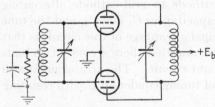

FIG. 12-20. Push-pull form of tuned-grid–tuned-plate oscillator.

In contrast, at very high frequencies in the circuit of Fig. 12-19a, there is considerable voltage developed across the inductance L_k of the cathode lead to ground. This modifies the behavior of the circuit in undesirable ways, and may even result in failure of the circuit to oscillate at certain frequencies.

Push-pull arrangements, such as the tuned-grid–tuned-plate system of Fig. 12-20, are often used in ultra-high-frequency oscillators. They have the advantage of being symmetrical with respect to ground. Also, since the interelectrode capacitances of the two tubes are in series, the total effective capacitance seen by the external circuit is half as great as when a single tube is employed. Again, since no alternating current flows from cathode to ground in a push-pull system, the inductance of the relatively long cathode-to-ground connection is eliminated, and replaced by the inductance of the lead connecting the two cathodes.   It is usually possible to arrange the tubes so that the inductance of this connecting lead can be quite small; this is particularly the case when the two tubes are in the same envelope, and have the cathodes interconnected inside the vacuum.

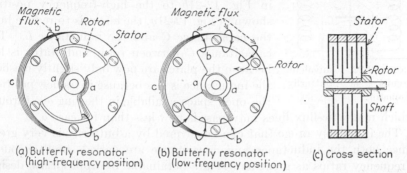

(a) Butterfly resonator
(high-frequency position)

(b) Butterfly resonator
(low-frequency position)

(c) Cross section

Fig. 12-21. Butterfly resonator, and rotor positions when resonant at low and high frequencies.

Butterfly Oscillators.[1]   At frequencies in the range 100 to 1000 Mc, the resonant circuit required in the oscillators of Fig. 12-19a and Fig. 12-19c is commonly provided by a "butterfly."

A typical butterfly is illustrated in Fig. 12-21.   It consists of a system of stationary and rotating plates shaped as shown, that mesh in the same manner as the stationary and rotating plates of a variable air-dielectric condenser.   Viewed from the points aa, this arrangement has the equivalent circuit shown in Fig. 12-22, which is seen to be a parallel resonant circuit with aa the points of high impedance.   Comparing Fig. 12-22 with Fig. 12-21, C is the capacitance between one side of the stator and the corresponding meshed portion of the rotor; two such capacitances are in series between points aa.   Similarly, each inductance L in the equivalent

[1] E. Karplus, The Butterfly Circuit, *Gen. Rad. Expt.*, vol. 19, October, 1944.   Oscillator circuits utilizing the butterfly and other similar wide-tuning-range circuits are described in "Very High Frequency Techniques," Chap. 30, McGraw-Hill Book Company, Inc., New York, 1947; also see E. Karplus, Wide-range Tuned Circuits and Oscillators for High Frequencies, *Proc. IRE*, vol. 33, p. 426, July, 1945; R. J. Ballantine and E. G. James, Oscillator Circuits for Wide-range Tuning, *J. IEE (Radiocomm. Conv.)*, vol. 94, pt. IIIA, p. 596, March–April, 1947; E. Karplus and E. E. Gross, A Standard-signal Generator for Frequencies between 50 and 920 Mc., *Gen. Rad. Expt.*, vol. 24, March, 1950.   Useful variations of the butterfly idea are described by D. K. Reynolds and M. B. Adams, Converters for UHF Television Reception, *Electronics*, vol. 22, p. 92, September, 1949; G. Franklin Montgomery and Peter G. Sulzer, Wide-range Resonators for VHF and UHF, *Electronics*, vol. 24, p. 200, May, 1951.

circuit of Fig. 12-22 is supplied by the inductance represented by the one-turn loop *aba* of Fig. 12-21; two such inductances are in parallel between points *aa*.

A variation in the position of the butterfly rotor changes both the

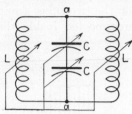

FIG. 12-22. Equivalent circuits of butterfly resonator.

inductance and capacitance of this equivalent resonant system. Thus, when the butterfly rotor is changed from the low-frequency position in Fig. 12-21*b* to the high-frequency position shown in Fig. 12-21*a*, the effect is to reduce both the capacitance *C* and the inductance *L*. The capacitance *C* between rotor and stator is less because the plates are now only slightly meshed; the inductance is less because in its new position, the open space available in the ring *aba* through which magnetic-flux lines may pass is now less than for case *b*.

The frequency range that can be covered by a butterfly is very great, since both the inductance and capacitance are varied simultaneously. Frequency ratios as great as 5:1 are obtainable by appropriate design. The circuit has reasonably high *Q*, good mechanical stability, and no sliding contacts. Because of these characteristics the butterfly is a uniquely desirable form of tunable circuit in the frequency range 100 to 1000 Mc. At higher frequencies the butterfly becomes too small to be practical; at lower frequencies it is unduly large and moreover, alternative arrangements are equally satisfactory at lower frequencies.

Butterfly oscillator circuits are usually based on Fig. 12-19*c*, with the butterfly supplying the tunable circuit *LC*. The plate and grid electrodes of the tube are connected to points *aa* on Fig. 12-21, and the plate choke is connected to a point on the stator such as *c*. Since the butterfly is not grounded, its stator is mounted on ceramic rods, and its rotor is provided with a ceramic shaft. Output may be obtained from a butterfly oscillator by a coupling loop placed near point *b* and oriented to link with the magnetic field produced by the current flowing in arm *b*.

12-9. Triode Oscillators Using Transmission Lines as Resonant Elements. At frequencies above about 100 Mc, resonant lines are frequently used in place of resonant circuits having lumped constants. Resonant lines have relatively high *Q* and also are capable of developing very large resonant impedances. Resonant lines of the parallel-line type are particularly easy to construct.

The disadvantage of resonant lines is that a sliding contact is usually required[1] to adjust the resonant frequency of the line. Lines are likewise

---

[1] It is of course possible to employ noncontact plungers, such as employed with reflex klystron oscillators and illustrated in Fig. 12-35; however, this adds complications and mechanical design problems.

physically awkward at the lower frequencies, as the length required is inversely proportional to frequency. Although it is possible to overcome this latter limitation to some extent by coiling the line, this introduces mechanical complications, particularly in the tuning arrangements.

Parallel-line Oscillators.[1] In the parallel-line oscillator, each resonant circuit required in the oscillator system is supplied by a two-wire line, the effective length of which is adjusted by means of a short-circuiting bar to give quarter-wave resonance when the lead inductance and interelectrode capacitance of the tube are considered as a part of the resonant line.

Examples of parallel-line oscillators are given in Fig. 12-23. The arrangement at *a* is similar to the circuit of Fig. 12-19c, except that the coil and condenser combination *LC* is replaced by a resonant line and the

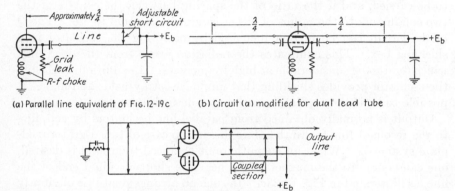

(a) Parallel line equivalent of Fig. 12-19c   (b) Circuit (a) modified for dual lead tube

(c) Parallel line equivalent of Fig. 12-20

Fig. 12-23. Oscillator circuits employing parallel lines as resonators.

radio-frequency choke coil in the plate circuit is omitted. It will be observed that the lead inductances and the interelectrode capacitances of the tube act as a terminal load, or extension, of the transmission line. To obtain oscillations at a particular frequency, the position of the short-circuiting bar is so adjusted that the line as loaded by these tube reactances exhibits quarter-wave resonance.

Some ultra-high-frequency triode tubes are provided with two leads to the grid and plate electrodes. With such tubes, it is possible to modify the circuit of Fig. 12-23a as shown in Fig. 12-23b. Here the tube is placed at the center of a half-wave line, and half the interelectrode capacitance of the tube can be considered as being associated with each quarter-wave section of this line. This halves the loading effect of the tube capacitance as compared with the circuit of Fig. 12-23a, and so permits higher resonant frequencies to be achieved. This arrangement has the disadvantage that now two tuning adjustments are called for instead of one. However,

[1] For more information, see "Very High Frequency Techniques," *op. cit.*, Chap. 14.

if the range over which the frequency is to be tuned is limited, one adjustment may be set at the optimum value for the middle of the frequency range, and then left unchanged as the position of the other short-circuiting bar is varied.

A typical push-pull circuit using parallel-line resonators is shown in Fig. 12-23c. This is analogous in every respect to the corresponding circuit of Fig. 12-20, the only difference being in the substitution of resonant lines for the lumped resonant circuits. Grounded-plate and dual-lead forms of push-pull parallel-line oscillators represent obvious variations that are possible.

Lines for use with oscillators will have the highest Q if the diameter of the conductors is made as large as is reasonable for the current and power to be carried, and if the ratio of the spacing between the centers of the two conductors to the radius of either conductor is equal to 3.6. The Q of the circuit can be further increased by enclosing the oscillator in a shielding box. This eliminates the radiation losses from the open line, which tend to be considerable at high frequencies. In addition, enclosing the oscillator provides shielding that minimizes stray fields and makes it possible to limit the oscillator output to a designated output terminal.

Output is normally obtained from parallel-line oscillators by coupling to the resonant line (or to the plate line in the case of tuned-grid–tuned-plate systems).[1] When an output circuit balanced to ground is desired, one can couple to the magnetic field near the short-circuited end of the line, as illustrated in Fig. 12-23c. In such an arrangement it is obviously necessary that the short circuit on the coupling line be varied as the position of the short circuit on the oscillator is varied to tune the oscillator. As an alternative to inductive coupling, one may connect the output symmetrically to the plate line, either conductively, or through coupling condensers.

When the output power is to be delivered to a load that is unbalanced with respect to ground, as for example, to a coaxial cable, one may employ a balanced-to-unbalanced transformer (sometimes called a balun) in combination with a balanced coupling system. Alternatively, conductive or capacitive couplings to one side of the parallel wire line may be employed.

Coaxial-line Triode Oscillators.[2,3] Coaxial lines provide higher Q resonant circuits than are obtainable with parallel lines. Also, if coaxial

---

[1] An excellent discussion of output coupling systems is to be found in "Very High Frequency Techniques," *op. cit.*, Chap. 16.

[2] For further information see "Very High Frequency Techniques," *op. cit.*, Chap. 15, also "Klystrons and Microwave Triodes" (Vol. 7, Radiation Laboratory Series), Chap. 7, McGraw-Hill Book Company, Inc., New York, 1948.

[3] The use of cavities in place of coaxial lines in connection with disk-seal triodes is

lines are used in conjunction with appropriately designed close-spaced parallel-plate triodes, oscillations can be generated at higher frequencies than with any other triode tube arrangement; powers of the order of a watt are obtainable at frequencies in excess of 4000 Mc.

The construction of a typical parallel-plane tube is illustrated in Fig. 12-24. The active part of the cathode, control grid, and plate lie in parallel planes as shown. The connections to these electrodes are provided by metal disks as shown, rather than by leads as is ordinarily the case. Because of this, parallel-plane tubes are also called disk-seal tubes.[1] This type of construction reduces the inductance of leads to a minimum,

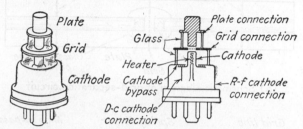

FIG. 12-24. Details of typical parallel-plane (lighthouse) tube.

and provides an arrangement that is particularly compatible with a coaxial transmission line.

The usual circuit arrangement of a coaxial-line oscillator using parallel-plane triodes is illustrated schematically in Fig. 12-25a. This is a tuned-grid–tuned-plate oscillator with a grounded grid; it is thus the same arrangement as shown in Fig. 12-18b, with the exception that resonant coaxial lines are used for tuned circuits. Since the control grid provides very effective electrostatic shielding between the grid and plate lines this arrangement is sometimes referred to as a grid-separation circuit.

In order to obtain oscillations, it is necessary to provide coupling between the grid and plate sides of the system; in practice this is done by means of a coupling loop or probe that extends from one resonant system to the other. Some parallel-plane tubes intended to be used only for

---

described in the paper by M. E. Hines, A Wide-range Microwave Sweeping Oscillator, *Bell System Tech J.*, vol. 29, p. 553, October, 1950. This particular oscillator is arranged so that the frequency can be mechanically swept over the frequency range 3600 to 4500 Mc.

[1] Tubes having the configuration of Fig. 12-24 are also sometimes called "lighthouse" tubes as a result of a fancied similarity of their silhouette to that of a lighthouse. A modification used in some power tubes consists in making the plate connection of large size in order to radiate a large amount of heat, and the cathode end small in diameter. This construction is called an "inverted lighthouse," and is illustrated by the 2C39 tube type.

oscillator service have built-in coupling between the cathode and plate sides of their control grids.

A practical form of a coaxial-line oscillator is shown in Fig. 12-25b. Here the grid-plate and grid-cathode lines are arranged concentrically, thus reducing over-all length and simplifying the problem of inserting and withdrawing the oscillator tube. Coupling between the grid and cathode lines is provided by means of coupling loops as illustrated. Typically, three such loops are employed, arranged symmetrically around

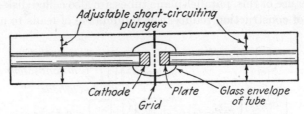

(a) Schematic diagram of grid-separation circuit

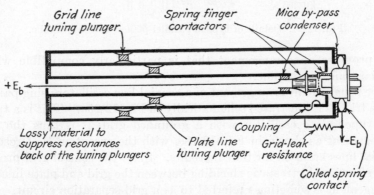

(b) Details of practical coaxial line oscillator

FIG. 12-25. Coaxial-line oscillator employing parallel-plane (lighthouse) tube.

the periphery of the cavity, and placed as close as practical to the tube end of the line. Alternatively, one may employ small probes which project through the wall separating the two resonant circuits, and provide electrostatic coupling. The sizes and locations of these coupling devices are usually determined empirically.

The coaxial lines are adjusted by means of short-circuiting plungers. The achievement of good high-frequency electrical contact between the surfaces of the coaxial lines and the tubes, and with the short-circuiting plunger, is one of the major problems in the construction of coaxial-line oscillators. Silver-plated and specially heat-treated beryllium copper flexible fingers are commonly used for the contacts. They must be precisely fabricated and assembled, as must most of the other components of the coaxial oscillator. For these reasons, it is not advisable to attempt the construction of such an oscillator unless adequate machine-shop facilities are available.

In order to introduce plate and bias voltages, it is necessary that the grid, plate, and cathode electrodes of the tube be electrically insulated from each other. This is commonly accomplished by building by-pass condensers into the coaxial-line system as illustrated in Fig. 12-25b. These by-pass condensers are normally formed by mica that separates silver-plated brass plates. A by-pass condenser separating the actual cathode from the grounded or cathode part of the tube envelope is built into some types of parallel-plane tubes.

Mode Separation in Resonant-line Oscillators.   A resonant transmission line of given physical length will be resonant at a series of frequencies, such that the effective electrical length of the line is $\lambda/4$, $3\lambda/4$, etc.   The existence of these different modes introduces the possibility that an oscillator can operate at two or more frequencies with a given tuning adjustment.   In such a case, the particular frequency at which the oscillator chooses to operate depends on the relative loaded Q of the resonant system for the different frequencies, the relative feedback coupling, whether or not transit-time effects differ significantly, etc.   In particular, if there is a significant difference in loaded Q, and other things are approximately equal, then the oscillator will pick the frequency for which the loaded Q is highest, *i.e.*, the frequency at which the oscillator delivers the least possible amount of output power. Thus, one way to avoid an undesired mode, is to couple the output load in a manner that provides loading for the undesired as well as the desired mode.

If a capacitance such as that represented by the interelectrode capacitance of a tube is connected across the open end of a resonant line, then the various resonant modes are no longer harmonically related. This fact can be taken advantage of to restrict operation to a desired mode. Thus in the tuned-grid–tuned-plate type of circuit illustrated in Fig. 12-23 and Fig. 12-25, conditions favorable for oscillator operation at more than one mode will occur only if the product of characteristic impedance and terminal loading capacitance is the same for both resonant lines.   Single-mode operation, *i.e.*, mode separation, can accordingly be achieved by making the product of terminal capacitance times characteristic impedance as greatly different as possible for the grid and the plate lines;[1] in this way adjustments that cause the two lines to have the same resonant

[1] See "Very High Frequency Techniques," *op. cit.*, p. 344; H. J. Reich, Mode Separation in Oscillators with Two Coaxial-line Resonators, *Proc. IRE*, vol. 36, p. 1252, October 1948; P. J. Sutro, Theory of Mode Separation in a Coaxial Oscillator, *Proc. IRE*, vol. 24, p. 960, December, 1946.

frequency for one mode, say $\lambda/4$, will result in the resonant frequencies for the other modes being different for the two lines. Mode separation can also be achieved by operating the grid and plate lines on different modes, as for example $3\lambda/4$ and $\lambda/4$, respectively.

12-10. Holes and Discontinuities in the Tuning Characteristic of Triode Oscillators Having Wide Tuning Range.[1] Ultra-high-frequency oscillators that are tunable over a wide frequency range often cease to oscillate, or oscillate only very weakly, at certain frequency settings. When this behavior occurs, the oscillator is said to possess a "hole." In other cases, even when no holes are present, the tuning curve of the oscillator may possess a discontinuity, with the actual frequency at certain settings of the tuning control being different when the setting is approached from the low-frequency side from what it is when the setting is approached from the high-frequency side.

These anomalies arise either from parasitic resonant circuits coupled with the oscillator-tuned circuit, or from undesired resonances in some portion of the oscillator itself. Holes may also be caused by inadequate feedback coupling at certain frequencies, either as a result of undesired resonances in the oscillator, or as a result of a change of voltage and current distribution with frequency altering the coupling.

Parasitic resonant circuits can stop the oscillations (or can at least make them weak) at the resonant frequency of the parasitic circuit, as a result of the resistance that the resonant parasitic circuit then couples into the oscillator system. If the parasitic system has high Q, and the coefficient of coupling is greater than the critical value, then the resulting coupled arrangement possesses double peaks with two possible resonant frequencies. Under these conditions a discontinuity in the tuning curve will occur.

Parasitic resonant circuits may arise in many ways. Thus by-pass condensers may resonate with associated leads. Another example is when the shielding box enclosing the oscillator has the proper dimensions to act as a cavity resonator at some frequency within the tuning range of the oscillator. The unused back sides of coaxial or parallel lines are also possible sources of hole trouble, since they are resonant systems that are coupled to the oscillator tank circuits by leakage or stray fields. In coaxial lines of very short length, it is possible for the resonant frequency of the first circumferential higher order mode to coincide with resonant frequency of the normal coaxial mode, thereby giving the equivalent of a coupled parasitic circuit.

Trouble from coupled parasitic resonant circuits can be avoided by such expedients as eliminating the parasitic resonant circuit or the coupling to it, or shifting the resonant frequency outside of the tuning range of the

---

[1] See "Very High Frequency Techniques," *op. cit.*, p. 371.

oscillator.   Alternatively, one may introduce so much loss in the parasitic resonant circuit as to make the coupled effects negligible.   Thus in Fig. 12-25b, lossy material arranged as shown will eliminate trouble from resonances in the space back of the plungers.

Radio-frequency chokes are an important source of holes in oscillators having a wide tuning range.   If at some frequency within the tuning range, the choke ceases to perform its normal function of supplying a high impedance, and instead acts as a series resonant circuit with resulting low series impedance, then a hole may occur.   In other cases the radio-frequency choke may resonate with a capacitance in the system, as, for example, a tube interelectrode capacitance, to produce a resonance that alters the normal voltage and current relations of the oscillator.   The leads in conjunction with electrode capacitances can also cause trouble. For example, when the oscillator circuit of Fig. 12-19a is used to generate extremely high frequencies, it is found that the inductance of the lead from cathode to ground will resonate with the cathode-to-ground capacitance.   This causes a change in the phase of the alternating voltage of the cathode with respect to the other electrodes that greatly reduces the normal feedback action occurring in this circuit.   Thus, with 955 or 9002 triodes in a butterfly oscillator, the result is a broad hole in the vicinity of 450 Mc, although oscillations are obtained at both higher and lower frequencies.   The remedy in such a case is to insert a radio-frequency choke in the cathode lead; the inductance of this choke should be such that the frequency of the resonance causing the hole is shifted to a low frequency that is outside the tuning range.[1]

12-11. The Reflex Klystron Oscillator.[2]   The reflex klystron finds wide use as a laboratory oscillator at frequencies above 1000 Mc.   It is essentially a low-power device, typically generating 10 to 500 mw.   At frequencies in the range 1000 to 3000 Mc the reflex klystron is competitive with the coaxial-line triode oscillator; at frequencies in the range 3000 to 25,000 Mc it has no satisfactory alternative for low-power laboratory applications.

[1] For further discussion of this particular situation see "Very High Frequency Techniques," op. cit., p. 835.

[2] The principles involved in reflex klystron oscillators are summarized in "Very High Frequency Techniques," op. cit., Chap. 31; J. R. Pierce, Reflex Oscillators, Proc. IRE, vol. 33, p. 112, February, 1945; F. E. Terman, "Radio Engineering," 3d ed., p. 442, McGraw-Hill Book Company, Inc., New York, 1947; "Technique of Microwave Measurements" (Vol. 11, Radiation Laboratory Series), pp. 21–58, McGraw-Hill Book Company, Inc., New York, 1947.   For more extensive treatments of the subject see J. R. Pierce and W. G. Shepherd, Reflex Oscillators, Bell System Tech. J., vol. 26, p. 460, July, 1947 (also appears in "Radar Systems and Components," pp. 488–761, D. Van Nostrand Company, Inc., New York, 1949); "Klystrons and Microwave Triodes," op. cit., pp. 311–566; A. E. Harrison, "Klystron Tubes," McGraw-Hill Book Company, Inc., New York, 1947.

The structure of a reflex klystron tube is illustrated in Fig. 12-26. The tube consists of a cathode, a focusing electrode at cathode potential, a coaxial line or re-entrant cavity resonator that also serves as an anode, and a repeller electrode that is at a moderate negative voltage with respect to the cathode. The cathode is so shaped in relation to the focusing electrode and anode that an electron beam is formed that passes through a gap in the resonator as shown, and travels toward the repeller.

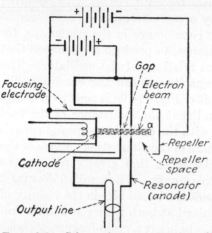

FIG. 12-26. Schematic representation of a reflex klystron oscillator.

Because the repeller has a negative potential with respect to the cathode, it turns these electrons back toward the anode when they have reached some point such as a in the repeller space; these returning electrons then pass through the gap a second time.

If one now assumes that oscillations are being generated, a radio-frequency voltage exists across the gap. This voltage acts on the electrons traveling toward the repeller, causing the velocity that these electrons have as they emerge from the gap into the repeller space to vary with time in accordance with the radio-frequency voltage, i.e., the electron stream entering the repeller space is velocity-modulated. Because of this velocity modulation, electrons emerging from the gap at different parts of the cycle take different lengths of time to return to the gap. As a result, the electrons returning through the gap tend to group together in bunches, whereas the original stream of electrons from the cathode toward the repeller passed through the gap at a uniform rate.

These returning bunches of electrons interact with the alternating voltage existing across the gap. If the bunches return at such a time during the radio-frequency cycle that the electrons are slowed down by the alternating gap voltage, then energy is delivered to the gap voltage and this tends to sustain the oscillations. Conversely, if the transit time in the repeller space is such that the returning electron bunches arrive at the gap at a time such that they are accelerated by the alternating gap voltage, then the electron beam absorbs energy from the oscillations in the resonator, and the oscillations tend to die out. In the event that the returning bunches pass through the gap when the alternating gap voltage is passing through zero, then the bunches give rise to an interaction that is of a purely reactive character.

The interaction that takes place between the returning electrons and the alternating voltage across the gap, is equivalent, as far as the resonant cavity is concerned, to shunting an admittance across the gap. This is illustrated schematically in Fig. 12-27, where this admittance Y_e, commonly called the electronic admittance, is represented as a conductance G_e shunted by a susceptance B_e. The magnitude of the electronic admittance is affected by the geometry and dimensions of the tube, the current in the electron beam, the electron transit time in the repeller space, and the amplitude of the alternating voltage across the gap. The phase angle of this admittance is determined solely by the electron transit time in the repeller space, and is proportional to transit time N measured in cycles. The conductive and susceptive components vary with N as shown in Fig. 12-28. It will be noted that the conductance is

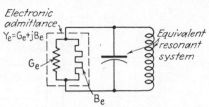

FIG. 12-27. Schematic representation of the resonant system of a reflex klystron oscillator, showing the relationship of the electronic admittance to the resonant system.

alternately negative and positive. Since oscillations occur most easily when the conductance is most negative, oscillations are strongest when

$$N = n + \tfrac{3}{4} \text{ cycles}$$

where n can be any integer, including zero.

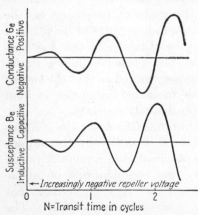

FIG. 12-28. Conductance and susceptance components of the electronic admittance of a reflex klystron.

To generate oscillations, the frequency of the resonant system is tuned to the desired value, and the transit time in the repeller space is adjusted to a suitable value by varying the negative bias voltage applied to the repeller. The more negative the repeller, the more quickly will the electrons passing into the repeller space be returned to the gap, and hence the less the transit time.

Reflex klystrons in which the resonant system is included in the evacuated portion of the tube, can be tuned by mechanically flexing the walls of the resonator and/or simultaneously varying the gap spacing. This method of tuning is based upon the fact that the resonant frequency is affected by the dimensions of the cavity, and by the loading effect introduced by the capacitance between the two sides of the gap. It is possible in this way to tune over a frequency range of the order of 1.3 to 1.

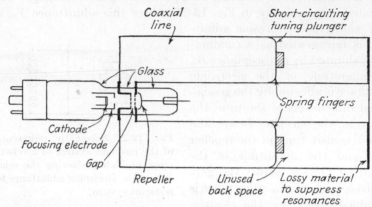

Fig. 12-29. Schematic representation of a reflex klystron oscillator with external resonant system supplied by a coaxial line.

In reflex klystrons that employ a resonant system that is external to the tube, as illustrated in Fig. 12-29, the resonant frequency can be adjusted by means of a tuning plunger. A tuning range of over 2 to 1 may be obtained in this way provided the repeller voltage is simultaneously varied so that the transit time measured in cycles is kept approximately constant.

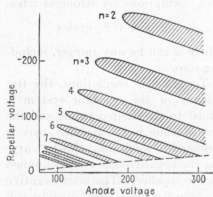

Fig. 12-30. Repeller-mode pattern of a reflex klystron oscillator. The shaded areas correspond to those combinations of voltages at which oscillations occur.

Operating Characteristics of Reflex Klystron Oscillators. Oscillations are obtained from a reflex klystron only for combinations of anode voltage and repeller voltage that give a favorable transit time. The situation existing in a typical klystron at a given frequency is illustrated in Fig. 12-30. Each shaded area corresponds to oscillations at a particular transit time mode n.

If the frequency of the oscillations is changed appreciably, the pattern still has the same general character shown in Fig. 12-30, but the locations of the regions of oscillation are shifted. This is because with a new frequency, a different transit time in seconds is required to give the same transit time in cycles.

When the frequency of oscillation and the anode voltage at which the tube is operated, are both kept constant, then the amplitude of the oscilla-

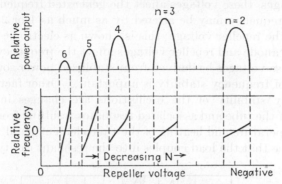

Fig. 12-31. Variation of output power and frequency of reflex oscillator as a function of repeller voltage for the tube of Fig. 12-30.

tions obtained from a reflex klystron varies with the repeller voltage as shown in Fig. 12-31. The different oscillating regions correspond to different values of n in Fig. 12-30, *i.e.*, to different transit-time modes. Oscillations have the maximum amplitude when the transit time is exactly $n + \frac{3}{4}$ cycles, corresponding to maximum possible negative conductance. As the transit time departs from this optimum condition, the negative conductance is less and the oscillations have progressively smaller amplitude.

The effect of a load coupled into the resonant system is illustrated in Fig. 12-32 for a particular transit-time mode. As the coupling of the load to the resonator is increased, the frequency range over which oscillations are produced is less. At the same time, the power output is maximum for a particular coupling, and is less for greater or smaller coupling.

Frequency. The frequency of the oscillations obtained from a reflex klystron is determined primarily by the resonant system. However, the electronic susceptance B_e also has a small effect as a result of the fact that it is a part of the equivalent resonant circuit (see Fig. 12-27). This elec-

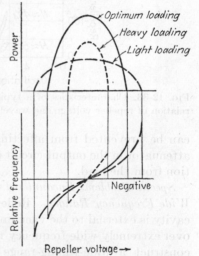

Fig. 12-32. Effect on output power and frequency of coupling different values of load impedance into the resonant system; these results are for a particular mode.

tronic susceptance depends upon the repeller-space transit time as shown in Fig. 12-28. Since the transit time depends on both the anode and repeller voltages, these voltages affect the generated frequency. In particular, the frequency may be altered by as much as 1 or 2 per cent by variation of the repeller voltage; this is known as electronic tuning.

Since both anode and repeller voltages affect the frequency, it is necessary that these voltages be derived from stabilized power sources when a high degree of frequency stability is important. Other factors affecting the frequency stability of the oscillations are changes in mechanical dimensions of the tube and associated resonator resulting from changes in ambient temperature and heating of the tube elements, and variations in the impedance that the load couples into the resonant cavity. The load

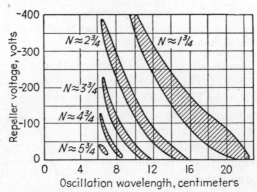

Fig. 12-33. Characteristics of a typical reflex klystron; the shaded areas show the relation of repeller voltage and wavelength for conditions which give oscillations.

can be prevented from affecting the frequency by inserting a resistive attenuator in the output circuit of the klystron resonator to provide isolation from the load.

Special Problems Encountered in Reflex Klystron Oscillators Tunable over Wide Frequency Ranges. Reflex klystron tubes in which the resonant cavity is external to the vacuum system, are inherently capable of tuning over extremely wide frequency ranges. However, when one attempts to construct a wide-tuning-range oscillator, a number of problems are encountered which must be understood and taken into account if satisfactory results are to be obtained.

Thus the required repeller voltage depends upon the frequency being generated, as shown in Fig. 12-33 for a typical case, and so must be varied simultaneously with the tuning control. One obvious means of doing this is to derive the repeller voltage from a potentiometer that is appropriately tapered, and which operates from the same shaft as does the tuning control. It is not necessary to maintain precise tracking, but for satisfactory results the repeller potential must ordinarily lie within ± 5 volts of a predetermined curve.[1]

It is apparent from Fig. 12-33 that it is possible to cover a frequency range greater than 2 to 1 using a single repeller-space transit-time mode provided the repeller voltage is properly tracked.   By changing from one mode to another a still greater frequency range can be covered by a single tube; thus the tube of Fig. 12-33 could readily cover the wavelength range 7 to 22 cm using two modes.

When a reflex klystron oscillator is tuned over a very wide frequency band, it is commonly found that holes, or discontinuities, occur at certain points in the tuning curve.   These are caused by parasitic resonances in exactly the same way that parasitic resonances introduce holes, or discontinuities, in wide-band tunable triode oscillators, as discussed in Sec. 12-10.   The commonest sources of parasitic resonances in reflex klystron oscillators are resonance in the space behind the short-circuiting plunger, resonance due to higher order modes in the active part of the cavity, particularly the first circumferential coaxial mode, and resonance in the plunger.[2,3]

Under certain conditions, a reflex klystron tube with a given tuning adjustment and repeller voltage, can operate at either of two frequencies which differ considerably in value.   This effect is called *mode interference*, and is illustrated in Fig. 12-34.   It arises as a result of the fact that ordinary resonators such as transmission lines or cavities are simultaneously resonant at a number of frequencies, while at the same time a given repeller voltage will correspond to different values of transit time N measured in cycles as the frequency is changed.   Mode interference, as illustrated in Fig. 12-34, can then arise whenever a coincidence exists in the frequency of such a higher order resonant mode, and the frequency for which the transit time N approximates a whole number of cycles plus three-fourths of a cycle.   The details involved are complicated by the fact that the loading of the resonator by the lumped capacitance of the tube prevents the resonator modes from being in harmonic relationship to each other, while at the same time several factors enter into the ease with which oscillations are generated on any particular mode.   Whenever a reflex klystron oscillator is tuned over a very wide frequency range, mode interference will nearly always occur at one or more places in the tuning

[1] For further information see "Very High Frequency Techniques," *op. cit.*, p. 872.

[2] A full discussion of these effects and their control is given in "Very High Frequency Techniques," *op. cit.*, Chap. 32.

[3] Discontinuities and irregularities in the tuning characteristic can also be introduced by electrons which make more than one round-trip passage through the gap of the reflex klystron tube.   This phenomenon is called electronic hysteresis, and is a characteristic of the tube.   In the more recently designed reflex klystron tubes, the electron optics have been so arranged that electronic hysteresis is largely absent.

range unless very great care has been exercised in coordinating tube and circuit design.[1,2]

Noncontacting Plungers.[3]   In reflex klystrons employing external resonators, a tuning plunger with flexible spring fingers can be used, as in Fig. 12-29.   However, with laboratory oscillators which are frequently being tuned, there are advantages in using a plunger of the noncontacting type, since in this way wear, contact noise, contact resistance, etc., are

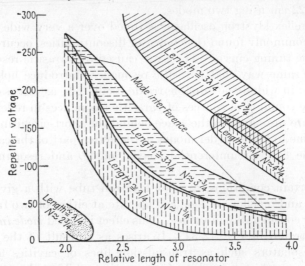

Fig. 12-34. Mode interference in a reflex klystron.

avoided.   Various forms of noncontacting plungers are illustrated schematically in Fig. 12-35.   In all of these there is a low-reactance gap between the plunger and the sides of coaxial cavity that serves as a low-impedance short circuit.

If a noncontacting type of plunger is to be effective over a wide frequency range, it must be very carefully designed.   The power dissipated in the plunger itself, together with the power that is permitted to leak past the plunger, must be small.   Likewise, resonances in the plunger system must either be suppressed, or shifted to frequencies outside of the

[1] See "Very High Frequency Techniques," *op. cit.*, Chap. 32.

[2] These problems of design and coordination are simplified if the coaxial tuning system of Fig. 12-29 is replaced by a system in which the outer conductor of the coaxial line is replaced by a rectangular waveguide to form a resonant slab line (see Fig. 4-8) that is completely enclosed.   Details are given by W. D. Myers, A 3800–7600 Mc Signal Generator Using a Parallel-plane Type of Resonator, *Hewlett-Packard J.*, vol. 2, September, 1950.

[3] A thorough discussion of this problem is given by William H. Huggins, Broadband Non-contacting Short Circuits for Coaxial Lines, *Proc. IRE*, vol. 35, pp. 906, 1085, 1324, September, October, November, 1947.

desired tuning range.   Finally, the plunger must act as a low-impedance termination throughout the desired frequency range.   By careful attention to details it is possible to design a noncontacting plunger that will perform satisfactorily over a frequency range in excess of 2 to 1.

Modulation of Reflex Klystron Oscillators.   Frequency modulation of a reflex klystron oscillator is readily carried out by superimposing the modulating voltage upon the repeller potential.   This varies the transit time in the repeller space and hence modulates the electronic susceptance shunted across the resonant circuit, as discussed in connection with Figs. 12-27 and 12-28.   The result is a variation in frequency of the character shown in Fig. 12-31.   It is seen that there is a region about the

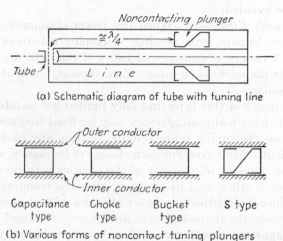

(a) Schematic diagram of tube with tuning line

(b) Various forms of noncontact tuning plungers

Fig. 12-35. Schematic representation of noncontact tuning plungers for a coaxial line.

center of each mode where substantially linear frequency modulation can be obtained by variation of the repeller voltage.   Accompanying this frequency modulation there is amplitude modulation of the generated oscillations which is less the smaller the frequency swing.   The useful frequency deviation that it is practical to obtain in this way depends on the load coupled to the resonator, the repeller-space transit-time mode n that is being used, the beam current, etc.; peak-to-peak deviations such as 1 per cent of the center frequency are easily obtainable in a typical case.   It will be noted that since the repeller electrode need not draw any current, the modulating power required is very low.

When an amplitude-modulated wave is required for test purposes from a reflex klystron oscillator, it is customary to employ square-wave modulation.   The modulating voltage is applied either to the repeller or to the anode, and is arranged with an amplitude such that the oscillations are alternately turned on and off in accordance with the modulation frequency. In this way, frequency modulation is avoided, since when the oscillations are being generated the electrode voltages are constant. In contrast, if a sinusoidal modulating wave were employed, the resulting variation of electrode voltage, during the period when oscillations were being generated, would introduce excessive frequency modulation along with the amplitude modulation.

Pulse modulation of a reflex klystron oscillator can be carried out by pulsing either the anode or the repeller voltage, whichever is most convenient.[1] The amplitudes are so arranged that conditions favorable for oscillation exist only during the period of the pulse; in addition, the pulse must have a flat top if excessive frequency modulation of the generated wave is to be avoided.

Multiple-cavity Klystrons. When the power obtainable from a reflex klystron is inadequate, it is possible to employ a two- or three-cavity klystron.[2] A variety of commercial tubes of this type are available for frequencies in the microwave range; these typically generate powers of a few tens of watts.

Power klystrons of this type find only limited use as laboratory oscillators, and then are really satisfactory only for fixed-frequency operation. This is because the tuning range obtainable from any particular tube is relatively small. Moreover, for each change of frequency, it is necessary to retune the resonant frequencies of the cavities very precisely in relationship to each other, and in addition, alter the coupling between the cavities. Since these adjustments are all quite critical, it is not a simple matter to change the frequency over an appreciable range.

12-12. Magnetron Oscillators. Magnetron oscillators of the cavity type are sometimes used as sources of microwave power in measurement work. Such oscillators are relatively high-power devices, and thus find use when reflex klystrons cannot develop sufficient output. Magnetron oscillators have the disadvantage for measurement work that they are of either fixed frequency, or limited tuning range, and that they cannot be modulated satisfactorily except by pulses or square waves.

Numerous magnetron tubes are commercially available as a result of radar and other developments that employ magnetrons. Most of these tubes have been designed for use with short pulses, although several types have been developed for continuous-wave operation at powers of the order of 50 watts or even higher.

The frequencies available in magnetron oscillators center about those used in radar work, such as 3000 and 10,000 Mc. The tubes available

---

[1] See "Very High Frequency Techniques," *op. cit.*, vol. 2, p. 1014.

[2] See Russell H. Varian and Sigurd F. Varian, A High-frequency Oscillator and Amplifier, *J. Applied Phys.*, vol. 10, p. 321, May, 1939; Harrison, *op. cit.;* "Klystrons and Microwave Triodes," *op. cit.*, pp. 201–310.

commonly have no tuning adjustment, or alternatively are tunable only over very limited frequency ranges, such as ±10 per cent or less. Tubes without tuning adjustment can have their frequency controlled to some extent by reactance coupled into the tube resonators through the use of a high-Q resonator external to the tube; however, the frequency range thereby obtainable is at best quite small.

The principles of operation of the magnetron are well discussed in the literature,[1] and attention will be confined here to the operating characteristics which determine output power, frequency, etc. In general it can be said that two conditions must be met to provide power at a given frequency. The first of these is the proper combination of magnetic field strength and anode voltage to provide suitable electron trajectories, while the second condition is that a resonant cavity or circuit must be provided for storing the radio-frequency energy.

The frequency, power, and efficiency, of a magnetron oscillator, are a function of the anode voltage and magnetic field strength, as illustrated by the typical performance chart shown in Fig. 12-36. Because of the frequency variations produced by variations in the anode voltage, it is difficult to obtain amplitude modulation without excessive frequency modulation. Hence if pulses free of frequency modulation are desired, the tops of the modulating pulses must be flat, so that a constant voltage will be applied to the tube while oscillations are being generated.

The frequency, power, and efficiency of a magnetron oscillator, are also affected by the load impedance connected to the output terminals of the tube. In oscillators for laboratory purposes the effect of the load impedance on the frequency is particularly important. This effect is commonly termed "pulling," and can be eliminated by placing an attenuator between the magnetron and its load.

A related phenomenon peculiar to magnetrons is termed the "long-line effect," and influences the action of the magnetron oscillator in the following way: Assume that the load is connected to the receiving end of a *long* transmission line, and that this load represents a considerable mismatch to the line. Then as the frequency of a tunable oscillator is varied, the impedance seen by the oscillator at the transmitting end of the line goes through extreme variations of impedance for relatively small frequency changes. Not only does this seriously influence the frequency

[1] J. B. Fisk, H. D. Hagstrum, and P. L. Hartman, The Magnetron as a Generator of Centimeter Waves, *Bell System Tech. J.*, vol. 25, pp. 1–188, April, 1946 (also reprinted in "Radar Systems and Components," D. Van Nostrand Company, Inc., New York, 1949); "Very High Frequency Techniques," *op. cit.*, Vol. 1, pp. 473–554; "Microwave Magnetrons" (Vol. 6, Radiation Laboratory Series), McGraw-Hill Book Company, Inc., New York, 1948. An excellent summary of the subject is given by H. D. Hagstrum, The Generation of Centimeter Waves, *Proc. IRE*, vol. 35, p. 548, June, 1947.

of oscillation, it generally also causes frequency "jumps," or discontinuities in the tuning; in extreme cases, the oscillator may cease to oscillate at certain points in the tuning range. Alternatively, when the line length is varied, the curve of frequency as a function of length will have

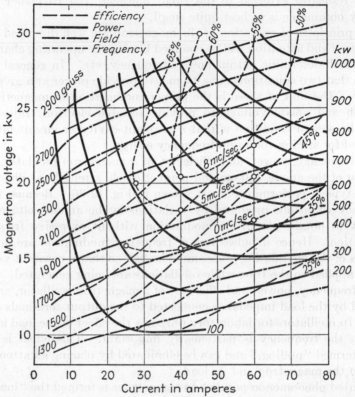

FIG. 12-36. Typical performance chart of a 10-cm pulsed magnetron for an arbitrarily chosen load impedance (*from* "Microwave Magnetrons"). The values of frequency marked on the curves represent deviations from an arbitrarily chosen reference frequency.

discontinuities in it. Long-line effect can be eliminated by placing the load as close to the oscillator as possible, or by carefully matching the load impedance to the transmission line, or finally, by placing an attenuator pad between the oscillator and the line.

CHAPTER 13

GENERATORS OF SPECIAL WAVEFORMS

13-1. Introduction. Extensive use is made in the field of measurements, as well as in other electronic work, of nonsinusoidal waves of special shapes. Common examples are square and saw-toothed waves and pulses.

Special waveforms can be obtained by using vacuum-tube circuit arrangements that directly generate the desired waveform. Alternatively, one may start with some other type of wave, as for example, a sine wave, and shape it by the use of vacuum tubes and circuits to give the desired waveform. The various techniques involved are described in some detail in this chapter, since they are not as familiar to most radio engineers as are those involved in conventional sine-wave oscillators.

Also included in this chapter is a section on the generation of a time interval. Such a time interval is ordinarily defined by two short pulses, one of which marks the beginning of the time interval, and a second that is delayed in time by the desired number of microseconds, and so marks the end of the interval. Such a time interval is readily produced with the aid of circuits that generate pulses and triangular voltage waveforms; hence the discussion of time-interval generation proceeds naturally from the material in the other sections of this chapter.

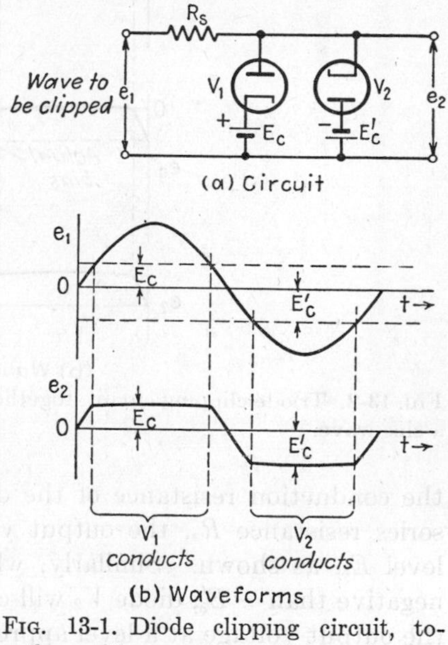

13-2. Wave-shaping Circuits. The principal methods used to convert an available waveform into a different desired wave shape are clipping, differentiation, and integration.

(a) Circuit

(b) Waveforms

Fig. 13-1. Diode clipping circuit, together with waveforms involved when clipping a sine wave.

Clipping. In clipping, a portion of a wave is flattened off or *limited* to some arbitrary level, irrespective of the amplitude of the original wave.

A simple, commonly used clipper circuit employing diode tubes is illustrated in Fig. 13-1. Here, when the instantaneous value of the input voltage wave lies between E_c and $-E_c'$, neither of the two diodes conducts, and the input wave is transmitted directly to the output terminals without change. On the other hand, when the input voltage is more positive than E_c, diode V_1 will conduct, and will tend to prevent the output voltage from rising appreciably above E_c. In fact, to the extent that

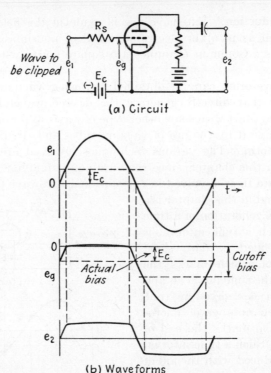

(a) Circuit

(b) Waveforms

FIG. 13-2. Triode clipping circuit, together with waveforms illustrating the clipping of a sine wave.

the conduction resistance of the diode is negligible compared with the series resistance R_s, the output voltage will be clipped exactly at the level E_c, as shown. Similarly, when the input voltage becomes more negative than $-E_c'$, diode V_2 will conduct and clip the negative peaks of the output voltage at a level approximating $-E_c'$.

A clipping circuit employing a triode tube is shown in Fig. 13-2.[1] Here the control grid and cathode function similarly to diode V_1 in Fig. 13-1, and in conjunction with bias E_c and series resistance R_s clip the positive

---

[1] A pentode tube could be employed instead of the triode, if desired.

peaks of the applied voltage at a level E_c, as shown.   In addition, if the instantaneous grid potential is driven more negative than the value corresponding to plate current cutoff, then the output waveform will be clipped at an amplitude corresponding to cutoff.   Thus both positive and negative peaks are clipped by the arrangement illustrated in Fig. 13-2, with the actual clipping levels for the positive and negative peaks being determined by the amplification factor of the tube and by the bias and plate voltages used.   The triode clipper of Fig. 13-2 can be regarded as being roughly the equivalent of the diode clipping system of Fig. 13-1, plus one stage of amplification.

A cathode-follower form of triode clipper is shown in Fig. 13-3.   Here the negative peaks of the input wave are clipped at a level corresponding to plate-current cutoff, exactly as in Fig. 13-2.   It is possible for the positive-going peaks of the input wave to be clipped as a result of grid current, as in the case of the triode clipper of Fig. 13-2; however, the clipping of the positive peaks is not very pronounced, and in fact, unless the amplitude is very large there is no clipping of the positive peaks.[1]   This is because when e_1 in Fig. 13-3 is positive, e_2 is likewise positive, and this fact increases the value that e_1 must have to cause the grid to draw current.   The usefulness of the cathode-follower arrangement is therefore as a negative-peak clipper, and in this connection it has a number of valuable properties. In the first place, the cathode-follower clipper develops an output wave having the same polarity as the input wave, whereas the triode clipper of Fig. 13-2 reverses the polarity; for some applications this is of considerable convenience.   In the second place, for input amplitudes less than the clipping levels, the output will

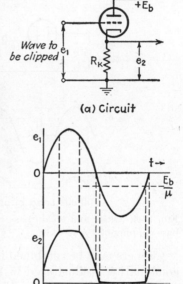

(a) Circuit

(b) Waveforms

FIG. 13-3. Cathode-follower clipper, together with waveforms illustrating the clipping of a sine wave.

more closely follow the variations of the input voltage than in the case of the triode clipper in Fig. 13-2; this results from the negative-feedback action inherent in the cathode-follower connection.   Finally, to its output circuit, the cathode-follower system acts as a source of very low

[1] A two-tube cathode-coupled arrangement that clips both positive and negative peaks is described by L. A. Goldmutz and H. L. Krauss, The Cathode-coupled Clipper Circuit, *Proc. IRE*, vol. 38, p. 1172, September, 1948.

impedance for amplitudes less than the clipping level; this is likewise important in many circumstances.

The arrangements described above are all *peak* clippers, in that they flatten off the positive or negative peaks of waves. Circumstances sometimes arise, however, when it is desired to reduce to zero all amplitudes below some minimum value. *Base clipping* of this type can be obtained with circuit arrangements such as illustrated in Fig. 13-4. In Fig. 13-4a the diode tube is biased to a voltage E_c corresponding to the level of base clipping desired, so that no output current flows until the applied voltage exceeds this value. In Fig. 13-4b, base clipping is accomplished by biasing the control grid of the amplifier tube to a value that is more negative than cutoff by an amount equal to the desired level of base clipping.

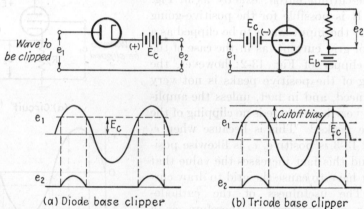

(a) Diode base clipper   (b) Triode base clipper

Fig. 13-4. Diode and triode base clippers, together with waveforms illustrating the base clipping of a sine wave.

Clippers may be combined in various ways. A particularly important combination is illustrated in Fig. 13-5. Here the combination of diode V_1, resistance R_s, and bias E_c serves as a peak clipper, while diode V_2 in association with bias E'_c simultaneously functions as a base clipper. The result is that all input voltages in excess of E_c are clipped in such a manner as to produce an output voltage having a value $E_c - E'_c$, while all values of input voltage that are less than E'_c are reduced to zero amplitude in the output. An arrangement of this type is termed a *slicer*, since the output wave can be regarded as consisting of a slice of the input waveform.

The above discussion of clippers has been idealized by neglecting certain second-order effects. Thus in actual practice, the level at which clipping occurs will ordinarily increase slightly with the amplitude of the wave being clipped. In diode clippers this is a result of increased voltage drop in the tube as the diode current becomes greater, while in the case of clippers using plate-current cutoff the failure of the tube to have a perfectly distinct and sharp cutoff leads to a similar end result.   The above discussion also does not consider the effects produced by tube capacitances or stray circuit capacitances, and so applies strictly only at the lower frequencies.   When a voltage of very high frequency is applied to the clipping system, these capacitances round off the sharp edges that the clipped wave would otherwise possess.   These distortions in the form of the clipped wave at high frequencies can be minimized by the same techniques used to give wide-band behavior in amplifiers, *i.e.*, low tube and circuit capacitances, high tube conductance, and the use of low values of resistance in the circuits.

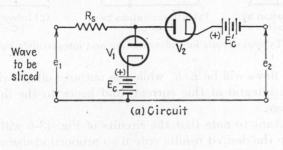

(a) Circuit

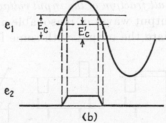

(b)

Fig. 13-5. A slicer circuit, together with waveforms showing the behavior in the case of a sine-wave input.

Differentiating and Integrating Circuits.   A differentiating circuit develops an output voltage that is proportional to the rate of change dE/dt of applied voltage.   A typical differentiating circuit consists of a small capacitance in series with a small resistance, as in Fig. 13-6a.   If the time constant RC is small enough so that the output voltage is very small compared with the applied voltage E, the current that flows in such a circuit is $C\,dE/dt$.   The voltage developed across the resistance R is then equal to $RC\,dE/dt$.   An alternative differentiating arrangement consists of a large resistance in series with a small inductance, as shown in Fig. 13-6b.   Here the circuit current is E/R, and the voltage across the inductance will be $L\,di/dt = (L/R)\,dE/dt$; this assumes that the time constant L/R is small enough so that the voltage developed across the inductance is very small compared with the applied voltage.

In an integrating circuit the output voltage is made proportional to the integral $\int E\,dt$ of the applied voltage.   A typical integrating circuit consists of a large capacitance in series with a high resistance, as shown in Fig. 13-6c.   In such an arrangement, if the time constant RC is so large that the output voltage is a negligible fraction of the applied voltage, the

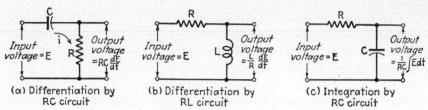

(a) Differentiation by   (b) Differentiation by   (c) Integration by
        RC circuit   RL circuit   RC circuit

FIG. 13-6. Typical circuits for differentiating and integrating a voltage wave.

current that flows will be E/R, while the output voltage will be proportional to the integral of this current, and hence to the integral of the applied voltage.

It is important to note that the circuits of Fig. 13-6 will operate correctly to give the desired results only if so proportioned that the output voltage is *a negligibly small fraction of the input voltage*.   To obtain differentiated or integrated output waves of reasonable amplitude, it is therefore customary to associate the output with some form of vacuum-tube

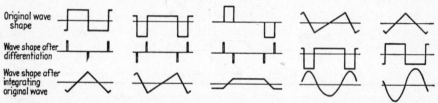

FIG. 13-7. Effects produced by differentiating and integrating typical idealized wave shapes.

amplifier.   A particularly desirable method of obtaining the amplification in integrator circuits is provided by the Miller integrator circuit discussed in connection with Fig. 13-37.

Differentiation and integration provides a straightforward means of converting from one type of wave shape to another type.   This is illustrated in Fig. 13-7, which shows the effect produced by differentiation and integration of some typical standard types of waves.   Thus differentiation of a square wave produces a succession of alternately positive and negative pulses of relatively short duration; in contrast, integration of a square wave results in a triangular wave.   Conversely, a square wave can be produced by integration of a succession of alternately positive and negative pulses that are of very brief duration, or by differentiation of a triangular wave.

13-3. The Multivibrator.[1] An important circuit in many areas of electronics, the multivibrator possesses a versatility that makes it an especially useful circuit in the field of measurements. In particular, it is applicable to the generation of square waves, pulses, and time intervals, as well as finding extensive use for frequency division and as a harmonic generator. Accordingly, a review of the principles of operation of the several forms of the multivibrator circuit is in order.

The multivibrator can be thought of as a two-stage resistance-coupled amplifier in which the voltage developed by the output of the second tube is applied to the input of the first tube, as shown in Fig. 13-8a, where the schematic of the plate-coupled form of multivibrator has been arranged to bring out this interpretation.[2] Such an arrangement will oscillate because each tube produces a phase shift of 180°, thereby causing the output of the second tube to supply to the first tube an input voltage that has exactly the right phase to sustain oscillations. The usefulness of the multivibrator arises from the facts that the wave that is generated is very rich in harmonics, that the frequency of oscillation is readily controlled by an injected voltage, and that it can be used as a generator of square waves, pulses, or time intervals.

The operation of the multivibrator can be understood by reference to the oscillograms shown in Fig. 13-9.[3] Oscillations are started (prior to

[1] Among the many possible references on the multivibrator, the following recent books and articles may be given: A rather complete coverage of the numerous multivibrator forms and applications will be found in "Waveforms" (Vol. 19, Radiation Laboratory Series), pp. 163–195, McGraw-Hill Book Company, Inc., New York, 1949. Techniques of analysis are given by E. H. Bartelink, A Wide-band Square-wave Generator, *Trans. AIEE*, vol. 60, p. 371, 1941; M. V. Kiebert and A. F. Inglis, Multivibrator Circuits, *Proc. IRE*, vol. 33, p. 534, August, 1945, and also in MIT Radar School Staff, "Principles of Radar," pp. 2-44–2-58, McGraw-Hill Book Company, Inc., New York, 1946. Papers on the design of actual circuits include A. E. Abbot, Multivibrator Design by Graphic Methods, *Electronics*, vol. 21, p. 118, June, 1948; E. R. Shenk, The Multivibrator—Applied Theory and Design, *Electronics*, vol. 17, pt. I, p. 136, January, pt. II, p. 140, February, pt. III, p. 238, March, 1944.

[2] Persons experienced in circuits such as the multivibrator have found it more effective to draw the circuit as shown in Fig. 13-8b. The point of view involved here is well advanced by F. C. Williams, Introduction to Circuit Techniques for Radiolocation, *J. IEE (Radiolocation Conv.)*, vol. 93, pt. IIIA, p. 289, March–May, 1946; especially the footnote on p. 302. Batteries are not shown in Fig. 13-8b, but points of fixed potential are designated, such as E_b, with more positive points toward the top of the schematic. Electrode voltages rise or fall in accordance with current flow through load resistors, and voltage waveforms can readily be visualized.

[3] The small exponential transients designated as A in Fig. 13-9 are not of consequence in a discussion of the main principles of operation of the circuit, and so for the moment will be ignored. However, they do affect the limiting frequency of oscillation, and will be mentioned later in this regard.

$t = 0$) by a minute voltage at the grid of one of the tubes, say a positive potential on the grid of tube V_1. This voltage is amplified by the two tubes, and reappears at the grid of the first tube to be reamplified. This action takes place almost instantly and is repeated over and over, so that the grid potential of tube V_1 rises suddenly to a positive value, while the grid potential e_{c_2} of tube V_2 just as suddenly becomes more negative than cutoff. The immediate result is that amplification ceases, and for the time being tube V_1 draws a heavy plate current while the tube V_2 takes

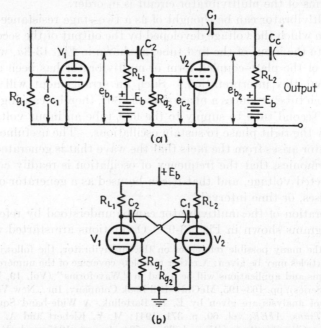

(a)

(b)

FIG. 13-8. Typical multivibrator circuit. The schematic diagram at (a) is drawn in such a way as to emphasize the similarity of a multivibrator to a two-stage amplifier. In (b) the same circuit is presented in a form that is particularly convenient for tracing instantaneous voltage changes.

no plate current. This situation, depicted in Fig. 13-9 for $0 < t < t_1$, is not permanent, however, because the current through the grid-leak resistance R_{g_2} of tube V_2 gradually brings the grid potential e_{c_2} back toward zero. At the time t_1 the grid potential e_{c_2} has reached the cutoff level, and the tube V_2 can now amplify once more. The rising voltage e_{c_2} will be amplified to produce a sudden fall in voltage e_{c_1}, with an end result that tube V_2 now becomes conducting and tube V_1 is cut off. This action, which is clearly evident in the oscillograms, takes place almost instantly and is exactly the same as the initial action except that the relative functions of the two tubes have been interchanged. Next the potential e_{c_1} on the grid of tube V_1 gradually dies away as the result of leakage through resistance R_{g_1} just as before, and finally the cycle repeats.

The output voltage is usually taken from the plate of one of the tubes through a coupling capacitor (C_c in Fig. 13-8). The output waveform is therefore that of e_{b_1} or e_{b_2} in Fig. 13-9. The amplitude is readily determined by a graphical "load-line" construction as depicted in Fig. 13-10, where a straight line of slope $-1/R_L$ is superimposed upon the static plate-voltage–plate-current characteristic curve for the tube. The intersection with the tube curve for zero grid voltage is the operating point for whichever tube is conducting. The voltage E_0 that represents the difference between the plate voltage when the tube is conducting and when it is cut off, is the amplitude of the output voltage wave.

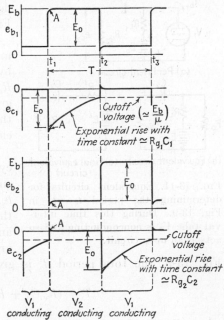

Fig. 13-9. Waveforms in the multivibrator of Fig. 13-8 for the symmetrical case where $R_{L_1} = R_{L_2}$, $R_{G_1} = R_{G_2}$, and $C_1 = C_2$.

The oscillograms of Fig. 13-9 are for the case where the circuits associated with the two tubes have the same constants. Except for the minor imperfections indicated by A, the waveforms at e_{b_1} and e_{b_2} are square waves. When the circuits are not symmetrical, and in particular when the time constants $R_{g_2}C_{g_2}$ and $R_{g_1}C_{g_1}$ of the two grid leak–condenser combinations differ greatly, the length of successive half cycles will differ correspondingly. By making one set of time constants very small, it is therefore possible to generate very short pulses by such an unbalanced or unsymmetrical multivibrator.

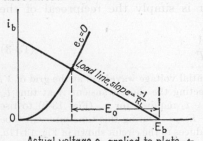

Fig. 13-10. Graphical load-line construction for determination of E_0, the amplitude of the square-wave component of e_{b_1} and e_{b_2} in Fig. 13-9.

Frequency of Multivibrator Oscillation. A multivibrator oscillating as above at a frequency determined solely by the characteristics of the multivibrator system, is commonly termed a *free-running* multivibrator.

This is in contrast to the situation that exists when the frequency is controlled by an injected voltage as described below in connection with Fig. 13-13.

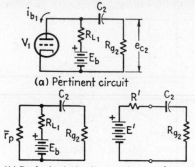

(a) Pertinent circuit

(b) Equivalent circuit   (c) Final equivalent circuit

FIG. 13-11. Equivalent circuits for determining the period $t_3 - t_2$ in Fig. 13-9. During this time interval tube V_2 is nonconducting and so acts as an open circuit.

The frequency of a free-running multivibrator is determined primarily by the time constants $R_{g_1}C_1$ and $R_{g_2}C_2$, and the potentials to which the grid return leads are brought, although the remaining circuit constants and electrode voltages have a slight effect.

The total period T (Fig. 13-9) of a cycle of multivibrator operation is the sum of the two intervals $t_2 - t_1$ and $t_3 - t_2$. In the symmetrical case these two intervals are equal, but in any case if the grid leak resistances are returned to the cathode as in Fig. 13-9, the total period T is given by[1]

$$ T = (R_{g_1}C_1 + R_{g_2}C_2) \log_\epsilon \frac{\mu E_0}{E_b} \tag{13-1} $$

where R_{g_1}, C_1, R_{g_2}, C_2 are as designated in Fig. 13-8 and

  μ = amplification factor of V_1 and V_2 (assumed the same for both tubes)

  E_0 = plate-voltage drop as illustrated in Figs. 13-9 and 13-10

  E_b = plate-supply voltage

The frequency f of the multivibrator is simply the reciprocal of the period, *i.e.*

$$ f = \frac{1}{T} \tag{13-3} $$

[1] Each interval is determined by an exponential voltage waveform at the grid of V_1 or V_2. Consider the interval $t_3 - t_2$. Neglecting the short transient A at time t_2, the duration of this interval is the time $t_3 - t_2$ required for e_{c_2} (Fig. 13-9) to rise exponentially from $-E_0$ to the cutoff level $-E_b/\mu$. During this time interval, tube V_2 carries no plate current, so that Fig. 13-9 reduces to the circuit shown in Fig. 13-11a. Replacing tube V_1 by the d-c plate resistance $\bar{r}_p$ (that is, $\bar{r}_p$ is the ratio of d-c voltage e_b applied to the plate to the d-c plate current i_{b_1}) gives the equivalent circuit of Fig. 13-11b, which can be simplified as shown at Fig. 13-11c, where

$$ E' = E_b \frac{\bar{r}_p}{\bar{r}_p + R_{L_1}} $$

$$ R' = \frac{\bar{r}_p R_{L_1}}{\bar{r}_p + R_{L_1}} $$

In this final circuit one ordinarily finds that $R' \ll R_{g_2}$, so that the time constant of the

The frequency of the free-running multivibrator can be controlled by returning the grid circuit to an adjustable positive potential, as illus-

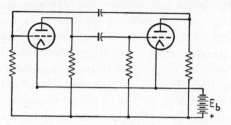

(a) Multivibrator with positive bias on grids

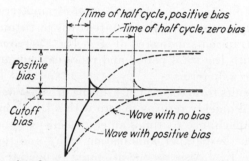

(b) Effect on grid voltage waves of positive bias

FIG. 13-12. Multivibrator with positive bias, together with grid-voltage waveforms, showing how the positive grid return reduces the time of a half cycle.

trated in Fig. 13-12.[1]   Such a positive bias shortens the time of each half cycle by an amount that increases with the bias by causing the instanta-

circuit can generally be taken to be $R_{g2}C_2$, although the true value is $(R_{g2} + R')C_2$.

Assuming therefore that the exponential voltage rise across R_{g2} has the time constant $R_{g2}C_2$, then since this voltage starts with an amplitude $-E_0$ at t_2 and has an amplitude $-E_b/\mu$ at $t_3 - t_2$, one can write

$$\frac{E_b}{\mu} = E_0 \epsilon^{-\frac{t_3 - t_2}{R_{g2}C_2}}$$

The interval $t_3 - t_2$ is obtained by rearranging, and taking the natural logarithm of both sides

$$\epsilon^{\frac{t_3 - t_2}{R_{g2}C_2}} = \frac{\mu E_0}{E_b}$$

$$\frac{t_3 - t_2}{R_{g2}C_2} = \log_\epsilon \frac{\mu E_0}{E_b}$$

$$t_3 - t_2 = R_{g2}C_2 \log_\epsilon \frac{\mu E_0}{E_b} \tag{13-2}$$

[1] See Bartelink, *loc. cit.*

neous grid potential to reach the cutoff value earlier in the discharge period than would otherwise be the case.[1] The frequency range that can be obtained by varying the bias when using any one set of circuit components is quite large, of the order of 10 to 1. By using feedback to linearize the discharge of the grid condensers, the frequency can be moreover made to vary linearly with bias voltage.[2]

A positive bias also increases the frequency stability of the multivibrator by making the curve of instantaneous grid potential intersect the cutoff grid-bias line in Fig. 13-12 at a greater slope. This means that variations in the voltages E_b or E_0 will result in smaller variations in the time of intersection.

By and large it can be said that a multivibrator can be made to oscillate at any frequency in the range where resistance-coupled amplification is possible.[3] Alternatively, it could be stated that in the normal range of frequencies, the transients indicated at A in Fig. 13-9 are of short duration compared with the total period and represent only small imperfections on the basic waveforms.

Transient A results from the grid of V_2 being driven somewhat positive. The grid potential quickly returns to zero with a time constant equal to the product of capacitance C_2 times an equivalent resistance formed by R_{L_1} in series with the parallel combination of R_{g_2} and the grid-cathode resistance of tube V_2. Also, as one attempts to operate a given multivibrator at higher and higher frequencies, a limitation results from the fact that the vertical segments in the waveforms of Fig. 13-9 really have

---

[1] With positive-bias voltage E, instead of zero bias, the interval $t_3 - t_2$ previously given in Eq. (13-2) now becomes

$$t_3 - t_2 = R_{g2}C_2 \log\epsilon \frac{E + E_0}{E + (E_b/\mu)} \tag{13-4}$$

If both grids are returned to the same positive-bias voltage E, then the total period T becomes

$$T = (R_{g1}C_1 + R_{g2}C_2) \log\epsilon \frac{E + E_0}{E + (E_b/\mu)} \tag{13-5}$$

[2] Thus see Sidney Bertram, A Degenerative Positive-bias Multivibrator, *Proc. IRE*, vol. 36, p. 277, February, 1948; Julian M. Sturtevant, A Voltage Controlled Multivibrator, *Electronics*, vol. 22, p. 144, October, 1949. This second reference also shows how one can make the frequency proportional to the square of a control voltage.

[3] By using care in the design details, very low frequencies can be generated, such as 1 cycle per hr; see Carl J. Quirk, Low Frequency Multivibrators, *Electronics*, vol. 18, p. 350, December, 1945. Likewise, by replacing each of the coupling resistors R_{L_1} and R_{L_2} by a tuned circuit shunted by a rectifier, it is possible to generate multivibrator type of oscillators at the resonant frequency of the tuned circuit. In this way it is possible to generate frequencies much higher than possible with the resistance-coupled multivibrator; see A. E. Johanson, A Tuned Plate Multivibrator, *Bell Labs. Record*, vol. 28, p. 208, May, 1950.

a finite slope.   These segments are more nearly vertical for high trans-conductance g_m and low input and output capacitances for the tubes,[1] i.e., the same properties that produce good high-frequency amplification.

Synchronizing the Multivibrator.   When a pulsed or alternating voltage from an outside source is introduced into the circuits of a multivibrator, the multivibrator oscillations tend to adjust themselves in frequency so that the ratio of the injected to multivibrator frequency is exactly a ratio of integers.   This ratio may be unity, or greater or less than unity.   The mechanism by which such synchronization occurs is illustrated in Fig. 13-13a, which shows a symmetrical multivibrator arranged to generate a frequency that is exactly one-seventh the injected frequency of the injected voltage e_s.   The voltage to be injected is capacitively coupled to either or both grids of the multivibrator, with the resulting waveform e_{c_1} or e_{c_2} as shown in the figure (contrast this with Fig. 13-9).   The ratio of one to seven comes from the fact that $3\frac{1}{2}$ cycles of the sine wave occur during the interval t_2 to t_3, which is a half period of the wave generated by the multivibrator.

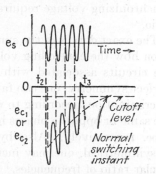

(a) Synchronizing with a sine wave in ratio of 7 to 1

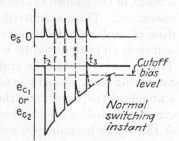

(b) Synchronizing with a pulsed voltage

Fig. 13-13. Synchronizing the multivibrator.

In a like manner the multivibrator can be synchronized with pulses, as in the example illustrated in Fig. 13-13b.   Here there are four pulses during the half period of the multivibrator, so the division ratio is one to eight.   Thus if an output pulse were obtained from the multivibrator by differentiating either the rising or the falling edge of the square waveform of plate voltage, there would be one output pulse for each eight input pulses.

In both cases in Fig. 13-13 it will be observed that the injected voltage superimposed upon the variation of grid potential that results from the discharge of the grid leak–condenser combination, controls the instant at which the instantaneous grid voltage of the multivibrator reaches the cutoff value.   In this way, the length of the multivibrator period $t_2 - t_3$ is controlled by the injected voltage, thus achieving synchronization.   If

---

[1] A detailed analysis is too complicated for inclusion here, but is given by E. M. Williams, D. F. Aldrich, and J. B. Woodford, Jr., Speed of Electronic Switching Circuits, *Proc. IRE*, vol. 38, p. 65, January, 1950.

the amplitude of the injected oscillation is increased, the multivibrator oscillation will synchronize at a lower ratio; *i.e.*, the multivibrator frequency is "drawn" toward the frequency of the injected voltage. The stability of control at a particular frequency ratio can be increased by the use of a positive grid bias, as this increases the change in amplitude of synchronizing voltage required to cause the frequency to jump to a new ratio.

The exact details of the synchronizing action in a multivibrator depend upon how the controlling voltage is introduced, and the extent to which the circuits associated with the two tubes are dissymmetrical. With perfect symmetry, one can favor either even or odd ratios, or can show no discrimination, according to whether the injected voltage is introduced in the same or opposite phases in the two tubes, or is introduced only in one tube, respectively. Also by making the multivibrator appropriately dissymmetrical, one may increase the tendency to synchronize at a particular ratio of frequencies.

The waveform of the multivibrator oscillations is rich in harmonics as a result of the sudden changes in amplitude that occur during the cycle of operation. Thus, a multivibrator operating at 10 kc can typically produce all sine-wave harmonics up to at least the 200th with an amplitude sufficient to be detected by a radio receiver of only moderate sensitivity. This property makes the multivibrator particularly useful in frequency-measuring work, since by synchronizing the multivibrator frequency with a standard frequency, one then obtains a whole series of frequencies, all exactly related to the standard frequency (see Sec. 5-1). The amplitude of the higher harmonics is greatest when the resistance-coupled stages of which the multivibrator is composed maintain their amplification up to frequencies that are high compared with the frequency of oscillation, since in this way the abrupt changes in wave shape are more pronounced.

"One-shot" Multivibrators. In certain applications, it is required that the multivibrator be quiescent until its action is initiated by a pulse of voltage from an external source. The multivibrator then goes through one cycle of operation, after which it reverts to the original quiescent condition, provided the initiating pulse is no longer present. Such an arrangement is called a *one-shot multivibrator*, and can be realized by biasing the grid of one of the multivibrator tubes to a voltage more negative than cutoff for the plate-supply potential employed.

A widely used form of one-shot multivibrator is shown in Fig. 13-14, which differs from the multivibrator of Fig. 13-8 in that cathode coupling replaces grid leak–condenser coupling in one of the amplifier stages. One-shot operation is achieved by returning the grid of tube V_2 to the plate-supply voltage through a grid-leak resistance R_{g_2}, while the grid of tube V_1 is returned to an adjustable positive-bias voltage through grid-leak resistance R_{g_1}.   Under quiescent conditions, tube V_2 carries a large plate current which causes the cathodes of both tubes to be considerably positive with respect to ground, thus causing the plate current of tube V_1 to be cut off.   However, when a large positive pulse is applied to the grid of tube V_1 multivibrator action is initiated, causing the plate current to be transferred to tube V_1, while the grid of tube V_2 is simultaneously driven negative, as shown in Fig. 13-14b, so that the plate current of tube V_2 is cut off.   This condition persists until the charge on condenser C_2 is

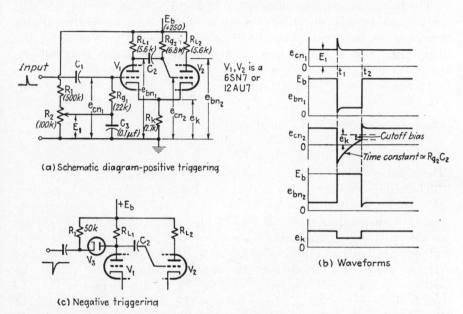

(a) Schematic diagram-positive triggering

(c) Negative triggering

(b) Waveforms

Fig. 13-14. Cathode-coupled "one-shot" multivibrator.   For the circuit values shown, the duration $T = t_2 - t_1$ of the plate-voltage pulse e_{bn1} or e_{bn2} is adjustable from a small value to about 120 μsec by means of potentiometer R_2.

able to leak off through resistance R_{g_2} sufficiently to reduce the negative voltage on the grid of tube V_2 to the point where this tube can again amplify.   The plate current then switches back to tube V_2, and the original quiescent condition is restored.

The cathode-coupled one-shot circuit can be utilized for the generation of a rectangular pulse of prescribed duration, viz., the waveforms e_{bn_1} or e_{bn_2} in Fig. 13-14.   Alternatively, it can be employed to obtain a trigger-type pulse that follows an initial triggering pulse by a prescribed time delay $T = t_2 - t_1$; this is achieved by differentiating either e_{bn_1} or e_{bn_2} by means of one of the circuits of Fig. 13-6, and using the pulse occurring at t_2 and associated with the trailing edge of e_{bn_1} or e_{bn_2}.   The duration of the rectangular pulse, and hence of the delay interval $t_2 - t_1$, is readily adjustable by means of the potentiometer R_2 in Fig. 13-14a. This adjustment controls the d-c bias voltage on V_1, and hence the plate current in V_1 during the interval between t_1 and t_2 (Fig. 13-14b). This plate current sets the cathode potential during this interval, and consequently determines the level to which e_{cn_2} must rise before V_2 can again conduct, and hence the time at which conduction starts. A feature of considerable advantage is that the time duration T between t_1 and t_2 is closely linear[1] with respect to the bias voltage E_1.

The particular circuit values shown in Fig. 13-14a are typical, and give an adjustable pulse duration or delay time that is continuously variable from a very small value up to 120 μsec. A general expression for the delay time $T = t_2 - t_1$ in terms of the circuit parameters is as follows:

$$T \approx R_{g_2}C_2 \log_\epsilon \frac{E_b - I_{b_2}R_k + I_{b_1}R_{L_1}}{E_b - I_{b_1}R_k} \tag{13-6}$$

where I_{b_1} = current in V_1 when conducting

I_{b_2} = current in V_2 when conducting

E_b = plate-supply voltage

The notation relating to circuit elements is as given in Fig. 13-14.

The circuit of Fig. 13-14a is shown as being triggered with a positive pulse, but a negative pulse would work, provided that the input connections are modified as shown in Fig. 13-14c. Here, when tube V_1 carries no current the coupling diode V_3 is nonconducting because its plate and cathode are both at the same potential E_b; hence prior to t_1 there is no voltage across V_3. However, the negative trigger pulse drives the cathode momentarily negative, causing V_3 to conduct, and thus to couple the negative-going trigger pulse to the plate of V_1 and the grid of V_2 (via C_2). This action initiates the sequence of events previously described for the instant t_1. As a result of these events, V_1 becomes conducting, causing a larger voltage drop across R_{L_1}, thereby making the anode of V_3 negative with respect to its cathode. Thus the trailing edge of the trigger impulse at the cathode of V_3 is unable to influence the circuit because V_3 is an open circuit. If this were not the case, a positive-going trailing edge of a large trigger pulse could prematurely restore the initial circuit conditions such as existed prior to time t_1, and thus the duration $t_2 - t_1$ would depend only upon the trigger-pulse duration, and not upon the circuit constants of the multivibrator.

13-4. The Blocking Oscillator. The arrangement shown in Fig. 13-15 is termed a *blocking oscillator*, and finds wide use as a generator of short pulses.

---

[1] A proof of this linearity is given by K. Glegg, Cathode-coupled Multivibrator Operation, *Proc. IRE*, vol. 38, p. 655, June, 1950.

The basic element of the block-ing oscillator is a special trans-former T that provides coupling between the grid and plate circuits of the tube. This transformer is normally wound on a high-perme-ability magnetic core in such a manner as to give the minimum possible leakage inductance be-tween the plate and grid windings, consistent with small distributed and interwinding capacitances (shown schematically as C_p in the figure).[1] The inductance L_p of the plate winding is made as large as possible, with the maximum per-missible value determined by the fact that the resonant frequency f_0 resulting from L_p and the trans-former capacitance must be such that $1/2f_0$ is of the order of the length of the desired pulse.

Mechanism of Operation of the Blocking Oscillator.[2] The circuit of the blocking oscillator, as shown in Fig. 13-15a, is identical with the circuit of the ordinary tuned-plate feedback oscillator. The actual operating details differ greatly, however; this is a result of the very high inductance-to-capacitance ratio of the resonant system represented by the transformer T, and the fact that in the blocking oscillator the time constant R_gC_g of the grid

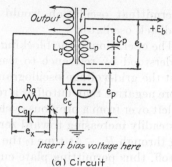

(a) Circuit

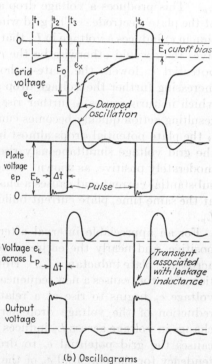

(b) Oscillograms

FIG. 13-15. Blocking-oscillator circuit, together with typical oscillogram.

leak–condenser combination is made so great that an exaggerated case of

[1] This transformer is frequently provided with a third winding as shown in Fig. 13-15. Such a tertiary winding makes it possible to obtain an output free of d-c volt-ages and independent of ground potential.

[2] A particularly useful discussion of the operation of the blocking oscillator is given by R. Benjamin, Blocking Oscillators, *J. IEE (Radiolocation Conv.)*, vol. 93, pt. IIIA, p. 1159, 1946. Additional information is to be found in "Principles of Radar," *op. cit.*, pp. 2-82–2-88, and in "Waveforms," *op. cit.*, Chap. 6.

intermittent oscillation would exist in the corresponding tuned-plate feedback oscillator.

The operation of the blocking oscillator under typical conditions can be understood by reference to the oscillograms of Fig. 13-15b.[1] Consider first the grid-voltage oscillogram. In the region t_1-t_2 the grid potential is more negative than cutoff as a result of a charge present on grid condenser C_g left over from a previous cycle of operation; however, the grid potential is steadily increasing toward zero as a result of the condenser C_g discharging through R_g. At time t_2 the grid potential becomes less negative than cutoff, thus permitting plate current to start flowing through inductance L_p. This produces a voltage drop across L_p that reduces the voltage e_p at the plate electrode. The grid winding L_g is so connected that a reduction in e_p induces a voltage in L_g that makes e_c more positive (or less negative) than would otherwise be the case. The resulting increase in grid potential e_c lowers the plate-cathode resistance of the tube, thereby increasing further the voltage drop across L_p; this reduces e_p still more, which in turn causes a further rise in grid potential, and so on. The resulting action quickly becomes cumulative, with the result that at time t_2 the plate potential drops almost instantly to a very small value, while the grid voltage simultaneously rises equally rapidly to a value that is moderately positive, as shown. Under these conditions the grid draws a substantial current and causes a charge to build up in grid condenser C_g; at the same time, plate current builds up steadily in the plate inductance L_p.

For an appreciable interval after t_2 the control-grid voltage remains positive, and nearly the entire plate-supply voltage E_b appears as drop across the plate inductance L_p. However, at some later time, a combination of factors causes a new sequence of events to occur, in which the plate voltage e_p begins to rise at a relatively rapid rate with corresponding reduction of the voltage drop across the plate inductance L_p. This change in voltage across L_p induces a voltage in the grid winding L_g that causes the grid potential e_c to drop, which still further increases the tendency for the potential e_p of the plate to rise. At time t_3 this action becomes cumulative, and hence suddenly drives the grid more negative than cutoff as shown. The factors that control the time t_1 when the pulse t_2-t_3 ends are quite complicated, and involve the saturation of the

[1] Several different modes of operation are possible in a blocking oscillator, and the details associated with each of these modes become very complicated when the non-linear effects of the tube and magnetic core are taken into account. The explanation given here represents a qualitative discussion of the mechanism of operation commonly employed when the blocking oscillator is arranged to generate a relatively flat-topped pulse with steep sides. For further details on the various possible modes of operation, see Benjamin, *loc. cit.*

transformer core, the effect of capacitance C_p of the transformer, and to some extent the grid condenser C_g, as well as the tube characteristics.

The energy that is stored in the transformer inductance L_p at the instant t_3, is dissipated in a damped oscillation that is superimposed upon the bias voltage e_x developed across the grid condenser C_g, as shown. The frequency of this oscillation is the resonant frequency resulting from the inductance L_p and capacitance C_p of the transformer. The transformer is intentionally designed with high core loss and winding resistance, so that this oscillation is almost completely damped out after a few cycles; in some cases a resistance is also shunted across one of the transformer windings in order to cause the oscillation to die out even more rapidly.

During the period t_2-t_3 of the pulse, grid current flows into condenser C_g and builds up a negative-bias voltage e_x across C_g that is considerably greater than cutoff. In the following time interval t_3-t_4 this bias voltage e_x dies away with the time constant $R_g C_g$, as shown, as a result of the charge on C_g leaking off through R_g. Finally, at time t_4 the conditions correspond to those existing at time t_2, and the cycle repeats.

Pulse Length and Shape. The voltage wave generated across L_p by the blocking oscillator is seen to be a periodic repetition of a short pulse, approximately rectangular in shape, that is followed by an oscillation that dies out rapidly. The most important single factor determining the *length* of the rectangular pulse produced is the transformer. The second most important factor is the grid condenser C_g. Reduction in the capacitance of this condenser increases the bias voltage that is built up by the grid current that flows during the pulse; as a result, a small value of capacitance tends to terminate the pulse sooner than would be the case if the capacitance were large. It is also possible to accelerate the termination of the pulse by the delay-line technique discussed in connection with Fig. 13-27.

The *shape* of the pulse generated by a blocking oscillator is determined primarily by the transformer. The steepness of the leading and lagging edges of the pulse are determined mainly by the leakage inductance, and will be greater the less the leakage. The flatness of the top (or bottom) of the pulse is determined primarily by the transformer characteristics in relationship to the tube and circuit constants with which the transformer is used.

It is rather typical in blocking oscillators for the initial portion of the pulse to have superimposed upon it a small, very high-frequency, highly damped transient oscillation, as shown in Fig. 13-15. This oscillation is produced by shock excitation of the resonant system represented by the leakage inductance and the distributed capacitance C_p of the transformer. In contrast, the damped oscillation following the pulse has a much lower frequency that corresponds to the primary inductance L_p resonating with the associated transformer capacitance C_p, as has already been noted.

A careful balance must exist between transformer and tube characteristics in order to achieve a sharply defined pulse having a flat top and a specified length. Once this result has been achieved, then any attempt to use the resulting transformer to generate pulses of substantially different length, will usually result in marked deterioration in the shape of the pulse.

The design factors that cause the blocking-oscillator transformer to produce a pulse of desired length are so complicated that a considerable amount of cut and try is ordinarily involved in arriving at suitable proportions. As a result, the final design of a transformer to give high-quality performance can be expected to represent a considerable amount of development time. It is therefore expedient, whenever possible, to purchase a transformer intended for a blocking oscillator of the pulse duration desired, and then to use this transformer with the tube and under the conditions for which it was designed.

Repetition Frequency of Pulses and Synchronization with External Voltages. The repetition frequency of the free-running blocking oscillator, *i.e.*, the number of cycles of operation per second, is given by the following relation, which is analogous to Eq. (13-5):

$$\text{Repetition frequency} = \frac{1}{\Delta t + R_g C_g \log_\epsilon \dfrac{E + E_0}{E + (E_b/\mu)}} \quad (13\text{-}7)$$

where Δt = length of pulse, sec

E_0 = voltage on C_g at end of pulse

E_b = plate-supply voltage

μ = amplification factor of tube

E = positive bias voltage applied to control grid at point x in Fig. 13-15a (E is assumed zero in the oscillograms of Fig. 13-15b)

R_g = grid-leak resistance

C_g = grid-condenser capacitance

This notation is illustrated in Fig. 13-15. The quantity E_0 is a complex function of transformer and tube characteristics, pulse length, grid-condenser capacitance, and plate-supply voltage.

The repetition frequency can be controlled satisfactorily over a very wide range of values without change in pulse shape or length by varying the grid-leak resistance R_g. For any given value of R_g, continuous control over a substantial range can be achieved readily by means of an adjustable positive-bias voltage applied at point x in Fig. 13-15a, which in analogy with the positive-bias multivibrator, increases the repetition frequency. Although Eq. (13-7) indicates that the repetition frequency depends upon C_g as well as R_g, this fact is seldom made use of to control the repetition frequency, as any substantial change in C_g will change the pulse length, and also may adversely alter the pulse shape.

The repetition frequency of a blocking oscillator will readily synchronize in harmonic relation with the frequency of an injected voltage, just as in the case of the multivibrator. The mechanism involved in such synchronization is essentially the same as that discussed in connection with Fig. 13-13; i.e., the injected voltage controls the instant t_4 at which the pulse is initiated.

One-shot Operation of the Blocking Oscillator. When a fixed negative bias somewhat greater than cutoff is inserted in the circuit of a blocking oscillator at point x in Fig. 13-15, operation analogous to that of the one-shot multivibrator results, as shown in Fig. 13-16. Such a system is inactive until an incoming positive trigger pulse is superimposed on the bias and momentarily reduces the grid potential of the tube to a value that is less negative than cutoff. The blocking oscillator then generates one pulse followed by a damped oscillation. After this oscillation dies out, the blocking oscillator again becomes inactive and remains quiescent with a grid bias greater than cutoff until the next positive pulse arrives. Operated in this manner, the multivibrator produces pulses that are accurately controlled by the incoming pulses, irrespective of whether these pulses arrive regularly or irregularly.

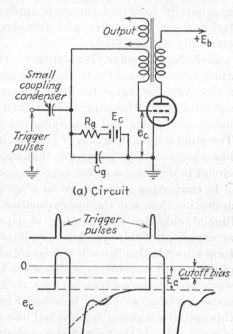

(a) Circuit

(b) Grid-voltage oscillogram

Fig. 13-16. One-shot blocking oscillator.

Practical Applications of the Blocking Oscillator. The principal use of the blocking oscillator is as a generator of short pulses. This application is discussed further in the next section. It is sufficient here to note that by the use of a suitably designed transformer, a pulse width anywhere in the range 0.1 to 25 μsec can be readily generated. The pulses have relatively steep leading and lagging edges, and a fairly rectangular shape. The peak energy of the pulses obtainable from the blocking oscillator is relatively large. This arises from the fact that the tube carries current only during a small fraction of the time, so that very large peak plate and grid currents are permissible without overheating the tube. Finally, the blocking oscillator has the merit that the pulse repetition frequency can be readily controlled by an external voltage.

The blocking oscillator can also be used to generate harmonics and subharmonics of a synchronizing voltage. However, the multivibrator is generally preferred for such applications, as the blocking-oscillator transformer is expensive, and also produces stray magnetic fields unless unusually well shielded.

13-5. Square-wave Generation.[1] There are two main ways of generating square waves of voltage. The first of these consists in starting with a sine-wave oscillator having a frequency equal to that of the desired square wave. The sine wave is then converted to a square wave by means of clipping and amplifying circuits as will be presently discussed. The other approach is that of using a circuit like the multivibrator, which has a plate-voltage waveform that approximates a square wave; such a circuit is therefore a direct generator of square waves.

In converting a sine wave to a square wave, the result is at best an approximation, but the approximation can be made as good as desired, limited only by the number of circuits employed. An elementary arrangement of this type has been illustrated by Fig. 13-1. In the waveform shown in this figure it will be noted that the top and bottom portions of the output waveform correspond to the horizontal portions of a square wave, but the transitions between them are sloping rather than approximately vertical as would be desired for the square wave. However, if this output waveform is amplified, the steepness of these sloping portions is increased. If the amplified waveform is then clipped again by passing it through another circuit of the type shown in Fig. 13-1, the output from this second clipping circuit is a much closer approximation to a square wave. This operation of alternately amplifying and clipping can be repeated until the final output waveform approximates a square wave as closely as desired. The circuit of Fig. 13-2 is even more convenient for the purpose of repeated amplification and clipping, in that the same tube which provides the clipping also provides the amplification. Thus several clipping circuits of the type shown in this figure can be connected in tandem through the coupling capacitor indicated in the figure, to give a simple and effective system of converting sine waves to square waves.

---

[1] Bartelink, *loc. cit.*; K. H. Martin, A Simple 60-cycle Square-wave Generator, *Electronics*, vol. 14, p. 46, July, 1941; J. R. Cosby and C. W. Lampson, An Electronic Switch and Square-wave Oscillator, *Rev. Sci. Instruments*, vol. 12, p. 187, April, 1941; Charles Markley and Herbert L. Polak, Square-wave Calibrator, *Electronics*, vol. 22, p. 193, November, 1949; L. B. Arguimbau, Network Testing with Square-waves, *Gen. Rad. Expt.*, vol. 16, p. 1, December, 1939.

The process of generation of square waves by clipping a sine wave is a convenient technique for experimental work. Sine-wave oscillators of accurately known and readily variable frequency are usually available in the laboratory, and the system of clippers and amplifiers can be assembled as a piece of auxiliary equipment for use with the oscillator, and will work over a wide range of frequencies.

The alternative approach to the generation of square waves is to produce them directly by means of the multivibrator circuit of Fig. 13-8. As can be seen from the oscillograms shown in Fig. 13-9, the plate-voltage waveform on either tube very closely approximates a square wave.[1] There are small imperfections in the waveform indicated as the transients A in the figure, but these imperfections can be removed by passing the waveform through a clipping circuit.

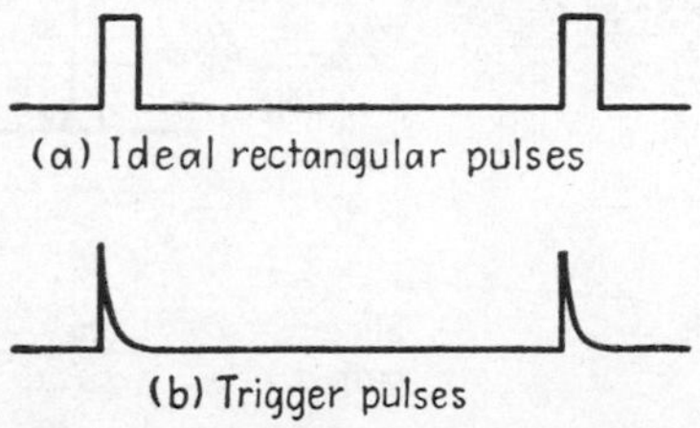

13-6. Pulse Generation—General Considerations. Two types of pulses as shown in Fig. 13-17 are to be distinguished. The *rectangular* pulse can be thought of as an unsymmetrical square wave, in which the positive (or negative) portion is of very short duration, and the remaining portion is of relatively long duration; its waveform in the ideal case consists of accurately horizontal and

(a) Ideal rectangular pulses

(b) Trigger pulses

Fig. 13-17. Rectangular and trigger pulses; the distinguishing feature of the trigger pulse is a rapid initial rise, with the remainder of the pulse shape being relatively unimportant.

vertical segments. Alternatively, a *trigger* pulse is characterized by a steep rise and a short duration, with the exact waveform being not critical. Such a pulse is used to initiate an action in other circuits.

The trigger-type pulse is usually generated by differentiating either a square wave or a steeply rising portion of some other waveform. Generation of a rectangular pulse calls for more refinement, however, and as in the case of square waves can be accomplished either by shaping operations performed upon another waveform, or by direct generation.

An example showing how the rising edge of a square wave can be converted to a trigger-type pulse by means of a differentiating circuit is shown in Fig. 13-18. This trigger-type pulse can in turn be converted to a pulse that is very nearly rectangular by clipping or slicing and then amplifying. The slicing circuit of Fig. 13-5 is particularly valuable in such an operation, as shown.

Circuits for directly generating rectangular pulses will be described in the next paragraphs.

13-7. Common Types of Pulse Generators. There exists a wide variety of circuits suitable for the direct generation of rectangular pulses,

[1] When an unsymmetrical multivibrator is used, a rectangular waveform is obtained.

only a few of the more important of which can be included in a brief treatment.[1] The choice among these is influenced by the desired duration of the pulses, the rate at which they must occur, whether they are to be continuously generated or generated one by one in accordance with trigger pulses, and whether they are to be of low voltage (or low power) on

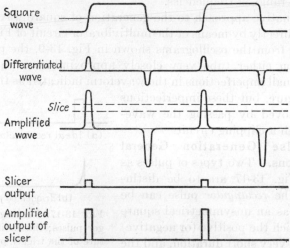

Fig. 13-18. Generation of a trigger pulse by differentiation of a square wave, together with conversion of the trigger pulse to a rectangular pulse by clipping and amplifying.

the one hand, or high voltage (or high power) on the other hand. Moreover, it may be important in some cases that the pulse be readily adjustable in length (duration), while in other cases the pulse duration need not be variable but must instead have a very precise value. Any reasonable combination of these requirements can be met with the circuits about to be described.

Pulse Generation by Use of Unsymmetrical Multivibrators. As described in Sec. 13-3, it is possible to obtain short rectangular pulses from the

[1] Other types and modifications will be found throughout the literature, particularly in references dealing with radar. Useful references on the subject include "Pulse Generators" (Vol. 5, Radiation Laboratory Series), McGraw-Hill Book Company, Inc., New York, 1948; "Waveforms," *op. cit.;* "Principles of Radar," *op. cit.;* E. L. C. White, The Use of Delay Networks in Pulse Formation, *J. IEE (Radiolocation Conv.),* vol. 93, pt. IIIA, p. 312, 1946; M. Levy, Power Pulse Generator, *Wireless Eng.,* vol. 23, p. 192, July, 1946; D. C. Espley, Generation of Very Short Pulses, *J. IEE (Radiolocation Conv.),* vol. 93, pt. IIIA, p. 314, 1946; C. R. Smitley and R. E. Graber, Electronic Switch for the Production of Pulses, *Electronics,* vol. 20, p. 128, April, 1947; H. A. Stone, Jr., Non-linear Coils for Pulse Generators, *Bell Labs. Record,* vol. 24, p. 450, December, 1946; L. W. Hussey, Nonlinear Coil Generators for Short Pulses, *Proc. IRE,* vol. 38, p. 40, January, 1950; W. S. Melville, The Use of Saturable Reactors as Discharge Devices for Pulse Generators, *Proc. IEE,* pt. III, vol. 98, p. 185, May, 1951.

plate-voltage waveform of the multivibrator by using the unsymmetrical form of this circuit. Thus the time constant of one combination of grid-leak resistor and coupling capacitor is made very small, while the time constant of the other is made relatively large. For example, in Fig. 13-9, the period between t_1 and t_2 can be made very small compared with the period between t_2 and t_3, by making the product $R_{g_1}C_1$ very small compared with the product of $R_{g_2}C_2$. The transient designated by A can be removed by clipping if necessary.

The pulse length is determined by the time constant $R_{g_1}C_1$ (when the period between t_1 and t_2 in Fig. 13-9 is to be the pulse) and by the bias voltage to which R_{g_1} is connected. If the pulses are to be of very short duration, it is best to connect the grid-leak resistor to a positive-bias voltage such as the plate-supply voltage. If it is desired that the pulse duration be adjustable, the resistor can be returned to a variable positive voltage.

The interval between pulses, $i.e.$, their recurrence frequency, is determined by the other time constant $R_{g_2}C_2$, and the voltage to which R_{g_2} is connected. Since this interval is relatively long, the resistor R_{g_2} is usually returned to ground. If the period between pulses is to be varied, this can be accomplished by adjusting the time constant $R_{g_2}C_2$, or the bias voltage to which grid-leak resistor R_{g_2} is returned. To the extent that the pulse duration is very small compared with the interval between pulses, these two quantities are accordingly independently controllable.

The arrangement just described is of the free-running variety, in that it oscillates continuously and will provide a steady succession of pulses. On the other hand, the one-shot form of the multivibrator described on page 546 will provide one rectangular pulse for each trigger pulse received. Means for adjusting the duration of this pulse have already been described, and are illustrated in Fig. 13-14.

The multivibrator as a generator of pulses has the advantage of flexibility of adjustment of pulse duration and rate. It has the disadvantage, however, that one of the tubes must carry current during the period between pulses and so must be able to handle almost continuously an amount of power corresponding to the peak power of the pulse. Thus advantage cannot be taken of the ability of small tubes to handle large amounts of power for relatively short intervals. In addition, the duration of the pulse is dependent somewhat upon the supply voltages and tube characteristics; however, this can be remedied by incorporating a delay line as part of the multivibrator circuit as will be discussed in Sec. 13-9.

Pulse Generation by Use of the Blocking Oscillator. The blocking oscillator, whose principles have been discussed in Sec. 13-4, can be used as a source of rectangular pulse waveforms. This circuit is capable of producing pulses of large voltage (or large power) with small tubes and minimum power-supply requirements.   This results from the fact that power is drawn by the tube only during the short pulse, whereas during the long interval between pulses the plate current of the tube is cut off. A disadvantage of the circuit is that it is relatively inflexible as to the duration of the pulse.   The duration and the exact shape of the waveform are dependent upon the characteristics of the transformer, which must be carefully designed at the outset.   With a given transformer, the duration and shape of the pulse are then fixed, except that the pulse length can be controlled by a delay line as discussed in connection with Fig. 13-27. With proper design the rectangularity of the pulses is fairly good, and can moreover be improved by clipping, just as in the case of pulses generated by a multivibrator.   In particular, clipping makes it possible to eliminate the high-frequency transient illustrated in Fig. 13-15.

The blocking oscillator can be arranged either for continuous oscillation (free-running), or for one-shot operation as discussed in Sec. 13-4.

Pulse Generation by Use of the Class C Amplifier.[1]   Occasionally the problem arises of obtaining pulses at a high repetition frequency.   Circuits such as the multivibrator and the blocking oscillator are limited in this regard, because of the small but finite time required after the completion of a pulse before another pulse can be generated.   An expedient which permits the generation of high-frequency pulses consists in using a Class C amplifier with a resistive load impedance.   It is well known that the plate current in a Class C amplifier, operating under conditions of large negative-bias voltage and large amplitude of the driving sinewave, consists of short pulses, somewhat sinusoidal in shape although flattened on the top.   Such pulses are not ideally rectangular, although if the frequency is not so high as to preclude the use of clipping circuits (which are impaired in function at higher frequencies by virtue of their stray capacitances), it is possible to improve the waveform.

Pulse Generation Using a Tuned Circuit.[2]   Another method of generating pulses is illustrated in Fig. 13-19.   Here a resonant circuit LC is placed between ground and the cathode of tube V_1.   In the absence of an applied signal the grid of V_1 is at cathode potential, and plate current I_p flows through L.   Assume now that a control voltage e_s of large amplitude is applied to the grid of V_1.   When this signal goes negative, the plate current of V_1 is suddenly cut off.   The current originally flowing through L is then forced to flow into C, and in the absence of diode clipper V_2

[1] R. D. Carman, Producing High-frequency Pulses, *Wireless Eng.*, vol. 25, p. 164, May, 1948.

[2] An application of this principle is incorporated in a pulse modulator described by R. G. Hibberd, J. H. Shankland, and A. Bruce, A Pulse-modulated Signal Generator for 260–800 Mc/s, *J. IEE (Radiolocation Conv.)*, vol. 93, pt. IIIA, p. 1331, 1946.

would set up a damped oscillation as shown in Fig. 13-19*b*. The frequency of this oscillation is the resonant frequency of the circuit *LC*, and the peak amplitude of the voltage developed across *LC* is $I_p \sqrt{L/C}$. However, the diode clipper tube V_2 prevents the output voltage e_0 from becoming positive. As a result, V_2 stops the damped oscillation after the first half cycle, as shown. Under these conditions the output voltage e_0 consists of a pulse shaped like a half cycle of a sine wave, and having a length corresponding to a half cycle of the resonant frequency of the circuit *LC*. The repetition frequency of the pulses generated is equal to the frequency of the control voltage e_s.

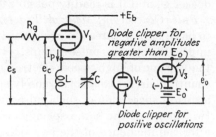

(a) Circuit

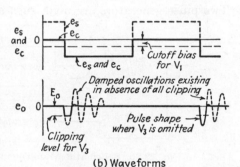

(b) Waveforms

FIG. 13-19. Generation of a short pulse by the use of a clipped transient of a resonant circuit.

Rectangular pulses can be obtained by clipping the sine-wave pulse at a level such as E_0 in Fig. 13-19*b* that is a small fraction of the peak amplitude. This can be accomplished by adding a second clipping diode V_3 to the system, as shown in Fig. 13-19*a*. Further improvement in pulse shape can be achieved by amplification, followed by further clipping.

The control voltage e_s must change from zero amplitude to a value equal to the cutoff bias of V_1 in a time that does not exceed half of the length of the pulse to be generated. When very short pulses of low or moderate repetition frequency are desired, e_s must be a square wave with appropriately steep sides, and an amplitude preferably considerably greater than cutoff, as shown in Fig. 13-19*b*. However, in many cases it is permissible to employ a sine wave of large amplitude. Thus if a sine wave has an amplitude 32 times the cutoff bias, the time interval between zero and cutoff amplitude is 1.8° corresponding to a pulse that lasts not less than 3.6°. For a 2000-cycle wave, this means that a pulse less than 5 μsec in length cannot be generated with this particular sine wave.

The high resistance R_g in series with the grid in Fig. 13-19*a* is for the purpose of producing a clipping action such that on the positive half cycles of the control voltage e_s (whether it be sinusoidal or square) the grid will remain at very close to cathode potential.

The circuit of Fig. 13-19 provides a very simple means of generating pulses. The pulse length can moreover be easily controlled simply by varying the resonant frequency of the tuned circuit with variable condenser C, and it is readily possible to obtain pulse lengths less than 1 μsec.

Pulse Generation: Multiple Pulses. There are times when it is desirable to have two or three closely spaced pulses, occurring with relatively long intervals between pulse groups. It has been found for instance that in the testing of high-speed electronic counting circuits, the ability of the counting circuit to resolve closely spaced pulses is different for the case of a steady succession of such pulses in contrast with the appearance of only two pulses of the same spacing, with long quiescent periods before and after the incidence of the two pulses.

An arrangement for generating a double pulse is shown in Fig. 13-20. Two pulse generators are used, such as one-shot blocking oscillators, or

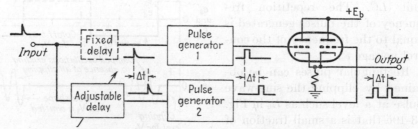

FIG. 13-20. Schematic arrangement for generating a double pulse.

one-shot multivibrators, which generate a single pulse upon the application of a trigger pulse at the input. The input pulses for the two generators are obtained from a common source, but the input to pulse generator 2 is delayed by passing it through an adjustable delay line of the type described in Sec. 13-8. Since any practical adjustable delay circuit introduces some delay, a second delay circuit is introduced ahead of pulse generator 1 as shown; this circuit is commonly designed to provide a fixed delay equal to the minimum delay of the adjustable circuit. Then when the delay time of the circuit for pulse generator 2 is at its minimum value, the separation between the two pulses applied to the generator is zero. The outputs of the two pulse generators are added in a mixing circuit, an example of which is shown in the figure; it is essentially a pair of cathode followers with separate inputs and a common load resistor.

The circuit shown in Fig. 13-20 generates a double pulse, but obviously groups of three or more pulses can be provided by adding additional delay and pulse-generator paths.

It is also possible to generate multiple pulses by operating a blocking oscillator under special conditions.[1]

[1] See Benjamin, *op. cit.*, p. 1169.

13-8. Lines and Pulse-forming Networks in Pulse Generation. It is possible to use a short length of transmission line either (1) to generate a pulse, or (2) as an auxiliary circuit element that precisely controls the pulse length in a multivibrator or blocking-oscillator type of pulse generator. In either case the action of the transmission line depends upon transient waves on the transmission line.

Behavior of Transient Waves on a Lossless Transmission Line.[1]   When voltage is suddenly applied to or removed from a transmission line, transient waves are produced.[2]   Consider for example the situation illustrated in Fig. 13-21a.   Here a d-c voltage E_0 is applied to the line by means of a switch S through a series resistance R_L which for reasons to be discussed later is made equal to the characteristic impedance R_0 of the line.   Immediately upon closing the switch, the line input terminals act as a resistance equal to the characteristic impedance R_0 of the line.   A voltage $E_0/2$ thus appears across the input terminals of the line and travels down the line at a speed or group velocity equal to the phase velocity.   Associated with this voltage is a current $I_{12} = E_0/2R_0$.   The voltage and its accompanying current constitute the transient wave.

When the transient wave reaches the end 3-4 of the line, the action depends upon the terminating impedance at 3-4.   When this impedance is a resistance equal to the characteristic impedance of the line, then the wave is absorbed, and that is all that happens.   However, for any other value of terminating impedance a reflection occurs, just as discussed in connection with Fig. 4-1 for the case of traveling waves.   In lines used in pulse generators the terminations employed at 3-4 are either open circuits or short circuits.

Consider first the situation that results when 3-4 is an open circuit. When a transient wave strikes such an open-circuit termination, it is completely reflected with reversal in polarity of current, but with no change in polarity of voltage.   That is, the voltage of the reflected wave adds to the voltage of the incident wave, doubling the voltage on the line, while

---

[1] Discussions of transient waves are to be found in numerous textbooks; for example see H. H. Skilling, "Transient Electric Currents," 2d ed., Chap. 9, McGraw-Hill Book Company, Inc., New York, 1952.

[2] A distinction exists between the traveling waves discussed in connection with Fig. 4-1 and the transient waves being considered here.   Traveling waves represent a steady-state condition, whereas transient waves represent the transient effects which ultimately settle down to create the steady-state result.   However, in the case of an ideal transmission line with zero losses, there are certain similarities between the two situations.   In particular, the velocity with which the transient wave travels is then identical with the phase velocity of the traveling wave, and the ratio of the voltage to current in the transient wave is equal to the characteristic impedance of the traveling wave.   These simple relations do not necessarily hold, however, if the transmission line possesses losses.

the current of the reflected wave cancels the current of the incident wave
to give zero total current; this is illustrated in Fig. 13-21b. Thus when
the reflected wave reaches the input terminals 1-2 of the line, the voltage
everywhere on the line is twice the voltage of the incident wave, *i.e.*, is

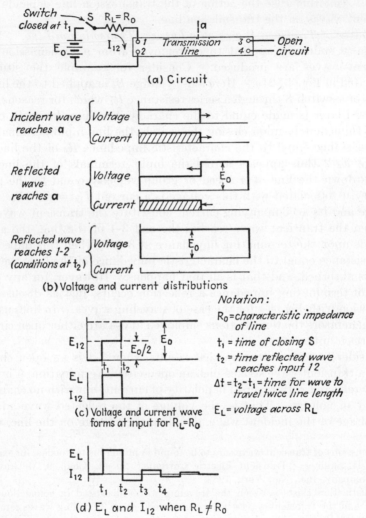

(a) Circuit

(b) Voltage and current distributions

(c) Voltage and current wave
forms at input for $R_L = R_0$

Notation:

R_0 = characteristic impedance
of line

t_1 = time of closing S

t_2 = time reflected wave
reaches input 12

$\Delta t = t_2 - t_1$ = time for wave to
travel twice line length

E_L = voltage across R_L

(d) E_L and I_{12} when $R_L \neq R_0$

FIG. 13-21. Behavior of an open-circuited transmission line when a d-c voltage is suddenly applied.

E_0, and the current everywhere on the line is zero.   To the reflected wave
the input terminals 1-2 of the line appear to have a resistance R_L.   When
this resistance is chosen so that $R_L = R_0$, the reflected wave is completely
absorbed when it reaches 1-2, and no further waves travel along the line.

The oscillograms of Fig. 13-21b show the voltage and current distributions that exist on the transmission line during this process, while the oscillograms of Fig. 13-21c show the current and voltage at the input terminals of the transmission line, and the voltage across the resistance R_L. In these oscillograms, t_1 is the time switch S is closed, while t_2 is the time the returning reflected wave reaches the input terminals. It will be noted that the current that flows into the line, and hence the voltage developed across the resistance R_L, is a rectangular pulse having a duration equal to the time $\Delta t = t_2 - t_1$ required for a transient wave to travel twice the length of the line. After t_2 no current flows into the line, and the line voltage is everywhere E_0, that is, the line is charged to the supply voltage E_0.

The above discussion has been for the case $R_L = R_0$. However, if $R_L \neq R_0$, then the reflected wave returning to the input terminals 1-2 is again reflected at least in part, to produce a new wave traveling toward terminals 3-4, where it again is reflected, to be returned to the terminals 1-2 for further reflection, and so on. Under these conditions the waveform of the current entering the line will have a character such as illustrated in Fig. 13-21d for a typical case. Thus to obtain a single clean pulse, it is necessary that the resistance R_L associated with the input of the line have a value that equals the characteristic impedance R_0 of the line.

Next consider the case shown in Fig. 13-22, where the terminals 3-4 of the line are short-circuited, instead of being open-circuited as in Fig. 13-21. The reflection at 3-4 now takes place with reversal of voltage, but no change in the sign of the current. As a result, the voltage and current distributions on the line have the character shown in Fig. 13-22b, and the waveforms of voltage and current at the input terminals 1-2 of the line for $R_L = R_0$ are shown in Fig. 13-22c; these oscillograms are to be compared with those of Fig. 13-21b and c, respectively. In Fig. 13-22 it will be observed that the voltage existing across the input terminals of the line is a rectangular pulse having an amplitude $E_0/2$ equal to half the applied voltage, and a length equal to the time $\Delta t = t_2 - t_1$ required by the transient wave to travel twice the length of the line.

The behavior of the line in the two cases just described can also be interpreted in a slightly different way. When the switch S is first closed at time t_1, the line behaves like a simple resistance R_0. Then, in the case of the open-circuited line of Fig. 13-21, at the time t_2 the line suddenly becomes equivalent to an open circuit at its input terminals. Thus the line acts like a *delayed open circuit*, the magnitude of the delay being accurately the amount of time $t_2 - t_1$ required for a transient wave to travel down the line and back. Similarly, in the case of the short-circuited line of Fig. 13-22, the line acts at its input terminals first like a resistance R_0, and then at the time t_2 like a short circuit. Thus in this case the line can be regarded as a *delayed short circuit*. This action as a delayed open or short circuit can be used to control the pulse length of a multivibrator or blocking oscillator, as described below.

A third transmission-line arrangement of importance in the generation of pulses is illustrated in Fig. 13-23a. Here while switch S is open, the

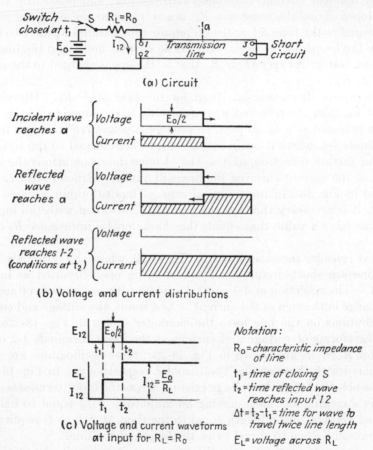

(a) Circuit

(b) Voltage and current distributions

(c) Voltage and current waveforms at input for $R_L = R_0$

Notation:

R_0 = characteristic impedance of line

t_1 = time of closing S

t_2 = time reflected wave reaches input 12

$\Delta t = t_2 - t_1$ = time for wave to travel twice line length

E_L = voltage across R_L

FIG. 13-22. Behavior of a short-circuited transmission line when a d-c voltage is suddenly applied.

transmission line is charged to a voltage E_0 as a result of current flowing through relatively high series resistance R_1. This charging occurs during the period between pulses, and so can take place relatively slowly as compared with the time represented by the length of the pulse to be generated. The transient represented by the charging of the line is illustrated by the waveform in interval t_0 to t_1 in Fig. 13-23b. Sometime after the line is thus charged, switch S is closed, placing the resistance $R_L = R_0$ directly across the input terminals of the line.   The electrostatic energy stored in the charged line is then discharged into the resistance R_L to form a pulse, as shown in Fig. 13-23c.   This pulse has a length equal to the time it takes a transient wave to travel twice the length of the line, and has an amplitude $E_0/2$.   The mechanism by which this result is achieved is as follows: Upon closing S the flow of current into R_L causes a wave to start traveling from terminals 1-2 toward 3-4.   This wave has a voltage equal to half the voltage E_0 to which the line was originally charged; the polarity of this wave is opposite to the polarity of the voltage with which the line was charged.   This wave then travels down the line toward terminals 3-4, wiping out half the line voltage as it goes, as shown in Fig. 13-23d, and also causing a current $E_0/2R_0$ to flow on the line; it is also the current that flows into the resistance R_L.   When the wave reaches terminals 3-4 a reflection occurs, in which the voltage of the reflected wave has the same polarity as the voltage of the incident wave, so that the voltage of the incident wave plus that of the reflected wave add up to a voltage that is equal and opposite to the charging voltage E_0, giving zero resultant voltage on the line.   Also, wherever this occurs on the line, the current of the reflected wave cancels the current of the incident wave, giving zero resultant line current.   That is to say, at points along the line where the incident and reflected waves are both present, the line is completely discharged and quiescent (see Fig. 13-23d).   When the reflected wave reaches the input terminals 1-2 all of the electrostatic energy originally stored in the line has now been delivered to the resistance R_L, and no voltage or current exists anywhere on the line.   After the line has thus been completely discharged, switch S is opened, thereby permitting the line again to be charged to the voltage E_0, so that another pulse can be formed upon subsequent closing of switch S.

Use of Special and Artificial Lines to Represent Real Lines.   In the above discussion it was assumed that the transmission lines were ideal, continuous, and with negligible losses.   An example of this would be a coaxial line with air dielectric, or a low-loss solid dielectric cable.   Because of the relatively high velocity of propagation on such lines, it is feasible to use them only for the generation of extremely short pulses.   For instance, if a coaxial cable with polyethylene insulation were used in the circuit of Fig. 13-23 to generate a pulse 1 μsec in duration, the length of the cable would have to be about 300 ft.   If a high-voltage pulse was involved, the insulation requirements of the cable would call for a large diameter, and thus the bulk and weight of the cable would be excessive for many applications.   Accordingly, various special forms of transmission line have been devised for use in pulse-generating circuits.

One approach is provided by the so-called high-impedance or spiral

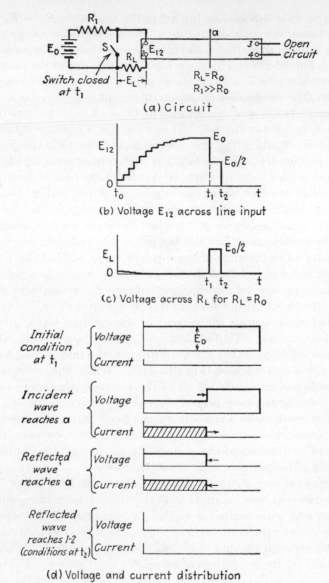

(a) Circuit

(b) Voltage E_{12} across line input

(c) Voltage across R_L for $R_L = R_0$

(d) Voltage and current distribution

FIG. 13-23. Pulse generation by discharging a charged transmission line through a load resistance.

delay line.[1] This is a coaxial line in which the inner conductor consists of a continuous coil of small wire, wound on an insulating core running along the central axis of the line. The effect of this coiled center conductor is to increase the inductance per unit length of the line, thereby reducing the line velocity (see Eq. 4-8b), and increasing the time delay per unit length. With such a line it is possible to obtain a time delay of 1 μsec in a length as short as 2 ft. The ultimate possibilities of the spiral delay line are limited by the fact that in such a line the velocity of propagation tends to vary with frequency. This effect becomes greater the higher the frequency, i.e., the shorter the pulse being generated, and the lower the velocity per unit length that the spiral line is designed to possess. The result of a variation of velocity with frequency is to distort the shape of the pulse produced

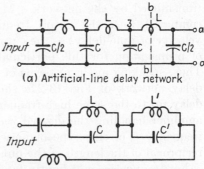

(a) Artificial-line delay network

(b) Pulse-forming network

FIG. 13-24. Lumped-element networks equivalent to the open-circuited lines of Figs. 13-21 and 13-23.

by the line. If such distortion is to be minimized, the delay line must have a velocity of propagation (i.e., group velocity) that is substantially constant up to the same high-frequency limit that would be involved in the design of a video amplifier used to amplify the same pulse.

Another means of avoiding a physically long transmission line is to use an artificial transmission line composed of inductors and capacitors in place of the actual line. Such an arrangement is commonly called a *delay network*, or *pulse-forming network*,[2] and is shown in Fig. 13-24a in a very elementary form. This particular network is a low-pass filter, with a cutoff frequency f_c given by the equation[3]

[1] H. E. Kallman, High Impedance Cable, *Proc. IRE*, vol. 34, p. 348, June, 1946; J. P. Blewett and J. H. Rubel, Video Delay Lines, *Proc. IRE*, vol. 35, p. 1580, December, 1947.

[2] B. Trevor, Jr., Artificial Delay-line Design, *Electronics*, vol. 18, p. 135, June, 1945; H. E. Kallman, Equalized Delay Lines, *Proc. IRE*, vol. 34, p. 646, September, 1946; "Waveforms," *op. cit.*, pp. 730–750; "Components Handbook" (Vol. 17, Radiation Laboratory Series), pp. 191–217, McGraw-Hill Book Company, Inc., New York, 1949. Descriptions of networks for high-power applications, including those devised by E. A. Guillemin, which provide better pulse waveforms with fewer components than networks based on the simple artificial line of Fig. 13-24, will be found in "Pulse Generators" *op. cit.*, pp. 175–224; White, *loc. cit.*; M. C. Wooley, Capacitors for High-voltage Pulse Networks, *Bell Labs. Record*, vol. 25, p. 207, May, 1947.

[3] As shown, the network of Fig. 13-24a corresponds to an open-circuited line. By connecting terminals *aa* together it becomes a short-circuited line. In this case the final capacitor $C/2$ may be omitted since it is short-circuited, and the line then ends in

$$f_c = \frac{1}{\pi \sqrt{LC}} \qquad \text{cycles per second} \qquad (13\text{-}8)$$

where L = inductance per section, henrys

C = capacitance per section, farads

The significance of the cutoff frequency is that higher frequencies are not transmitted by the network. Moreover, only frequencies that are low compared with the cutoff frequency are transmitted with constant velocity or time delay; as the cutoff frequency is approached the velocity of propagation for this particular network tends increasingly to vary. Thus, speaking again in terms of a video amplifier, and noting that the delay network of Fig. 13-24a should have substantially constant time delay up to the same high-frequency limit that would be required in an amplifier handling the desired waveform, it is necessary that the cutoff frequency f_c of this type of network be several times greater than the reciprocal of the length of the pulse to be generated.

For frequencies sufficiently far below cutoff, the delay time τ per section for the structure of Fig. 13-24a, is constant and is given by

$$\tau = \sqrt{LC} \qquad (13\text{-}9)$$

This value of τ is the time required for a transient wave to travel through one section, i.e., from 1 to 2 in Fig. 13-24a. It will be noted that if the cutoff frequency given by Eq. (13-8) is high, the LC product must be small, and the delay time per section given by Eq. (13-9) will likewise be small. Accordingly, a larger number of sections is required for a given time delay when one increases the cutoff frequency in order to obtain a better delay characteristic. This represents the price paid for improved constancy of time delay, and the better waveforms that result.

The artificial line of Fig. 13-24a has a characteristic impedance which is the counterpart of the line impedance R_0 in the previous discussions. For frequencies far below cutoff this impedance is constant and given by

$$R_0 = \sqrt{\frac{L}{C}} \qquad (13\text{-}10)$$

It can be seen by comparing Eqs. (13-9) and (13-10) that the designer has independent control over the time delay and impedance, inasmuch as one is proportional to the product LC, while the other is proportional to the quotient L/C.

The simple network of Fig. 13-24a illustrates the principles involved in artificial lines, but does not make the most efficient use of the inductors

---

a short circuit that is in series with an inductance L. However, sometimes the final inductance placed in series with the short circuit is given the value $L/2$ instead of L. This is equivalent to short-circuiting the line at the point bb in Fig. 13-24a.

and capacitors involved because of the simple structure and the uniformity of the successive sections.   A more sophisticated approach makes use of artificial lines in which the successive sections, while having the same impedance and cutoff frequency, are dissimilar in structure, just as are the different sections of an m-derived filter.   Practical considerations also make it desirable to transform such artificial lines into equivalent two-terminal networks of the type illustrated in Fig. 13-24b.   By means of such refinements, it is possible to obtain the same quality of waveform as given by Fig. 13-24a, while employing a smaller number of network elements.[1]

Pulse Generation with Lines.[2]   Practical pulse generators can be based upon the circuits of Figs. 13-21, 13-22, or 13-23.   For the line required in these circuits it is possible to use a length of actual transmission line (if the desired pulse duration is short), or the spiral delay line, or a pulse-forming network.   The switch shown in the circuits can take various forms, depending on the requirements of voltage, switching rate, etc. For example, a mechanical commutator or rotating contactor is sometimes used.   Alternatively, a rotary spark gap may be preferable for high-voltage applications, in which case a low-resistance spark discharge takes the place of the mechanical contact.   Finally, electronic switching may be utilized, as provided by a gas triode or a high-vacuum triode or pentode.   In this case a square wave of the desired frequency is applied to the control grid of the tube in order to permit or prohibit the flow of plate current, thus providing a switching action in the plate circuit.

The circuit most commonly used in transmission-line-type pulse generators is that of Fig. 13-23.[3,4]   When applied to small laboratory-type

[1] The design of pulse-forming networks of the type shown in Fig. 13-24b is discussed in "Pulse Generators," *loc. cit.*

[2] For discussion of details see "Pulse Generators," *op. cit.*, pp. 225–248; also "Radar System Engineering" (Vol. 1, Radiation Laboratory Series), pp. 374–383, McGraw-Hill Book Company, Inc., New York, 1947.

[3] The charging resistance R_1 in Fig. 13-23 can be replaced if desired by an inductance. In this way all of the energy supplied by the voltage E_0 to the system is delivered to the line to form pulses, instead of only half of the energy as is the case with resistance charging.   Inductance charging is thus always used instead of resistance charging where power efficiency is important, as for example in line-type pulses for radar transmitters.   The considerations involved in the design and analysis of systems using inductance charging are given in "Pulse Generators," *op. cit.*, pp. 354–416.

[4] This circuit is sometimes modified for laboratory applications to permit variation of the pulse length.   The general idea is to associate a gas-triode tube with the output amplifier of the pulse generator in such a manner that when the gas tube is triggered the amplifier output is cut off.   Thus by controlling the instant at which this tube is triggered in relation to the instant the line discharge is started, it is possible to control the pulse length up to a maximum equal to the length of the pulse generated by the line.   For circuit details see G. S. Kan, New 0.07-10 Microsecond General-purpose Pulse Generator, *Hewlett-Packard J.*, vol. 1, February, 1950.

generators, the switching is accomplished by mechanical commutators or relays, or gas triodes. In high-power applications, the switch is normally a rotary spark gap or a large thyratron, frequently of the hydrogen-filled variety because of shorter deionization time compared to the mercury-filled thyratron. The circuit of Fig. 13-23 is particularly applicable for high-power requirements, because in contrast to the circuits in Figs. 13-21 and 13-22 the power source does not need to supply the peak current delivered to the load during the pulse. Instead, the pulse-forming line or network can be slowly charged between pulses from a high-voltage low-current supply.[1]

There are occasions, however, when a long period between pulses is not available for charging the line, thus precluding the use of the circuit of Fig. 13-23. The pulse-generating arrangement shown in Fig. 13-25a can then be used. This is a modification of Fig. 13-22, in which the pentode tube V_1 acts as a switch to give the equivalent circuit of Fig. 13-25b. When a square wave e_1 is applied to the grid of V_1 then a current I_p, corresponding to the plate current of the tube for zero bias,[2] is alternately turned on at time t_1 and off at time t_2. Turning this current on at t_1 produces a pulse of voltage across R_0 having a magnitude equal to $I_p R_0/2$, and a duration equal to twice the length of time it takes a transient wave to travel the length of the line. This pulse is equivalent to the one produced across the line input terminals in Fig. 13-22. Similarly, when the current I_p is turned off at t_2, a similar pulse of opposite polarity is produced, as shown in Fig. 13-25c. If pulses of only one polarity are desired, a clipping circuit can be employed to reject the pulses having the unwanted polarity.

The circuit of Fig. 13-25a can be extended to provide the useful function of generating multiple pulses of precisely fixed duration and time separation. An example of such a circuit is shown in Fig. 13-25d, wherein a lumped-element delay line is shown. The time intervals T_1, T_2, and T_3 designate the one-way delay time of the corresponding sections of the

---

[1] The magnitude of the charging current during the interval $t_0 t_1$ in Fig. 13-23b is determined primarily by the size of resistor R_1. If $R_1 \gg R_0$, the maximum current is E_0/R_1; hence the larger the value of R_1 the smaller is the current. On the other hand, a large value of R_1 results in a longer charging time. The stepped charging curve depicted in Fig. 13-23b follows an exponential path having a time constant approximately equal to $R_1 C'$, where C' is the total capacitance of the line as measured at a low frequency. Since the charging period must last for a time that is three or four times as great as this time constant, if the exponential charging curve is to approach its ultimate value within a few per cent, the period available between successive pulses, i.e., the pulse repetition frequency, is the factor that determines the largest value of R_1 that can be used.

[2] The circuit composed of the capacitor C_c, the diode V_2, and the grid resistor R_g is termed a *clamping* circuit, and serves to set the peak positive level of the square wave e_1 exactly at zero volts, regardless of the amplitude of the square wave.

line.   The various waveforms that result are illustrated in Fig. 13-25e. The waveform at A (the voltage between the point A and ground) is the same as that of e_0 in the original circuit of Fig. 13-25a.   The pulse has a duration equal to twice the total delay time from the terminals where the tube is connected to the short-circuited end of the line [*i.e.*, the pulse length is $2(T_2 + T_1)$].   This same pulse also travels toward the resistive termination R_0, arriving at B after a time T_3.   The pulse at B has the

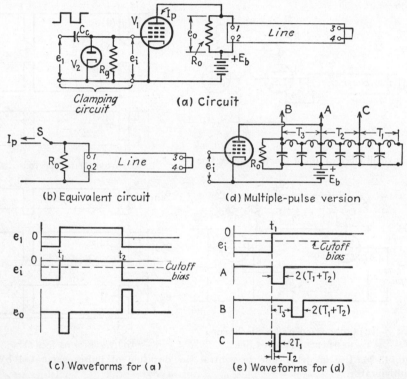

FIG. 13-25. Pulse generator using short-circuited line with high-vacuum pentode as switching element.

same duration as that at A.   In contrast, the pulse appearing at C has a shorter duration, namely, $2T_1$, and is delayed by an amount T_2.   Thus, if it is desired, the two pulses at B and C can be made to occur at the same instant by making T_2 equal to T_3, but one pulse can be made shorter than the other by any specified amount.   On the other hand, two identical pulses having a time separation between their leading edges of T_3 are obtained at terminals A and B.

13-9. Delay-line Control of Pulse Length in the Multivibrator and Blocking Oscillator.   As explained above, in connection with Fig. 13-21, the behavior of the open-circuited line can be interpreted as a delayed open circuit.   Similarly, the short-circuited line illustrated in Fig. 13-22 can be interpreted as representing a delayed short circuit.   These properties can be used in pulse generators of the multivibrator or blocking oscillator types, to control precisely the length of a generated pulse.

Typical circuits of multivibrator pulse generators using delay lines to control the pulse length are illustrated in Fig. 13-26.   The circuit of Fig. 13-26a is the same as that of Fig. 13-8b except that the grid-leak

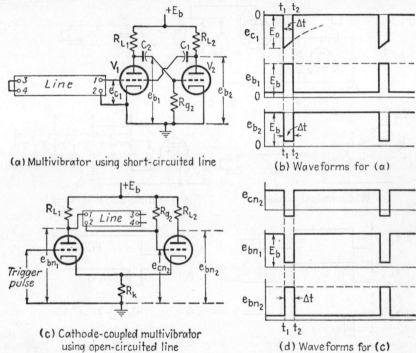

(a) Multivibrator using short-circuited line

(b) Waveforms for (a)

(c) Cathode-coupled multivibrator
using open-circuited line

(d) Waveforms for (c)

Fig. 13-26. Use of delay line to control the duration of pulses generated by a multivibrator.

resistor R_{g_1} of the latter has been replaced by a short-circuited transmission line as shown.   The effect of this change can be explained by reference to the waveforms of Figs. 13-9 and 13-26b.   In Fig. 13-9 the grid voltage e_{c_1} of tube V_1 drops at time t_1 to a large negative value E_0 that is greater than cutoff, after which e_{c_1} rises exponentially according to a time constant approximating $R_{g_1}C_1$.   When the short-circuited delay line of characteristic impedance R_0 is substituted for R_{g_1} then immediately after V_1 stops conducting, $i.e.$, just after t_1, the system behaves as though the grid-leak resistance in Fig. 13-9 had the value R_0, as explained above.[1]

[1] It is to be noted that since the maximum characteristic resistance R_0 that it is practical to obtain in a line is low, of the order of 1000 ohms, the circuit of Fig. 13-26a is the equivalent of a multivibrator with relatively low grid-leak resistance.

However after a time interval $\Delta t = t_2 - t_1$ such that the wave starting down the line at time t_1 has had time to be reflected by the short circuit and return to the line input, then the input terminals 1-2 of the line suddenly behave like a short circuit, causing tube V_1 to start conducting. At this instant, indicated by t_2 in Fig. 13-26b, the half cycle of operation therefore ends. The duration $\Delta t = t_2 - t_1$ of this half cycle depends only upon the delay introduced by the line, provided that Δt does not exceed the corresponding period of the free-running multivibrator in which $R_{g_1} = R_0$. As shown in Fig. 13-26b, the voltage at the plate of tube V_1 contains a positive pulse of duration Δt, while the voltage at the plate of tube V_2 simultaneously possesses a component representing a negative pulse of the same duration.

An open-circuited line can be used in the circuit of Fig. 13-14 to replace the coupling capacitor C_2, as shown in Fig. 13-26c; it will be noted that the line capacitance provides d-c isolation just as does C_2. Referring to the waveforms in Fig. 13-14b, the action taking place at time t_1 is seen to be very much the same as in Fig. 13-14b. At this instant the plate voltage e_{bn_1} on V_1 drops, and causes the grid voltage e_{cn_2} on V_2 to fall simultaneously because of the coupling provided by the equivalent input resistance R_0 that the delay line presents immediately after t_1. The grid potential of V_2 is thereby made more negative than cutoff immediately after t_1. However, at a time t_2 after an interval $\Delta t = t_2 - t_1$ such that a wave can travel the length of the line and return to the input terminals, the input terminals 1-2 suddenly act like an open circuit instead of like a resistance R_0, that is, the delayed open circuit becomes effective as explained above. When this happens the grid of V_2 is suddenly isolated from the plate of V_1, and the grid potential of V_2 jumps from a value more negative than cutoff to a value that is slightly positive, as determined by E_b applied to the grid through the grid-leak resistance R_{g_2}. Tube V_2 accordingly becomes conducting and the half cycle of operation ends. The result is the production of a pulse having a length Δt, as shown in Fig. 13-26d, that is determined only by the length of the line.

Similar results can be obtained with the blocking-oscillator circuit of Figs. 13-15 and 13-16. In Fig. 13-27a, a short-circuited delay line is used. Here the delay line is for convenience connected to the system by means of the third winding on the transformer; its effect is then equivalent to placing a short circuit across the grid winding of the transformer at the delayed time t_2. In Fig. 13-27b the delay line replaces the grid coupling capacitor, and serves as a delayed open circuit in the same way as with the multivibrator in Fig. 13-26c.

In the circuits of Figs. 13-26 and 13-27 the action will correspond exactly to a delayed open circuit or short circuit only if the equivalent resistance of the circuit connected to the input terminals 1-2 of the delay line during the time interval $\Delta t = t_2 - t_1$ of the pulse is equal to the characteristic resistance R_0 of the line. This result can be achieved by placing an appropriate resistance in shunt (or in series) with the input terminals of the line; however, in practice failure to meet this requirement

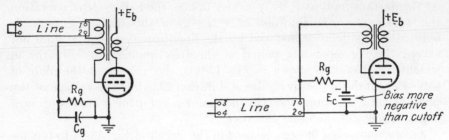

(a) Blocking oscillator with short-circuited control line

(b) One-shot blocking oscillator with open-circuited control line

Fig. 13-27. Use of delay line to control the pulse duration of a blocking oscillator.

does not cause the line to lose control of the pulse length, and such resistors are ordinarily omitted, as in Figs. 13-26 and 13-27.

13-10. Saw-tooth Voltage Generation. A *saw-tooth waveform* is characterized by intervals during which the voltage rises (or falls) linearly with time. It is sometimes referred to as a *triangular waveform,* or a *linear voltage slope.* Two commonly used forms of saw-tooth voltage

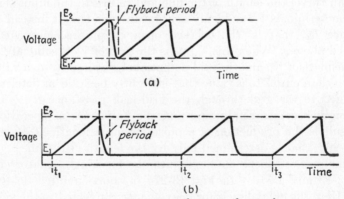

Fig. 13-28. Common types of saw-tooth waveforms.

waveforms are illustrated in Fig. 13-28. In the first type, the successive rising portions are separated by relatively short intervals during which the voltage returns to the starting level; this return is often called the *flyback* period. The second type of waveform is illustrated in Fig. 13-28b, and involves a quiescent period before each linear rise. The starting or triggering times t_1, t_2, etc., of the linear sections of such a wave may then occur either at regular or irregular intervals.

Both types of waveforms shown in Fig. 13-28 find their principal use in connection with the cathode-ray oscilloscope, and are discussed from this point of view in Sec. 13-15 and in Chap. 6.   Such waveforms may also form the basis of circuits for generating a precise time delay, in the manner described in Sec. 13-17.   In both of these applications it is desired that the rising portion of the wave be linear, that the flyback time be a minimum, that there be precise uniformity of the waveform from cycle to cycle,[1] and that synchronization with other waveforms be easily achieved.

13-11. Thyratron Saw-tooth Generator.   A very widely used form of saw-tooth generator is illustrated in Fig. 13-29a.   Here a voltage E_b is

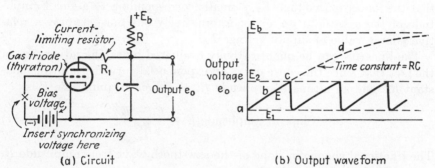

(a) Circuit   (b) Output waveform

FIG. 13-29. Gas-triode (thyratron) type of saw-tooth-wave generator, together with typical waveform.

applied to a circuit consisting of a resistance R and a capacitance C in series.   The plate-cathode circuit of a thyratron is then shunted across C as illustrated in the figure, and the bias of the thyratron is adjusted so that the tube will ionize and thus start conducting when the voltage on the plate, *i.e.*, the voltage across C, reaches a value E_2 chosen by considerations discussed below.

When E_b is first applied to the system, the voltage across C rises exponentially according to the time constant RC, as illustrated by $abcd$ in Fig. 13-29b.   However, when the voltage across C reaches the value E_2 at which the thyratron ionizes, the charge that has been built up on C rapidly flows through the tube,[2] thus causing the voltage across C to drop quickly.   When the voltage across C has fallen to the value E_1 at which ionization can no longer be maintained in the tube, the tube becomes

---

[1] Lack of this uniformity is called "jitter" because it causes the pattern on a cathode oscilloscope to jitter about when a saw-tooth generator possessing a nonuniformity is used to provide the horizontal sweep voltage.

[2] A current-limiting resistance R_1 must in fact be provided in order to prevent the plate current of the tube from being so large as to damage the tube.   The smallest permissible value of R_1 as determined by this consideration, thus determines the shortest flyback time that can be obtained without harming the tube.

nonconducting, voltage again starts to build up across C, and the cycle repeats. The result is a saw-tooth wave of the type illustrated in Fig. 13-29b, consisting of an interval where the voltage rises gradually and approximately linearly (actually exponentially), followed by a rapid fly-back, immediately after which the voltage begins to rise again.

The extent to which the voltage wave in Fig. 13-29b rises linearly with time is determined by the accuracy with which the section abc of the exponential curve can be represented by a straight line. This approxima-tion is better the smaller the ratio E_2/E_b. Thus when linearity is impor-tant, as is usually the case, it is necessary either to adjust the thyratron so that the ionization voltage E_2 is small (corresponding to a small ampli-tude of the saw-tooth wave), or alternatively one must employ a rela-tively large value of supply voltage E_b.

The linearity can be quantitatively evaluated by taking advantage of the fact that since the curve abc is an exponential curve with a time con-stant RC and an ultimate amplitude E_b, the slope at amplitude E is

$$\text{Slope at amplitude } E = \frac{E_b - E}{RC} \qquad (13\text{-}11)$$

The fractional change in slope of the saw-tooth wave from amplitude E_1 to amplitude E_2 is accordingly

$$\begin{aligned}
\left.\begin{array}{l}\text{Fractional change}\\ \text{in slope}\end{array}\right\} &= \frac{(\text{slope at } E_1) - (\text{slope at } E_2)}{\text{slope at } E_1} \\[2mm]
&= \frac{E_2 - E_1}{E_b - E_1} \qquad (13\text{-}12)
\end{aligned}$$

Examination of Eq. (13-12) shows that if E_1 is negligible compared with E_2 and E_b, as is usually the case, then the fractional change in slope is E_2/E_b; that is, if $E_2 = 0.1E_b$, then there is a 10 per cent variation in the slope.

The amplitude of the saw-tooth wave generated in Fig. 13-29 is seen to be $E_2 - E_1$. The value E_1 is determined by the characteristics of the tube, and is usually quite small, such as 10 volts. The ionization voltage E_2 of the thyratron tube can be controlled by adjusting the grid bias of the tube, and where desired can be made only slightly less than the supply voltage E_b. Thus the circuit of Fig. 13-29 is capable of generating a saw-tooth wave having an amplitude $E_2 - E_1$ that is only moderately less than the supply voltage E_b. However, as explained above, the linearity of the waveform will be poor unless E_2 is made much less than the supply voltage E_b. Thus under practical conditions the amplitude that can be generated with a reasonable supply voltage is limited by linearity con-siderations to a relatively small value. If the amplitude desired is larger than can be obtained with reasonable linearity, then amplification of the saw-tooth wave can be resorted to.

Frequency. The time required for each cycle of the saw-tooth voltage wave is approximately the period of the rise from E_1 to E_2, since the time for the flyback is usually small in comparison. Thus the period T is the quotient of the voltage rise $E_2 - E_1$, and the slope as given by Eq. (13-11) for the average amplitude $(E_1 + E_2)/2$;

$$T = RC \frac{E_2 - E_1}{E_b - \dfrac{E_1 + E_2}{2}} \approx RC \frac{E_2}{E_b - \dfrac{E_2}{2}} \tag{13-13}$$

As the frequency approximates $1/T$, one has

$$f \approx \frac{1}{RC} \frac{E_b - (E_2/2)}{E_2} \tag{13-14}$$

The frequency is readily adjustable without altering the amplitude of the waveform by changing either R or C. In practice it is common to provide a coarse adjustment by switching among several capacitors, usually in steps of 10. Then for fine adjustment between steps the resistor R is made continuously variable.

The highest frequency that can be generated with a thyratron saw-tooth generator is determined by the finite time required for the gas ions in the thyratron tube to recombine following the voltage fall. Typically this limit is of the order of 50 kc for tubes employing the lighter gases, and is below 10 kc for mercury-vapor thyratron tubes.

The low-frequency limit is determined by the leakage resistance associated with condenser C; for proper operation this condenser must retain, for the period of one cycle, most of the change it receives from E_b during that cycle. That is to say, the time constant R_2C must be large compared with the period of one cycle, where R_2 is the leakage resistance associated with C. When C is a high-quality condenser, it is possible to generate frequencies of less than 1 cycle per sec.

Synchronization. The thyratron saw-tooth generator, like the multivibrator, will readily synchronize with another waveform. The synchronizing waveform can be a sine wave, square wave, or regularly repeating pulses.

The synchronizing voltage is applied in series with the control grid as indicated in Fig. 13-29a. This causes the ionizing voltage of the thyratron to vary sinusoidally with time as illustrated in Fig. 13-30a, the ionizing voltage being reduced when the synchronizing voltage is positive, and increased when it is negative. If the frequency generated by the free-running saw-tooth-wave oscillator in the absence of the synchronizing voltage approximates or is slightly less than the frequency of the synchronizing voltage, then the presence of the latter voltage will cause exactly one cycle of saw-tooth wave to be generated for each cycle of synchronizing voltage, as in Fig. 13-30a. The extent to which the free-running frequency may be varied without losing synchronization depends upon the amplitude of the synchronizing voltage, and the bias voltage on the thyratron. It is, however, usually desirable for the free-running frequency to be slightly lower than the synchronized frequency.

Increasing the amplitude of the synchronizing voltage produces the effects illustrated in Fig. 13-30b and c. A moderate increase in amplitude will slightly reduce the amplitude of the generated saw-tooth wave, as shown in Fig. 13-30b. However, if the amplitude of the synchronizing voltage is very large, then the amplitude of the saw-tooth wave is greatly reduced, and in addition the possibility is introduced of generating a double saw-tooth, as in Fig. 13-30c.

Synchronization can also be accomplished when the saw-tooth frequency approximates a subharmonic of the sine-wave frequency, as in Fig. 13-30d. In the particular case shown, synchronization occurs in such a manner that four cycles of sine wave elapse for one cycle of the saw-tooth wave. It will also be noted that the free-running frequency of the saw-tooth-wave generator in the absence of synchronizing voltage will be somewhat lower than the synchronized frequency, to the extent that the ionizing voltage E_2'' at point B, compared with the free-running ionizing voltage E_2 at point A, gives a lower frequency in Eq. (13-14). This behavior is typical of subharmonic operation. If the amplitude of the synchronizing voltage in Fig. 13-30d is increased, as shown at e, then the synchronizing ratio will jump to a new value, in this case from 4:1 to 3:1. Still further increase in amplitude would result in the synchronizing ratio becoming first 2:1, and then 1:1.

Successful synchronization with sinusoidal synchronizing voltages depends upon the synchronizing voltage having an adequate but not excessive amplitude, together with a free-running frequency in the absence of synchronization that is properly related to the frequency at which synchronization is to occur. If the amplitude of the synchronizing wave is too small, then the free-running frequency of the saw-tooth generator must approximate very closely the synchronized frequency, and any slight variation of either frequency will cause the two oscillations to fall out of step. On the other hand, excessive amplitude of the synchronizing voltage will unnecessarily reduce the amplitude of the saw-tooth wave. In addition, other undesirable effects may also result from excessive synchronizing amplitude, such as two nonidentical saw-tooth waves per cycle as illustrated in Fig. 13-30c, or in the case of subharmonic operation, synchronization at the wrong frequency ratio. With a suitable amplitude of synchronizing voltage, the ability to maintain synchronization with variations in operating conditions is greatest when the free-running frequency of the saw-tooth-wave generator is lower than the synchronized frequency. This is increasingly the case the greater the amplitude of the synchronizing voltage and the higher the subharmonic

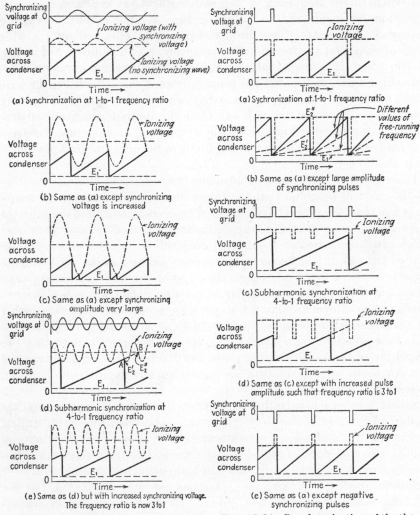

Fig. 13-30. Synchronization of the thyratron saw-tooth generator of Fig. 13-29 with a sine-wave synchronizing voltage.

Fig. 13-31. Synchronization of the thyratron saw-tooth generator of Fig. 13-29 with regularly repeating pulses.

ratio. In general, both the amplitude of the synchronizing voltage and the free-running frequency of the saw-tooth-wave generator become more critical in subharmonic operation as the frequency ratio increases.

Synchronizing with a pulse waveform is illustrated in Fig. 13-31a for the case of positive-going pulses applied to the grid of the thyratron. Each such pulse momentarily reduces the ionizing potential of the thyratron tube as shown, and causes the tube to conduct if the saw-tooth-wave amplitude at that moment is at all appreciable.   When it is desired that the synchronized frequency of the saw-tooth wave be the same as the repetition frequency of the pulses, pulses of large amplitude can be employed.   Satisfactory synchronization is then obtained over a wide range of values for the free-running frequency.   This is illustrated in Fig. 13-31b, where it is seen that any value of free-running frequency corresponding to E_2 in Eq. (13-14) ranging from E_2' to E_2'' will synchronize satisfactorily.   It will be noted, however, that the free-running frequency must always be equal to or lower than the desired synchronized frequency.   Within this limitation, the only effect of changing the free-running frequency is to alter the amplitude of the synchronized saw-tooth wave that is generated.

Pulse synchronization at subharmonic frequencies is illustrated in Fig. 13-31c.   It will be noted that the free-running frequency must be somewhat less than the desired synchronized frequency, and that the range of free-running frequencies (*i.e.*, the variation in slope of the saw-tooth over which synchronization at the desired ratio will occur) is now much more limited than in b, and becomes increasingly limited as the subharmonic ratio becomes greater.   In the case of subharmonic synchronization, increasing the amplitude of the synchronizing pulses will cause the frequency ratio of synchronization to decrease progressively, accompanied by a decrease in amplitude of the saw-tooth, as illustrated in Fig. 13-31d. It is thus apparent that increasing care must be used in adjusting the amplitude of the synchronizing pulse and the free-running frequency of the saw-tooth-wave generator, as subharmonic synchronization at an increasingly great frequency ratio is desired.

Satisfactory synchronization cannot be obtained with negative pulses applied to the grid of the thyratron tube.   This condition is illustrated in Fig. 13-31e, and allows synchronization to occur only over a very limited range of slope of the saw-tooth wave; *i.e.*, the free-running frequency must be critically adjusted to obtain synchronization.

Synchronization with a square wave has not been illustrated, but the behavior closely follows that of pulses.   In general, the ease of adjustment and the stability of the synchronization are nearly as good with a square wave as with pulses, and in both cases are considerably better than with a sine wave of the same frequency.

13-12. Saw-tooth Generators Using High-vacuum Tubes.   The switching function provided by the gas triode in the circuit of Fig. 13-29 can also be provided by a high-vacuum tube.   However, since the high-vacuum tube does not have ionizing and extinction voltages, free-running operation is not possible.[1]   Instead, tube V_1 is alternately switched between conducting and nonconducting action by a suitable control voltage applied to the grid of the high-vacuum triode, as shown in Fig. 13-32a.   This control voltage is preferably a square wave e_1 that is passed through the clamping circuit represented by C_c, V_2, and R_g (see footnote 2, page 570).   In this way the grid voltage of V_1 alternates between zero and a bias sufficiently negative to cut off the plate current.

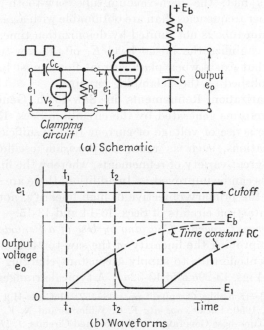

(a) Schematic

(b) Waveforms

Fig. 13-32. Saw-tooth-wave generator employing high-vacuum triode, together with typical waveforms.

During the interval when the plate current is cut off, the output voltage e_0 across the condenser C rises exponentially in exactly the same way as does the voltage e_0 in the thyratron circuit of Fig. 13-29 when the thyratron tube is nonconducting.   During the next interval, when the voltage at the grid is zero, a large plate current flows.   Condenser C then discharges rapidly until its voltage falls to the value E_1 corresponding to the voltage that would exist at the plate if condenser C were removed and the

---

[1] Free-running action can be obtained, however, by modifying the circuit so that the discharge tube is controlled by a trigger action that is initiated when the linear portion of the wave reaches the desired maximum amplitude; thus see H. den Hartog and F. A. Muller, Oscilloscope Time Base Circuit, *Wireless Eng.*, vol. 24, p. 287, October, 1947; also see O. S. Puckle, "Time Bases," 2d ed., John Wiley & Sons, Inc., New York, 1951.

tube operated at zero bias with supply voltage E_b applied to the plate in series with resistance R. The voltage across C then remains at the value E_1 until the next half cycle of the switching voltage, when V_1 becomes nonconducting and the cycle repeats. The resulting output waveform is as shown in Fig. 13-32b, and is seen to be of the type illustrated in Fig. 13-26b. In order for the time of fall of the saw-tooth wave to be small, it is necessary that the current drawn by the tube be very large. When this requirement is met, the high-vacuum-tube saw-tooth generator can operate at higher frequencies than are obtainable with a gas tube, because the high-vacuum tube is not limited by deionization time.

In order to stabilize the initial level E_1 of the saw-tooth, the grid-voltage level that exists when plate current flows must be carefully set. This is accomplished by the "clamping circuit."

13-13. Linearization Refinements in Saw-tooth Generators.[1] The saw-tooth waveforms generated by the circuits in Secs. 13-11 and 13-12 do not provide a rise of voltage or current that is sufficiently linear for certain applications, such as radar or precision oscillographic work. There exists a great variety of refinements, whereby the linearity of most of these circuits can be improved.[2] In addition, there are several circuits designed with the primary objective of high linearity, notably the feedback and phantastron circuits of Secs. 13-14 and 13-15.

Constant-current Capacitor Charging by Use of a Pentode. A standard approach to improving the linearity of the saw-tooth generator involves the use of a pentode tube to supply a constant charging current to the capacitor C in Figs. 13-29a and 13-32a. A typical arrangement[3] is shown

[1] S. Seely, "Electron-tube Circuits," pp. 448–452, McGraw-Hill Book Company, Inc., New York, 1950; Puckle, *op. cit.;* F. C. Williams and N. F. Moody, Ranging Circuits, Linear Time-base Generators and Associated Circuits, *J. IEE (Radiolocation Conv.*), vol. 93, pt. IIIA, p. 1188, March–May, 1946; Arthur C. Clarke, Linearity Circuits, *Wireless Eng.*, vol. 21, p. 256, June, 1944, vol. 22, p. 72, February, 1945; H. den Hartog and Robert P. Owen, Linear Sweep Circuits, *Electronics*, vol. 19, p. 136, December, 1946.

[2] One linearization technique of only minor importance utilizes the curvature of the plate-current–plate-voltage characteristic of the tube to compensate for the curvature of the exponential charging curve. This technique has only limited utility, because it depends too much on the details of the tube characteristics, and hence the linearization will vary from tube to tube.

[3] In practical circuits the screen battery E_s is usually replaced by a resistance connected between E_b and the screen, together with a large by-pass condenser between screen and cathode which maintains a constant screen voltage during the saw-tooth oscillation. The only effect of this change is to cause the condenser charging current L_{b_2} to be augmented by the d-c component of the screen current. However, if the plate voltage always exceeds the value a in Fig. 13-33d, the charging current is still independent of variations in the voltage e_{b_2} acting between plate and cathode.

An optional circuit element often included is the unby-passed cathode resistor shown dotted in Fig. 13-33a. This provides negative current feedback that assists in

in Fig. 13-33a which differs from Fig. 13-32a only in that the resistor R has been replaced by the plate-cathode circuit of pentode V_2.   To the extent that the operating conditions are properly chosen, a matter to be taken up shortly, the pentode will deliver a constant current to the capacitor C during the time interval between t_1 and t_2.   Accordingly, the

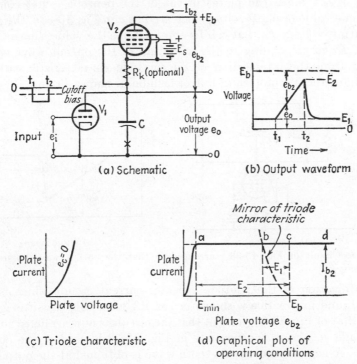

(a) Schematic

(b) Output waveform

(c) Triode characteristic

(d) Graphical plot of operating conditions

FIG. 13-33.   Saw-tooth-wave generator of Fig. 13-32 modified by use of a pentode to obtain constant-current charging.

capacitor voltage will rise linearly with time as a result of this constant charging current, instead of exponentially as in Fig. 13-32.   The slope of the rise is I_{b_2}/C volts per second, where I_{b_2} is the pentode plate current in amperes, and C is in farads.

The tube operating conditions necessary for proper functioning of this circuit can best be explained by reference to c and d of Fig. 13-33.   Here the plate-voltage–plate-current characteristic of triode V_1 is shown at c for zero grid bias, $i.e.$, for the condition that exists when tube V_1 conducts. Similarly, the plate-voltage–plate-current characteristic for the constant-

making the magnitude of the current I_{b_2} still less sensitive to variations in e_{b_2}.   Another variation consists in replacing the pentode by a triode that is given a constant-current characteristic by the use of current feedback provided by a large cathode resistor; see David Sayre, Linear Sweep Generation, *Electronics*, vol. 23, p. 171, July, 1950.

current pentode V_2 is given at d for the screen and control-grid voltages at which this tube operates.   This characteristic exhibits the usual region $abcd$ over which the plate current is substantially independent of plate voltage e_{b_2}.   The plate voltage e_{b_2} actually applied to the tube is the difference between the supply voltage E_b and the output voltage e_0, that is, $E_b = e_{b_2} + e_0$.   Since the plate current of the pentode is not constant below some value of plate voltage indicated as a in Fig. 13-33d, the maximum output voltage E_2 that can be obtained has the value shown.   The value of E_1 corresponding to the minimum of the output wave can be obtained from the intersection of the pentode characteristic with the triode characteristic plotted in mirror fashion as shown in d.

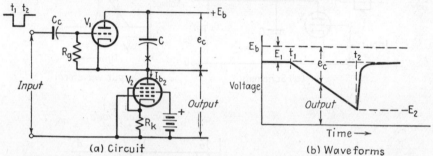

(a) Circuit   (b) Wave forms

FIG. 13-34. Circuit of Fig. 13-33 rearranged so that the output wave possesses a negative slope.

A modification of the pentode constant-current circuit which is frequently found in practice is shown in Fig. 13-34.   This circuit is equivalent to that of Fig. 13-33,[1] except that the circuit is now arranged so that the voltage e_{b_2} across the pentode in Fig. 13-33 is used as the output voltage.   A negative-going saw-tooth wave is obtained at the output, as indicated.   Such a waveform is as useful in most applications as is the positive-going saw-tooth previously discussed.

Although a high-vacuum triode has been shown as the switching tube in the circuits of Figs. 13-33 and 13-34, it is equally feasible to use a gas triode. In such a case it is possible to make the circuit self-oscillating, as was the gas-triode circuit of Fig. 13-29; the limits E_1 and E_2 in Figs. 13-33 and 13-34 would then correspond to the extinction and ionization potentials, respectively, of the gas triode.

Bootstrap Circuit.   Another means of obtaining a constant current for the charging of a capacitor is provided by the so-called *bootstrap circuit* shown schematically in Fig. 13-35.   Here the capacitor C is charged through the resistor R by a voltage consisting of E plus the output voltage e_0 of the cathode-coupler stage V_1.   Since the cathode-coupled stage has

[1] In this circuit, C_c, R_g, and the rectifying action between the grid and cathode of V_1, provide a clamping action that causes the grid-cathode voltage of V_1 to be zero when the rectangular input wave is positive.

an amplification only barely less than unity, then $e_0 \approx e_c$, and the voltage available to act across resistance R approximates the value E quite closely. The current flowing through R to charge the condenser C is hence very nearly constant at the value E/R. The result is constant-current charging of C that is substantially equivalent to that obtained by the use of the pentode in Fig. 13-33a. Saw-tooth waves are then generated by shunting C with a switching system consisting of a gas triode, or a high-vacuum triode with square-wave control voltage. The output voltage e_0 is the voltage e_c developed across the condenser C, as amplified by the cathode-follower stage V_1; this provides the incidental benefit of a low output impedance typical of a cathode-follower circuit.

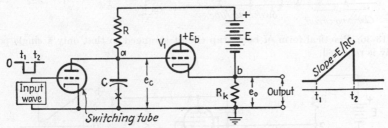

FIG. 13-35. Bootstrap saw-tooth-wave generator.

The name "bootstrap" comes from the fact that the potentials at points a and b in Fig. 13-35 rise simultaneously with respect to ground as the capacitor C charges. These potentials are thus "raised by their own bootstraps."

The bootstrap circuit is extremely effective in generating a closely linear voltage rise. Also, an output saw-tooth voltage waveform of very large amplitude can be obtained by making E_b large, and using a transmitting tube for V_1.

A practical form of the bootstrap circuit is shown in Fig. 13-36, in which the triode V_3 serves as the switch to which is applied a square wave clamped as in Fig. 13-32a. Also the ungrounded battery E in Fig. 13-35 has been replaced by the voltage E_{c_2} resulting from a charge built up on capacitor C_2 by the aid of diode V_2. Thus prior to the time t_1, when the capacitor C is essentially short-circuited by triode V_3, the capacitor C_2 is charged through diode V_2 and R_k to a voltage that is only slightly less than E_b. By using a capacitance C_2 that is very large compared with capacitance C, the voltage E_{c_2} across C_2 remains essentially constant during the interval while the capacitor C is charging, and serves the same function as the battery voltage E in Fig. 13-35.

The voltage slope that results from the bootstrap circuit can be readily computed by assuming that the gain of the cathode-follower stage is exactly unity. If this is the case, the current through the resistor R is equal to E/R in Fig. 13-35, and is almost, but not quite, $(E_b - E_1)/R$ in

Fig. 13-36. When this constant current flows into the capacitor C, the rate of voltage rise across the capacitor is equal to the current divided by the capacitance.

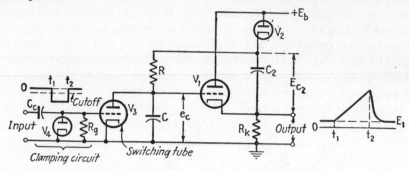

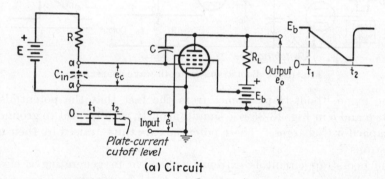

Fig. 13-36. Practical form of bootstrap circuit arranged so that only a single power supply is required.

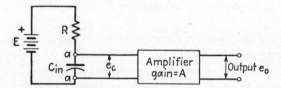

(a) Circuit

(b) Equivalent circuit between t_1 and t_2

Fig. 13-37. A simple form of feedback, or Miller integrator, circuit for generating a linear saw-tooth wave.

13-14. Linearization Refinements in Saw-tooth-wave Generators. Feedback (Miller Integrator) Circuits.

The circuit shown in Fig. 13-37a is a form of saw-tooth generator having very desirable characteristics. It is known as a feedback, or "Miller" integrator,[1] and possesses a very

[1] The circuit described here is frequently referred to in the literature as the "Miller" integrator. This has come about from the fact that the circuit exploits and enhances the so-called "Miller effect," a phenomenon first noted in connection with the input

linear slope, a saw-tooth voltage having a peak-to-peak value only slightly less than the supply voltage, and insensitivity to tube and circuit characteristics.

The tube in the circuit provides several functions.   First, it is an amplifier of the saw-tooth waveform which is generated at its grid in a manner to be explained.   Second, it is a switching device; a control voltage is applied to the suppressor grid, thereby turning the plate current on or off. Finally, the tube provides an input capacitance C_{in} which is charged from the battery[1] E through high series resistance R to provide the basic saw-tooth waveform.

The operation of the circuit of Fig. 13-37 can be understood by the following explanation, with the aid of the oscillograms shown in Fig. 13-38: To begin with, a rectangular control waveform e_1 is applied to the suppressor grid of the tube in order to switch the plate current on at time t_1 and off at time t_2.   This waveform of voltage is applied through a clamping circuit (not shown in the figure but analogous to that in Fig. 13-32a) so that the most positive portion of the wave is at zero voltage, which corresponds to the normal suppressor-grid voltage for a pentode amplifier tube.   Prior to the time t_1, and also following the time t_2, the control waveform e_1 makes the suppressor grid sufficiently negative so that plate current in the tube is cut off.

Just prior to the time t_1, the plate current is zero, and hence the output voltage is equal to E_b.   The control-grid voltage e_c is approximately zero, although very slightly positive by virtue of the grid being connected to the positive voltage E through the resistance R.   The control grid cannot go appreciably positive, because the resistance R is large compared with the plate resistance of the equivalent diode comprising the grid-cathode portion of the tube.

At the time t_1 when plate current is permitted to flow in the tube, there occurs a slight readjustment of the circuit voltages before generation of the saw-tooth voltage begins.   Plate current will immediately begin to flow through the load resistor R_L, and there will be a fall in voltage at the plate.   This fall in plate voltage is coupled through capacitor C to the grid, thus driving the grid voltage in the negative direction.   The grid

impedance of triodes, and described by J. M. Miller in Dependence on the Input Impedance of a Three Electrode Vacuum Tube upon the Load in the Plate Circuit, *Natl. Bur. Standards (U.S.) Sci. Paper* 351, 1918.   The application of this effect to integrating circuits or saw-tooth-voltage generators is credited to the late A. D. Blumlein by his colleague F. C. Williams; see Introduction to Circuit Techniques for Radiolocation, *J. IEE (Radiolocation Conv.)*, vol. 93, pt. IIIA, p. 303, 1946.   Further discussion of the circuit is given by Williams and Moody, *op. cit.;* also see "Waveforms," *op. cit.*, pp. 37, 195, 278–287.

[1] A separate battery E is shown for clarity.   In practice the plate-supply voltage E_b is commonly used for this purpose.

voltage will fall by an amount shown as E_0 in Fig. 13-38, which is just sufficient to counteract further increase in plate current, and further fall in plate voltage. Because of the coupling through capacitor C, both grid and plate voltages fall by the same amount E_0.

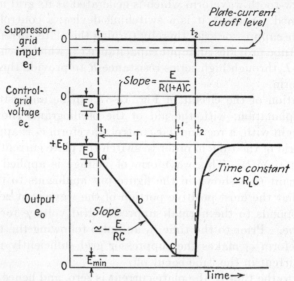

FIG. 13-38. Waveforms showing the behavior of the feedback (Miller integrator) circuit of Fig. 13-37.

The tube is now ready to function as an amplifier, and the action during this stage of the operation can best be understood by reference to the equivalent circuit of Fig. 13-37b. The amplifier provides a gain A, which is equal to the usual product of the transconductance g_m times the load resistance R_L. In addition, the amplifier provides the input capacitance C_{in} at the terminals aa. The value of the input capacitance C_{in} is determined primarily by the feedback action through the capacitor C, and assumes the value[1]

$$C_{in} \approx C(1 + A) \tag{13-15}$$

where C = feedback capacitance (see Fig. 13-37a)

　　A = amplification of pentode circuit ($= g_m R_L$)

The capacitor C_{in} now is charged by the battery E through the resistor R. The capacitor voltage e_c rises exponentially, with a time constant equal to RC_{in}. The initial portion of this curve of voltage is very closely a straight line, with a slope equal to

[1] F. E. Terman, "Radio Engineers' Handbook," p. 467, McGraw-Hill Book Company, Inc., New York, 1943. Capacitance C is large compared with the interelectrode capacitances of the tube, and hence the latter are neglected in Eq. (13-15).

$$\text{Slope of } e_c \text{ waveform} = \frac{E}{RC_{in}} \qquad (13\text{-}16)$$

The notation is as in Fig. 13-37 and Eq. (13-15).

This rising voltage e_c across C_{in} is amplified by the tube, which also reverses its polarity.   The voltage hence appears as a linearly falling voltage e_0 at the output terminals, as shown by the line segment abc in the oscillogram of Fig. 13-38.   The magnitude of this slope will be $-A$ times the slope at the input of the amplifier as given by Eq. (13-16), so that

$$\text{Slope of } e_0 \text{ waveform} = -A\,\frac{E}{RC_{in}} \qquad (13\text{-}17)$$

$$= -A\,\frac{E}{R[C(1+A)]}$$

When $A \gg 1$ this becomes

$$\text{Slope of } e_0 \text{ waveform} \approx -\frac{E}{RC} \qquad (13\text{-}18)$$

The interval T (Fig. 13-38), during which the output voltage e_0 falls linearly with time, can be terminated in either of two possible ways.   The first of these is illustrated in the figure.   When the output voltage, which is also the plate voltage of the tube, has fallen to some value designated as E_{min} in Fig. 13-38, the tube ceases to amplify.   This minimum voltage corresponds to the condition in a pentode when a virtual cathode is formed in the suppressor-grid region, and the plate current is thus not appreciably influenced by control-grid voltage.   Under these conditions the amplification drops, which causes the input capacitance to become small [see Eq. (13-15)].   The control-grid potential then quickly returns to the potential it possessed prior to the time t_1.   The plate, on the other hand, continues to conduct current, and the plate voltage will remain at the level E_{min} until the time t_2, when the control voltage e_1 applied to the suppressor grid cuts off the plate current.   At this time, the plate voltage will return to the level of the battery voltage E_b, but in so doing the capacitor C must be charged through the load resistor R_L.   Thus the plate voltage will rise exponentially, with a time constant[1] closely equal to $R_L C$.

The second way of terminating the interval T during which the output voltage falls linearly, is for the control waveform to cut off the plate current before the output voltage reaches its minimum level.   For this to happen, the time t_2 of the control wave applied to the suppressor in Fig. 13-38 must occur before the sloping wave decreases to its minimum value E_{min}.   When this happens both grid and plate voltages would return to

[1] The charging current also flows through the grid-cathode circuit of the tube, but the resistance of this circuit is usually small compared with the load resistance R_L and so does not appreciably affect the time constant.

their initial values simultaneously, although the plate-voltage return curve would be controlled by the time constant $R_L C$ as before. This method of terminating the linear wave is shown in Fig. 13-39.

A remarkable and valuable feature of the circuit is apparent from Eq. (13-18), where it can be seen that the slope of the output voltage is independent of the magnitude of amplification A, provided only that A is much greater than unity. Thus the slope depends only upon the voltage E, the resistance R, and the capacitance C, and is independent of other circuit constants and of the tube characteristics.

Another important feature is that the amplitude of the linear falling portion of the output-voltage waveform can be made a substantial percentage of the supply voltage E_b without introducing nonlinearity. This is in contrast to the simpler circuits of Figs. 13-29, 13-32, and 13-33, where the output amplitude must not exceed a small fraction of the total supply voltage if the saw-tooth waveform is to be closely linear. This feature results from the fact that the large amplification of the small charging voltage waveform e_c, makes it possible to limit e_c to a very small fraction indeed of the supply voltage E. At the same time, the feedback action associated with condenser C causes the output slope to be independent of the tube amplification A, and hence of tube nonlinearities. The result obtained is therefore superior to simply adding an amplifier to the saw-tooth generator of Fig. 13-29 or 13-32.

From the above discussion it can be seen that the feedback, or Miller integrator, circuit possesses an important combination of features. Moreover, the circuit is not only usable in its basic form as shown in Fig. 13-37, but there are several modifications to be described below which provide additional valuable properties.

Modifications. One modification of the basic Miller integrator circuit eliminates the initial voltage drop E_0 shown in Fig. 13-38. Actually this drop is only about 5 volts for $E_b = 300$, but if circumstances require a saw-tooth waveform without this drop, the circuit of Fig. 13-39 can be used. The new circuit differs from the original version by virtue of the fact that prior to the time t_1, when the saw-tooth voltage is to be initiated, the control grid is held at exactly the potential $-E_0$, and is thus ready to commence its linear slope without further readjustment. The control waveform is applied through diode V_3, which prior to time t_1 is not conducting. Diode V_2 is conducting, however, and prevents the grid voltage from rising above the level $-E_0$, as determined by the bias battery E_c and the voltage divider consisting of resistors R_1 and R_2. This same pair of resistors is designed to draw sufficient current through the load resistor R_L to set the initial plate-voltage level at the value $E_b - E_0$, which in Fig. 13-38 was the level existing just after the initial readjustment had taken place. Accordingly, the circuit of Fig. 13-39 is in readiness at the time t_1 to commence the generation of a linear slope if diode V_2 can be then "disconnected." This is accomplished by the fact that at time t_1 the positive-going input wave causes conduction in diode V_3; this raises the cathode of diode V_2 to a potential more positive than its anode. Thus V_2 ceases conduction, and is effectively disconnected. The circuit is now free to function in the same manner as the original circuit, and a linear voltage slope will be generated as illustrated by the waveforms in Fig. 13-39b. At the time t_2, the control waveform restores the circuit to its

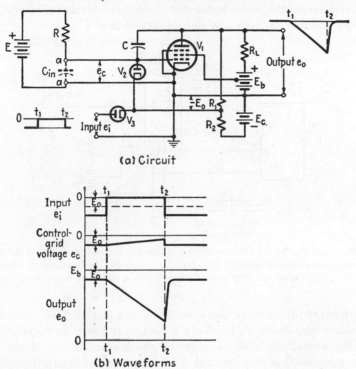

FIG. 13-39. Modification of the feedback (Miller integrator) circuit of Fig. 13-37 that eliminates the initial voltage jump at the beginning of the linear slope.

original condition, except that, as before, the plate voltage will rise at a rate corresponding to the time constant $R_L C$.

In some circumstances it may be important that the circuit of Fig. 13-37 be restored to its original plate voltage as quickly as possible following the time t_2, so that another saw-tooth wave can be initiated immediately thereafter. All that is required to achieve this result is a low-resistance circuit for charging the capacitor C; such a circuit is provided by the modification shown in Fig. 13-40.[1] In this modification, cathode-follower stage V_2 is introduced as shown. Since the voltage gain of such a stage approximates unity, the feedback effect associated with C is just as

[1] Separate batteries E, E_b, and E_{b_2} are shown for clarity. In practice a common supply voltage E_b serves for all three.

though terminal b of this capacitor were connected directly to d as in Fig. 13-38. However, at time t_2 the capacitor C is now charged from battery E_{b_2} through a low resistance that is effectively the parallel combination of R_k and the plate resistance of V_2. This provides a very small time constant, and as a result the cathode of V_2 and the plate of V_1 rise very quickly after t_2 to their original voltage levels. A further advantage of the modified circuit of Fig. 13-40 is that the linear voltage slope can now be obtained across the cathode resistor R_k of the cathode follower. Thus the circuit will have a very low output impedance.

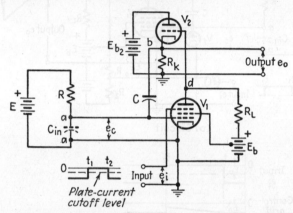

FIG. 13-40. Modification of the feedback (Miller integrator) circuit of Fig. 13-37 in which the recovery time of the output voltage at the end of the linear slope is shortened by employing a cathode-follower tube V_2 to provide a low-resistance charging circuit for condenser C.

A further modification of the original circuit of Fig. 13-37 is shown in Fig. 13-41, where diode V_2 has been added to provide a convenient control of the amplitude and duration of the linear voltage slope. This diode, in combination with battery E_2 and potentiometer P_1, functions as a clipping circuit, and limits the positive excursion of the plate voltage for output waveform e_0.* Three settings of the potentiometer P_1 are designated as A, B, and C; the corresponding waveforms that result are shown in Fig. 13-41b. Here the initial level of the output waveform e_0 has three different values corresponding to the three potentiometer settings, but the slope of the linear fall, and also the minimum voltage level $E_{\min}$ are the same in each case. As a result, the length of time required for the output voltage to drop to the minimum level is different in the three cases, resulting in three different periods T_A, T_B, and T_C.

* A diode connected like V_2 in Fig. 13-41 is usually referred to as a "plate-catching diode" because of the way it "catches," or arrests, the positive excursion of the plate voltage. Diodes are used to advantage in this way to set quiescent plate-voltage levels in various other circuits such as multivibrators.

13-15. Linearization in Saw-tooth-wave Generators. The Phantastron Circuit.[1] The phantastron is a modified Miller integrator circuit which is arranged so that a control voltage in the form of a trigger pulse will cause the circuit to go through one cycle of operation and then become quiescent until a new cycle is initiated by a later pulse. Thus a trigger

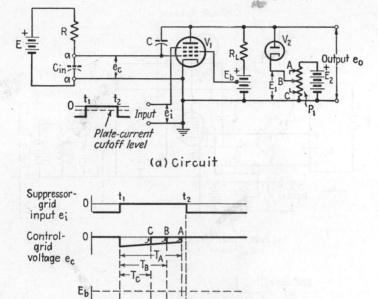

(a) Circuit

(b) Waveforms

FIG. 13-41. Feedback (Miller integrator) circuit in which the maximum value of the output voltage is controlled by the setting of the potentiometer P_1.

pulse initiates the sequence of events in the Miller integrator, but the circuit is arranged to terminate its own operation.

A functional circuit diagram, together with resulting waveforms, is shown in Fig. 13-42. In Fig. 13-42a the circuit has been drawn to resemble the basic circuit of Fig. 13-37 together with the cathode-follower

[1] An excellent summary of the origin and practical possibilities of the phantastron circuit is given by R. N. Close and M. T. Lebenbaum, Design of Phantastron Time Delay Circuits, *Electronics*, vol. 21, p. 100, April, 1948; the design data in Fig. 13-43 are taken from this paper. Other descriptions of the phantastron are to be found in "Waveforms," *op. cit.*, pp. 195–204, 287; Williams and Moody, *loc. cit.*; "Principles of Radar," *op. cit.*, pp. 2-58–2-56.

and diode-clipper modifications as described in connection with Figs. 13-40 and 13-41. An important difference is that a cathode resistor R_{k_1} has been added to the integrator circuit; the consequences of this are discussed below. A pentagrid tube is shown in Fig. 13-42a for V_1; it functions the same as the pentode amplifier in Fig. 13-37, but has the advan-

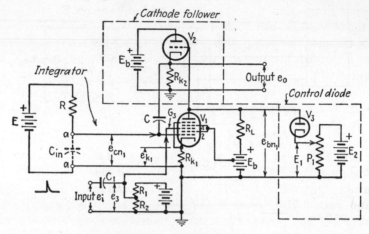

(a) Functional circuit diagram

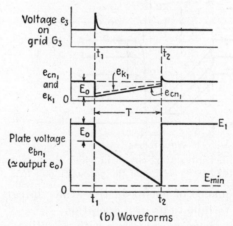

(b) Waveforms

Fig. 13-42. Functional circuit and waveforms of phantastron circuit.

tage that the required control voltage amplitude is less than with the pentode tube. Grids 2 and 4 are connected together to serve as a screen grid, while grid 3 serves to turn the plate current on and off, as did the suppressor grid in the pentode of Fig. 13-37.

The action taking place in Fig. 13-42a can be explained with the aid of the waveforms in Fig. 13-42b. Prior to the time t_1, when a trigger pulse initiates the cycle of operation, the voltage divider comprising resistors R_1 and R_2 sets the d-c voltage on grid 3 at a level that cuts off the plate current in tube V_1.   The plate voltage e_{bn_1} is then at its maximum positive value E_1 as limited by the diode V_3.   To the extent that the gain of the cathode follower V_2 is equal to unity, the output voltage will also be equal to E_1 prior to the time t_1.   The control-grid voltage on V_1 approximates the cathode voltage, although it is slightly positive with respect to the cathode because the control-grid connection is returned to the positive voltage E through high resistance R.   Since the cathode voltage e_{k_1} of V_1 is substantially positive with respect to ground by virtue of the screen current flowing through the cathode resistor R_{k_1}, the control-grid voltage e_{cn_1} prior to t_1 is also positive with respect to ground by an amount approximating e_{k_1}.

At the time t_1, a large positive trigger pulse is superimposed upon the steady voltage on grid 3 of V_1, which carries grid 3 sufficiently positive to permit plate current to flow.   Exactly as in the case of the basic Miller integrator circuit of Fig. 13-37, there now occurs an initial readjustment in plate and control-grid voltages, whereby both are driven negative by an amount E_0.   The phantastron circuit behavior is different, however, owing to the presence of the cathode resistor R_{k_1}.   As the control-grid voltage of V_1 drops, so also will the cathode voltage because the reduced space current reduces the voltage drop in R_{k_1}; the result is that although the trigger pulse quickly disappears, the d-c voltage on grid 3 is now sufficiently positive with respect to the new and lower cathode voltage so that plate current can continue to flow.   Therefore the circuit continues to function as a generator of a linear voltage slope, until the time when the plate voltage reaches the minimum value E_{min} where the tube ceases to amplify.   At this time, shown as t_2 in Fig. 13-42b, the control-grid[1] and cathode voltages e_{cn_1} and e_{k_1}, respectively, simultaneously rise quickly. The change in cathode voltage results from the fact that the presence of R_{k_1} in the circuit causes the cathode voltage to ground to vary with the space current, and hence to rise and fall as the control grid becomes more and less positive, respectively, as shown in the second oscillogram of Fig. 13-42b.   As a result, both the plate voltage e_{bn_1} and the output voltage e_0 return at time t_2 to their original quiescent values E_1, since the cathode voltage rises to a value sufficiently positive with respect to the d-c potential of grid 3 to stop the flow of plate current.   Thus the cycle of

---

[1] The momentary overshoot shown for the waveform of e_{cn_1} arises from the fact that at t_2 the charge delivered to C during the interval $T = t_2 - t_1$ must be discharged through the grid-cathode circuit of the tube and so causes the control-grid voltage to be momentarily appreciably positive with respect to the cathode.   This overshoot is not transmitted to the output, however, because the plate current of V_1 has already been cut off.

operation is completed, and the circuit will remain in a quiescent condition until another input pulse is applied.

The duration of the period T is readily varied by adjusting the voltage E_1 associated with diode V_3, as explained in connection with Fig. 13-41. This voltage affects only the initial level of the output waveform; the slope of the linear fall in voltage, and the minimum level E_{min} are both

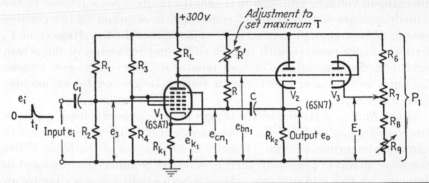

Maximum period T	Recommended circuit constants[1] including permissible manufacturers' tolerances and required wattage rating of resistors													
	R_L 20% 1w*	R_1 5% 2w	R_2 5% 1w	R_3 5% 10w	R_4 5% 1w	R_6 20% 1w	R_7 Linear to 0.1%	R_8 20% 10w	R_9 Variable 2w	R_{k_1} 5% 2w	R_{k_2} 20% 5w	R 10% 1w	R' 20% 2w	C 10%
500 μsec	1 meg	68,000	5,600	20,000	8,200	12,000	20,000	3,000	5,000	10,000	25,000	1 meg	0.1 meg	90 μμf
2,500 μsec	2 meg	68,000	6,200	20,000	6,200	12,000	20,000	3,000	5,000	10,000	25,000	1 meg	0.1 meg	475 μμf
10,000 μsec	5 meg*	50,000	5,000	15,000	5,600	12,000	20,000	3,000	5,000	10,000	25,000	1 meg	0.1 meg	2,000 μμf
50,000 μsec	5 meg*	50,000	5,000	15,000	5,600	12,000	20,000	3,000	5,000	10,000	25,000	1 meg	0.1 meg	10,000μμf

* Required rating 5 megohm resistor = 0.5 watt

[1] From Close and Lebenbaum.

FIG. 13-43. A practical form of phantastron circuit, together with recommended circuit constants for typical designs.

unchanged by altering E_1. As a consequence of this situation, the duration T is accurately proportional to E_1.

It is to be observed that in Fig. 13-42 the termination of the interval T is now determined by the instant that the plate voltage on V_1 reaches its minimum level E_{min}, and is not due to an external control waveform. This, and the fact that the control wave is a trigger pulse instead of a square or rectangular waveform, are the essential features of the phantastron, in contrast to the basic Miller integrator circuit. The slope of the waveform is the same in both cases, and is still independent of tube amplification and all circuit constants except E, R, and C, as in Eq. (13-18).

A practical form of the phantastron is given in Fig. 13-43, together with design information that will be found useful if a circuit of this type is to be

built.   This circuit differs from Fig. 13-42 only in details, as for example
the use of a single voltage supply.   In order to show the similarity the
notation is the same in both figures as far as possible.   A phantastron
circuit designed as in Fig. 13-43 requires a trigger pulse of about 30 volts
amplitude, while the amplitude of the output voltage has a maximum
value of about 250 volts.

A properly designed phantastron is capable of outstanding performance.
The slope of the output wave is highly linear, and is independent of tube
conditions and of all circuit constants except R and C.   The amplitude is
continuously adjustable without change in slope up to a value that is
only moderately less than the supply voltage E_b.   Finally, the fact that
the time interval T, from the moment t_1 when the sloping wave begins
until the instant t_2 when it ends, is very precisely proportional[1] to
the voltage E_1 makes the phantastron valuable as a generator of a controllable time delay; this is discussed further in Sec. 13-18.

An important feature of the phantastron is that it goes through exactly
the same cycle of operation each time a pulse is applied to the input or
control circuit.   This is true irrespective of whether the pulses are
applied regularly or irregularly.   Thus the phantastron can be regarded
as a one-shot saw-tooth- or sloping-wave generator, in analogy with the
one-shot multivibrator discussed in connection with Fig. 13-14.

13-16. Oscilloscope Applications of Saw-tooth-waveform Generators.
In measurement work, one of the principal applications of saw-tooth
waveforms is to cause the spot in a cathode-ray oscillograph to travel
horizontally with displacement proportional to time.   Virtually all of
the saw-tooth-wave generators described in the preceding sections have
been so used in commercial or experimental oscilloscopes.   The choice
among the various available saw-tooth generators depends upon the
particular features or requirements associated with the oscilloscope in
question.

The saw-tooth-generator circuit most widely used in general-purpose
oscilloscopes is the gas-triode circuit of Fig. 13-29.   This arrangement is
simple, and has considerable flexibility, in that it can be operated free-
running at a rate that is readily adjustable, or can be synchronized with
an external waveform as described in connection with Figs. 13-30 and
13-31.

Gas-tube systems, however, have the disadvantage that successive saw-
tooths are not always absolutely identical because ionization and extinction may occur at very slightly different voltages from cycle to cycle.
This causes successive sweeps of the cathode-ray spot to fail to be precisely identical and produces a "jitter" in the motion of the pattern.   In

---

[1] Thus in a circuit designed according to Fig. 13-43, the departure from linearity
between the voltage E_1 and the time interval $t_2 - t_1$ does not exceed 1 to 5 parts in
1000, with the exact degree of linearity depending upon the time interval involved.

addition, the deionization time of the gas tube sets an upper limit to the frequency of operation.

High-vacuum circuits do not have this high-frequency limit or the inherent tendency toward jitter.   Also, the high-vacuum-tube circuits lend themselves more readily to starting and stopping of the saw-tooth waveform than do gas-tube arrangements, and hence are better adapted to oscilloscopes intended for observing single or irregularly repeated transient waveforms.   Of the high-vacuum circuits, that of Fig. 13-32 is the simplest; however, the addition of a pentode as in Fig. 13-33 or 13-34 is not a difficult step, and produces a great improvement in linearity.[1] Free-running operation can be obtained, but ordinarily involves additional tubes and circuit complications.

Oscilloscopes requiring the utmost in linearity of the sweep voltage employ such circuits as the bootstrap or phantastron.   These arrangements not only provide a high degree of linearity, but in addition are sufficiently precise in terms of constancy of the rate of voltage rise with respect to variations in operating conditions to permit a direct time calibration to be inscribed on the sweep controls.

Synchronization Procedures.   When the gas-triode saw-tooth-waveform generator is to be synchronized with an external waveform, it is important that the operator understand the basic mechanism involved, and follow an orderly procedure for accomplishing the synchronization.   It is therefore helpful to restudy Figs. 13-30 and 13-31 in terms of the oscilloscope application.[2]   Thus the spot moves horizontally across the screen during the time the saw-tooth is rising from its minimum to its maximum value, with a speed determined by the slope of the saw-tooth wave in volts per second.   At the same time the magnitude of the horizontal displacement is proportional to the amplitude of the saw-tooth.   When the waveform to be observed is also used as the synchronizing voltage, then what is actually seen on the face of the cathode-ray tube is that portion of the waveform occurring during one stroke of the saw-tooth wave.   Accordingly, for the situation in Fig. 13-30*a* and *b*, the observer sees one complete cycle of a sine wave.   The situation in Fig. 13-30*c* is one of faulty adjustment, and the observer sees two superimposed sweeps, one of which would show about three-fourths of a cycle of the sine wave, while the

---

[1] Examples of the use of a pentode for constant-current charging or discharging will be found in various commercial oscilloscopes.   An interesting application of the constant-current principle, in which the same tube charges one capacitor and discharges another simultaneously to provide two saw-tooth voltages of opposite polarity for push-pull deflection, is described by Y. P. Yu, H. E. Kallman, and P. S. Christaldi, Millimicrosecond Oscillography, *Electronics,* vol. 24, p. 106, July, 1951.

[2] Although this discussion is presented in terms of the gas-triode saw-tooth generator, the same principles apply without change to any free-running system employing high-vacuum tubes.

other displays only a small portion of the sine-wave cycle on a sweep of small amplitude.   At d and e there will be four and three cycles, respectively, displayed on the oscilloscope screen.

Two principal controls are used in adjusting the synchronization.   The first of these sets the free-running frequency of the sweep oscillator; in Fig. 13-29, this involves varying the capacitor C in steps for coarse adjustment, and varying the resistor R continuously for fine control.   The second control adjusts the amplitude of the synchronizing voltage; the effect of different settings of this control is seen by comparing a and b in Fig. 13-30.

The proper procedure to follow in accomplishing synchronization is first to adjust the frequency of the saw-tooth generator or sweep generator to a value slightly *less* than the frequency that will give synchronization with the waveform to be observed.   Second, the amplitude of the synchronizing voltage is set to a very small value, and is then increased to a value that is slightly more than enough to achieve synchronization. When the saw-tooth generator is to be synchronized with a pulse waveform, then the synchronizing pulses applied to the grid of the gas triode should be negative, as discussed in connection with Fig. 13-31.

13-17. Production of Saw-tooth Current Wave in an Inductance-Resistance Circuit.[1]   The saw-tooth-wave generators discussed above all produce voltage waveforms.   However, in some circumstances it is necessary to pass a saw-tooth wave of current through an inductance.   An example occurs in the production of a magnetic field that will cause the deflection of a cathode-ray spot to be proportional to time; such an arrangement is used in many television receivers.

An understanding of the problems involved when a saw-tooth wave of current flows through an inductor can be gained by considering the voltage and current relations that exist in a circuit consisting of an inductance in series with a resistance, as shown in Fig. 13-44a.   Resistance must always be included in such a circuit along with the inductance, since every inductor possesses some resistance.

The saw-tooth wave of current I passing through the inductance will cause the voltage drop E_{L_0} across the inductance to have the wave shape shown.   During the interval when the current rises linearly, the voltage across the inductance is positive and constant, while during flyback it is a negative pulse.[2]   The voltage drop E_{R_0} produced by the saw-tooth wave

[1] For further discussion of this subject see "Principles of Radar," *op. cit.*, pp. 3-34–3-48; "Waveforms," *op. cit.*, pp. 317–324; Seely, *op. cit.*, pp. 460–467; O. H. Schade, Magnetic Deflection Circuits for Cathode-ray Tubes, *RCA Rev.*, vol. 8, p. 506, September, 1947.

[2] The exact shapes of the waves in Fig. 13-44b for the flyback interval can vary considerably according to the shape of the current wave involved.   The situation shown is representative, but by no means the only possibility.

of current flowing through the resistance R_0 has the same shape as the current wave. The total voltage across the resistance-inductance com-

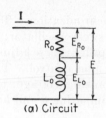

(a) Circuit

bination L_0R_0 is given by the final oscillogram in Fig. 13-44b, and is seen to be trapezoidal in shape.

It is to be noted that during the flyback period the voltage across the inductance is large. This is because the current through the inductance is then changing rapidly, with resulting large self-induced voltage. The peak magnitude of the voltage during the flyback period will increase as the time interval available for flyback decreases; hence very rapid flyback is undesirable for saw-tooth-current generators.

Three general methods are available for producing a saw-tooth wave of current in an inductance-resistance circuit. These are (1) application of a trapezoidal wave of suitable characteristics to the inductance-resistance circuit, (2) derivation of a saw-tooth current wave directly from a saw-tooth voltage wave by the aid of negative feedback, and (3) direct generation of a saw-tooth current wave.

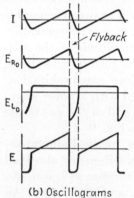

(b) Oscillograms

Fig. 13-44. Typical voltage and current relations existing when a saw-tooth wave of current is passed through an inductance-resistance circuit. The voltage wave shapes during the flyback interval will depend upon the exact shape of the current waveform during this period.

Generation of Trapezoidal Voltage Waveforms and Their Use to Produce Saw-tooth Current Waves. When a trapezoidal voltage wave such as E of Fig. 13-44b is applied to an inductance-resistance circuit, then the saw-tooth current waveform I will be produced.[1] The required trapezoidal-shaped voltage waveform can be generated by the arrangement illustrated in Fig. 13-45a, which is the same as the circuit of Fig. 13-29a except for the added resistor R_2. The waveforms that result are shown in Fig. 13-45b.

It will be noted that during the period T, the approximately constant current flowing through resistance R produces a linearly increasing voltage across C and a constant voltage across R. During flyback, condenser C discharges rapidly through the tube; this causes the current through R_2 to reverse in direction and be large, causing a negative pulse in the waveform of e_{R_2}. The total output voltage e_0 then has a trapezoi-

---

[1] In the special case when the resistance R_0 associated with the inductance L_0 is negligible, a saw-tooth current wave results when the applied voltage has the shape given by E_{L_0} in Fig. 13-44b.

dal shape, as shown. The slope of the top of the trapezoid can be adjusted by varying either C or R. The height E'_L of the pedestal upon

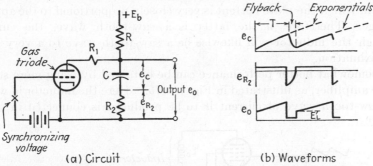

(a) Circuit (b) Waveforms

FIG. 13-45. Circuit of Fig. 13-29a modified to generate a trapezoidal wave shape.

which this sloping part of the wave is superimposed can be controlled by varying R_2. It is to be noted that if the trapezoidal voltage wave is then applied to an inductance L_0, the slope of the resulting saw-tooth current wave is determined by R_2 and R, but is not affected by C.

The trapezoidal voltage wave is ordinarily applied to the inductance-resistance circuit with the aid of an amplifier.[1,2] A typical arrangement is illustrated in Fig. 13-46.

Saw-tooth Current Waves from Saw-tooth Voltage Waves by the Aid of Negative Feedback. A saw-tooth wave of current can be forced through an inductor by deriving the current from the output of an amplifier that is excited by a saw-tooth voltage wave,

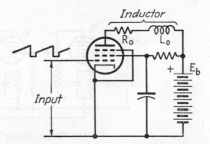

FIG. 13-46. A pentode amplifier circuit for applying a trapezoidal wave shape of voltage to an inductor in order to produce a saw-tooth wave of current in the latter.

and which at the same time, employs negative *current* feedback to ensure that the *output current* waveform will resemble the *input voltage* waveform. A simple arrangement of this type is illustrated in Fig. 13-47a. Here the fact that the plate current of the pentode tube tends to be proportional to

---

[1] Even with amplification, the current requirement may be so high as to require several tubes in parallel, or, more commonly, a transformer to step up the plate current. Such a transformer must have properties similar to those required for pulse transformers as used in the blocking oscillator. See A. W. Friend, Television Deflection Circuits, *RCA Rev.*, vol. 7, p. 98, March, 1947.

[2] Beam power tubes are generally used in place of pentodes, where large currents are required. Special insulation is called for because of the high plate-cathode voltage during the flyback.

control-grid voltage and independent of voltage drop in the plate load impedance, together with the fact that the resistance R_k provides current feedback that accentuates this property still further, results in an arrangement in which the plate current is very closely proportional to the applied voltage. Therefore, if the latter is a saw-tooth wave, the current through the inductor will likewise be a saw-tooth wave to a very good approximation.

A somewhat better performance can be obtained by using more stages in the amplifier, as illustrated in Fig. 13-47b. Here the inductor in which the saw-tooth wave of current is to be produced is connected in series

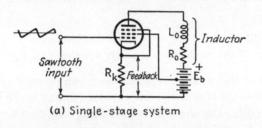

(a) Single-stage system

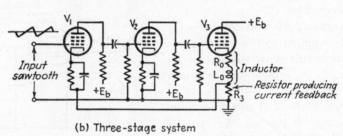

(b) Three-stage system

Fig. 13-47. Feedback amplifier arrangements for obtaining a saw-tooth wave of current in an inductor from a saw-tooth voltage wave.

with the cathode of tube V_3 of the three-stage amplifier $V_1V_2V_3$, as shown. Negative feedback proportional to the *current* in the inductor is introduced into the system with the aid of resistance R_3 as illustrated. Such an arrangement has the advantage that the amount of negative feedback that can be obtained is much greater than in Fig. 13-47a because of the increased amount of amplification available. The result is that non-linearities introduced by curvature of the tube characteristics will be much less.

Direct Generation of Saw-tooth Current Waves. A saw-tooth wave of current can be directly generated in an inductor by an arrangement of the type illustrated in Fig. 13-48a. Here tube V_1 acts as a switch that is alternately turned on at time t_1 and off at t_2 by a rectangular waveform applied to the control grid. Some form of clamping arrangement such as illustrated in Fig. 13-32a would ordinarily be employed so that the control-grid voltage of this tube would be approximately zero on the positive portion of the switching waveform.　Diode V_2 conducts only during the flyback interval between times t_2 and t_3.

Operation of this arrangement can be explained with the aid of the oscillograms of Fig. 13-48d.　Just before t_1, tube V_1 is cut off and no current flows through L_0.　However, beginning at t_1 and continuing until t_2 the tube V_1 is conducting, $i.e.$, the switch is turned on.　The system

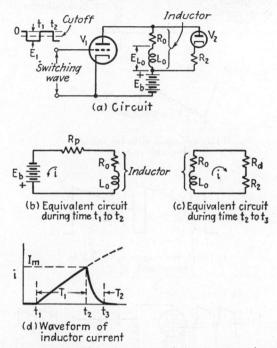

(a) Circuit

(b) Equivalent circuit during time t_1 to t_2

(c) Equivalent circuit during time t_2 to t_3

(d) Waveform of inductor current

FIG. 13-48.　Direct generation of a saw-tooth current wave in an inductor.

then has the equivalent circuit shown in Fig. 13-48b, where R_p is the plate resistance of V_1.　Beginning with t_1, current starts flowing in L_0 and builds up exponentially during the interval T_1 with the time constant $L_0/(R_0 + R_p)$.　The initial rate of current rise approximates E_b/L_0 amperes per second.

At time t_2 the grid of V_1 goes negative, cutting off the plate current, and the current in L_0 drops rapidly.　It does not stop instantly, however, because of the inertia effect of the inductance.　When the current through L_0 begins to fall, there is a large self-induced voltage across L_0 such that current can flow through the diode V_2.*　The system now has

---

* In some cases the diode is omitted, and L_0 is simply shunted by a resistance.　This has the merit of simplicity, but does not give as good performance.

the equivalent circuit of Fig. 13-48c. During this flyback interval T_2 the current in the inductor dies away according to the time constant $L/(R_0 + R_2 + R_d)$, where R_d is the equivalent resistance of the diode V_2.

Saw-tooth *current* waves obtained as in Fig. 13-48a by direct generation are analogous to saw-tooth *voltage* waves obtained by the systems

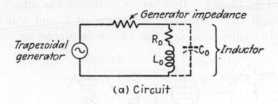

(a) Circuit

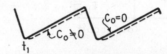

(b) Current wave with trapezoidal
generator voltage

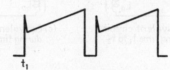

(c) Generator wave required to
compensate for C_0

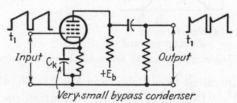

(d) Circuit for producing waveform at (c)

Fig. 13-49. Complications introduced when it is desired to pass a saw-tooth wave of current through an inductor possessing distributed capacitance.

illustrated in Figs. 13-29a and 13-32a, and have the same limitations in that the current waveform is the initial section of an exponential curve, rather than being linear. Such arrangements are therefore satisfactory only when the requirements as to linearity are not too severe. When the current wave is to be precisely saw-tooth, it is necessary to use systems such as illustrated in Figs. 13-46 and 13-47.

Effect of Distributed Capacitance. In the above discussion it was assumed that the inductor L_0 had no capacitance associated with it. However, there is always some distributed capacitance which acts as a shunt condenser C_0, as illustrated in Fig. 13-49a. The effect of this capacitance is to delay slightly the start of the saw-tooth current wave. Thus when a trapezoidal voltage waveform having a source resistance is applied to an inductance-resistance circuit having distributed capacitance, then the voltage across the inductor at time t_1 does not start rising until capacitance C_0 has had time to acquire charge; this causes the start of the linear wave to be delayed as illustrated in Fig. 13-49b. It is possible to compensate for the effect of the capacitance by adding a spike to the waveform of the trapezoidal generator at time t_1, as shown in Fig. 13-49c; this spike quickly charges C_0.

The required spiked trapezoidal wave can be produced in a variety of ways. For example, consider the circuit of Fig. 13-49d, in which the by-pass condenser C_k across the cathode resistor of the amplifier tube is intentionally made very small. Then when a trapezoidal wave is applied to the amplifier input, the amplification at time t_1 will be large because C_k is an effective by-pass to the rapidly changing voltage occurring at time t_1. However, immediately subsequent to t_1 the rate of change of the applied voltage is so much lower that the small size of C_k makes it ineffective as a by-pass, and negative feedback is produced by R_k. Thus the trapezoidal waveform possesses a spike at its leading edge because at this moment t_1 the momentary absence of negative feedback causes the amplification to be greater than before (or after) t_1 when C_k is ineffective and negative feedback due to R_k is present.

13-18. Time-delay Circuits. In measurements work it is occasionally necessary to obtain a voltage pulse or an abrupt voltage change that is delayed in time by a known and adjustable interval following a reference pulse. The waveform of the delayed pulse (or step) need not be identical with that of the reference pulse, since in most applications both of the pulses are merely used to trigger other circuits.

Two circuits have already been described in this chapter which can be used to generate such a time delay. These are the cathode-coupled multivibrator of Fig. 13-14 and the phantastron of Fig. 13-42; their use as time-delay generators is discussed on pages 548 and 597, respectively.[1] Both of these circuits are actuated by a trigger pulse at the time t_1. Likewise, both of these circuits provide an output waveform having a sharply rising portion that is delayed by a known interval with respect to the input pulse. If this rising portion of the waveform is applied to a

---

[1] A tabulation of comparative characteristics of the phantastron and the cathode-coupled multivibrator as time-delay circuits is given by J. R. McDade, The "Phantastron" Control Circuit, *Elec. Eng.*, vol. 67, p. 974, October, 1948.

differentiating circuit (see Fig. 13-6), this latter circuit will provide a positive trigger pulse; this is illustrated in Fig. 13-50 for the phantastron output waveform.

In the multivibrator type of time-delay generator (see Fig. 13-14) the delay time T is controlled by the positive bias E_1 on the control grid of tube V_1, and is very nearly linearly proportional to this bias. The multivibrator arrangement has fewer components than does the phantastron, but is more affected by variations in supply voltage, and tube and circuit characteristics.

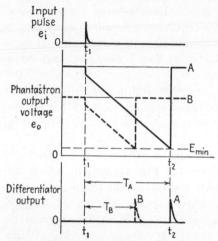

Fig. **13-50.** Phantastron waveforms corresponding to two values of time delay.

The phantastron is capable of developing very precisely known values of time delay that are linearly proportional to the voltage E_1 in Fig. 13-42, as discussed on page 596. The behavior for two values of E_1 is given by A and B in Fig. 13-50, which shows pulses A and B corresponding to delay times T_A and T_B, respectively.

Time-delay Generation by Sloping Wave and Comparator. A third method of producing an adjustable time delay is illustrated in Fig. 13-51. Here the output from any convenient type of saw-tooth generator is connected to a circuit called a *comparator*,[1] which is actuated when the rising or falling saw-tooth wave reaches a specific level. When this level is reached, a voltage step or pulse is generated. This pulse or step is obviously delayed in time with respect to the waveform that initiated the saw-tooth, by the interval required for the saw-tooth to reach the specified level. This delay time is readily controlled by adjusting the specified level.

A typical system is depicted schematically in Fig. 13-51a. Here at time t_1 a reference or control wave initiates the generation of a saw-tooth wave, as shown. This wave is applied to the comparator, which in Fig. 13-51a consists of a diode tube biased by adjustable voltage E_1 so that no current flows through the tube until a time T has elapsed such that the amplitude of the saw-tooth wave has fallen by an amount E_1, as shown in the second oscillogram of Fig. 13-51b. At this moment current begins to flow through V_1 and a voltage suddenly appears across R_1. This voltage

---

[1] The comparator circuit "compares" the amplitude of the time-varying saw-tooth with a fixed voltage, and then is actuated when the two amplitudes become equal. Another name used frequently in the literature is "pick-off" circuit.

is amplified by V_2, thus producing an indication in the output that is delayed with respect to t_1 by the interval T.

A typical comparator circuit is shown in detail in Fig. 13-52. Here the input sawtooth wave is assumed to be of the type shown in Fig. 13-51, and is associated with a clamping circuit located between the saw-tooth-generator output and the input of the comparator circuit as shown, in order that the most positive level of the saw-tooth waveform will be at zero volts. The operation of this system can now be explained as

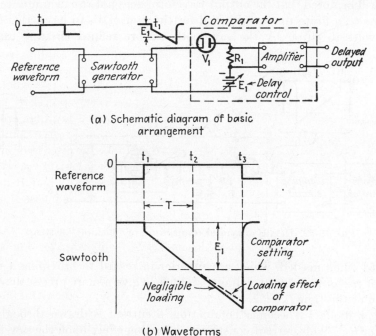

(a) Schematic diagram of basic arrangement

(b) Waveforms

FIG. 13-51. Generation of time delay by means of a sloping waveform and voltage comparator, or "pick-off," system.

follows: Prior to time t_2, the diode anode is more negative than the voltage applied to the cathode by the saw-tooth wave. Under these conditions no current flows through V_1, and there is hence no voltage across R_1. Pentode amplifier V_2 is conducting by virtue of the positive control-grid bias resulting from returning grid-leak resistor R_g to $+E_b$. However, at the time t_2, when the saw-tooth waveform has fallen to the level E_1, the cathode of V_1 becomes negative with respect to the anode and the diode thus conducts. The saw-tooth waveform is then coupled through capacitor C_c to the control grid of the pentode V_2, and this grid is quickly carried sufficiently negative in voltage to cut off the plate current in V_2. The plate voltage of the pentode therefore rises to the supply voltage E_b, thus providing a voltage rise at the output terminal. This constitutes the delayed waveform, with the delay interval T being the time difference between t_1 and t_2. The output waveform could be differentiated to provide a pulse at t_2 if desired. The cycle of operation terminates at time t_3, when the reference waveform returns the saw-tooth generator to its original quiescent condition, thereby cutting off the diode current and allowing the grid of V_2 again to become positive, with a resulting drop in output voltage.

It will be noted that the output waveform does not rise instantaneously at time t_2; a finite time is required for the grid of V_2 to be carried from zero volts to cutoff by the saw-tooth. More refined circuits[1] can be

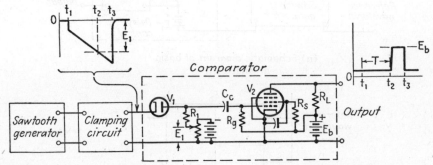

Fig. 13-52. Details of typical comparator, or "pick-off," system.

devised when needed, which are superior in regard to providing a more abrupt rise of the output voltage, and hence give a more precise determination of the time t_2.

When diode V_1 becomes conducting, a current is drawn through the resistor R_1. This current constitutes a loading effect upon the saw-tooth generator, and may cause the saw-tooth to assume the form shown by the dotted line in Fig. 13-51b. If the loading is made negligible, however, it is possible to operate several comparator circuits from the same saw-tooth generator. Thus several independently delayed signals can be controlled by one master waveform.

By using a highly linear saw-tooth generator such as the Miller integrator, the delay time becomes a precisely linear function of the control voltage E_1. If this feature of linearity is not required, other saw-tooth generators can be used. Indeed, it is not even necessary to use a saw-tooth waveform; an exponential or sine wave would serve to provide an

---

[1] See for instance the "multiar" described by F. C. Williams and N. F. Moody, Ranging Circuits, Linear Time-base Generators and Associated Circuits, *J. IEE*, vol. 93, pt. IIIA, p. 1188, March–May, 1946.

adjustable time delay provided only that the waveform be initiated at a specified reference time, and that the comparator circuit be arranged to operate when the waveform reaches a second specified level.

Still other schemes for generation of a time delay will be found in the literature.[1]

[1] "Electronic Time Measurements" (Vol. 20, Radiation Laboratory Series), McGraw-Hill Book Company, Inc., New York, 1949; Britton Chance, Time Modulation, *Proc. IRE*, vol. 35, p. 1039, October, 1947; Some Precision Circuit Techniques Used in Waveform Generation and Time Measurement, *Rev. Sci. Instruments*, vol. 17, p. 396, October, 1946.

CHAPTER 14

REACTANCE AND RESISTANCE STANDARDS AND DEVICES

14-1. Variable Air-dielectric Standard Condensers. Condensers provide the most desirable form of standard reactance because practical condensers approximate ideal reactances much more closely than do practical inductances. As a consequence, condensers are nearly always used as reactance standards in radio-frequency measurements; they also are preferred in very precise reactance measurements at audio frequencies, although inductance standards are also satisfactory for most audio-frequency applications. Standards of capacitance covering the range up to about 0.002 μf are always variable air-dielectric condensers.

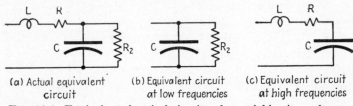

(a) Actual equivalent circuit   (b) Equivalent circuit at low frequencies   (c) Equivalent circuit at high frequencies

FIG. 14-1. Equivalent electrical circuits of a variable air condenser.

Equivalent Circuit, and Frequency Effects. A variable air-dielectric condenser can be represented by the equivalent electrical network in Fig. 14-1a.[1] Here C is the capacitance of the condenser, while R_2 is the equivalent shunt resistance introduced by the presence of the solid dielectric used to support the stator. This resistance is independent of the capacitance setting of the condenser, but is inversely proportional to the frequency. The inductance L in Fig. 14-1a takes into account the magnetic flux produced by the current flowing in the condenser and its leads, and is to first approximation independent of the capacitance setting and of the frequency. It is proportional to the physical size of the condenser, and also depends upon where the connections are made to the two sets of

---

[1] The determination of the constants of this equivalent circuit is discussed by R. F. Field and D. B. Sinclair, A Method for Determining the Residual Inductance and Resistance of a Variable Air Condenser at Radio Frequencies, *Proc. IRE*, vol. 24, p. 255, February, 1936; R. Faraday Proctor, Variable Air Condensers, *Wireless Eng.*, vol. 17, p. 257, June, 1940.

plates.   The series resistance R results from the resistance of the leads, washers, connecting rods, etc.; this resistance is substantially independent of the capacitance setting, but increases with frequency as a result of skin effect.   At high frequencies R is accordingly proportional to the square root of the frequency.   Values of these circuit elements for a particular laboratory-type precision condenser designed especially for use at radio frequencies are given in Table 14-1; the physically compact variable condensers used in radio-receiver circuits would have much smaller L.

TABLE 14-1

CIRCUIT CONSTANTS OF PRECISION LABORATORY VARIABLE CONDENSER*

$C = 1100$ μμf (maximum)

$L = 0.024$ μh

$R = 0.008$ ohm at 1 Mc (proportional to square root of frequency at higher frequencies)

$R_2 = 3.2$ megohms at 1 Mc (inversely proportional to frequency for all frequencies)

Figure of merit (= power factor × capacitance) = $DC = 0.05$μμf at low and moderate frequencies

Temperature coefficient of capacitance = $+20$ parts in a million per °C

* Data from General Radio Company.

At low and moderate frequencies, the effects of the inductance L and series resistance R are negligible, and the equivalent circuit reduces to that shown in Fig. 14-1b, where the resistance R_2 is independent of capacitance setting, but varies inversely with frequency.[1]   Under these conditions the power factor of the condenser for any given setting is independent of frequency.   However, as the capacitance setting increases, the power factor is inversely proportional to capacitance.[2]   This power factor is quite small (that is, R_2 is large) because only a small amount of solid dielectric is involved, and this moreover has low losses.   As a result, the power factor of a variable condenser at low and moderate frequencies is extremely low; for most practical purposes one can consider the capacitance to be an ideal lossless reactance.

At very high frequencies, the reactance of the series inductance L cannot be neglected compared with the reactance of the condenser capacitance C.   This causes the apparent capacitance as observed at the con-

[1] In very precise work involving air condensers, it is necessary to take into account the fact that the humidity of the air affects the dielectric constant of the air, and causes a moisture film to form on the plates.   Changes in capacitance of the order of 3 parts in 10,000 can be produced in this way under ordinary conditions; see L. H. Ford, The Effect of Humidity on the Calibration of Precision Air Condensers, *Proc. IEE* (*Radio & Comm.*) vol. 96, pt. III, p. 13, January, 1949.

[2] A useful figure of merit for a variable condenser under these conditions is the quantity DC, where D is the power factor (sometimes called dissipation factor) and C the capacitance; for a given air-dielectric condenser DC will be constant, irrespective of frequency or capacitance setting.

denser terminals to be greater than the actual capacitance, according to the relation

$$\text{Apparent capacitance} = \frac{C}{1 - \omega^2 LC} = \frac{C}{1 - (f^2/f_0)^2} \qquad (14\text{-}1)$$

where $f = \omega/2\pi$ is the actual frequency, f_0 is the frequency at which L and C are resonant, and L and C are as shown in Fig. 14-1a. The difference between the apparent and actual capacitance becomes an important factor in measurements made at very high frequencies. Thus for the condenser of Table 14-1, the apparent capacitance is in error by about 10 per cent at 10 Mc when the capacitance setting is 1000 $\mu\mu$f; a physically smaller condenser would exhibit much better behavior. If the inductance of the condenser is known, Eq. (14-1) can be used to calculate a correction factor.

At very high frequencies, the resistance R in the equivalent circuit of Fig. 14-1a can no longer be neglected. This resistance increases as the square root of the frequency, while the capacitive reactance varies inversely with frequency. As a consequence, at high frequencies the power factor of the variable condenser rises, and is determined primarily by the losses in the series resistance R rather than by the losses in the shunt resistance R_2. The equivalent circuit then takes the form given in Fig. 14-1c. For any given capacitance setting, the power factor tends to be proportional to the $\frac{3}{2}$ power of the frequency, while for a given frequency the power factor at very high frequencies will be proportional to the capacitance setting.

To summarize, it is seen that although a variable air-dielectric condenser has excellent characteristics, it is not a perfect device, particularly at short-wave and higher frequencies. At low and moderate frequencies, the variable air condenser approaches an ideal reactance in that the capacitance is independent of frequency, and the power factor is extremely small. However, at very high frequencies, the apparent capacitance as observed at the terminals will commonly differ appreciably from the capacitance at low and moderate frequencies, and this effect increases with frequency. Also, at very high frequencies the power factor increases with both frequency and capacitance setting, and is much higher than at low frequencies, although still low compared with the power factor of a typical inductance. The power-factor characteristics of a representative laboratory condenser are shown in Fig. 14-2.

Temperature Effects. The capacitance of an ordinary air-dielectric condenser varies with temperature changes as a result of (1) differential expansion of different parts of the condenser, particularly effects causing bending of the plates, (2) linear expansion that causes changes in surface areas, etc., (3) changes of the dimensions and dielectric constant of the solid insulation used for mounting, and (4) changes in residual stress with temperature that give rise to deformations.[1]

The temperature coefficient of capacitance of actual air-dielectric condensers may vary over a wide range. Thus, values from $+150$ to -65 parts per million per °C have been observed for different designs. The behavior of many condensers with respect to changes in temperature is noncyclic, *i.e.*, the capacitance does not return to its original value after the temperature returns to normal.

Air condensers with small temperature coefficients, and having cyclic behavior, can be realized by proper design.[2] Such a result is facilitated by making the fixed- and rotating-plate assemblies of the same material throughout, and annealing to relieve residual stress. The air gap should be large so that the capacitance will not be critical

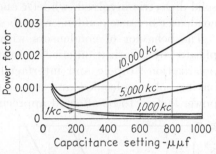

Fig. 14-2. Power factor at various frequencies of a particular variable air-dielectric condenser as a function of capacitance setting.

with small deformations of the plates. The insulating supports should have low temperature coefficients of expansion and low dielectric constant. Certain of the ceramics and plastics are the best materials for this purpose. The exact temperature coefficient of such a condenser can be adjusted as desired by controlling the axial position of the rotating plates with respect to the fixed plates by means of metal rods of a second material having a different coefficient of expansion. In this way, it is possible to obtain zero temperature coefficient of capacitance by providing an appropriate initial displacement of the rotating plates away from the mid-position between fixed plates; alternatively one can obtain either a positive or a negative temperature coefficient as desired by using a greater or less displacement than that giving zero coefficient.[3]

---

[1] The measurement of the temperature coefficient of capacitance is discussed by W. Schick, Temperature Coefficient of Capacitance, *Wireless Eng.*, vol. 21, p. 65, February, 1944.

[2] H. A. Thomas, The Development of a Small Variable Air Condenser Compensated for Rapid Changes of Temperature, *J. IEE*, vol. 84, p. 495, 1939; also *Wireless Sec., IEE*, vol. 14, p. 157, June, 1939; The Electrical Stability of Condensers, *J. IEE*, vol. 79, p. 297, 1936; also *Wireless Sec., IEE*, vol. 11, p. 202, September, 1936; W. H. F. Griffiths, The Temperature Compensation of Condensers, *Wireless Eng.*, vol. 19, p. 101, March, 1942; also see p. 148, April, 1942, and pp. 199 and 200, May, 1942.

[3] Another method of obtaining zero coefficient in a variable condenser involves a condenser in which all parts determining length are aluminum, as are also all the stator plates, while half of the rotor plates are invar and half aluminum. See T. Slonczewski,

14-2. Fixed Standard Condensers with Solid Dielectric. Standards of capacitance larger than about 0.002 μf are normally fixed condensers with mica dielectric. When properly constructed, such condensers have very low losses, and are stable in their characteristics. The equivalent circuit of Fig. 14-1 also applies to fixed condensers having solid dielectric, except that R_2 now tends to be less because of the increased amount of solid dielectric involved, while R and L are smaller than in the usual air condenser because condensers with solid dielectric are more compact.

The behavior of condensers with solid dielectric is commonly complicated by polarization effects in the dielectric. There are two types of polarization,[1] dipole and interfacial. The former occurs in dielectrics having polar molecules, and causes the dielectric constant (and also the power factor) to be affected appreciably by temperature and frequency;

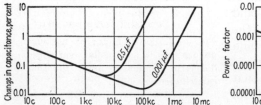 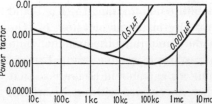

FIG. 14-3. Effect of frequency on the properties of typical standard mica-dielectric capacitors.

polar dielectrics are therefore not suitable for use when the capacitance is to have a precise value. Interfacial polarization (also sometimes called dielectric absorption) occurs in composite dielectrics, and at very low frequencies causes the capacitance to increase slightly and to have a higher power factor. Mica has no dipole polarization, but does exhibit interfacial polarization to a small extent.

The characteristics of typical standard mica condensers of several different capacitances are shown in Fig. 14-3. The slight rise in capacitance at low frequencies is a result of interfacial polarization; the increase in apparent capacitance at high frequencies is due to the series inductance of the condenser. The increase in power factor at very low frequencies likewise results from interfacial polarization of the dielectric, while the increase in power factor at high frequencies is caused by skin effect.

A change in temperature can cause the capacitance of solid-dielectric condensers to vary as a result of the effect of temperature on the dimensions and dielectric constant, and on the mechanical pressure to which the

---

High Accuracy Heterodyne Oscillators, *Bell System Tech. J.*, vol. 19, p. 407, July, 1940.

[1] For a discussion, see R. F. Field, Frequency Characteristics of Decade Condensers, *Gen. Rad. Expt.*, vol. 17, October, 1942.

condenser assembly is subjected.[1] In ordinary mica condensers, the effect of the temperature upon the pressure of an assembly consisting of alternate mica and metal foil is the most important of these factors causing the capacitance to change with temperature. A low coefficient of temperature can therefore be obtained by clamping the assembly together with metal rods having a carefully chosen temperature coefficient of expansion. Alternatively, one may eliminate pressure as a factor by depositing the electrodes directly upon opposite sides of the mica sheet; if the very best quality mica is used a temperature coefficient of the order of +20 parts per million per °C can be obtained.

When a standard fixed condenser is required to develop a specified capacitance to a high degree of accuracy, a problem arises as to how the capacitance can be adjusted to the desired value with the required precision. In the case of mica condensers in which the electrodes are deposited on the mica, it is possible to make minor adjustments by scraping off the metal coating by hand. An alternative procedure, quite widely used in commercial condensers, consists in building up the desired capacitance by combining two condenser units. If a large number of individual units is available, these can be individually measured, and then matched in pairs in such a manner that the total capacitance adds up to the desired value with the required precision.

Although mica is customarily used in standard condensers having solid dielectric, other dielectrics find some use. In particular, condensers with ceramic dielectrics are often employed to obtain controlled temperature coefficients, and for neutralization of temperature effects. This possibility arises because the temperature coefficient of most solid dielectrics is positive, whereas it is possible to obtain ceramic dielectrics that have a relatively high negative temperature coefficient. Thus one can obtain an over-all temperature coefficient of approximately zero by combining a large condenser with a moderately small positive temperature coefficient, with a small capacitance having a relatively high negative temperature coefficient.

Decade Condensers. In grouping condensers together to form decade units, it is desirable to employ the smallest possible number of condensers because of the cost of accurately adjusted units. A suitable arrangement is shown in Fig. 14-4, and permits a full decade to be covered with four condensers controlled by a four-gang 11-position switch. A continuous variation of capacitance can be obtained by using a variable air condenser having about 1100 $\mu\mu$f maximum capacitance to bridge between 0.001-$\mu\mu$f steps.

[1] It is important that solid dielectrics be free of moisture; not only does moisture increase the losses, but in addition water dielectric has a large negative temperature coefficient of capacitance.

Decade condensers should be mounted in a metal container or shield so that their capacitance will not be affected by outside objects. It is also necessary to shield each individual condenser and its associated switch if the capacitances of the various steps are to add up properly.[1] Suitable shielding is shown in Fig. 14-4. If the shielding is omitted, direct capacitances will exist between the upper sides of the various condensers, as illustrated in Fig. 14-5, and this introduces errors. Thus when one of the condensers C_1 is switched into the circuit, the capacitance added is not C_1, but rather C_1 plus shunting capacitances such as the capacitance consisting of C_2 in series with C_{12}. On the other hand, when all capacitances are switched in, the total capacitance is

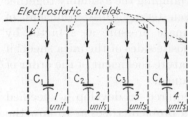

Fig. 14-4. Switching arrangements for decade. condenser. This requires a four-gang 11-position switch so wired that the necessary condensers are connected across the circuit for the various switch positions.

$C_1 + C_2 + C_3 + C_4$, and the direct capacitances C_{12}, C_{23}, etc., have no effect. The shield replaces the direct capacitances by capacitances to ground which are in parallel with the individual units and can be allowed for when each unit is constructed and adjusted. The effects of unshielded direct capacitances are particularly important in the 0.001- and

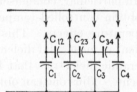

Fig. 14-5. Unshielded decade condenser, illustrating direct capacitances that introduce errors.

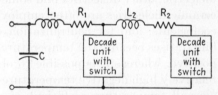

Fig. 14-6. Equivalent circuit of a two-decade condenser box, showing residual impedances of the leads.

0.01-μf decades, since the error introduced by the direct capacitance is not negligible in comparison with the size of these steps.

The equivalent circuit of a decade condenser is shown in Fig. 14-6. Here C is the capacitance that appears between terminals with all condenser units switched out; it represents the capacitance of leads and switches to ground. The resistances and inductances of the leads are represented by R_1, R_2, L_1, and L_2 as shown. In addition, each capaci-

[1] Also see R. F. Field, Connection Errors in Capacitance Measurements, *Gen. Rad. Expt.*, vol. 21, May, 1947.

tance switched into the circuit has an equivalent circuit such as shown in Fig. 14-1a.   When the condenser decades are arranged along a line as shown in Fig. 14-6, the largest capacitance decade should be placed next to the terminals, the next largest decade unit should come next, etc.   In this way, the series inductance is least for the largest capacitances (where series inductance is most harmful), and greatest for the smallest capacitance where it does least harm.

When the highest possible accuracy and stability are not required, it is possible to assemble decade units from small mica radio condensers having capacitances slightly less than the desired values, which are then built out with adjustable "trimmer" condensers of the type employed to line up intermediate-frequency transformers in radio receivers.   This method of construction is suitable for decade units having steps of 0.001 and 0.01 μf.   A variable condenser having a maximum capacitance in excess of 0.001 μf (such as a three-gang broadcast-receiver condenser with all sections in parallel) can be used for interpolating between 0.001-μf steps. Mica condensers suitable for 0.1-μf steps are expensive, and unless low losses are very essential it is often permissible to use good-grade paper condensers.[1]

14-3. Standards of Inductance and Mutual Inductance.   The desirable properties of a standard inductance are mechanical stability, low temperature coefficient of inductance, high Q, a minimum of external magnetic field, and the lowest possible distributed capacitance.   In the case of variable inductances, the bearings must be free from play and backlash that will affect the inductance associated with a given dial setting.

The distributed capacitance of a standard inductance is particularly important because it causes the apparent inductance observed between the coil terminals to increase with frequency in accordance with Eq. (3-11b).   If the apparent inductance is not to differ from the true inductance by more than 1 per cent, the frequency at which the coil is used must not exceed 10 per cent of the frequency at which the inductance would be resonant with the equivalent lumped value of the distributed capacitance. This sets an upper limit to the frequency at which it is permissible to use any given standard inductance.   At frequencies where skin effect must be considered, the inductance is reduced by the skin effect.   This is because skin effect and the related proximity effect cause the current to be redistributed over the conductor cross section in such a manner as to

---

[1] There are several types of telephone (Western Electric) condensers peculiarly well suited to building up decade units having steps of 0.01 μf and larger.   These consist of a large number of individual condensers of various sizes potted in a single can, and are relatively inexpensive.   It is possible to build up any desired capacitance to a high degree of accuracy by merely combining appropriate units in the one can.

reduce the total number of flux linkages. The resulting lowering of inductance may readily amount to a few per cent.

The fact that the effective inductance is affected by distributed capacitance and skin effect seriously limits the usefulness of standard inductances in measurement work at the higher frequencies. When reactance standards of high accuracy are required above audio frequencies, matters are normally arranged so that standard capacitances can be used.

Inductance standards for use at audio and the lower radio frequencies are normally air-cored coils wound with litz wire. In this way, skin effect and its attendant influence on inductance and resistance are minimized. The winding may be arranged in one of several ways, as illustrated in

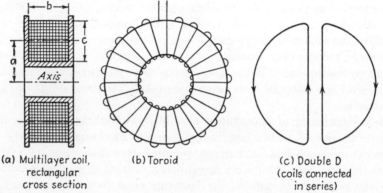

(a) Multilayer coil, rectangular cross section   (b) Toroid   (c) Double D (coils connected in series)

FIG. 14-7. Methods used to wind inductance standards for audio frequencies.

Fig. 14-7. The conventional multilayer coil shown in Fig. 14-7a gives the largest inductance in proportion to the d-c resistance, but has the disadvantage of a large external field.[1] Inductances of this type will have the minimum loss when proportioned so that $b = c$, and $c/a = 0.66$. The toroid has negligible external field, but requires a very large amount of wire in proportion to the inductance obtained, and so has high d-c resistance and low Q. The double-D winding consists of two D-shaped coils connected in series; it is intermediate in its characteristics between the toroid and the multilayer coil, with respect to both external field and d-c resistance. This arrangement has the advantage that the individual coils can be wound to approximately the correct number of turns, impregnated, taped, and mounted, all before final adjustment. The adjustment to give the exact value of inductance desired is then made by shifting

---

[1] The design of standard inductances of this type is thoroughly discussed by H. B. Brooks, Design of Standards of Inductance, and the Proposed Use of Model Reactors in the Design of Air-core and Iron-core Reactors, *J. Research Natl. Bur. Standards*, vol. 7, p. 289, August, 1931.

the relative positions of the two coils slightly with respect to each other before clamping them into final position.

Fixed inductances that are to be used as standards at radio frequencies should have low losses, good mechanical stability, low distributed capacitance, and a minimum of dielectric loss.   Single-layer solenoids are customary, and litz wire is desirable for frequencies up to and including standard broadcast frequencies.   The construction must be substantial, the coil form must be of good dielectric material, and the coil should be protected by a moistureproof coating.   Consideration should be given to temperature effects, as discussed below.

If an air-cored coil is placed in a shield, it must be mounted very rigidly with respect to the shield, and the latter must also be rigid.   Any change in position of the coil relative to the shield, or any flexing of the shield walls as a result of mechanical strain, aging, temperature changes, etc., will alter the effective inductance of the shielded coil.

At audio frequencies, coils with magnetic cores, as for example molybdenum permalloy dust rings, are suitable for the laboratory where an accuracy of the order of 1 per cent is permissible.[1]   Such coils will have very low losses at audio frequencies, and their inductance will not vary appreciably with reasonable changes in the alternating flux density.   It is important, however, that d-c magnetization be avoided, since this will affect the inductance, especially when high-permeability core material is used.   The resistance of such inductances depends on the frequency, but since the losses are small, this is not important in many applications. Coils with magnetic cores are seldom used as inductance standards in bridge measurements, however, because of their uncertain loss, and their lack of high accuracy.

Different magnetic materials differ considerably in their suitability as cores for laboratory inductances.   Thus molybdenum-permalloy dust cores are very much superior to cores of iron or permalloy dust in constancy of inductance with alternating flux density, and in effects produced by direct-current magnetization.

Temperature Effects.   The inductance of an air-cored coil varies with temperature as a result of (1) changes in dimensions with temperature, and (2) changes in current distribution in the wire as a result of change of wire resistivity with temperature modifying the skin and proximity effects.

In the ideal case of a freely suspended coil expanding according to the coefficient of linear expansion of the copper wire, the temperature coefficient of inductance (neglecting skin effect) would be the coefficient of linear expansion of copper, or approximately 17 parts per million per °C.

[1] Thus see H. W. Lamson, A New Decade Inductor, *Gen. Rad. Expt.*, vol. 24, July, 1949.

Actually, however, changes in temperature would commonly produce mechanical strains and cause a greater temperature effect. When the coil is wound on a form instead of being freely suspended, the changes of dimension with temperature tend to be controlled by the form. However, even here it is found that the temperature coefficient of inductance will normally be considerably greater than the expansion coefficient of either the form or the wire.[1]

The change in wire resistivity with a temperature change modifies the skin and proximity effects, and this in turn can affect the inductances, as discussed above. The change of inductance produced in this way is maximum at a frequency for which the skin and proximity effects are only moderate, so that the current distribution is particularly sensitive to resistance changes.[2]

The variation of coil inductance with temperature is often noncyclic. Thus if the coil undergoes a temperature cycle, the inductance will often not follow the temperature exactly, but rather will vary irregularly and will not return to the initial value when the temperature returns to normal. This is the result of mechanical changes such as result from slippage of the wire over the form, and permanent changes of physical dimensions occasioned by the relieving of initial stress.

It is impractical to achieve a particularly low temperature coefficient of inductance in multilayer coils because a several-layer arrangement cannot be made to have a high degree of mechanical stability. Wood impregnated with beeswax, and certain grades of porcelain, are the best material for the forms of such coils, while bakelite and hard rubber are not recommended because of their high coefficient of expansion.

In the case of a single-layer solenoid, several means have been used to obtain a stable inductance with a low temperature coefficient. One method consists in using a silver-plated invar wire wound on a ceramic form having a low temperature coefficient of expansion.[3] Alternatively,

[1] Mechanical effects that arise from temperature changes, and which influence the inductance of a coil are discussed by H. A. Thomas, The Stability of Inductance Coils for Radio Frequencies, *J. IEE*, vol. 77, p. 702, 1935; also *Wireless Sec.*, *J. IEE*, vol. 11, p. 44, March, 1936; E. B. Moulin, The Temperature Coefficient of Inductances for Use in a Valve Generator, *Proc. IRE*, vol. 26, p. 1385, November, 1938.

[2] Inductance changes that arise from changes in resistivity with temperature are discussed by A. Bloch, Temperature Coefficient of Air-cored Self-inductances, *Wireless Eng.*, vol. 21, p. 359, August, 1944; D. A. Bell, Temperature Coefficient of Inductance, *Wireless Eng.*, vol. 16, p. 240, May, 1939; H. A. Thomas, The Dependence on Frequency of the Temperature Coefficient of Inductance of Coils, *J. IEE*, vol. 84, p. 101, 1939; also *Wireless Sec.*, *J. IEE*, vol. 14, p. 19, March, 1939; Janusz Groszkowski, The Temperature Coefficient of Inductance, *Wireless Eng.*, vol. 12, p. 650, December, 1935.

[3] S. W. Seeley and E. I. Anderson, UHF Oscillator Frequency-stability Considerations, *RCA Rev.*, vol. 5, p. 77, July, 1940.

one can employ a ceramic form, with a conductor consisting of a conducting film deposited directly on the ceramic surface in such a manner as to form well-spaced turns that are in the form of a very thin, narrow, flat ribbon.[1]   In this way, the temperature coefficient of inductance will approximate very closely that of the ceramic form, will be largely independent of frequency, and will be stable over repeated temperature cycles.   By expedients of this type, temperature coefficients of inductance ranging from 1 to 10 parts per million per °C can be obtained in single-layer coils.[2]

Variable Inductances and Mutual Inductances.   The commonest type of variable inductance consists of two coils that are connected in series, and are rotatable with respect to each other in such a manner as to vary the mutual inductance between them.   The total inductance of the combination is then $L_1 + L_2 \pm M$, where L_1 and L_2 are the self-inductances of the individual coils, and M is the mutual inductance between them.   When the two inductances L_1 and L_2 are of equal magnitude, and the maximum coefficient of coupling obtainable is large, then the ratio of maximum to minimum inductance obtainable will be correspondingly great.   Ratios of the order of 10:1 are readily achieved in practice.

Two methods of constructing variable inductances are shown in Fig. 14-8.   In the variometer, the rotating coil is wound upon a spherical section, and mounted inside a corresponding fixed coil that is wound on the inner side of a spherical surface of slightly larger radius.   The two coils are preferably adjusted so that their self-inductances are equal.   In the Brooks inductometer, the same result is achieved in a slightly different way.   The Brooks inductometer[3] has the advantage that the calibration is not appreciably affected by axial displacement of the rotating coil; also by proportioning the coils as shown in Fig. 14-8a, the inductance varies linearly with the angle of rotation.

Any standard variable inductance can be converted into a variable mutual-inductance standard by connecting the leads of the fixed and moving coils to separate binding posts.   This is ordinarily done in variable-inductance standards, and permits such standards to be used as variable mutual inductances by the removal of a jumper connection.

Decade Inductances.   Inductances can be built up into decade units in the same way as resistances.   One method of accomplishing this is to

[1] H. A. Thomas, The Dependence on Frequency of the Temperature-coefficient of Inductance of Coils, *J. IEE*, vol. 84, p. 101, 1939; also *Wireless Sec.*, *J. IEE*, vol. 14, p. 19, March, 1939.

[2] Still another method of obtaining a low temperature coefficient is described by W. H. F. Griffiths, Recent Improvements in Air-cored Inductances, *Wireless Eng.*, vol. 19, p. 8, January, 1942.

[3] For detailed design information on the Brooks inductometer see A Variable Self and Mutual Inductor, *Natl. Bur. Standards (U.S.) Sci. Paper* 290.

cover an entire decade with a single tapped coil. It is difficult, however, to locate the taps properly unless the coil is wound by hand. A more satisfactory arrangement is to build up each decade from four untapped inductances of relative values 1, 2, 3, and 4 (or 1, 2, 2, and 5) and then to

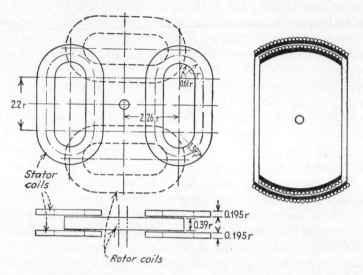

(a) Brooks inductometer   (b) Common variometer

FIG. 14-8. Types of variable inductances commonly employed as standards of self- and mutual-inductance.

use a four-gang 11-point switch to short-circuit the coils that are not required, as shown in Fig. 14-9. Care must be taken in mounting the coils to ensure that they have substantially zero coupling; if compactness is at all important it is necessary to employ toroidal coils with magnetic cores. Decade inductance boxes built up in this way are suitable for

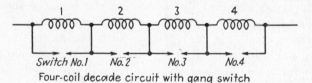

Four-coil decade circuit with gang switch

FIG. 14-9. Switching arrangement for decade inductance. A four-gang 11-point switch is required and is so wired that the undesired inductances are short-circuited.

audio-frequency use, where accuracies of the order of 2 per cent are suffi- cient. Inductance values as great as 1 henry per step can be obtained without difficulty.

14-4. Wire-wound Resistances. *Resistance Wire.* Typical resistance alloys used in wire-wound resistances of the type encountered in laboratory equipment, are listed in Table 14-2, together with their principal properties.[1]

The nichrome group of resistance alloys is capable of operating at high temperatures, and is the wire generally employed for rheostats, heating elements, enamel-coated resistance tubes, etc. The temperature coefficient of resistivity of nichrome is quite small compared with that of

TABLE 14-2

PROPERTIES OF RESISTANCE WIRE

| Material | Typical composition | Resistivity | | | Thermal emf against copper, μv per °C |
		Microhm-cm	Ohms per mil-ft	Temp. coefficient, ppm per °C	
Nichrome, nichrome I to V, chromel A, tophet, etc.	Ni 80%, Cr 20%	108	650	150	22
Advance, ideal, cupron, copel, constantan, etc.	Ni 45%, Cu 55%	48	290	±20	43
Manganin	Ni 4%, Cu 84%, Mn 12%	48	290	±15	< 3.0
Evanohm, Karma, 331 alloy	Ni 74.5%, Cr 20%, balance Al, and Fe or Cu	133	800	±20	< 2.5
Copper	Cu 99.9+%	1.724	10.37	3930	

NOTE: Above values are approximate, and will vary somewhat with the exact composition, details of manufacture, etc.

copper, although it is not zero. Manganin finds use in the construction of precision resistors; it is characterized by high stability of its resistance when annealed and not overheated, by negligible temperature coefficient, and by freedom from thermoelectric effects with copper. Advance and related alloys are characterized by zero temperature coefficient of resistance, and are often used in standard resistors. These alloys have a high thermoelectric coefficient against copper, however, and are frequently employed in thermocouples. Evanohm and Karma are more recently developed alloys characterized by unusually high resistivity, low temperature coefficient of resistivity, low thermoelectric coefficient against copper, and a high degree of stability over a period of time.

An important consideration in the choice of a resistance wire is often the thermoelectric voltage that it develops against copper. For example,

[1] Many alloys have at least some use as resistance material. Tables giving their properties are to be found in handbooks.

resistances used in a d-c bridge must have a very low thermoelectric coefficient; otherwise unequal temperatures of different parts of the bridge system can easily produce sufficient thermoelectric voltage to give a significant deflection of the bridge galvanometer.   Values for the thermoelectric effect are given in Table 14-2.

Resistors which are required to maintain their characteristics unchanged over long periods of time must be stabilized in some manner so that mechanical strains introduced in winding the wire will not cause the resistance, or the temperature coefficient of resistivity, to change with time.   This is sometimes done by aging the resistor at room temperature for a long period, such as 6 months, before it is finally adjusted and put into use.   Alternatively, annealing by baking at a temperature of 120°C

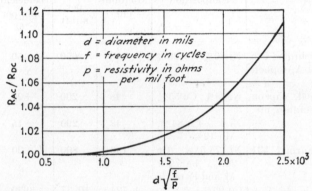

Fig. 14-10. Skin-effect resistance ratio as a function of frequency and wire characteristics.

for 24 hr will stabilize the characteristics provided the resistor is not subsequently heated above this annealing temperature.   Stabilization is especially important in the case of manganin, which is particularly sensitive to mechanical strains.

Frequency Effects in Wire-wound Resistors.   Skin Effect.   In resistances that are to be used at high frequencies, attention must be given to skin effect.   The ratio of a-c to d-c resistance of an isolated wire is determined by the factor $d \sqrt{f/\rho}$, where d is the wire diameter, f the frequency, and ρ the resistivity, and is given in Fig. 14-10 for low-resistance ratios.[1]   Table 14-3, derived from Fig. 14-10, gives the largest wire that can be used at various frequencies and still keep the difference between the a-c and d-c resistance within 1 per cent.   Corresponding values for ratios of 0.1 per cent or 10 per cent can be derived from the table by use of simple factors, as indicated.

[1] This has been calculated from the usual formulas for skin effect found in all handbooks; thus see F. E. Terman, "Radio Engineers' Handbook," p. 28, McGraw-Hill Book Company, Inc., New York, 1943.

TABLE 14-3

LARGEST PERMISSIBLE WIRE DIAMETER IN MILS FOR SKIN-EFFECT RATIO OF 1.01

Frequency, Mc	Nichrome	Advance and manganin	Copper
0.1	110	74	14
1	35	23	4.4
10	11	7.4	1.4
100	3.5	2.3	0.44
1,000	1.1	0.74	0.14
10,000	0.35	0.23	0.04

NOTE: For a ratio of 1.001 multiply above diameters by 0.55. For a ratio of 1.10 multiply above diameters by 1.78.

Inductance and Capacitance of Wire-wound Resistors. Every wire-wound resistor has a certain amount of inductance and capacitance associated with it. The inductance arises because whenever current

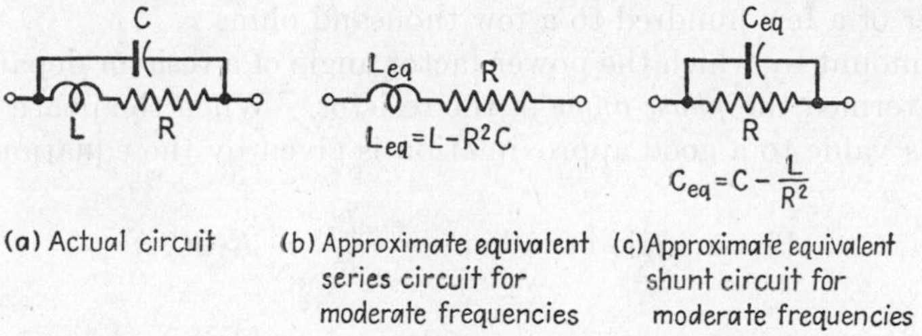

(a) Actual circuit   (b) Approximate equivalent series circuit for moderate frequencies   (c) Approximate equivalent shunt circuit for moderate frequencies

$$L_{eq} = L - R^2 C$$

$$C_{eq} = C - \frac{L}{R^2}$$

Fig. 14-11. Actual and equivalent circuits of a resistance, showing associated inductance and capacitance.

flows through a conductor, magnetic fields are produced. Capacitance is inevitably present because of the capacitance between terminals, and between parts of the resistor. The result is that at high frequencies, both the magnitude and phase angle of the impedance observed across the terminals of a resistor vary with frequency. To a first approximation, the situation that exists can be represented by the circuit of Fig. 14-11a, where R is the actual resistance of the wire (taking into account skin effect), L is an inductance resulting from the magnetic flux, and capacitance C takes into account the capacitance effects associated with the resistor.[1]

[1] The principal approximations in this equivalent circuit are that it neglects any losses that may be associated with C, and that it ignores the fact that part of C may be distributed capacitance. To the extent that these factors are not negligible, they produce an effect that causes the equivalent value of R to decrease with increasing frequency, as discussed in connection with Fig. 14-17.

At low and moderate frequencies, far below the resonant frequency of L and C, and also such that $R \gg \omega L$, and $R \ll (1/\omega C)$, the reactive effects associated with the resistor produce only a moderate modification of its properties.   Under these conditions, one can represent the actual resistor with its associated reactance by the equivalent series circuit of Fig. 14-11b, or by the equivalent shunt circuit shown in Fig. 14-11c.   In either case, it is to be noted that if R, L, C are so related that

$$R = \sqrt{\frac{L}{C}} \qquad (14\text{-}2)$$

then the reactive effects produced by the inductance and capacitance cancel each other.   For this particular case, the resistor is unaffected by the frequency as long as the frequency is not too high.[1]   However, when $R < \sqrt{L/C}$, as tends to be the case with low resistances, an inductive impedance or admittance is obtained, whereas if $R > \sqrt{L/C}$, as is typical when R is high, capacitive effects predominate.   The transition between these two conditions commonly occurs when the resistance is of the order of a few hundred to a few thousand ohms.

The amount by which the power-factor angle of a resistor departs from unity is termed the *phase angle* of the resistor.   When the phase angle is small, its value to a good approximation is given by the equation

$$\text{Phase angle in radians} = \frac{\omega L_{eq}}{R} = R(\omega C_{eq}) \qquad (14\text{-}3)$$

The merit of a resistance unit from the point of view of freedom from reactance effects, is also sometimes expressed in terms of the *time constant* $(= |L_{eq}/R| = |RC_{eq}|)$, which may be as low as 10^{-8} when care is taken to minimize capacitive and inductive effects.

Phase angles of some typical commercial resistance units at 1000 cycles are given in Table 14-4.   It is seen that most ordinary resistors will have a small or negligible phase angle over the audio-frequency range unless the resistance is very low, *i.e.*, below 10 ohms, or unless it is unusually high. However, at radio frequencies, special precautions are necessary if reactive effects are to be small.

---

[1] When the frequency is sufficiently high so that the inequalities upon which the equations given in Fig. 14-11b and c are based, do not hold, then one must analyze the equivalent circuit of Fig. 14-11a without making any approximations.   This is a parallel resonant system with low Q.   A full discussion of its properties is to be found in various places in the literature; for example, see the discussion on resistors in the General Radio Catalogue, or F. E. Terman, "Radio Engineers' Handbook," *op.cit.*, p. 45.   To the extent that the capacitance is distributed, this fact must be taken into account as discussed in Sec. 14-4.

TABLE 14-4

PHASE ANGLES OF TYPICAL COMMERCIAL WIRE-WOUND RESISTORS

Description	Resistance, ohms	Phase angle at 1000 cycles
50-watt vitreous-enamel tube............	10	26′ lag
Potentiometer.........................	27	9′ lag
50-watt vitreous-enamel tube............	100	14′ lag
Potentiometer.........................	360	8′ lag
1-watt wire-wound.....................	3,500	1′ lag
1-watt wire-wound.....................	28,000	6′ lead
Potentiometer.........................	50,000	24′ lead
Serviceman test box...................	50,000	1°40′ lead
200-watt vitreous-enamel tube...........	100,000	2°54′ lead

Wire-wound Resistors with Low Inductive and Capacitive Effects. Reactance effects associated with wire-wound resistors can be minimized by
special winding arrangements.

The inductance of a resistor is determined primarily by the number of
turns of wire and the area enclosed by the individual turns. To keep the
inductance low, each turn should enclose the minimum possible area, and
the wire should have as many ohms per foot of length as possible so that
the length required to obtain the desired resistance will be small. In
addition, it is desirable that adjacent turns carry current in opposite
directions so that the residual inductance of an individual turn is largely
neutralized by the effect of adjacent turns.

A low capacitive reactance associated with a resistor is obtained by
arranging the winding in such a way that adjacent turns of wire have a
low potential difference between them and are as far apart as possible.

Methods that can be used to minimize the reactive effects associated
with a resistor are shown in Fig. 14-12. The card type of resistor uses a
single-layer winding on a thin form, commonly mica, provided with
copper end strips that serve as terminals and reinforcing. A low inductance can be obtained by making the card very thin and using small wire
to give a high resistance per turn.[1] The Ayrton-Perry type of resistor is

---

[1] Resistance units wound on thin cards are the easiest to construct, hence it is
important to be able to determine their limitations. If the form is thin compared
with the axial length of the winding, the inductance is given by the formula

$$\left. \begin{array}{c} \text{Series inductance} \\ \text{of resistance card} \end{array} \right\} = 0.032AbT^2 \quad \mu h \qquad (14\text{-}4)$$

where A is the area enclosed by an individual turn in square inches (measurements
being made to the center of the wire), b the axial length of the winding in inches, and
T the turns per linear inch. Substitution of numerical values in this equation for

constructed by winding a spaced layer of insulated wire on a thin strip, after which a second wire is wound in the opposite direction between turns of the first winding. The two windings are connected in parallel and thereby produce practically zero resultant magnetic effect. The distributed capacitance is low, because adjacent turns have very little potential difference between them. The reversed-loop winding obtains low

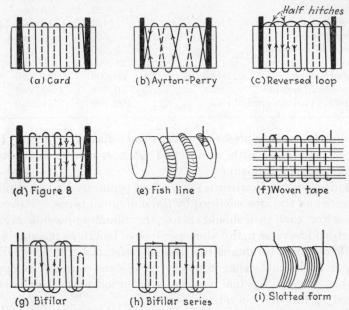

FIG. 14-12. Types of resistor windings that minimize reactive effects.

inductive effects by making a half hitch at the end of each turn and thus reversing the direction of current in adjacent turns. The winding of Fig. 14-12*d* accomplishes substantially the same result in a different way. It should be noted that in this winding the wire is passed through the slot only on the *alternate* times it comes to the slot. The fishline type of resistor consists of a fine resistance wire wound over a silk cord that serves as a core, and the resulting "fishline" is then space-wound on a cylindrical form. The tape resistor is made by weaving the resistance wire into a fabric in which the wire serves as the weft and silk thread functions as the

inductance shows that resistances of a few ohms or more which have entirely satisfactory characteristics at audio and the lower radio frequencies can be wound on cards of thin bakelite provided *small* wire is used. Thus a 1000-ohm winding with No. 43 manganin on a bakelite card 2 in. wide and $\frac{1}{32}$ in. thick, if wound 100 turns to the inch, will have an axial length of about 0.5 in. The inductance will be 10 μh, and in the absence of stray shunting capacitances the phase angle at 100 kc will be only 0.35°. Before they are wound, the bakelite cards should be baked for 24 hr at 120°C to stabilize the dimensions of the card and so prevent the wire from loosening upon annealing.

warp.[1]   The bifilar winding has negligible inductance, but the capacitance is relatively large, because the beginning and end of the resistance are close together.   This capacitance effect can be minimized to some extent by subdividing the total resistance into several bifilar sections, as shown in Fig. 14-12h.[2]   The slotted-form winding will have moderately low capacitance because of the subdivision of the winding, particularly if many slots are used; the inductance can be kept moderately low by reversing the direction of the winding in adjacent slots and by using small wire to keep down the number of turns and the physical size.

The mica-card, reversed-loop, and figure-eight types of resistors can be made to have very low phase angles and are the types used in radio-frequency attenuators.   The mica-card, fishline, and woven-tape types of construction are commonly used in decade resistance boxes designed to have a low phase angle at radio frequencies, particularly for the high-resistance units.   The Ayrton-Perry winding is also suitable for use at radio frequencies, particularly for resistances up to several thousand ohms.   The simple bifilar winding is suitable at radio frequencies only for resistances so low that capacitance effects are of no importance.   The slot type of winding is used in very high-resistance units where only moderately low phase angle is essential, as in the case of voltmeter multipliers.

Even when the utmost care is taken to arrange for a winding to have negligible inductance and a minimum of capacitance, there still remains a residual capacitance.   This arises because of the capacitance of one part of the resistor to other parts (see Fig. 14-17a), and is a function of the resistor geometry and dimensions.   This capacitance can be minimized by favorable geometry, but it cannot be avoided.   The effect of this distributed capacitance is discussed on page 88, and is important at very high frequencies, particularly for high resistances.

A radically different arrangement that is suitable for providing a fixed resistance having low reactance effects at very high frequencies is illustrated in Fig. 14-13.   Here the resistance element is a very short straight length of fine wire in which the inductance is minimized by mounting this wire against a metal plate with only a thin mica sheet for insulation. The shielding effect of the metal at high frequencies is such as to prevent the penetration of magnetic flux into the metal, with a consequent virtual elimination of the magnetic field around the wire.   Capacitance is still

[1] For a discussion of various types of weaves that may be used, see L. Behr and R. E. Tarpley, Design of Resistors for Precise High-frequency Measurements, *Proc. IRE*, vol. 20, p. 1101, July, 1932.

[2] For a detailed theory of the bifilar resistor, see H. Nukiyama and Y. Shoji, On a Design for a Bifilar Type of Non-reactive Resistance Coil, *Trans. AIEE*, vol. 44, p. 349, 1925.

present, but can be minimized by using a wire of such small diameter and high resistivity that only a short length is required; moreover, the proportions can be easily chosen so as to satisfy Eq. (14-2), thus minimizing reactance effects. This type of construction is particularly suitable for resistances of the order of 5 ohms to 200 ohms, and has good resistance and reactance characteristics to frequencies exceeding 10 Mc. The power-dissipating ability is reasonably large in spite of the small dimensions because of the proximity of the metal plates.[1]

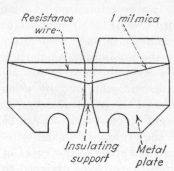

FIG. 14-13. Fixed resistor that can be designed to have low reactive effects at very high frequencies.

Resistance Boxes. A number of individual resistance units may be mounted in a box and provided with switches as in Fig. 14-14 to control the resistance; here the units are grouped in decades with each decade controlled by an 11-point switch, thus giving an overlap between dials.

When the best possible behavior at radio frequencies is desired the resistors should be of a type having low reactance. In a typical commercial resistance box, the bifilar winding is used below 1 ohm, the Ayrton-Perry arrangement for 1-, 10-, and 100-ohm units, mica-card resistors for 1000 and 10,000 ohms, and the fishline winding for greater values.

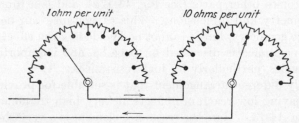

FIG. 14-14. Switching arrangements for decade resistance box.

When several resistances are assembled together with a switch to form an adjustable resistance box, the result is to increase the residual reactances and degrade the phase angle. Thus the inductance is increased as a result of the inductance of the leads and switches, while the capacitance is greater as a result of the additional capacitance introduced by the leads and case. The equivalent circuit for a single decade then takes the

[1] Further information on this type of resistance is given by D. B. Sinclair, Type 663 Resistor—A Standard for Use at High Frequencies, *Gen. Rad. Expt.*, vol. 13, p. 6, January, 1939.

form shown in Fig. 14-15.   Here ΔR and ΔL are the resistance and inductance increments, added as the switch advances one step, C is the equivalent shunting capacitance of the leads and switch, while R_0 and L_0 are the residual resistance and inductance observed at the terminals when the switch is at the first position where all resistance units are cut out.

In certain types of measurements, such as those involving the determination of small inductances at audio frequencies, and in the determination of resistance of radio frequencies by the substitution method, it is necessary that the equivalent series inductance of a resistance box be independent of the resistance setting, although the inductance need not be zero.

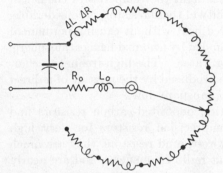

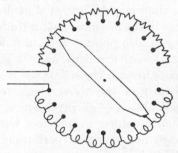

Fig. 14-15. Equivalent circuit of a single decade of a resistance box.

Fig. 14-16. Inductively compensated decade resistance.

This result can be obtained by an arrangement of the type illustrated in Fig. 14-16.   Here the opposite ends of the switch control, respectively, resistance units, and small coils each having an inductance equal to the inductance of an individual resistance unit but wound with copper wire. As the switch is rotated, the total inductance hence stays absolutely constant as the resistance is increased or decreased.

14-5. Carbon-film and Carbon-composition Resistors.[1] Wire-wound resistors are expensive, and are not suitable for use at extremely high frequencies; also very high resistance values cannot be obtained in physically small wire-wound units.   The most important alternatives to wire-wound resistors are deposited-carbon, carbon-composition-rod, and carbon-composition-film resistors.

Deposited-carbon Resistors.[2] The carbon-film resistor, also called a deposited-carbon resistor, consists of a ceramic core on which a thin layer

---

[1] An extensive summarizing discussion is given in "Components Handbook" (Vol. 17, Radiation Laboratory Series), Chap. 2, McGraw-Hill Book Company, Inc., New York, 1949.

[2] A. C. Pfister, Precision Carbon Resistors, *Bell Labs. Record.*, vol. 26, p. 401, October, 1948; W. van Roosbroeck, High-frequency Deposited Carbon Resistors,

of crystalline metallic carbon is deposited from a hydrocarbon vapor at high temperature. When this process is carried out under properly controlled conditions, a uniform, strongly adhering film of crystalline carbon is obtained, the resistance of which is very stable. Resistance values ranging from 1 ohm to tens of megohms are obtainable in this way, using rods several inches long.

Deposited-carbon resistors have excellent characteristics. The resistance is very stable with time, particularly when the resistor is protected from moisture by sealing in a glass envelope filled with an inert gas; temperature cycles produce negligible hysteresis effect of the resistance; the temperature coefficient of resistivity is of the order of 200 to 500 parts per million per °C, which is much less than the temperature coefficient of copper. The power-dissipating ability of these resistors is considerable. Thus they may be operated at dull red heat without causing permanent change in the resistance value if surrounded by a nonoxidizing atmosphere; they can also be immersed in flowing water. The high-frequency characteristics are excellent, and the noise produced by the passage of a direct current through the resistance is also unusually low.

Because of the above characteristics, deposited-carbon resistors find considerable use as precision or semiprecision resistors for very high resistance values. Compared with wire-wound resistors, they are much cheaper, have superior performance at radio frequencies, and are nearly as stable.

Carbon-composition Resistors. The carbon-composition-*rod* type of resistance so widely used in electronics equipment consists of a solid conducting rod formed of a mixture of fine carbon particles and an insulating binding medium. The resistance obtained with such an arrangement depends upon the length and cross section of the conducting rod, and the conductivity of the mixture of which it is formed. Such resistors are not suitable for precision work because of their poor stability, high temperature coefficient, variation of resistance with applied voltage, poor performance at very high frequencies, etc.

The carbon-composition-*film* resistor makes use of a conducting mixture of carbon particles and insulating binding medium that is used to provide a conducting film on the surface of an insulating support such as a ceramic or glass rod or tube. Resistors of this type are frequently called

Bell. Labs. Record., vol. 26, p. 407, October, 1948; P. R. Coursey, Fixed Resistors for Use in Communication Equipment, *Proc. IEE (Radio & Comm.)*, vol. 96, pt. III, p. 169, May, 1949; T. Holmes, Fixed High-stability Carbon Resistors, *J. IEE (Radiocomm. Conv.)*, vol. 94, pt. IIIA, p. 912, March–April, 1947; R. O. Grisdale, A. C. Pfister, and W. van Roosbroeck, Pyrolytic Film Resistors, *Bell System Tech. J.*, vol. 28, **p. 21**, March, 1951.

"metallized" resistors.[1]   Their characteristics with respect to temperature coefficient of resistance, stability of resistance with time, humidity, etc., as well as performance at very high frequencies, are vastly superior to those of the carbon-rod type of resistor, but are somewhat inferior to those of the deposited-carbon resistor.

Frequency Effects in Carbon-film and -rod Resistors, Including Effects Introduced by Distributed Capacitance.   Because of their small physical size and short current paths in proportion to resistance, carbon-film and -rod resistors have negligible series inductance in proportion to resistance. In the case of film resistors, the conducting film is ordinarily so thin that skin effect is not an important factor in the behavior.

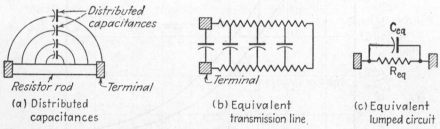

(a) Distributed capacitances

(b) Equivalent transmission line

(c) Equivalent lumped circuit

Fig. 14-17.   Distributed capacitance in a resistor, and equivalent circuit taking it into account.

In rod and film resistors, and also in noninductive wire-wound types as well, the equivalent circuit at low and moderate frequencies is as shown in Fig. 14-11a with $L = 0$.   The resistor then acts like a resistance of fixed value (except for possible skin effect) shunted by a fixed capacitance. However, at very high frequencies the behavior is affected by the fact that at least part of the capacitance associated with the resistor is distributed, as shown in Fig. 14-17a.

This distributed capacitance causes the resistance rod to act as a resistance-capacitance transmission line when viewed from the terminals of the rod, giving an equivalent circuit as illustrated in Fig. 14-17b.   The effective resistance R_{eq} that can be considered as connecting the terminals (see Fig. 14-17c) will then decrease with frequency in the manner illustrated in Fig. 14-18.   Theory, confirmed by experiment, shows that for any particular type of resistance of given size and geometrical configuration, the ratio R_{eq}/R of effective a-c resistance R_{eq} to low-frequency or d-c resistance R will depend only upon the product fR, and will be independ-

---

[1] Resistors which utilize sputtered or evaporated metal films, are also commercially available, but are not the same as the resistors commonly advertised as "metallized"; see "Components Handbook," *op. cit.*, p. 99.

ent of the particular value of resistance.[1] The ratio C_{eq}/C of equivalent shunting capacitance C_{eq} (exclusive of direct capacitance between terminals) to the equivalent lumped low-frequency value C also depends on the product fR as shown in Fig. 14-18. Thus if a particular type of 1-megohm resistance shows a drop in effective resistance of 10 per cent at a frequency of 1 Mc, then a 1000-ohm resistance of the same type having the same physical dimensions, will show a drop in effective resistance of 10 per cent at a frequency of 1000 Mc.

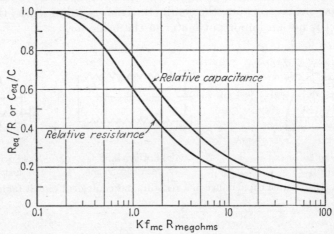

Fig. 14-18. Effect of the resistance-frequency product Rf on the relative resistance and capacitance of a resistor having distributed capacitance. The factor K is a constant that depends upon the type of resistor, and the physical size and shape of the resistor, and typically has a value of the order of 0.25 to 2.0 for small rod resistors.

The value of the resistance-frequency product fR corresponding to a particular value of resistance drop will depend on the geometry, size, and type of resistor, and also upon the capacitance to neighboring objects (particularly the terminal caps). Such differences are taken into account by the constant K in Fig. 14-18. In general, long thin resistors will perform better at high frequencies than will short resistors; to a first approximation the constant K will be inversely proportional to the length of a resistor of constant diameter. The value of K is typically in the range 0.25 to 2.0. The value is usually lowest for deposited-carbon resistors and for the best quality metallized resistors, and is higher for poor-quality metallized, and for wire-wound resistors. It tends to be quite high for

[1] G. W. O. Howe, The Behavior of High Resistance at High Frequencies, *Wireless Eng. and Exptl. Wireless*, vol. 12, p. 414, August, 1935; L. Hartshorn, The Behavior of Resistors at High Frequencies, *Wireless Eng.*, vol. 15, p. 363, July, 1938.

carbon-composition-rod resistors, and such resistors are consequently generally unsatisfactory for use at very high frequencies.

Resistance Noise Arising from Direct Current.[1]   When direct current is passed through a deposited-film, composition-film, or carbon-rod resistor, a noise voltage is developed across the resistor terminals in addition to thermal-agitation noise.   No such effect is observed in wire-wound resistances.   This noise voltage is maximum at low frequencies.   It is inversely proportional to frequency up to at least 10 kc, and sometimes drops off even more rapidly at higher frequencies.   At frequencies of the order of 1 Mc the excess noise arising from the passage of the direct current becomes negligible compared with thermal-agitation noise.

The rms value of the noise voltage developed across the terminals of a resistance by the passage of a direct current is found by experiment to be almost exactly proportional to the d-c voltage applied to the resistor, and so is commonly expressed in terms of microvolts of noise generated across the resistor terminals per volt of applied d-c potential.   The value of this coefficient will be the same for a particular type of resistor, irrespective of the value of its resistance.

Different types of resistors differ greatly in the noise that they generate. Of the several types that depend upon carbon as a conducting element, the deposited-carbon resistor has the lowest noise, its coefficient typically being less than 0.25 μv noise per d-c volt.   Carbon-film (metallized) resistors, can be nearly as good, while the carbon-rod type always has a high noise coefficient.   Carbon-rod and metallized resistors vary greatly from resistor to resistor, variations as great as 20 to 1 being typically found in a group of otherwise apparently identical resistors.

14-6. Loads for Dissipating Radio-frequency Power.[2]   In testing transmitters, power oscillators, Class C amplifiers, etc., it is frequently necessary to dissipate the generated power in a laboratory or "dummy" load.   Many arrangements are used for this purpose; the only requirements are that the dummy load have the ability to dissipate the required amount of power, and that at the same time it present a suitable impedance to the source of energy.

At the lower radio frequencies, as contrasted with microwave frequencies, it is possible to obtain lumped resistances that have fairly good impedance characteristics, and that are capable of dissipating small to moderate amounts of power.   Arrangements used include metallized,

---

[1] See C. J. Christensen and G. L. Pearson, Spontaneous Resistance Fluctuations in Carbon Microphones and Other Granular Resistances, *Bell System Tech. J.*, vol. 15, p. 181, April, 1936; R. H. Campbell, Jr., and R. A. Chipman, Noise from Current-carrying Resistors 20 to 500 Kc, *Proc. IRE*, vol. 37, p. 938, August, 1949.

[2] See "Very High Frequency Techniques," pp. 570–574, 580–581, McGraw-Hill Book Company, Inc., New York, 1947.

deposited-carbon, and noninductive wire-wound resistances cooled by air, forced air draft, oil, or water.[1]   For powers of 50 watts or less, mica-card resistors cooled by being mounted in a hydrogen-filled bulb are very satisfactory up to frequencies of 25 Mc.   Loads consisting of a lamp filament, preferably cooled by hydrogen, will handle up to 50 watts, and when specially designed with a "straight-through" filament may be used up to 3000 Mc.[2]

When very large amounts of power are to be dissipated at low or moderate frequencies, as for example 50 kw, water loads are often used. It is also possible to dissipate large amounts of power in a two-wire transmission line which is given a high attenuation by using iron or nichrome conductors.   Since the conductors of such a line may be long and may operate at a relatively high temperature, large amounts of power can be dissipated.

At microwave frequencies, the energy to be dissipated in a dummy load is ordinarily available in a coaxial line or waveguide.   The problem therefore becomes one of terminating the system in a manner that will dissipate the energy involved, and at the same time provide at least a reasonably fair impedance match, so that the power actually available in the system will be delivered to the dummy load.   When all tests are to be made at a single frequency, or when the frequency is changed only infrequently, it is possible to achieve the required impedance matching with the aid of tuning stubs, etc.   However, when it is required that the dummy load be suitable for operation over a wide frequency range, it is customary to use one of the nonreflecting terminations discussed below in Sec. 14-7. Alternatively, moderate amounts of power can be dissipated by hydrogen-cooled lamp filaments, which can be designed to operate satisfactorily up to frequencies of over 3000 Mc.

When it is not necessary to avoid radiation of energy, one very convenient means of dissipating power at very high frequencies is to deliver it to a radiating antenna.   Thus a quarter-wave grounded antenna provides a resistive load of 36.7 ohms, and can be readily matched to a coaxial line.   Similarly, a suitably designed tapered horn will radiate the power in a waveguide without introducing an appreciable reflection.

[1] A water-cooled load resistor is described by G. H. Brown and J. W. Conklin, Water-cooled Resistors for Ultra-high Frequencies, *Electronics*, vol. 14, p. 24, April, 1941.

[2] A good discussion of the cooling action of hydrogen is given by E. G. Linder, The Use of Gas-filled Lamps as High Dissipation, High-frequency Resistors Especially for Power Measurements, *RCA Rev.*, vol. 4, p. 83, July, 1939.   Various load lamps are described in "Technique of Microwave Measurements" (Vol. 11, Radiation Laboratory Series), p. 180, McGraw-Hill Book Company, Inc., New York, 1947.

14-7. Terminations for Coaxial Lines and Waveguides at Microwave Frequencies.[1] Innumerable circumstances arise in microwave work where it is necessary to provide a nonreflecting termination for a coaxial line or a waveguide.   In many cases the power involved is small, in which case avoidance of reflection is the only consideration involved; in other situations the power to be dissipated is large, and the ability of the termination to handle energy is also important.   In obtaining a low reflection, it is ordinarily highly desirable to avoid depending upon an adjustable impedance-matching arrangement, such as a stub tuner, which is generally rather sensitive to changes in frequency, and requires auxiliary devices to determine when it is properly adjusted.

The termination of a waveguide or coaxial system at microwave frequencies is commonly accomplished with the aid of an attenuator, as illustrated schematically in Fig. 14-19 when applied to a waveguide. The attenuator can be based on any one of the types of resistive attenuators described in Sec. 15-5.   It is simply necessary that there be a low reflection on the input side of the termina-

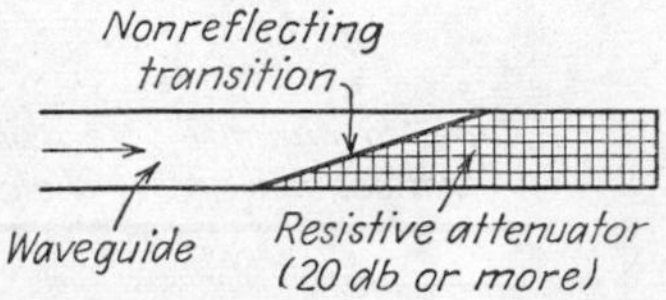

Fig. 14-19. Schematic diagram showing use of a resistive attenuator to provide a nonreflecting termination for a waveguide system.

tion, and that the total attenuation of the terminating attenuator be great enough so that a wave that traverses the attenuator and is reflected at its output side is reduced to negligible amplitude by the time it returns to the input end of the attenuator. An attenuator loss of 20 db is generally sufficient.   This gives a round-trip attenuation of 40 db, and even with complete reflection on the output side, the voltage standing-wave ratio introduced by the output reflection will then be only 1.01.   Tapering or otherwise providing a transition to minimize reflections, such as illustrated in Fig. 15-16, is required only for the input side of the termination; the output side of the terminating attenuator need not be tapered because an output impedance match is not required.

Special Considerations Applying to Coaxial-line Terminations.   A lossy cable provides a termination for coaxial systems that is capable of handling large amounts of power, and will provide a satisfactory termination over a very wide frequency band.   When the power to be dissipated in the cable is large, it is desirable to use several sections of lossy cable having progressively increasing rates of attenuation per unit length, as illustrated in Fig. 14-20a.   In this way, the dissipation of energy is distributed over a greater length of cable.   When a lossy cable is used to

[1] Further details, including particularly much useful design information, is given in "Technique of Microwave Measurements," *op. cit.*, pp. 720–743.

provide a termination over a wide frequency band, the length of cable required will be reduced if the output end of the lossy cable is terminated in some form of lumped impedance that approximates the characteristic impedance at the lower frequencies involved. In this way, the input terminals of the cable will provide an impedance approximating the characteristic impedance even at frequencies so low that the attenuation of the lossy line would not otherwise be adequate to give a satisfactory termination.

The resistive center conductor, as shown in Fig. 14-20b, and also discussed on page 664, provides a simple and effective means of terminating a

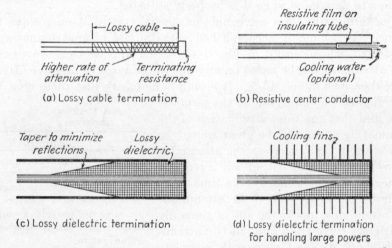

Fig. 14-20. Schematic representation of various methods of obtaining a nonreflecting termination for a coaxial system.

coaxial line. Such a system can be designed to introduce a low standing-wave ratio over a wide frequency range. Also, by the use of internal water cooling a considerable amount of power can be handled, particularly if the attenuation per unit length is not made too great. When large amounts of power are to be dissipated it is desirable that the resistivity of the center conductor be tapered from a relatively low value adjacent to the coaxial line, to an increasingly high value as the short-circuited termination is approached. In this way, the dissipation of energy can be distributed over an appreciable length while still keeping the total length of the attenuator a minimum. Tapering the resistivity of the center conductor in this way also improves the impedance match. When compactness in the termination is important, one should arrange so that the total resistance of the center conductor is equal to the characteristic impedance of the line to be terminated. At the same time, the characteristic impedance of the terminating section is made $\sqrt{3}$ times as great as the characteristic impedance of the line being matched.   This greater characteristic impedance of the terminating section may be achieved either by suitable choice of dielectric material for the terminating section, or by employing a different diameter from that part of the system.   With these proportions the voltage standing-wave ratio will not exceed 1.03 from the very lowest frequencies up to a top frequency such that the length of the terminating resistance is 0.05 wavelength.   If the length is expressed in inches, this leads to the formula[1]

$$\text{Maximum permissible frequency in Mc} = \frac{600}{\text{Resistor length in in.}} \quad (14\text{-}5)$$

Another method often used to terminate coaxial lines consists in introducing a tapered section of lossy dielectric as illustrated in Fig. 14-20c. The lossy dielectric provides a high attenuation, while the taper is for the purpose of providing a gradual transition that does not set up reflections. Several plastic and ceramic materials have been developed that are suitable for this application; it is also possible to use iron-dust cores (polyiron) as the lossy material, while another form of the same idea is illustrated in Fig. 2-10.   A simple arrangement suitable for dissipating large amounts of power is illustrated in Fig. 14-20d.   Here a tapered segment of lossy material composed of a mixture of graphite, cement, and water, is cast in place.[2]   When provided with fins to radiate heat, such an arrangement with a ⅞-in.-diameter outside conductor, will dissipate over 100 watts, and will have a low standing-wave ratio over a wavelength range from 8 to 12 cm.   The rate of taper is preferably made more gradual than the minimum necessary to avoid reflections, as in this way the energy loss can be distributed uniformly over an increased length.

Special Considerations Applying to Waveguide Terminations.   Waveguide terminations for low and moderate powers are generally adaptations of the waveguide attenuators discussed in Sec. 15-5.   Examples of such adaptations are illustrated in Fig. 14-21, and involve lossy vanes, iron-dust (polyiron) cores, wedges of lossy dielectric, etc., arranged with a taper on the entering side, and having a length sufficient to provide a total attenuation adequate to give a good termination.   In order to minimize the total length required to realize this required attenuation, the terminating attenuator is commonly provided with a double taper as shown; in the case of vanes this involves a multiplicity of staggered vanes.

Waveguide terminations suitable for dissipating large amounts of power can be constructed in several ways.   One approach is to employ the same

[1] The theory of compact terminations of this type, together with design curves, is given by D. Rogers Crosby and Carol H. Pennypacker, Radio Frequency Resistors as Uniform Transmission Lines, *Proc. IRE*, vol. 34, p. 62, February, 1946.

[2] For process details see "Technique of Microwave Measurements," *op. cit.*, p. 733.

techniques as are used in the calorimeter measurement of power in waveguides (see Sec. 2-3). Another approach is to employ a waveguide with a tapered ridge composed of steel or other material that introduces a high loss, making the ridge section sufficiently long to introduce an attenuation

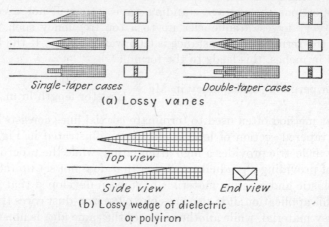

Single-taper cases   Double-taper cases

(a) Lossy vanes

Top view

Side view   End view

(b) Lossy wedge of dielectric
or polyiron

FIG. 14-21. Examples of nonreflecting terminations for waveguides.

of at least 20 db. Still another approach is that illustrated in Fig. 14-22, in which the walls of the waveguide are lined with lossy material. The lossy material is arranged so that the height (but not width) of the guide is tapered as shown; in this way the attenuation per unit length increases as the wave penetrates into the lossy section. This reduces the total

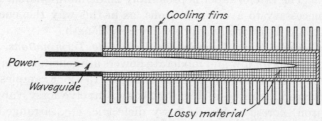

Cooling fins

Power

Waveguide

Lossy material

FIG. 14-22. Nonreflecting termination for a waveguide capable of dissipating large amounts of power.

length required to keep a low standing-wave ratio, and causes the heating to be more evenly distributed. The lossy material in Fig. 14-22 can be a mixture of graphite, cement, and water that is cast into place.[1] Radiating fins can be used as shown to assist in dissipating the heat. Such arrangements have a high power-handling capacity, a good standing-wave characteristic over a 1.5 to 1 frequency range, and can be built for wavelengths as short as 1 cm.

[1] For process details, see "Technique of Microwave Measurements," *op. cit.*, p. 737.

CHAPTER 15

ATTENUATORS AND SIGNAL GENERATORS

15-1. Attenuators Using Lumped Resistance Elements. Attenuators, sometimes also called *pads*, are devices used to reduce voltage, current, or power in controllable and known amounts. An important class of attenuators is composed of a network of resistance units that is connected between a pair of input terminals and a pair of output terminals.

Typical examples of such resistance attenuators are given in Fig. 15-1. A study of these networks reveals that as far as the characteristics observable at the terminals are concerned, every conceivable combination of

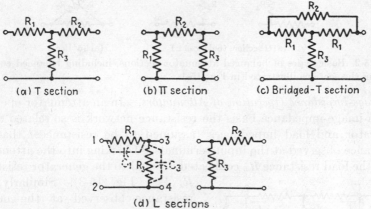

(a) T section   (b) π section   (c) Bridged-T section

(d) L sections

FIG. 15-1. Basic types of unbalanced attenuator sections.

resistances, however complex, can be reduced to a network composed of only three resistors. Thus the T and π networks are the most general arrangements possible. The more complicated bridged-T, while having desirable convenience and flexibility for certain practical purposes, always can be reduced to an equivalent T or π. In contrast, the L attenuator is more limited than the T or π in the properties it can realize, as it possesses only two resistors.

Of particular practical importance, is the special case in which the network is symmetrical about a vertical center line. In the case of the T network of Fig. 15-1a, this corresponds to $R_1 = R_2$, while with the π network it means that $R_1 = R_3$. The L network is inherently unsymmetrical.

In all the attenuator networks of Fig. 15-1, one input and one output terminal are connected directly together; where this is the case the attenuator is said to be *unbalanced* or *grounded*. When symmetry about a horizontal center line is achieved by rearranging so that the series resistances are divided equally between the two sides of the circuit as in Fig. 15-2, the network is then said to be *balanced*.

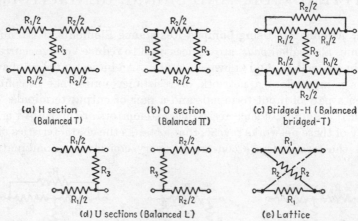

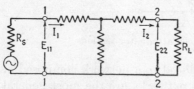

(a) H section
(Balanced T)

(b) O section
(Balanced π)

(c) Bridged-H (Balanced bridged-T)

(d) U sections (Balanced L)

(e) Lattice

Fig. 15-2. Basic types of balanced attenuator sections, including balanced counterparts of the sections illustrated in Fig. 15-1.

Image-impedance Operation of Attenuators. In an attenuator operated on an image-impedance basis the resistance network is so related to the generator and load impedances (assumed to be resistances) that the resistance observed at the input terminals 1-1 looking into the attenuator with the load resistance R_L connected is equal to the generator resistance R_s (see Fig. 15-3). Similarly, the resistance observed at the output terminals 2-2 when looking into the attenuator network with R_s present is equal to the load resistance R_L. Image-impedance operation is therefore the case in which impedance matching occurs *simultaneously* at both the input and output terminals. That is to say, with image operation the impedances at 1-1 are the same when looking toward the generator and toward the load; similarly the impedances at 2-2 are the same looking in both directions though not necessarily having the same numerical value as is associated with 1-1. Image operation thus corresponds to the condition for which the power delivered by the generator to the network has the maximum possible value; it likewise corresponds to the

Fig. 15-3. Attenuator associated with generator and load resistances.

condition where the load resistance has the value that will absorb the maximum possible power from the network.

The generator and load resistances that must be used with a network to give image-impedance operation are termed the *image impedances*, and are fundamental properties of the network.   A third fundamental characteristic of the network is the ratio of load to generator voltage (or current) under image-impedance conditions.   This property is commonly defined in terms of the attenuation constant α (sometimes called *image attenuation* or *transfer constant*), which is defined in terms of the relation

$$\frac{E_{22}}{E_{11}} = \sqrt{\frac{R_{I_2}}{R_{I_1}}}\, \epsilon^{-\alpha} \qquad (15\text{-}1a)$$

or

$$\frac{I_2}{I_1} = \sqrt{\frac{R_{I_1}}{R_{I_2}}}\, \epsilon^{-\alpha} \qquad (15\text{-}1b)$$

where R_{I_1} and R_{I_2} are the image impedances at the input and output terminals of the network, respectively, and E_{11}, E_{22}, I_1, and I_2 have the meanings indicated in Fig. 15-3.   For the particular case of a symmetrical network, $R_{I_1} = R_{I_2}$, and Eqs. (15-1) become

$$\frac{E_{22}}{E_{11}} = \frac{I_2}{I_1} = \epsilon^{-\alpha} \qquad (15\text{-}2)$$

An important consideration when dealing with attenuators is the ratio of the power delivered to the attenuator input to the power that the attenuator output delivers to the load resistance.   This ratio can be called the *transmission loss*, or the *power-loss ratio*, and is commonly represented by the symbol K^2.   Accordingly,

$$\text{Power-loss ratio in db} = 20 \log_{10} K \qquad (15\text{-}3)$$

In the case of *image-impedance operation*, as represented by Eqs. (15-1), it follows that[1]

$$\left. \begin{array}{l} \text{Power-loss ratio} \\ \text{for image operation} \end{array} \right\} = K^2 = \frac{I_1{}^2 R_{I_1}}{I_2{}^2 R_{I_2}} = \epsilon^{2\alpha} \qquad (15\text{-}4a)$$

or

$$\text{Power loss in db} = 8.686\alpha \qquad (15\text{-}4b)$$

Equation (15-4b) can be considered to be a definition of the attenuation constant.

Unbalanced attenuator sections are used wherever possible in prefer-

---

[1] Formulas and curves for obtaining the power-loss ratio K^2 in the general case where image matching does not exist are given by Arthur W. Melloh, Errors in the Calibrated Losses of Symmetrical Resistance Networks, *Proc. IRE*, vol. 29, p. 387, July, 1941.

ence to balanced sections, as the latter require more resistance units. However, when a balanced arrangement is required, this can be readily achieved, since every unbalanced section has its balanced counterpart, as seen by comparing Fig. 15-1 with Fig. 15-2.

Since the most general possible form of resistance network is composed of three independent resistances, it follows that specifying the two image

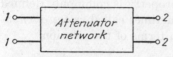

FIG. 15-4. Schematic representation of an attenuator network and its terminals.

resistances R_{I_1} and R_{I_2}, and the image attenuation constant α, defines a T (or π) network of resistances that has the same characteristics as the actual network, which is not necessarily either a T or π. When discussing the electrical properties of an attenuator, as distinct from the process of designing an attenuator, it is therefore customary to describe the attenuator in terms of its image resistances, and image attenuation constant.

The three attenuator parameters R_{I_1}, R_{I_2}, and α, can be calculated in terms of the open- and short-circuit resistances of the network, according to the relation

$$R_{I_1} = \sqrt{R_{oc}R_{sc}} \qquad (15\text{-}5a)$$

$$R_{I_2} = \sqrt{R'_{oc}R'_{sc}} \qquad (15\text{-}5b)$$

$$\tanh \alpha = \sqrt{\frac{R_{sc}}{R_{oc}}} = \sqrt{\frac{R'_{sc}}{R'_{oc}}} \qquad (15\text{-}5c)$$

Referring to Fig. 15-4, R_{oc} and R_{sc} are the resistances observed at terminals 1-1 with terminals 2-2 open-circuited and short-circuited, respectively, while R'_{oc} and R'_{sc} are the resistances observed between terminals 2-2 when terminals 1-1 are alternatively open and short circuited.

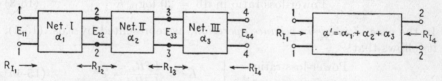

(a) Networks in cascade

(b) Equivalent network

FIG. 15-5. Cascade arrangement of attenuator networks matched on an image-impedance basis.

When a number of attenuator sections are connected in a cascade as illustrated in Fig. 15-5a, with image impedance matching existing at each junction, then the entire chain of attenuators can be regarded as a single attenuator as illustrated in Fig. 15-5b.[1] This equivalent attenuator has

[1] The effect of impedance mismatches at the junction of such a system are analyzed by R. W. Beatty, Cascade-connected Attenuators, *Proc. IRE*, vol. 38, p. 1190, October, 1950.

an attenuation constant α' equal to the sum of the attenuation constants of the individual sections that are connected in cascade, and has image impedances R'_{I_1} and R'_{I_2} that are the input image impedance of the first section and the output image impedance of the last section, respectively.[1] The characteristics of the over-all cascade chain of attenuators are then given by Eqs. (15-1) for these equivalent constants.   It will be noted that

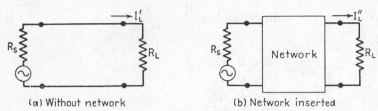

(a) Without network   (b) Network inserted

Fig. 15-6. Circuits illustrating insertion of network between a generator and a load.

the image impedances of the intermediate junctions do not enter into the over-all properties of the attenuator chain, provided that the intermediate junctions are matched on an image impedance basis.

Insertion Loss.   When a network is inserted between a sending end resistance R_s and a load resistance R_L as in Fig. 15-6b, the ratio of current I''_L in the load impedance when the network is present to the current I'_L in the load when the generator is connected directly to the load resistance (see Fig. 15-6a), is termed the *insertion loss*.   It will be noted that the insertion loss gives the effect of the attenuator on the load current, irrespective of whether or not image impedance matching exists.   While the

[1] This can be shown as follows: Referring to Fig. 15-5a, and following Eq. (15-1a), one can write,

$$\frac{E_{22}}{E_{11}} = \sqrt{\frac{R_{I_2}}{R_{I_1}}}\; \epsilon^{-\alpha_1}$$

$$\frac{E_{33}}{E_{22}} = \sqrt{\frac{R_{I_3}}{R_{I_2}}}\; \epsilon^{-\alpha_2}$$

$$\frac{E_{44}}{E_{33}} = \sqrt{\frac{R_{I_4}}{R_{I_3}}}\; \epsilon^{-\alpha_3}$$

Multiplying the first two of these equations together to eliminate E_{22} gives

$$\frac{E_{33}}{E_{11}} = \sqrt{\frac{R_{I_3}}{R_{I_1}}}\; \epsilon^{-(\alpha_1+\alpha_2)}$$

Multiplying this relation by the third equation to eliminate E_{33} gives

$$\frac{E_{44}}{E_{11}} = \sqrt{\frac{R_{I_4}}{R_{I_1}}}\; \epsilon^{-(\alpha_1+\alpha_2+\alpha_3)}$$

Comparison with Eq. (15-1a) shows this result is the same as given by a single section having input and output image impedances of R_{I_1} and R_{I_4}, respectively, and an attenuation constant $\alpha' = \alpha_1 + \alpha_2 + \alpha_3$.

insertion loss is defined above in terms of a current or voltage ratio, it can also be given in terms of the equivalent power ratio, in which case it is expressed in decibels.

The insertion loss can be conveniently expressed in terms of the two image impedances R_{I_1} and R_{I_2}, the attenuation constant α, and the generator and load resistances R_s and R_L according to the equation[1]

$$\text{Insertion loss } \frac{I'_L}{I''_L} = \frac{k_3}{\sigma k_1 k_2} \epsilon^\alpha \tag{15-6}$$

where

$$k_1 = \frac{2\sqrt{R_s/R_{I_1}}}{1 + (R_s/R_{I_1})}$$

$$k_2 = \frac{2\sqrt{R_{I_2}/R_L}}{1 + (R_{I_2}/R_L)}$$

$$k_3 = \frac{2\sqrt{R_s/R_L}}{1 + (R_s/R_L)}$$

$$\sigma = \frac{1}{1 - \left(\dfrac{R_{I_2} - R_L}{R_{I_2} + R_L}\right)\left(\dfrac{R_{I_1} - R_s}{R_{I_1} + R_s}\right)\epsilon^{-2\alpha}}$$

It is to be noted that the insertion loss is not the same as the power loss ratio K defined by Eq. (15-4a).

It is helpful in interpreting the significance of Eq. (15-6) to note that k_1 has the value of unity when an image impedance match exists between the generator resistance R_s and the input image impedance R_{I_1} of the network; for all other relations between these two impedances k_1 is less than unity and becomes smaller as the two impedances depart increasingly from an image match.   The quantity k_2 behaves in a similar manner, being unity when the output image impedance R_{I_2} of the network equals the load resistance.   In the same way, k_3 is unity when the load resistance is equal to the generator resistance, i.e., when the load represents an image impedance match to the generator.

The quantity σ is termed the *interaction factor*.   It is a second-order effect, representing the modification of the insertion loss that occurs when there is mismatching at *both* the input and output terminals of the network.   The interaction factor is unity if the generator resistance matches the input image resistance, or if the load resistance matches the output image impedance; the interaction factor is also unity even if mismatching occurs at both terminals provided the attenuation of the network is large (i.e., if $\alpha > 2$).   If none of these conditions is satisfied, the interaction

---

[1] Curves from which the insertion loss may be quickly determined for a symmetrical attenuator are given by Melloh, *loc. cit.*

faction will differ from unity, but under ordinary conditions will usually lie in the range 0.8 to 1.25.

The practical usefulness of the insertion-loss concept can be increased by keeping in mind the way the insertion loss behaves in type cases as follows:

Case 1.   Image-impedance operation.   Here k_1, k_2, and σ are all equal to unity.   The insertion loss accordingly becomes

$$\text{Insertion loss} = k_3\epsilon^\alpha$$

In the special case where the load resistance R_L also equals the generator resistance R_3, then k_3 is likewise equal to unity, and the insertion loss becomes simply

$$\text{Insertion loss} = \epsilon^\alpha$$

Case 2.   Image-impedance matching at one terminal of the network but mismatching at the other terminal.   In this case the interaction factor σ, and also the value of k applying to the matched terminal are both unity. From Eq. (15-6) it then follows that

$$\text{Insertion loss} = \frac{k_3}{k'}\,\epsilon^\alpha$$

where k' is either k_1 or k_2, whichever is not unity.

15-2. Considerations Relating to Practical Attenuators Using Lumped Resistance Elements.   Most resistance attenuators are used in situations that call for a symmetrical arrangement.   Under these conditions, and provided an impedance match exists at at least one of the attenuator terminals, then insertion of the attenuator into the system between the generator and load reduces the load current without in any way altering the impedance relations associated with the generator and load that had existed prior to the insertion of the symmetrical attenuator section.

Attenuator sections are occasionally called upon to provide image impedance matching to generator and load resistances that are unequal. This requires an unsymmetrical, or "tapered," attenuator.   It is characteristic of tapered attenuators that they cannot be designed to have an attenuation constant less than a certain minimum value which is determined by the ratio of the image resistances involved.   Also, when the attenuation has this minimum value, the unsymmetrical T or π section degenerates into an L section, as discussed below.

Design Formulas, and Discussion of Basic Resistance Attenuator Types. The basic types of attenuator sections are the T, π, L, and bridged-T arrangements, and their balanced equivalents, the H, O, U, and bridged-H, respectively.   There is also the lattice attenuator, which is a balanced structure that has no unbalanced equivalent.

TABLE 15-1.

DESIGN FORMULAS FOR ATTENUATORS OPERATED WITH IMAGE IMPEDANCE MATCHING

Type	T and H	π and O	Bridged T and H	Lattice
Circuit and notation — Unbalanced	 $R_{I_1} \neq R_{I_2}$	 $R_{I_1} \neq R_{I_2}$		
Circuit and notation — Balanced	 $R_{I_1} = R_{I_2} = R_I$			
Design formulas K^2 = power ratio	$R_1 = R_{I_1}\left(\dfrac{K^2+1}{K^2-1}\right) - 2\sqrt{R_{I_1}R_{I_2}}\left(\dfrac{K}{K^2-1}\right)$ $R_2 = R_{I_2}\left(\dfrac{K^2+1}{K^2-1}\right) - 2\sqrt{R_{I_1}R_{I_2}}\left(\dfrac{K}{K^2-1}\right)$ $R_3 = 2\sqrt{R_{I_1}R_{I_2}}\left(\dfrac{K}{K^2-1}\right)$ $R_1 = R_2 = R_I\left(\dfrac{K-1}{K+1}\right)$ $R_3 = 2R_I\left(\dfrac{K}{K^2-1}\right)$	$R_1 = R_{I_1}\left(\dfrac{K^2-1}{K^2-2K\sqrt{\frac{R_{I_1}}{R_{I_2}}}+1}\right)$ $R_2 = \dfrac{\sqrt{R_{I_1}R_{I_2}}}{2}\left(\dfrac{K^2-1}{K}\right)$ $R_3 = R_{I_2}\left(\dfrac{K^2-1}{K^2-2K\sqrt{\frac{R_{I_2}}{R_{I_1}}}+1}\right)$ $R_1 = R_3 = R_I\left(\dfrac{K+1}{K-1}\right)$ $R_2 = \dfrac{R_I}{2}\left(\dfrac{K^2-1}{K}\right)$	Always used in balanced form $R_1 = R_I$ $R_2 = R_I(K-1)$ $R_3 = R_I\left(\dfrac{1}{K-1}\right)$	Inherently balanced $R_1 = R_I\left(\dfrac{K-1}{K+1}\right)$ $R_2 = R_I\left(\dfrac{K+1}{K-1}\right)$

TABLE 15-2.
DESIGN FORMULAS FOR U AND L ATTENUATORS

Circuit and notation	Case I	Case II
L		
U		
Design Formulas for image match at 1-1 $R_A \neq R_B$ (General case)	$R_1 = \sqrt{R_A R_B}\left(\sqrt{\dfrac{R_A}{R_B}} - \dfrac{1}{M}\right)$ $R_3 = \sqrt{R_A R_B}\left(\dfrac{1}{M - \sqrt{\dfrac{R_A}{R_B}}}\right)$	$R_2 = \sqrt{R_A R_B}\left(M - \sqrt{\dfrac{R_A}{R_B}}\right)$ $R_3 = \sqrt{R_A R_B}\left(\dfrac{1}{\sqrt{\dfrac{R_A}{R_B}} - \dfrac{1}{M}}\right)$
$R_A = R_B$	$R_1 = R_A\left(\dfrac{M-1}{M}\right)$ $R_3 = R_A\left(\dfrac{1}{M-1}\right)$	$R_2 = R_A(M-1)$ $R_3 = R_A\left(\dfrac{M}{M-1}\right)$

NOTE 1: In the above: $M^2 = \dfrac{\text{Power input to terminals } 1-1}{\text{Power output delivered to } R_B}$

NOTE 2: The image resistance, R_{I_B}, of the attenuator at the unmatched terminals 2-2 can be calculated from the relations:

$$\text{Case I} \quad R_{I_B} = \frac{R_1 R_3}{R_A}$$

$$\text{Case II} \quad R_{I_B} = \frac{R_2 R_3}{R_A}$$

The design of these types of attenuator sections to give a desired combination of image impedances R_{I_1} and R_{I_2} and attenuation constant α can be carried out with the aid of the formulas in Tables 15-1 and 15-2.[1]   The

[1] For a derivation of these formulas, for tables giving resistance values calculated from them, etc., see P. K. McElroy, Designing Resistive Attenuating Networks, *Proc. IRE*, vol. 23, p. 213, March, 1935; Guy C. Omer, Jr., Lattice Attenuating Networks, *Proc. IRE*, vol. 25, p. 620, May, 1937; C. D. Colchester and M. W. Gough, Resistance Networks—Complete Design Tables, *Wireless Eng.*, vol. 17, p. 206, May, 1940; Dawkins Espy, Attenuator Design—Formulas for Calculating Resistance Networks, *Electronics*, vol. 14, p. 51, November, 1941.

T and π sections may be designed to have any arbitrarily chosen combination of image resistances, together with any specified attenuation constant not less than a minimum value determined by the ratio of the image resistances. The lattice section, on the other hand, is inherently symmetrical and requires that the image impedances of the input and output sides be the same. The bridged-T attenuator as used in practice is also designed to be symmetrical; although such a section could theoretically be made unsymmetrical, this is seldom done in practice.

The T attenuator is the most widely used of the unbalanced types. As compared with the π section, it has the advantage that if the attenuation is to be adjustable, the fact that all three resistances of the T have a common junction is of practical importance. The π section is an alternative for the T; the fact that the three resistances composing the π are connected in series is an advantage in some mechanical layouts. The bridged-T section is of practical importance only in symmetrical attenuators; it is widely used as an adjustable attenuator because, although it requires a total of four resistors, only two of these need be variable, whereas a variable T or π requires that three resistors be adjustable. For balanced systems, the O and lattice types have the advantage over the H and bridged-H in that they require a smaller number of resistances per section.

The L attenuator is covered by Table 15-2, and calls for special consideration. Since only two resistances are involved, it is not possible to achieve arbitrarily specified values of the three network parameters in an L section. In practice, the most common use of the L attenuator is to cause the power delivered to the load impedance to be less than the power supplied to the attenuator input by some desired amount, while providing an image impedance match at either the input or the output terminals (but not both). The magnitude of the mismatch in resistance at the unmatched side of the L attenuator will depend upon the attenuation, and upon the ratio of the generator and load resistances associated with the network. In general, the impedance that the L attenuator presents to the unmatched resistance will be higher than the unmatched terminating resistance when the series arm of the L points toward the unmatched resistance, as in Case II in Table 15-2, and will be less than the unmatched terminating resistance when the series arm of the L points toward the matched resistance, as in Case I of Table 15-2. Thus when it makes a difference whether the unmatched resistance presented by the attenuator is high or low, it becomes of importance which way the L attenuator is oriented.

Another use of the L attenuator is as a minimum-loss taper attenuator. Here the objective is to provide image impedance matching for unequal load and generator resistances, while introducing the minimum possible power-loss factor K^2 [see Eq. (15-2)]. This result is achieved by using an L (or U) section with the series arm turned toward the higher terminating resistance, and designing the section so that M has the value[1]

$$M = \sqrt{\frac{R_A}{R_B}} + \sqrt{\frac{R_A}{R_B} - 1} \qquad (15\text{-}7a)$$

The corresponding values of R_1 and R_3 are

$$R_1 = R_A \sqrt{1 - \frac{R_B}{R_A}} \qquad (15\text{-}7b)$$

$$R_3 = \frac{R_B}{\sqrt{1 - \frac{R_B}{R_A}}} \qquad (15\text{-}7c)$$

These relations assume $R_A > R_B$. It will be found that if either a T or a π section is designed according to Table 15-1 with K equal to this value of M, the T or π section degenerates into the same L that results by use of Eqs. (15-7) in Table 15-2.

Continuously Variable and Step Attenuators.   In many circumstances it is necessary to vary the attenuation constant α while maintaining the image impedance match at the two pairs of terminals without change.[2] A continuous variation of attenuation can be obtained by employing variable resistances for the attenuator arms, and controlling these resistances from a common shaft. Each variable resistance must be appropriately "tapered" to give a law of variation with angle of rotation that satisfies the relations between resistance elements called for by the design equations of the type of section involved.[3] The bridged-T attenuator is particularly suitable for such applications as only two variable resistances are required.

Attenuators that are adjustable in steps with the aid of switches are used in measurement work wherever precision is important. The step arrangement makes it possible to adjust the individual resistance elements composing the attenuators to a high degree of accuracy, and entirely avoids errors from failure of several variable resistances to track,

[1] For derivation of formulas see McElroy, *loc. cit.*, or M. F. Cooper, Audio-frequency Mixers, *Wireless Eng.*, vol. 21, p. 117, March, 1944.

[2] In the case of the L section the impedance match exists for only one side of the attenuator.

[3] For laboratory measurement work, continuously variable attenuators of this type must be made with wire-wound resistances in order to ensure reliability. However, when it is merely necessary that the attenuation be continuously adjustable, and it is not necessary that the attenuation be known or stable, then composition-type variable resistors can be employed at a considerable saving in cost.

and from the wear, noise, and the uncertain contact resistance associated with sliding contacts.

Step variation of attenuation may be obtained in either of two ways. One method is to vary the resistances of the individual elements composing the attenuator, using ganged tap switches, as illustrated in Fig. 15-7a. Alternatively, attenuator sections may be switched in and out of a cascade arrangement, as illustrated in Fig. 15-7b. If the individual sections are symmetrical, and all image impedances are the same, then adding or subtracting a section from the system changes the attenuation by the value of α associated with the section, without altering the imped-ance relations in any respect.

A decade attenuator can be obtained in this way, by employing four double-point double-throw switches to control four attenuator units, in which the relative decibel attenuation is of the ratio 1, 2, 3, 4. For example, if the individual units of such a system have attenuations of 0.1,

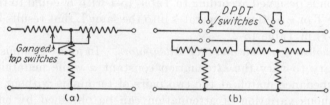

Fig. 15-7. Switching arrangements for obtaining step variation in the attenuation.

0.2, 0.3, and 0.4 db, then by manipulating the switches to cut into the system the proper sections, one can vary the total attenuation from 0 to 1.0 db in 0.1-db steps. A second decade connected in cascade with the first, and arranged to give 1-db steps, could then extend the total range to 11.0 db adjustable in 0.1-db steps, and so on. The required switching arrangement for each decade can be conveniently and compactly achieved in an 11-point rotary switch of the multideck wafer type; alternatively a double-point double-throw toggle switch may be used to control each individual attenuator.

The ladder attenuator, a typical form of which is shown in Fig. 15-8a, provides a rather specialized but nevertheless important means for obtain-ing variable attenuation. As shown in Fig. 15-8b, the attenuator itself consists of symmetrical π sections having identical image impedances; generally, the individual sections have the same attenuation per section although this is not required. A resistance R_s equal to the image resist-ance R_I of the sections is connected across terminals 1-1 of the attenuator, while terminals 2-2 are connected to a terminating resistance $R_L = R_s$ that is also equal to the image resistance R_I of the sections. The attenu-ator input is derived from a constant-current source, i.e., a current source having an internal impedance large compared with the input resistance of the attenuator. This input resistance is half the image impedance of the attenuator sections, since the resistance on each side of any top is equal to R_I, and these two resistances are effectively in parallel. Under these conditions, the attenuator output has the equivalent circuit shown in Fig. 15-8c, where the equivalent output resistance is half the image impedance of the attenuator sections, while the equivalent voltage E_{out} is

$$E_{out} = E_{in} \, \epsilon^{-\alpha n} \tag{15-8}$$

where E_{in} is the input voltage developed across the attenuator, and αn is the sum of the attenuation constants of the sections between the output and the point at which the input is connected.

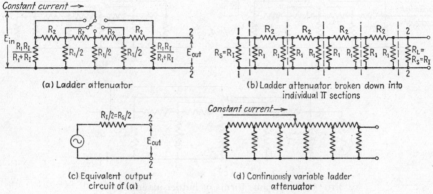

(a) Ladder attenuator

(b) Ladder attenuator broken down into individual π sections

(c) Equivalent output circuit of (a)

(d) Continuously variable ladder attenuator

FIG. 15-8. Various aspects of ladder attenuators.

A continuous variation of attenuation can be obtained by the arrangement shown in Fig. 15-8d, where the tap switch of Fig. 15-8a has been replaced by a slider that permits continuous rather than step variation of the input point. The resistance along the top of the ladder can then be supplied by an ordinary wire-wound potentiometer with sliding contact, to which suitable shunt resistances are connected at regular intervals to form the ladder arrangement. Such an attenuator is inexpensive to construct, and if the shunt resistances are placed close together so that the ladder has many sections with small or moderate attenuation per section, the attenuation is almost a linear function of position. Also, the input and output resistances will then likewise be maintained within narrow limits, except that with small attenuations the input resistance is dependent upon the load connected to the attenuator output.

Numerous variations of the arrangement of Fig. 15-8a are possible. Thus the input and output terminals may be interchanged as in Fig. 15-9a, or the resistance R_L in Fig. 15-8b can be used as the load resistance, as shown in Fig. 15-9*b*. Again, one may dispense with the constant-current generator, and instead use a voltage generator having an internal resistance R_s; this leads to Fig. 15-9*c*, which is derived from Figs. 15-8*b* and 15-9*a*.

Frequency Effects in Resistance Attenuators. At low and moderate frequencies, the resistance units which compose the attenuator act like pure resistances, and the behavior is independent of frequency. However, at very high frequencies, one must take into account various residual inductive and capacitive reactances, such as shown in Fig. 15-10*a* for a simple case. Here the inductances take into account the inductances of the resistor units, the leads, etc., while the various condensers that are shown

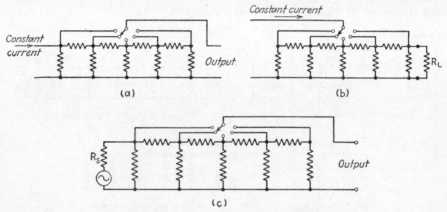

FIG. 15-9. Various forms of ladder attenuators.

represent the capacitances of the resistor units, capacitances of leads to ground, etc.

Frequency effects may be minimized in attenuators by using resistances of types having low inherent reactance effects (see Fig. 14-12), by proper electrostatic shielding that replaces capacitances between different parts of the system by capacitances to ground and by simple shunt capacitances (see Fig. 15-10*b* and *c*), and by proper layout to minimize lead inductance and capacitance to ground.[1] It is also possible largely to eliminate frequency errors in an arrangement such as that of Fig. 15-10*b* if the stray capacitance (after shielding to eliminate mutual capacitances) and residual inductance associated with each resistance unit, are so balanced as to cause all resistance units to have a phase angle that is the same and preferably small, as calculated from Eq. (14-3) and Fig. 14-11. That is to say, $(L/R) - RC$ should be the same for all resistance units,

---

[1] A discussion of shielding and frequency effects in step attenuators is given by Horatio W. Lamson, A Precision Attenuator Having a Wide Frequency Range, *Gen. Rad. Expt.*, vol. 24, p. 1, December 1949.

where R is the resistance, and L and C are the associated series induct-ance and shunt capacitance, respectively (see Fig. 15-10c). Special con-siderations relating to switches in ladder attenuators intended for use at very high frequencies are discussed in connection with Fig. 15-30.

Capacitive effects usually predominate when the resistance level (*i.e.*, image impedance) of the attenuator is moderate or high, such as hundreds or thousands of ohms. In this case, frequency errors can be minimized by making the capacitance C associated with each resistance R such that the product RC is the same for all of the resistance units in the attenuator.

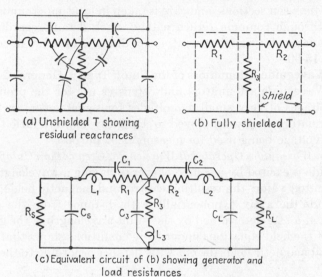

(a) Unshielded T showing
residual reactances

(b) Fully shielded T

(c) Equivalent circuit of (b) showing generator and
load resistances

FIG. 15-10. Residual reactances in a T section, and the effect produced by shielding.

A particularly important and commonly used application of this principle occurs when the L section on the left-hand side of Fig. 15-1d is used as a voltage divider. In this case, by adding shunt condensers C_1 and C_3 of such size that $R_1 C_1 = R_3 C_3$, then the ratio of the open-circuit voltage across terminals 3-4 to the voltage applied across 1-2 is constant irrespec-tive of frequency.

Alternatively, when the impedance level is low, as tens of ohms or less, the principal reactive effect arises from the inductance; and frequency effects can then be minimized by making L/R the same for all resistances of the attenuator. At some intermediate impedance level, the inductive and capacitive effects tend to balance and be a minimum, as mentioned above.

When care is taken, it is possible to construct attenuators that will not be seriously affected by frequency up to several hundred megacycles, provided an appropriate impedance level can be used and the associated inductive and capacitive effects are carefully balanced. In particular, ladder attenuators of the type illustrated in Fig. 15-8a are commonly used in signal generators up to over 100 Mc; in such applications it is necessary to obtain a maximum attenuation of 100 db adjustable in steps that are precisely 10 or 20 db, with negligible frequency effect.[1] To achieve such a result, an intermediate value of impedance level such as 10 to 100 ohms is chosen, and then the inductance and capacitance associated with each resistor in the attenuator are adjusted to give a low phase angle that is the same for all resistor units. In addition, electrostatic shielding is employed between sections, and care is taken in locating grounds to avoid coupling through common return paths. Such details regarding resistance attenuators for signal generators are discussed further in connection with Fig. 15-30.

15-3. Waveguide Attenuators of the Cutoff Type. General Considerations.[2] Waveguide attenuators find extensive use for the production of known voltages of very small magnitudes for signal-generator purposes. Such attenuators are also employed to change by a known ratio the amplitude of a voltage being used for measurement purposes.

Fields in Waveguides Operated at Wavelengths Greater than Cutoff. When a waveguide is excited by a source of energy having a wavelength greater than the cutoff value, the resulting electric and magnetic fields produced in the guide die away exponentially with distance from the source of excitation at a rate determined by the cutoff wavelength of the guide. A solution of the field equations under these conditions shows that both the electric and magnetic fields die out with distance according to the relation[3]

$$\left.\begin{array}{c}\text{Attenuation in db} \\ \text{per unit length}\end{array}\right\} = \frac{54.6}{\lambda_c} \sqrt{1 - \left(\frac{\lambda_c}{\lambda}\right)^2} \tag{15-9}$$

where λ is the actual wavelength in free space, and λ_c is the cutoff wavelength of the guide. This relation applies to all types of guides and for all possible waveguide modes. It will be noted that the rate at which the fields decay in a waveguide operated beyond cutoff is not affected by the losses in the walls, and is hence independent of the wall material.

Frequency enters into Eq. (15-9) only through the term λ/λ_c; when this ratio is small, the attenuation is accordingly substantially independent

[1] A similar result can also be obtained by an attenuator of the type shown in Fig. 15-7b; thus see "Vacuum Tube Amplifiers" (Vol. 18, Radiation Laboratory Series), p. 315, McGraw-Hill Book Company, Inc., New York, 1948.

[2] The original paper on this subject was by Daniel E. Harnett and Nelson P. Case, The Design and Testing of Multirange Receivers, *Proc. IRE*, vol. 23, p. 578, June, 1935.

[3] E. G. Linder, Attenuation of Electromagnetic Fields in Pipes Smaller than the Critical Size, *Proc. IRE*, vol. 23, p. 554, December, 1942.

of frequency,[1] and becomes

$$\left.\begin{array}{l}\text{Attenuation in db} \\ \text{per unit length}\end{array}\right\} = \frac{54.6}{\lambda_c} \tag{15-10}$$

Thus when $\lambda_c/\lambda \le 0.2$, the attenuation expressed in decibels will be within 2 per cent of the value given by Eq. (15-10).   However, for larger values of λ_c/λ_c, Eq. (15-9) should be employed; this formula is dependable until λ becomes so nearly equal to λ_c that $\lambda \le 1.05\lambda_c$.

TABLE 15-3

ATTENUATION FORMULAS FOR CUTOFF ATTENUATORS

Mode	Attenuation, db per unit length	Value of λ_c
Circular waveguides of radius r		
TE_{11}	$\dfrac{16.0}{r}$	$3.42r$
TM_{01}	$\dfrac{20.9}{r}$	$2.61r$
TE_{01}	$\dfrac{33.3}{r}$	$1.64r$
Rectangular waveguides of width a and height b		
TE_{10}	$\dfrac{27.3}{a}$	$2a$
TE_{11} and TM_{11}	$\dfrac{27.3}{a}\sqrt{1+\left(\dfrac{a}{b}\right)^2}$	$\dfrac{2a}{\sqrt{1+\left(\dfrac{a}{b}\right)^2}}$

The actual rate of attenuation of the fields in a waveguide operated beyond cutoff depends upon the waveguide mode with which these fields are associated.   The fundamental or dominant mode, $i.e$, the mode having the longest cutoff wavelength, is attenuated most slowly, while

[1] This neglects the fact that the depth of current penetration into the walls is affected by frequency.   To obtain maximum accuracy in using Eqs. (15-9) and (15-10) the effective internal dimensions of the guide used in calculating λ_c should be taken as extending into the walls a slight distance to take into account the current penetration. Since the depth of penetration varies with frequency, the value to be assigned to λ_c will likewise vary with frequency, and will increase slightly as the frequency is reduced. The depth to which the effective internal dimensions of the waveguide should be taken as extending into the walls, is of the order of one-fourth of the skin depth; for analysis of a particular case, see J. Brown, Corrections to the Attenuation of Piston Attenuators, *Proc. IEE (Radio & Comm.)*, vol. 96, pt. III, p. 491, November,1949.   This frequency-dependent correction is negligible at very high and microwave frequencies, and is too small to be of practical significance in ordinary cases even at lower radio frequencies, such as 1 Mc.

fields representing higher order modes are attenuated more rapidly. Thus with a rectangular waveguide, the TE_{10} mode attenuates most slowly, while with a circular guide, this is the case with the TE_{11} mode. The actual rates of attenuation for some of the more common modes, as calculated by Eq. (15-10), are given in Table 15-3.

Practical Cutoff Attenuators. Attenuators utilizing the exponential decay of fields in a waveguide operated beyond cutoff are variously termed cutoff, piston, and mutual-inductance (or mutual-capacitance) attenuators.

While the details of cutoff attenuators can be varied greatly, the general idea of all such arrangements is illustrated in Fig. 15-11a. Here, a magnetic field is excited in a circular waveguide by a coil L_1 oriented as indicated. A similarly oriented pickup coil L_2 is arranged so it can be slid

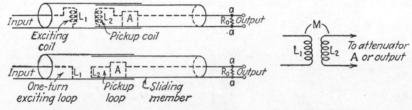

(a) Mutual inductance attenuator   (b) Equivalent circuit

FIG. 15-11. Schematic diagram of cutoff attenuators using multiturn and single-turn coils for excitation and pickup, together with equivalent circuit.

along the waveguide to vary the spacing between coils L_1 and L_2. The voltage induced in the pickup coil L_2 by the magnetic field will then vary with changes in the separation of the two coils according to Eq. (15-9) or (15-10). In this way, one can produce a *change* in the output which is accurately known. The system of Fig. 15-11a can be thought of as having the equivalent circuit of Fig. 15-11b, in which the pickup coil L_2 is to be regarded as possessing a mutual inductance M to the exciting coil L_1; the waveguide then causes M to vary with spacing in accordance with Eq. (15-9).

Instead of using a magnetic field one can instead employ an electric field in the cutoff attenuator.[1] When this is done, the exciting coil is replaced by an electrode or group of electrodes that excite the desired type of electric field: thus the disk electrode in Fig. 15-12a excites the TM_{01} mode. This field then attenuates in accordance with Eq. (15-9), just as does a magnetic field, and can be utilized by employing an insulated

[1] It is also possible to excite the attenuator by means of an iris coupling to a transmitting waveguide; for example see "Technique of Microwave Measurements" (Vol. 11, Radiation Laboratory Series), Chap. 11, McGraw-Hill Book Company, Inc., New York, 1947.

pickup electrode in place of the coil L_2. The equivalent circuit of such
an arrangement is illustrated in Fig. 15-12b.   Here the equivalent output
impedance of the pickup system is the capacitance C_2 of the pickup electrode to ground, while the coupling between this electrode and the exciting
electrode can be considered as being supplied by an extremely small
coupling capacitance C_m that is caused by the presence of the waveguide
to have a value that depends on distance in accordance with Eq. (15-9).
Cutoff attenuators of the mutual-capacitance type are only seldom used,
because the equivalent impedance of the output electrode has less satisfactory characteristics than when an output coil is employed.

The great advantage of the cutoff attenuator is that it provides a
standard of attenuation which can be simply related to geometrical dimensions. The magnitude of the attenuation can, accordingly, be determined by calculations, and the accuracy with which the attenuation is

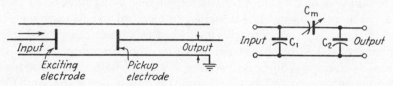

(a) Mutual capacitance attenuator   (b) Equivalent circuit

FIG. 15-12. Mutual-capacitance type of cutoff attenuator, together with equivalent
circuit.

realized is determined only by the ability to achieve mechanical precision.
When carefully made, the cutoff attenuator can be regarded as a primary
standard of attenuation for wavelengths longer than about 3 cm.

The principal disadvantage of the cutoff attenuator arises from the
fact that its insertion loss is high even when the attenuation has the
minimum usable value.   That is to say, the maximum power obtainable
from the output terminals is always much less than the power available at
the input to the attenuator.

Cutoff attenuators can be used at all frequencies; however they are particularly important at frequencies so high that resistance attenuators of
the ladder and similar types cannot be used.[1]   Satisfactory operation at
wavelengths as short as 1 cm can be readily realized, although it is not
always expedient under such conditions to make the guide small enough
for its cutoff wavelength to be very much less than the actual wavelength.
Under these conditions the attenuation per unit length will vary with frequency, and Eq. (15-9) must be used in determining the attenuation law
rather than Eq. (15-10).

[1] An extensive discussion of microwave waveguide cutoff attenuators that includes a
number of illustrative examples, is to be found in "Technique of Microwave Measurements," *loc. cit.*

15-4. Practical Considerations in Cutoff Attenuators. *Output Circuit of Cutoff Attenuator.* In cutoff-attenuator systems, a resistance attenuator is commonly placed between the pickup coil or electrode, and the output terminals of the system, as indicated schematically by A in Fig. 15-11. If the attenuation introduced in this way in the output system is of the order of 20 db or more, then to any load connected across the output terminals, the cutoff-attenuator system appears to be a voltage generator having an internal impedance that is a resistance equal to the image resistance of A.* Attenuator A may take a variety of forms. At low and moderate frequencies a T or π attenuator composed of wire-wound or film resistances can be employed; at microwave frequencies a section of lossy transmission line is often used (also see Sec. 15-5).

The output voltage developed by a cutoff-attenuator system is normally brought out to the output terminals by means of a coaxial transmission line terminated in its characteristic impedance R_0 as illustrated in Fig. 15-11. The attenuator A is designed to have an image resistance that matches the characteristic impedance R_0 of this line. As viewed from a load connected to the output terminals aa, the attenuator system then appears to have a source impedance equal to half the characteristic impedance of the transmission line, and this impedance is the same for all frequencies. Alternatively, if R_0 is supplied by the load connected to the output terminals, then this load sees a source resistance equal to the characteristic impedance R_0 of the terminated line.

At frequencies sufficiently low so that the transmission line connecting the pickup coil with the output terminals is only a small fraction of a quarter wavelength long, it is permissible to operate the system with the terminating resistance R_0 omitted. In this case the output impedance appears to be equal to the image resistance of attenuator A shunted by a capacitance equal to the equivalent lumped capacitance of the transmission line on the output side of A.

Determination of a Reference Level. In the attenuator arrangements discussed above, accurately known changes in output voltage can be produced by varying the position of the pickup system; the relative values of output obtained for different positions can then be accurately calculated from a knowledge of the axial displacement and the use of Eq. (15-9) or Table 15-3. In many cases, relative magnitudes are all that need be known. However, if the absolute voltages are also required, then it is necessary to establish a reference level, *i.e.*, to determine the actual output for some particular position of the pickup electrode.

---

* It is also sometimes desirable to place a similar attenuator between the source of power and the coil L_1 (or other input electrode) that excites the waveguide. This wastes a certain amount of the exciting power, but it enables the input of the attenuator system to provide an image impedance load to an associated transmission line.

A reference level can be established with the aid of a vacuum-tube or crystal voltmeter connected across either the input or the output of the attenuator A. Such a voltmeter can be used to determine the output associated with some convenient small value of spacing between the exciting and pickup coils. Alternatively, it can be employed to adjust the excitation of input electrode L_1 of the cutoff attenuator so that a predetermined output, such as 0.5 volt, is obtained for some convenient (and small) spacing.

An alternative arrangement for establishing a reference level makes use of a probe or loop that samples the fields produced by the exciting coil. Still another possibility consists of a thermocouple meter to indicate the current in the exciting coil, or a crystal or vacuum-tube voltmeter that gives the voltage across it. Finally, if the desired reference level is too small to be indicated by the usual means, a bolometer matched to the output cable of the attenuator can be employed.

Mode Considerations in Cutoff Attenuators, and Minimum Permissible Spacing. Since the field configurations representing different waveguide modes decay at different rates, it is necessary to have a pure mode if the attenuation is to be calculated by Eq. (15-9) or Table 15-3. This is most readily achieved by employing the fundamental mode; this means the TE_{10} mode in rectangular waveguides, and the TE_{11} mode in circular guides.

A particular mode is excited by employing a coil or electrode system that produces a field having the general character of the desired mode. Thus a coil (or one-turn loop) placed with its axis perpendicular to the axis of a waveguide will tend to excite the magnetic field of the TE_{10} mode if the plane of the turns is parallel to the short dimension of the rectangular cross section. In a circular guide, such a coil with its axis coinciding with the guide axis will cause the TE_{01} mode to be the one most strongly excited. Similarly, a launching system such as shown in Fig. 15-12a will tend to excite the electric field of the TM_{01} mode.

No practical system for launching a field will, however, produce an absolutely pure mode. In practice, the field in the vicinity of the point of origin, will, with a suitably chosen launching system, consist largely of the desired mode. Other modes will, however, also be present, particularly modes having the same general type of geometrical symmetry as the desired mode. Thus, if in a rectangular waveguide the mode most strongly excited is the TE_{10}, then one can also expect TE_{30}, TE_{50}, etc. modes of lesser amplitude to be present. However, if the launching system is symmetrical about the center of this rectangular guide, even-order modes such as the TE_{20} will not be excited in significant amount. In general, it is impossible to generate a mode so pure that all other modes are negligible in comparison.

Pure mode operation based on the fundamental mode can be readily obtained by taking advantage of the fact that the fields of the higher order modes attenuate more rapidly than does the fundamental field. Hence the greater the spacing the purer the mode, and to obtain pure fundamental mode behavior, one merely needs to keep the minimum spacing between pickup and exciting electrodes always great enough so that at this minimum spacing the higher order modes are already attenuated enough relative to the fundamental to be of no significance.[1,2] This minimum permissible spacing can be determined experimentally by observing the variation of output with displacement of the pickup system. A nonlinear relationship then denotes either that spurious modes are of significant amplitude, or that the spacing is so close that the coupling between exciting and pickup systems is excessive.[3]

In circumstances where it is necessary to use a mode other than the fundamental in a cutoff-attenuator system, then the system for exciting the field must be so designed as to minimize the generation of lower order modes to which the pickup system could respond. In addition, it is very desirable to employ some system for suppressing the lower order modes while leaving the desired mode unaffected.[4] By such expedients it is possible to employ higher order modes provided the maximum attenuation desired is not too large.

15-5. Resistance Attenuators for Microwaves. Resistance attenuators find extensive use in microwave systems for control of power levels, and as buffer devices that perform such functions as isolating an oscillator from its load so that changes in the load impedance will not react on the oscillator. Resistive attenuators are customarily used for such purposes; cutoff attenuators have the disadvantages of high insertion loss and poor

---

[1] At microwave frequencies a pure fundamental mode can also be obtained by first exciting a waveguide that is just large enough to transmit the fundamental mode without attenuation. Higher order modes will then be beyond cutoff and so will be attenuated. Thus if sufficient length of guide is used these undesired modes decay into insignificance. The resulting pure mode is fed through a suitable transition section into a guide that is beyond cutoff for the fundamental mode. If the transition section is so designed that it does not re-excite the higher modes, then one has an absolutely pure mode in the cutoff attenuator section. For further details see "Technique of Microwave Measurements," *op. cit.*, p. 693.

[2] One may also make use of a mode filter to help suppress unwanted modes; thus see G. F. Gainsborough, A Method of Calibrating Standard-signal Generators and Radio-frequency Attenuators, *J. IEE*, vol. 94, pt. III, p. 203, May, 1947.

[3] If the spacing is small, the impedance that the output coil L_2 couples into the exciting coil L_1 may be sufficient appreciably to alter the current in L_1. The fields initially established in the waveguide are then affected, and Eq. (15-9) no longer holds. This is in addition to any mode effects.

[4] For examples of mode filters see R. E. Grantham and J. J. Freeman, Microwave Attenuation Standard, *Trans. AIEE*, vol. 67, p. 329, 1948.

impedance characteristics.   Resistance attenuators can be adapted to both coaxial lines and waveguides, and can be made to introduce either a fixed or an adjustable attenuation.   A major consideration in the design of resistive attenuators for this purpose is the necessity that the standing-wave ratio that they introduce have a low value, and that the variation of the standing-wave ratio and of the attenuation be as little as possible as the frequency changes.

Resistance Attenuators for Coaxial Systems.[1]   Common forms of resistance attenuators suitable for coaxial systems at microwave frequencies are shown in Fig. 15-13.   The lossy cable of *a* achieves a high attenuation

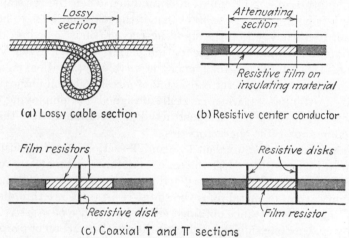

(a) Lossy cable section

(b) Resistive center conductor

(c) Coaxial T and π sections

FIG. 15-13.   Various forms of fixed attenuators for coaxial systems.

by such expedients as a high-loss dielectric and a center conductor composed of resistance material, and is commercially available in the same characteristic impedance values as standard cables.   The attenuation in decibels introduced by a section of lossy cable is proportional to the length of the section, and increases with frequency at a rate intermediate between the square root and first power of the frequency.   The attenuation also increases with temperature.   If the characteristic impedance of the lossy section is the same as that of the associated low-loss cable, the standing-wave ratio introduced by the lossy cable will be very low for all frequencies.   Attenuators of the lossy-cable type have the advantage of being simple and easy to use, but possess the disadvantage that they are bulky and have an attenuation that depends upon the frequency.

[1] Much detailed design and construction information on this subject is given in "Technique of Microwave Measurements," pp. 743–747, 751–774; also see C. W. Miller, M. C. Crowley-Milling, and G. Saxon, Note on Waveguide Attenuators, *J. IEE*, (*Radiolocation Conv.*), vol. 93, pt. IIIA, p. 1477, March–May, 1946.

In the attenuator of Fig. 15-13b, a short section of the center conductor consists of a glass or ceramic tube coated by a very thin high-resistance film of carbon or metal.[1] When carefully designed, such an arrangement will give a large attenuation in a small length, and at the same time cause very little reflection. Moreover, since the resistive film is so thin that skin effect is negligible even at microwave frequencies, the attenuation tends to be independent of frequency. The limiting factor in such coaxial film attenuators is that the high resistance per unit length of the center conductor causes the characteristic impedance of the attenuating section to have a reactive component; also the relationship between the resistance per unit length and the attenuation is modified when the resistance per unit length is high. Analysis shows that if the attenuation is to be independent of frequency, and if the standing-wave ratio is to be low, there is then a limit to the amount of attenuation permissible in a given physical length, and this limit is less the longer the wavelength.[2] Coaxial attenuators using a center conductor consisting of a resistive film find extensive use as fixed attenuators; when carefully designed and employing evaporated metal films, they can be constructed as precision devices that give reproducible and stable characteristics.

Coaxial attenuators equivalent to π and T sections, can be constructed as shown in Fig. 15-13c. Here the series resistance elements are resistive sections of center conductor constructed by coating a dielectric rod or tube with a thin carbon or metal film; the shunt resistances are thin dielectric disks having high resistance obtained either by the use of resistive dielectric, or by coating one side of a dielectric disk with a carbon or evaporated metal film. Attenuators of this type can be built so that up to 500 to 1,000 Mc they introduce a very low standing-wave ratio, and have an attenuation substantially independent of frequency.[3]

Continuously variable attenuation can be achieved in a coaxial system

[1] A suitable carbon film can be obtained by painting Aquadag, a colloidal suspension of fine carbon powder, on a glass or ceramic rod or tube, and drying in an oven at 100°C. The attenuation per unit length will then depend on the thickness of the coating. This method is simple and convenient. However, a thin metallic film composed of resistance material such as nichrome, has greater long-time stability and a lower temperature coefficient; moreover, when deposited by evaporation in a vacuum, such metallic films are very reproducible in production. As a result, in commercially made precision attenuators using resistive films, these films are normally of metal rather than of carbon. For details on processes for depositing metal films see "Technique of Microwave Measurements," *op. cit.*, pp. 757–762.

[2] See H. J. Carlin and J. W. E. Griemsmann, A Bead Supported Coaxial Attenuator for the Frequency Band 4,000–10,000 Mc/sec., *Proc. Natl. Electronic Conf.*, vol. 3, p. 79, November, 1947; also "Technique of Microwave Measurements," *op. cit.*, p. 752.

[3] For further details, see J. S. Elliott, Coaxial Attenuation Standards, *Bell Labs. Record*, vol. 27, p. 221, June, 1949.

by the expedients shown in Fig. 15-14, where the effective length of the resistive section of the center conductor is adjustable. At *b* the variation in effective length is achieved by covering the resistive film with a hard, thin protective coating and then sliding a metal cylinder over it as shown; at *a* the resistive film is coated on a tube provided with an internal adjustable metal plunger as shown. In the actual design of these arrangements, a variety of details must be worked out if impedance matching is

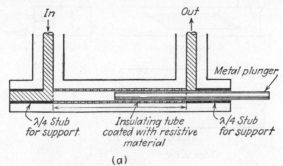

(a)

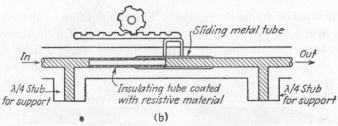

(b)

FIG. 15-14. Variable coaxial attenuators.

to be maintained for all values of attenuation. When these are properly attended to, the variable attenuators have characteristics that closely approximate those of the corresponding fixed attenuators.[1]

Fixed Resistive Attenuators for Waveguides.[2] The usual fixed waveguide attenuator consists of a dissipative element in the form of a thin vane that is suspended in the waveguide with its flat side parallel to the electric field, as shown in Fig. 15-15. The dissipative element can be a film of carbon or metal coated on a thin low-loss dielectric, or it may be a strip of lossy dielectric. In either case, this attenuator element can be mounted on struts that are supported from the side walls of the guide and oriented at right angles to the electric field. In order to minimize reflections, it is

[1] See "Technique of Microwave Measurements," *op. cit.*, pp. 769–774.

[2] Further information, particularly of a design and performance character, is given in "Technique of Microwave Measurements," *op. cit.*, pp. 747, 774–783; also G. K. Teal, M. D. Ringterink, and C. J. Frosch, Attenuator Materials for Microwaves, *Elec. Eng.*, vol. 67, p. 754, August, 1948.

customary to taper the two ends of the vane, or provide some form of transition at the ends; common methods in use are illustrated in Fig. 15-16.

The vane attenuator is capable of giving an excellent performance. By proper design the standing-wave ratio it introduces can be made small

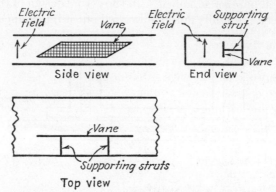

Fig. 15-15. Waveguide attenuator consisting of a lossy vane.

over a substantial frequency range.   The attenuation is also reasonably constant over a moderate frequency range, although it will vary somewhat with frequency because of the changes in field configuration that take place in the guide as the ratio of actual wavelength to cutoff wavelength varies.

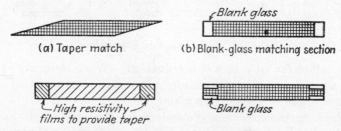

Fig. 15-16. Common methods of tapering a vane attenuator to minimize reflection; in these cases the attenuator is a resistive film coated on a thin low-loss glass sheet.

Attenuation may also be introduced in a waveguide system by means of an appropriately shaped piece of iron-dust (polyiron) magnetic material.   Shaping is required to provide a transition at the input and output ends that minimizes reflections.[1]   Still another method of introducing attenuation in a waveguide system is to arrange matters so that the walls of a section of the guide have high resistance.   The idea is illustrated in

[1] For examples see "Technique of Microwave Measurements," *op. cit.*, p. 726.

Fig. 15-17, and can be carried out by making the walls of resistance alloy in case a small attenuation rate is desired, or by using walls consisting of a dielectric coated with a thin resistive film in case a moderate or high rate of attenuation is required.

Variable Resistive Attenuators for Waveguide Systems.[1] The simplest form of variable resistance attenuator for waveguides is the "flap" or "guillotine" attenuator illustrated schematically in Fig. 15-18. Here, a thin lossy vane is shaped so that it approximates a circular arc, and is then hinged at one corner as shown so that it can be inserted any desired amount into the waveguide through a slot cut in the broad side of the guide. The attenuation is controlled by the depth of the insertion. The shape of the lossy member provides a taper that minimizes reflection for all possible positions of the attenuating vane. When the lossy element consists of a stable metal film pro-

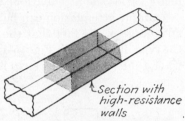

Fig. 15-17. Waveguide attenuator utilizing a section of waveguide in which the walls have high resistivity.

tected by a suitable coating, and when the mounting system is also well designed mechanically, variable attenuators of this type can be used as calibrated precision standards of attenuation.

In the flap attenuator, the lossy element acts as an antenna and causes power to leak from the waveguide through the slot. In order to avoid

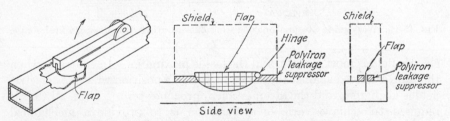

(a) General view of flap (guillotine) attenuator

(b) Flap attenuator details

Fig. 15-18. Schematic view of variable waveguide attenuator of the flap type.

production of undesirable stray fields, the entire flap system can be enclosed in a cavity, as illustrated in Fig. 15-18b. However, energy that leaks into this cavity from the input side of the attenuator, can leak back from the cavity through the slot into the waveguide on the output side of the attenuator. This by-passing action limits the maximum attenuation

---

[1] For further information, with particular reference to design and performance details, see "Technique of Microwave Measurements," *op. cit.*, pp. 748–751, 784–799.

that it is possible to achieve in a simple flap arrangement to about 40 db. However, this limitation can be removed by lining the slot with lossy material such as iron-dust material (polyiron), that absorbs the energy that would otherwise leak into the cavity (see Fig. 15-18b).

A modification of the flap attenuator is shown in Fig. 15-19. Here, the attenuating lossy vane is cut in the form of a spiral, as illustrated. Rotation of this spiral varies the depth of penetration into the waveguide, and hence varies the attenuation.

Variable attenuation can be obtained in a waveguide system by taking advantage of the fact that the attenuation introduced by a lossy vane of the type illustrated in Fig. 15-15 depends on the position of the vane in the wave guide. When the strip is located at the guide center it is where the

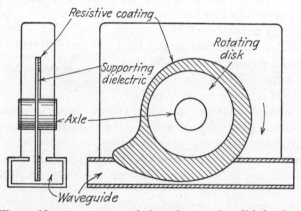

Fig. 15-19. Waveguide attenuator consisting of a rotating disk having spiral shape.

electric field is most intense, and the loss is maximum. In contrast, when the vane is moved against the side wall, it is in a position where the electric field is negligible, and the attenuation approaches zero. Thus, all that is required to achieve variable attenuation is to provide a mechanical arrangement such that the strut system on which the lossy vane is mounted can be displaced sidewise. A modification of this arrangement involves two lossy vanes symmetrically arranged on either side of the center line of the guide, with a mechanical system that moves these vanes closer together or farther apart, to vary the attenuation.

15-6. Microwave Attenuators of the Sampling Type. Large and fixed values of attenuation can be readily obtained by the use of sampling methods. The idea is illustrated in Fig. 15-20. Here the power to be attenuated is transmitted down a coaxial or waveguide line, and dissipated in a load that provides a characteristic impedance termination for the line. A small fraction of this power is then diverted into an auxiliary transmission line or waveguide system by means of a coupling device, as indicated.

Sampling arrangements of this type permit measurements involving high power levels to be made with equipment designed to operate at nominal power magnitude, as discussed in Sec. 2-5; in addition, they are useful in other applications requiring a fixed value of attenuation. The coupling device called for in Fig. 15-20 may be a probe as illustrated, a small loop, or simply a hole. In addition, directional couplers such as discussed in Sec. 2-5 can be regarded as a form of sampling attenuator.

The magnitude of the attenuation that is obtained in Fig. 15-20 depends upon the design details. A large attenuation is readily realized by

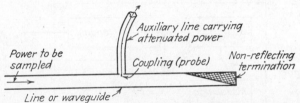

FIG. 15-20. Schematic diagram illustrating sampling type of attenuator.

making the coupling to the auxiliary line small. Small values of attenuation are not practical, however, as they involve a coupling great enough to introduce a serious reflection in the system. The magnitude of the attenuation of sampling-type attenuators is ordinarily fixed. It is possible, however, to control the magnitude in some circumstances; for example, it is possible to employ a mechanical arrangement that permits adjustment of the depth to which the probe in Fig. 15-20 projects into the transmission line (or waveguide).

The effect of frequency on the attenuation of a sampling system depends upon the type of arrangement employed, and the design details. In general, the attenuation is not critically dependent upon frequency. With some types of coupling arrangements, it is, in fact, possible with careful design to cover very wide frequency ranges, such as 3 to 1.[1]

15-7. Signal Generators.[2] A signal generator is a device for producing known and controllable voltages that simulate radio-frequency signals.

[1] For example, see H. J. Carlin and E. N. Torgow, Microwave Attenuators for Powers Up to 1000 Watts, *Proc. IRE*, vol. 38, p. 777, July, 1950.

[2] For descriptions of representative signal generators of various types, see A. G. Bosquet, General-purpose A-M Standard-signal Generator, *Gen. Rad. Expt.*, vol. 24, p. 1, September, 1949; Eduard Karplus and Ervin E. Gross, A Standard-signal Generator for Frequencies between 50 and 920 Mc, *Gen. Rad. Expt.*, vol. 24, p. 1, March, 1950; A. V. Haeff, T. E. Hanley, and C. B. Smith, Wide-range Ultra-high-frequency Signal Generators, *Proc. IRE*, vol. 35, p. 1137, October, 1947; D. M. Hill and M. G. Crosby, Design of F-M Signal Generator, *Electronics*, vol. 19, p. 96, November, 1946; D. B. Sinclair, A Simple Standard-signal Generator for F-M Broadcast Use,

They are used for testing receivers and amplifiers, and are also often employed as a source of test power for exciting standing-wave detectors, radio-frequency bridges, etc.

A typical signal generator is shown schematically in Fig. 15-21. It consists of (1) an oscillator, (2) an associated modulating system, (3) an attenuator, (4) means for establishing a reference level of voltage or power, and (5) shielding that prevents oscillator power from reaching the output terminals or the apparatus under test by any means other than passing through the attenuator.

Signal generators intended for general use are ordinarily purchased, rather than constructed by the user. However, the signal generator is

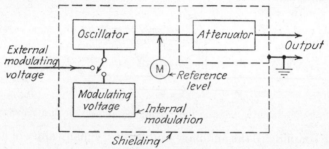

Fig. 15-21. Schematic diagram of signal generator.

such an important piece of laboratory apparatus that even when purchased the user should have some understanding of the principles and practices involved in its construction. Moreover, there are cases where it may be necessary to construct special signal generators to meet particular needs that are not satisfied by available commercial equipment.

Oscillators for Signal Generators. The oscillator used in a signal generator must be tunable over the necessary frequency band; in the case of general-purpose signal generators this means a tuning range such as 3 to 1 together with provision for band switching. The oscillator output is preferably as nearly constant as possible over any one tuning range, and from one band to the next; in some cases automatic amplitude control is used to achieve this result. The oscillator should have good inherent frequency stability.

The same types of oscillators are used in signal generators as for general laboratory applications (see Chap. 12). Thus the Hartley or

Gen. Rad. Expt., vol. 24, p. 1, November, 1949; R. G. Hibberd, J. H. Shankland, and A. Bruce, A Pulse-modulated Signal Generator for 260–800 Mc/s, *Jour. IEE (Radiolocation Conv.)*, vol. 93, pt. IIIA, p. 1331, March–May, 1946; W. R. Piggott, Producing Rectangular R. F. Pulses of Known Amplitude, *Wireless Eng.*, vol. 22, p. 119, March, 1945; E. D. Hart, Methods of Pulse Modulation of Signal Generators Covering 5–300 Mc/s, *J. IEE*, (*Radiolocation Conv.*), vol. 93, pt. IIIA, p. 1315, March–May, 1946.

equivalent tuned-circuit oscillator is suitable for frequencies below about 200 Mc.   Butterfly oscillators find use in the frequency range 50 to 1200 Mc, while reflex klystron oscillators are commonly used at higher frequencies.   Beat-frequency arrangements find occasional use to meet special requirements,[1] but are generally avoided as being cumbersome and tending to introduce spurious frequencies into the system.

Master-oscillator–power-amplifier arrangements are practical at frequencies below about 1000 Mc.   They have the advantage of permitting amplitude modulation to be applied to the amplifier instead of the oscillator, thus minimizing incidental frequency modulation.   This is particularly important in signal generators operating at the higher frequencies.   Although the use of a power amplifier complicates the electrical design, the advantages are such that the master-oscillator–power-amplifier arrangement is used in most commercial general-purpose signal generators intended to produce amplitude-modulated signals in the very high-frequency and lower frequency ranges.

Modulation of Signal-generator Oscillators.   Signal-generator oscillators are usually provided with some form of amplitude or frequency modulation.   The exact type of modulation and its details depend upon the application for which the signal generator is to be used.

Three types of amplitude modulation are to be distinguished: sine wave, square wave, pulse.   Sine-wave modulation is used to simulate a signal modulated by a voice or video wave.   Square-wave modulation is commonly used in microwave signal generators instead of sine-wave modulation, particularly in connection with reflex klystron oscillators.   In this way, one can obtain amplitude modulation free of incidental frequency modulation (see page 529).   Pulse modulation is used when it is desired to simulate signals such as used in radars, and in pulse communication systems.   Signal generators with this type of modulation are required for the intermediate frequencies that are commonly used in such systems, as well as for the signal frequencies.   In order to avoid incidental frequency modulation during the period of the pulse, it is important that the modulating pulse have a flat top and steep sides.

Two types of frequency modulation find wide use in signal generators. The first employs a sine-wave modulating voltage to simulate a signal that is modulated by a voice or equivalent wave.   In the case of triode oscillators, reactance-tube modulation is normally employed.[2]   With

[1] For example, see Alfred W. Barber, C. J. Franks, and A. G. Richardson, A Signal Generator for Frequency Modulation, *Electronics*, vol. 14, p. 36, April, 1941.

[2] In the ordinary reactance-tube arrangement, the frequency deviation produced by a given amplitude of modulating voltage will vary with the carrier frequency.   Means of overcoming this characteristic and obtaining a deviation that is substantially independent of carrier frequency are described by Hill and Crosby, *loc. cit.;* Sinclair, *loc. cit.;* Barber, Franks, and Richardson, *loc. cit.*

reflex klystron oscillators, frequency modulation is ordinarily achieved by applying the modulating voltage to the repeller electrode (see page 529).

The second type of frequency modulation used in signal generators is represented by the sweeping oscillator (see page 501). Here the instantaneous frequency of the generated oscillation is continuously swept over a wide band in order to trace out response curves, etc.[1]

Signal generators are commonly arranged so that modulation can be obtained either from an internally generated modulating voltage, or by a modulating voltage supplied from a source external to the signal generator. The internal arrangement ordinarily provides modulation corresponding to standard test condition. Thus in the case of signal generators intended for testing broadcast receivers, the internal modulation is a 400-cycle sine wave adjustable in amplitude to give a percentage modulation ranging up to at least 80 per cent. Similarly, in the case of signal generators designed for the testing of pulse systems, one would use internal modulation that would give pulse modulation corresponding to several typical values of pulse length and repetition frequency. More flexible or more elaborate forms of modulation can then be obtained by using an external modulating voltage in place of the modulating voltage available internally in the signal generator.

Amplitude Modulation of Attenuator Output. In some circumstances there is an advantage to be gained by modulating the output of the signal-generator attenuator, rather than modulating the signal-generator oscillator or power amplifier. Amplitude-modulation systems of this type are illustrated in Fig. 15-22. The arrangement at *a* is an untuned Class A amplifier that is grid-modulated.[2] By using a very low value of plate load resistance R_L such that the voltage gain of the stage is of the order of 0.1, this arrangement will give substantially constant amplification up to frequencies of the order of 150 Mc. Control-grid modulation is employed, using a relatively large modulating voltage.[3] In this way satisfactory modulation up to about 80 per cent is possible. The degree of modulation produced is independent of the amplitude of the radio-frequency voltage applied by the signal generator provided this voltage is small compared with the modulating voltage.

[1] Examples of such signal generators are described by R. G. Hibberd, A Wide-band Visual-alignment Signal Generator for 10–100 Mc/s, *J. IEE* (*Radiolocation Conv.*), vol. 93, pt. IIA, p. 1328, March–May, 1946; C. M. Burrell, W. R. Savery and P. B. F. Evans, An Alignment Signal Generator for 5–35 Mc/s and 38–32 Mc/s Incorporating a Display System, *J. IEE* (*Radiolocation Conv.*), vol. 93, pt. IIIA, p. 1352, March–May, 1946.

[2] See D. B. Sinclair, A Versatile Amplitude Modulator for V-H-F Standard-signal Generators, *Gen. Rad. Expt.*, vol. 24, p. 3, November, 1949.

[3] This arrangement is sometimes called a modulated Class A amplifier of the van der Bijl type.

In the arrangement at Fig. 15-22*b*, the modulating element is a crystal rectifier placed between input and output terminals, as illustrated.[1] Modulation is accomplished by biasing the crystal to give a suitable operating point, and then superimposing a modulating voltage much larger than the radio-frequency voltage.   In this way the resistance of the crystal is varied in accordance with the modulating voltage, thereby varying the transmission of the radio frequency between the input and output terminals, and producing a modulated output wave.   An arrangement of this type will operate satisfactorily up to carrier frequencies of at

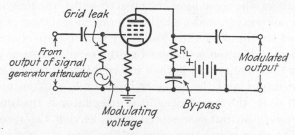

(a) Grid-modulated amplifier

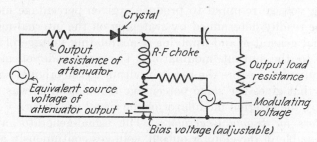

(b) Crystal-rectifier modulator

Fig. 15-22. Two arrangements that can be used to obtain amplitude modulation of a signal-generator output.

least 1000 Mc.   The degree of modulation obtained with a given modulating voltage is independent of the carrier amplitude of the applied signal, and likewise can be made independent of the modulating frequency up to nearly 5 Mc.   The maximum percentage of modulation that can be obtained with a reasonably linear characteristic drops off at the higher carrier frequencies, and at 1000 Mc is of the order of 30 per cent.

Modulating arrangements such as illustrated in Fig. 15-22 are particular useful where it is desired to avoid incidental frequency modulation.   They can also be applied to the output of a frequency-modulated signal generator to give signals that possess combined amplitude and fre-

[1] W. F. Byers, An Amplitude Modulator for Video Frequency, *Gen. Rad. Expt.*, vol. 24, p. 6, March, 1950.

quency modulation for testing the effectiveness of limiters, etc.   Finally, the crystal-rectifier modulator of Fig. 15-22b introduces the possibility of obtaining a video modulated signal for testing television receivers, using a signal generator designed for other purposes.   It is merely necessary to use the video output from a high-quality television receiver as the modulating voltage; the result is then a signal useful in testing certain aspects of television receivers.[1]

The modulators of Fig. 15-22 introduce an insertion loss that must be allowed for.   This loss can be determined in the following manner: The output terminals of the signal-generator attenuator are first connected directly to a radio receiver, and with the internal modulation of the signal generator turned on, the attenuator and receiver gain control are adjusted until a convenient indication is obtained on the receiver output indicator.   The modulator to be calibrated is then inserted into the system between the attenuator output and the receiver input, and with no modulating voltage applied to it, the signal-generator attenuator is readjusted until the original receiver output is restored while leaving the receiver gain unchanged.   The change in attenuator setting then obviously gives the insertion loss introduced by the output modulator under test.   The modulating voltage required to produce a given percentage modulation can next be readily determined by switching off the internal modulation of the signal generator and applying a modulating voltage of the same frequency to the output modulator.   The amplitude of modulating voltage required to restore the receiver output to the original value is the amplitude that gives the same percentage modulation as was originally produced by the internal modulator of the signal generator.

Attenuators for Signal Generators.   The signal-generator attenuator must be capable of developing output voltages continuously adjustable from less than 1 μv to over 0.1 volt, a range in excess of 100 db.   Both resistive and waveguide attenuators are satisfactory at frequencies below about 200 Mc.   At higher frequencies, waveguide attenuators are employed almost exclusively, although occasional use is made of systems involving flap and rotating-disk arrangements.

General-purpose signal generators of commercial design that cover the broadcast and short-wave bands almost universally employ resistive attenuators.   These attenuators are ordinarily of the ladder type, adjustable in steps as illustrated in Figs. 15-8a and 15-9, and designed to present an equivalent impedance at the output terminals of the order of 10 to 50 ohms.   A continuously variable output voltage between attenuator steps is obtained by means of an adjustment that varies the input to the attenuator.   Provision is made for establishing a reference input level

---

[1] It is to be noted, however, that the modulated output possesses double-side-band modulation, whereas the standard television signal is of the vestigial-side-band type.

to the attenuator; either a vacuum-tube voltmeter or a thermocouple meter can be used for this purpose.

Attenuators based upon a waveguide operated at frequencies lower than the cutoff frequency are discussed in detail in Secs. 15-3 and 15-4. When such arrangements are used in signal generators, they are always provided with means for establishing a known reference level to which all values of attenuation can be referred, as discussed on page 660.

The output voltage of the signal-generator attenuator is ordinarily delivered to a binding post in the case of signal generators operating at short-wave and lower frequencies. However, at very high frequency and higher frequencies, the capacitance and inductances of leads connecting such an output terminal with apparatus under test will cause the voltage actually applied to this equipment to differ from the voltage at the attenuator output terminals by a substantial and unknown amount. At these higher frequencies, it is accordingly customary to employ a cable to deliver the attenuator output to the apparatus under test. This cable must be terminated at the apparatus end in its characteristic impedance, and is preferably but not necessarily excited from a signal generator having an equivalent output impedance likewise equal to the characteristic impedance of the cable.[1] In such an arrangement, the length of the cable does not affect the voltage actually present at the output terminals of the cable, provided only that the total attenuation of the cable is small.

The accuracy of well-made attenuators is quite high even at attenuation values as great as 100 to 120 db. The waveguide attenuator can, in fact, be used as a primary standard of attenuation, since when free of spurious modes its attenuation is determined only by the mechanical dimensions, in accordance with Eq. (15-9). The accuracy of resistive attenuators depends upon the details of design and construction, and can be made quite good at frequencies below 200 Mc. However, there is no way of being certain that the attenuation at the higher radio frequencies will be as anticipated except by calibrating against an attenuator that is known to be accurate, particularly a waveguide attenuator.[2] Unless the signal-generator shielding is very good, the principal error resulting from the use of a signal generator at very large values of attenuation will ordinarily arise through energy leaking from the signal generator to the equipment under test, rather than from attenuator inaccuracies.

Signal Generators for Audio Frequencies. Signal generators for audio frequencies are used in determining the amplification, and variation of

[1] For a detailed discussion of the properties of signal generator output systems involving cables, see Arnold Peterson, Output Systems of Signal Generators, *Gen. Rad. Expt.*, vol. 21, p. 1, June, 1946.

[2] Methods for accurately calibrating signal-generator attenuators are described by Gainsborough, *loc. cit.;* Grantham and Freeman, *loc. cit.*

amplification with frequency, of audio amplifiers.   A signal generator for this purpose is composed of an audio oscillator, typically of the resistance-capacitance type, the output of which is applied to an adjustable-resistance attenuator.   The input to the attenuator is commonly indicated by a vacuum-tube voltmeter.

Only elementary precautions need be taken with respect to shielding of audio-frequency signal generators.   Reasonable separation between parts of the system that are at greatly different power levels, a little thought regarding the location of grounds, the use of separate leads to ground for different parts of the system that are to be grounded, and very simple electrostatic shielding, will always be adequate to meet the needs of the situation.   As a result, it is possible to realize an audio-frequency signal generator by combining an ordinary laboratory audio-frequency oscillator that is in a metal case, with a standard attenuator unit that is external to the oscillator.   Commercial models of laboratory audio-frequency oscillators are sometimes provided with built-in attenuator and level indicator so that they can also be used as signal generators.

15-8. Shielding of Signal Generators and Similar Equipment.[1]   In a signal generator the oscillator circuits carry potentials of the order of tens of volts, whereas the attenuator output may be 1.0 μv or less.   It is necessary that the signal-generator shielding prevent the strong fields associated with the oscillator from inducing in the apparatus under test, voltages comparable with a microvolt or less obtained from the attenuator output. Achievement of this result requires a carefully designed shielding system, in which great attention is paid to many details.   The principles involved in such shielding are of fundamental importance in connection with signal generators, and are of sufficient general interest in many classes of equipment to warrant careful study.

The shielding of radio-frequency fields, both electric and magnetic, is ordinarily accomplished by taking advantage of the fact that such fields are almost perfectly shielded by a good conductor such as copper or aluminum.   The effectiveness of the shielding obtained in this way will be very great if the thickness of the shield is much greater than the skin depth.   When the magnetic field is parallel to the shield, the ratio of magnetic field strengths on the two sides of a shield of thickness a is

$$\text{Ratio of field strengths in db} = 8.69 \frac{a}{\delta} \tag{15-11}$$

---

[1] Useful discussions of shielding techniques are given by Bosquet, *loc. cit.;* Haeff, Hanley, and Smith, *loc. cit.;* D. C. Rogers, The Design of Signal Generators for Centimetre Wavelengths, *J. IEE (Radiolocation Conv.)*, vol. 93, pt. III*A*, p. 1457, March–May, 1946.

where δ is the skin depth, and which for nonmagnetic materials is given by the equation

$$\delta \text{ in cm} = \frac{6.62}{\sqrt{f\gamma}} \qquad (15\text{-}12)$$

where f is the frequency in cycles, and γ is the *relative* conductivity of the shield compared *to the conductivity of copper*.   By using conducting shields of suitable thickness, it is possible to obtain very complete shielding at all radio frequencies, and particularly at broadcast and higher frequencies.

It is apparent that if the apparatus producing the undesired field is placed inside of a copper box that is then sealed perfectly with well-made soldered joints, the shielding will for all practical purposes be perfect if the thickness of the walls is adequate.   It is also apparent that such an

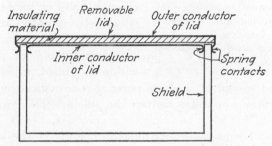

Fig. 15-23. Sandwich type of lid for a shielded compartment.

arrangement would not be very practical; to be useful, leads must pass through the shield to supply power, shafts must be provided that permit adjustments of the equipment inside the shield, access is required to permit changing tubes, etc.   These practical considerations are the things that give trouble in shielding, and which require special attention if excessive leakage is to be avoided.

The first requirement for obtaining effective shielding under practical conditions is good mechanical construction of the shield.   Joints are preferably soldered; where this is not possible, surfaces that are in contact should be constructed to give a good mechanical fit that provides a continuous low-resistance contact.

Lids which must be frequently opened provide a particularly difficult problem.   One solution is to employ a refrigerator-type door, preferably supplemented by clamping with wing nuts.   A very ingenious and effective method of handling the lid problem is illustrated schematically in Fig. 15-23.   Here the lid is in the form of a sandwich, the center of which is insulating material.   The inner conducting surface of the lid makes a spring contact with the inner side of the shield, while the outer conductor

of the lid makes a spring contact with the outer side of the shield.   Such
an arrangement is several hundred times as effective as a simple all-metal
lid with spring fit, and is satisfactory
under many circumstances that
would otherwise require wing-nut
clamping arrangements.

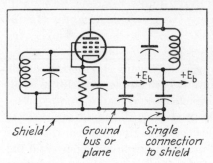

Shield   Ground   Single
             bus or   connection
             plane   to shield

FIG. 15-24. Schematic diagram of
shielded compartment containing tube
and circuits, showing how a ground
bus, or ground plate, can be used so
that only a single ground connection
need be made to the shield.

Grounds for the apparatus housed
within a shield should be arranged so
that the shield is not used as a return
conductor.   In this way the current
that flows in the walls of the shield
is reduced to a very small value, and
the tendency for energy to leak out
through holes or joints in the shield
is thereby greatly reduced.   The
ideal grounding system makes use of
a "ground bus," or ground plate,
within the shield, which is insulated
from the shield except at a single point that provides the only ground
connection for the apparatus within the shield.   This is illustrated in
Fig. 15-24.

Lead Filters.   Leads passing through the walls of the shield for the
purpose of supplying anode and filament power, modulating voltage,

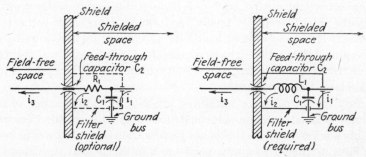

(a) Resistance-capacitance filter   (b) Inductance-capacitance filter

FIG. 15-25. Resistance-capacitance and inductance-capacitance filter arrangements.
The "feed-through" capacitors C_2 shown in the diagram can be replaced if desired by
condensers connected from the left-hand end of R_1 to the shield.

direct current to operate meters, etc., are normally equipped with resistance-capacitance filters to prevent leakage of radio-frequency energy.
The principles involved are illustrated in Fig. 15-25a.   Here capacitance
C_1 tends to by-pass to the ground bus current i_1 attempting to pass out
along the lead passing through the shield.   At the same time, the rela-

tively high resistance R_1 reduces to a very small value whatever current i_2 still flows through resistance R_1 as a result of the potential developed across C_1 by the current i_1; furthermore, the current i_2 is largely by-passed to the shield by the capacitor C_2 (commonly of the feed-through type as in the illustration) that provides capacitance from the lead to the shield.   In this way the current i_3 that finally emerges from the filter can be made very very much smaller than the original current i_1.   However, if still more filtering is required, several resistance-capacitance sections can be added to the right of R_1C_1 in Fig. 15-25a; in this case, part or all of the filter is placed in a shielded space as indicated in Fig. 15-25a, to protect the filter from whatever fields may be present.

Where d-c voltage drops are to be avoided in filters, as in the case of leads carrying modulating voltages or used to deliver the d-c output of a

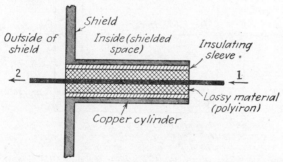

Fig. 15-26. Lossy transmission-line type of filter.

thermocouple to an indicating instrument, it is possible to replace the filter resistances by inductances, as illustrated in Fig. 15-25b.   In this case, it is necessary to shield the filter inductance in the inner compartment in order to prevent the magnetic fields that are to be shielded from inducing a voltage in the inductance and nullifying the effect of the by-pass capacitance C_1.

Another means of preventing leakage of energy while at the same time avoiding the introduction of a d-c voltage drop is illustrated in Fig. 15-26. Here the filter consists of a short section of coaxial line having a high-loss dielectric, typically an iron-dust cylinder made of polyiron material. Such an arrangement operates by dissipating the energy entering the filter at 1 to such an extent that very little of this energy emerges from the end 2 of the filter.   The insulating sleeve lining the inside of the outer conductor is to prevent leakage of direct current between the inner and outer conductor.

Multiple Shields.   When the shielding must be very effective, it is customary to employ multiple shields, *i.e.*, shields within shields.   For example, the most important and serious source of fields in a signal generator is the coil of the oscillator circuit; the effectiveness of the shielding system is therefore greatly increased if the coil is enclosed in an auxiliary shield, which is then placed inside the main shield.   In some cases the entire tuned circuit, or even the oscillator tube and associated radio-frequency tuned circuit and chokes, are placed in a separate shield that is within the main shield.   In general, refinements such as filters for leads or single-point grounding, are not used in such a coil or tuned-circuit shield.   If the shielding that results with such an arrangement, is not adequate, the main shielding container is then placed inside of an outer shield, as illustrated in Fig. 15-27.

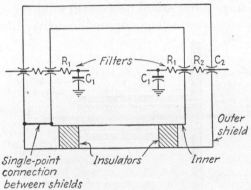

Fig. 15-27. Schematic diagram illustrating a multiple shielding system provided with a single point connection between the shields.

In Fig. 15-27, the inner shield is insulated from the outer shield, except for a single connection between the two.   This avoids the possibility that currents will circulate around a loop completed by two or more connections between the shields.   Leads passing through both inner and outer shields in such an arrangement are commonly provided with additional filtering located in the space between the shields, as illustrated by $R_2 C_2$; also shafts extending from the outside to the inner compartment must be of nonconducting material in order to avoid introducing additional connections between the shields.

Waveguide-attenuator Method of Shielding.   In certain cases it is possible to use the waveguide-attenuator principle to prevent leakage of fields. For example, when it is necessary to circulate air through a shielded space, one may use tubular metal ducts as illustrated in Fig. 15-28, to provide the attenuation.   By using a tube with an internal diameter small compared with a half wavelength, then the attenuation will be as given by Eq. (15-9), and will generally be adequate if the length is of the order of five diameters or more.

If the tube is filled with dielectric, it is necessary to take into account the fact that the distance corresponding to a wavelength is thereby reduced.   This reduces the largest permissible tube diameter that can be used and still obtain waveguide attenuation; at the same time, the length corresponding to five tube diameters is reduced.

Elimination of Shaft Leakage.   Shafts which must pass through the wall of a shield, or walls of a succession of shields, in order to adjust a tuned circuit, a potentiometer, or switch, can cause considerable difficulty.   Ceramic or plastic shafts have many advantages, particularly when multiple shields are employed.   In this case, it is possible to employ the waveguide-attenuator technique, as illustrated in Fig. 15-29*a*, in order to prevent leakage through the hole introduced by the shaft.   However, in such an arrangement, the fact that the dielectric constant of the shaft is greater than that of air may increase the cutoff wavelength to a point where transmission through the waveguide takes place with negligible attenuation.

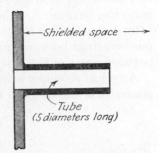

Fig. 15-28. Diagram showing a tube serving as a waveguide attenuator; such an arrangement permits access to the shielded space for the circulation of air or other purposes, without allowing leakage of energy.

An expedient that has been found quite effective in eliminating leakage via the shaft is illustrated in Fig. 15-29*b*.   This consists in enclosing the end of the shaft, whether it be of metal or nonconducting material, with a

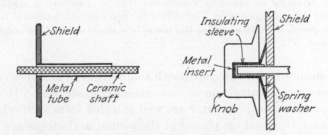

(a) Waveguide attenuator method   (b) Grounded metal insert on knob

Fig. 15-29. Methods that can be used to prevent leakage when a shaft passes through a shield.

knob that is provided with a metal insert that completely encloses the end of the shaft; in the case of a metal shaft this conducting insert of the knob is insulated from the actual shaft by a thin phenolic sleeve.   The metal insert of the shaft is then grounded to the shield by means of a spring washer.

Shielding of Attenuators.   Waveguide attenuators require no particular attention with respect to shielding because they are completely enclosed in a metal tube which is long enough so that fields emerging from the output end are attenuated to negligible amplitude compared with the signal-generator output.   On the other hand, resistive attenuators must be carefully designed from the point of view of shielding in order to avoid spurious couplings between input and output portions of the attenuator, and between parts of the switching system.

A typical shielding arrangement for the resistive attenuator of a signal generator is illustrated in Fig. 15-30.   Here the shield consists of a circular

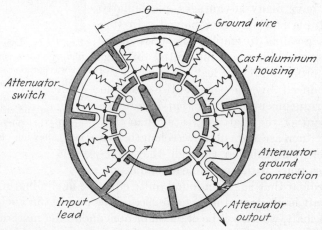

Fig. 15-30. Example of shielding system suitable for use with a signal-generator attenuator of the resistance type.   Note that the attenuator is grounded to the shield at only one point, thereby avoiding the use of the shield as a return conductor that carries current.

cast-aluminum housing, provided with compartments as shown, with each compartment containing one or two attenuator sections.   In this way different parts of the attenuator are well shielded from each other.   The switch with its contacts is placed in the center, and means are provided whereby unused contacts at high power level are not significantly coupled electrostatically to switch points associated with very low power levels. It is to be noted, that if the maximum cross-sectional dimension of the portion of the shield housing the attenuator units is small compared with a wavelength, then the attenuation of the fields due to waveguide-attenuator action tends to be high as one goes from one attenuator section to the next.   In fact, if the proportions are such that when one travels an angular distance θ, the attenuation of the fields due to waveguide-attenuator action is as great as or greater than the attenuation of the resistive sections physically occupying this same distance, then it is possible to dispense with the radial shielding partitions.

Test for Leakage. The effectiveness of a shielding system can be determined by connecting a one- to four-turn coil to the input terminals of a sensitive receiver and exploring for pickup. The pickup should be negligible when the coil is at least several inches away from the shield, and in particular, there should be no pickup when the coil is brought into the proximity of the leads which go through the shield. When a signal generator is properly shielded, a sensitive receiver connected to the attenuator posts will show negligible response when the attenuator is set for the smallest possible output voltage and its output posts are short-circuited.

AUTHOR INDEX

A

Abate, Anthony, 308
Abbot, A. E., 539
Adams, M. B., 513
Affel, H. A., 64
Affenhouse, R. P., 230
Aggers, C. V., 465
Aiken, C. B., 35, 303
Aldrich, D. F., 545
Alford, Andrew, 135
Allan, H. R., 59, 204
Alsberg, D. A., 274, 275
Altar, W., 145
Ames, Millard E., 488, 501, 507
Amstel, J. J. A. Ploos van, 6
Anderson, E. I., 496, 620
Andrews, P., 254
Apker, L., 251
Appleton, E. V., 477
Archer-Thomson, H., 459
Arguimbau, L. B., 246, 498, 554
Artzt, Maurice, 4, 507
Ashwell, G. E., 462

B

Bagley, A. S., 220, 221
Bagno, S., 275
Bailey, F. M., 510
Bailey, R., 475
Baker, W. N., 141
Ballantine, R. J., 513
Ballantine, Stuart, 36, 386
Bangert, J. T., 59, 64
Barber, Alfred W., 671
Barco, A. A., 105
Barfield, R. H., 470, 480
Barker, P. L., 462
Barlow, H. M., 122, 173
Barnett, A., 275
Barrett, M. A. S., 477
Barrett, R. M., 508
Barrow, W. L., 163, 208

Bartelink, E. H., 230, 539, 543, 554
Bartlett, B. W., 74
Bartlett, J. G., 230
Batcher, Ralph R., 101
Bath, C. C., 49
Bauer, Brunton, 483
Bayly, B. de F., 226
Beatty, R. W., 189, 644
Becker, J. A., 44
Bedford, A. V., 257, 327
Behr, L., 71, 629
Bell, D. A., 620
Bell, J., 510
Bell, J. F., 303
Bell, R. L., 367
Benjamin, R., 549, 550, 560
Bennett, W. S., 193
Bentley, E. P., 38
Bertram, Sidney, 544
Best, J. E., 477
Bethe, H., 62
Beverage, H. H., 453
Birdsall, L. C., 35
Black, F. W., 39
Blackband, W. T., 128
Blanchard, A., 487
Blass, J., 48
Bleaney, B., 42
Blewett, J. P., 262, 501, 567
Bloch, A., 620
Blumlein, A. D., 587
Bocking, Geoffrey, 309
Booker, H. G., 472
Booth, C. F., 194, 195
Bosquet, A. G., 669, 676
Bourne, W. A., 251
Bown, Ralph, 453
Brand, S., 267, 275
Bray, W. J., 380
Breit, G., 470
Brewer, G. R., 181
Briggs, A. J., 90
Brooks, Frederick E., 466
Brooks, H. B., 618, 621

SUBJECT INDEX